# SWOOPE'S
## LESSONS IN
# PRACTICAL ELECTRICITY

---

**EIGHTEENTH EDITION**
REVISED AND ENLARGED

*By*

## ERICH HAUSMANN, E.E., Sc.D.
*Thomas Potts Professor of Physics and Dean of the College*
*Polytechnic Institute of Brooklyn*

## D. VAN NOSTRAND COMPANY, Inc.
### PRINCETON, NEW JERSEY
### NEW YORK

TORONTO                                      LONDON

D. VAN NOSTRAND COMPANY, INC.
120 Alexander St., Princeton, New Jersey (*Principal office*)
24 West 40 Street, New York 18, New York

D. VAN NOSTRAND COMPANY, LTD.
358, Kensington High Street, London, W.14, England

D. VAN NOSTRAND COMPANY (Canada), LTD.
25 Hollinger Road, Toronto 16, Canada

076111r35

PRINTED IN THE UNITED STATES OF AMERICA

# PREFACE

This eighteenth edition of Swoope's "Lessons in Practical Electricity" is a completely rewritten book. Some of the material of the preceding edition has been omitted as no longer essential, some has been condensed to make space for later developments, and rearrangement has been made to integrate the old with the new material. The basic structure of the book and its methods of presentation have been retained, however, for these features have been favorably commented upon repeatedly by instructors and students.

The original book grew out of the experiences of Coates Walton Swoope as a teacher of electricity and as a designer and constructor of electrical apparatus. The text was prepared to combine statements of electrical principles, instructions for the experimental demonstration of these principles, descriptions of apparatus and devices then used in the electrical arts, and practical methods employed in calculating and measuring electrical quantities.

The success of the book, in presenting the subject of electricity to the beginner in a manner that is both easily understood and sufficiently complete, is evidenced by the satisfaction it has given to teachers and by the achievements of their former students. It has also been found particularly suited to those who desire to study for themselves the fundamentals of practical electricity.

The specific improvements in the present edition, made in keeping with the advances in electrical engineering, are as follows: an introductory lesson on the structure of matter, presenting the electron, and its companion particles of modern electrical theory, and the behavior of electric charges; a merger of the two lessons on magnets and on magnetism, of those on voltaic cells and on chemical effects of current, of those on Ohm's Law and on its applications, of those on electromagnetism and on electrodynamics, of those on galvanometers and on ammeters and voltmeters, and of those on wattmeters and on watthour meters; an earlier presentation of the lessons on storage batteries and on alternating currents; a separate lesson devoted to inductance and capacitance; the expansion of the lesson on alternating-current circuits into two, of the two lessons on alternating-current machinery into three, and of the two lessons on radio into four lessons. In this way the thirty-four lessons of the preceding edition have been brought back to thirty despite the addition of many new topics.

To give an impression of the scope of the modernization, it will suffice to list the additions in the radio lessons, as follows: multi-electrode tubes, the newer radio circuits, automatic volume control, facsimile transmission, frequency modulation, the electron gun, television, loran and radar signaling. These and all the other new features are described in a manner that will be understood by the reader upon reaching them in a sequential study of the book.

The volume contains the directions for conducting 115 experiments so expressed that the reader without experimental facilities can appreciate the results expected; it contains 175 worked-out problems to give him experience in handling electrical computations. Also at the ends of chapters are given an aggregate of 620 questions and 270 problems, the latter with answers, all designed to enable the student to test for himself the comprehension he has gained of electrical principles and techniques.

Thanks are extended to my friend and colleague, Frank E. Canavaciol, Professor of Electrical Engineering at Polytechnic Institute, for his help throughout the text and particularly in the radio lessons. Appreciation is expressed to a number of manufacturers for the photographs of electrical instruments and machinery which they supplied for the book; their names are mentioned with the figure captions.

E. Hausmann

Polytechnic Institute of Brooklyn
June 1, 1948

# CONTENTS

# Lesson I

## ELECTRICITY AND MATTER

Electric charges—Elements and compounds—Atomic structure—Atomic number and atomic weight—Characteristics of atoms—Insulators and conductors—The electroscope—Charging by induction—Toepler-Holtz generator—Van de Graaff generator—Electric current and electron flow—Questions.

**1. Electric Charges.**—Experimental science extends back many centuries. The first electrical experiment is credited to the Greek philosopher Thales who observed, about 600 B. C., that a piece of amber when rubbed with cloth was able to attract light objects placed near it. Nowadays, the act of rubbing the amber, or of bringing about a very close contact between it and the cloth, is said to give the amber a *charge of electricity,* and the attraction is called an electric or *electrostatic attraction.* The term electricity is derived from *elektra,* the Greek word for amber.

Charges of electricity can be established on many substances by rubbing them with various materials. A glass rod rubbed with silk, or a hard-rubber rod stroked with fur, becomes electrically charged. The action produced by such charges can be demonstrated best by using light materials, because the effects on them can be observed readily. A very satisfactory material for this purpose is *pith,* the soft spongy tissue found at the center of stems and branches of certain plants.

Two small balls of pith, each suspended by a thread and hung about an inch apart, will serve in detecting electric charges and in distinguishing between two kinds of charge. When a charged glass rod is touched to both pith balls, they fly apart and remain separated; such repulsion is also observed when both are touched with a charged hard-rubber rod. But, if one pith ball is touched by the glass rod and the other by the rubber rod, then the two balls will attract and approach each other. From these tests it is evident that there is some difference between the electricity on the glass and that on the hard-rubber; and quite arbitrarily, the charge on the glass rod is said to be *positive* and that on the rubber rod *negative*. The plus (+) and minus (−) signs are used respectively to represent these charges.

Since the charges placed upon the two pith balls by touching them with the glass rod are positive and since these balls repel each other, the result can be summed up briefly by stating that two + charges repel each other. When negative charges are placed upon the pith balls by touching them with the hard-rubber rod repulsion occurs again, and the test shows that two − charges repel each other. With one ball charged positively and the other negatively there will be attraction between the two and, consequently, a + charge is said to attract a − charge. These facts are of basic importance in electrostatics and may be summarized by stating that *like charges of electricity repel each other and unlike charges attract.*

Attraction and repulsion are terms used to indicate the direction of the *force* on one body with respect to that on another. It will be sufficient to state that force can be measured in *pounds* (English system of units) or in *grams* (metric system of units), and to defer the technical definition of force, §91. The strength of the force exerted between electric charges depends upon the amounts of the charges involved and the distance between them. While the effects of charges on light objects can be demonstrated easily, their effects on larger ones can be observed also when the objects are supported to swing freely.

**Experiment 1.**—Charge a hard-rubber rod by rubbing it with fur and place it horizontally in a wire stirrup which is suspended by a thread. Hold near its ends another rubber rod similarly electrified and observe that there is repulsion between them. Repeat, using a glass rod rubbed with silk; it will attract the suspended rubber rod. Try also with pieces of rosin and sulfur rubbed with a woolen cloth, and show that their charges are negative.

Examples illustrating the production of electric charge are familiar to everyone. The effect may be observed by passing a rubber comb through the hair or by shuffling the feet on a woolen carpet. A leather belt traveling on iron pulleys may acquire sufficient electricity to produce an electric spark to a person's finger held nearby. The paper in a printing press exhibits a charge when it is separated from the rollers, and means must be provided to dissipate the electricity. Charges can also be produced by liquids, such as gasoline and other petroleum products, when they are pumped through pipe lines under turbulent or rapid flow, and dangerous conditions may develop by the accumulation of these charges at the terminal containers.

**2. Elements and Compounds.**—The word *matter* is applied to all substances in the universe when it is unnecessary to specify them more definitely. Technically, matter is defined as anything which occupies space and has weight. Matter may be recognized in three forms, namely as *solids, liquids,* or *gases.* Water is an example of matter in the liquid form; as the temperature is lowered it will freeze and become a solid, as ice, and as the temperature is raised it will vaporize and become a gas, as steam. Whether it has changed to ice or steam, the chemical composition remains the same as that of water.

Everyone is familiar with many kinds of matter, and each kind is distinguished from the others by certain *properties.* Such properties include the obvious characteristics of color and smell, as well as a host of physical and chemical properties, such as hardness, melting point, oxidation, solubility, and electrical behavior. A knowledge of the various properties of a substance determines its suitability for any particular experimental or industrial use.

The various substances known to man may be classified broadly into basic substances called *elements,* and other substances called *compounds,* each compound being formed of two or more elements in definite proportions. There are over ninety elements, which are distinguishable through physical and chemical differences; some elements are very common, others are rare. Among the elements are aluminum, carbon, iron, mercury, nickel, oxygen and tungsten. The number of compounds that can be formed from the elements is almost limitless. Some of the compounds familiar in daily life are alcohol, carbon dioxide, gasoline, table salt, and water.

An *element is composed of atoms,* and the atom is regarded as the smallest particle into which matter may be divided by purely chemical means. The atoms of any one element differ from those of the other elements. Atoms of all the elements are very small, much too small to be seen, but despite their minuteness many things are definitely known about them. In fact, effects produced by individual atoms can actually be observed experimentally.

A *compound is composed of molecules* that are all alike, and a molecule is a permanent combination of two or more atoms. The molecules of one compound differ from those of another. A molecule of water consists of two atoms of hydrogen (H) and one atom of oxygen (O); it is written chemically to indicate this composition as $H_2O$. Both components are colorless, odorless and tasteless gases, which themselves can be liquefied and solidified at very low temperatures. Table salt consists of atoms of sodium (Na) and of chlorine (Cl) in equal numbers; it is designated as NaCl. A molecule of sulfuric acid consists of two atoms of hydrogen, one atom of sulfur (S), and four atoms of oxygen; it is expressed as $H_2SO_4$.

The smallest unit of an element is an atom, and the smallest unit of a compound is a molecule. In some elements the atoms also combine to form molecules, for example, hydrogen has two atoms to the molecule. This is ordinary hydrogen, a gas that can be used for inflating balloons. Under high temperatures the molecules of hydrogen may be split apart into atoms; when a stream of atomic hydrogen strikes a substance the atoms recombine with a large liberation of heat to form ordinary hydrogen. This fact is made use of in the atomic hydrogen flame for the welding and cutting of metals; its temperature is over 6000° F.

To give an idea how small atoms really are, it may be stated that in a cubic inch of rock salt (NaCl) there are 729 thousand billion billion atoms. This huge number is expressed more conveniently in multiples of 10. The product of 10 times 10, or 100, is spoken of as ten *square,* or ten to the *second power,* and is written $10^2$. Similarly, the product $10 \times 10 \times 10$, or 1000, is called 10 *cube,* written $10^3$. Proceeding in this way, it follows that 1 million $= 10^6$, and 1 billion $= 10^9$. Hence, a thousand billion billion $= 10^3 \times 10^9 \times 10^9 = 10^{21}$, read ten to the 21st power. Consequently, one cubic inch of rock salt contains $729 \times 10^{21}$ atoms. Fig. 1 illustrates the structure of rock salt as a lattice of cubes with atoms at the corners, alternately sodium and chlorine.

**Problem 1.**—Calculate the distance between neighboring atoms in rock salt, as measured along the lines shown in Fig. 1.

*Solution.*—The number of atoms along a single edge of the crystal one inch long will be that number which when cubed equals $729 \times 10^{21}$, the number of atoms in one cubic inch of rock salt. The number of atoms in one inch of length will then be the cube root of $729 \times 10^{21}$, or $\sqrt[3]{729 \times 10^{21}} = \sqrt[3]{729} \times \sqrt[3]{10^{21}} = 9 \times 10^7 = 90$ million. The distance between adjacent atoms will be the reciprocal of this number, that is, 1 divided by 90 million.

Some kinds of matter are recognized as *mixtures* and others as *alloys*. For example, the air of the atmosphere is a mixture of a number of gases, mostly oxygen and nitrogen in the proportions of about one to four, and among the other elements are helium, argon and neon. An alloy is a blend of metals produced by melting them together; for example, brass is formed by the fusion of copper and zinc, and bronze by the fusion of copper and tin. Steel is essentially an alloy of iron (Fe) and carbon (C), the fusion being effected in a furnace; the carbon ranges in proportion from a few hundredths of 1 per cent up to about 1.6 per cent, the grade known as mild steel having less than 0.25 per cent.

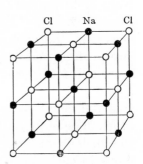

FIG. 1. Lattice structure of rock salt (NaCl)
Solid dots represent sodium atoms and circles represent chlorine atoms.

**3. Atomic Structure.**—Even though atoms are extremely small, they can be divided by physical means into still smaller particles, some of which have electric charges. The actual structure of an atom is not completely known, but there is ample experimental and theoretical evidence to conclude that it comprises three types of particles, called electrons, protons and neutrons. The *electron* has a tiny but definite charge of negative electricity. The *proton* has an equal charge of positive electricity but has a weight about

1800 times that of the electron. The *neutron* possesses no charge and weighs about the same as a proton.

Research with cosmic rays has demonstrated the existence of still another tiny particle, named the *positron*. Its weight and quantity of charge are about the same as those of an electron, but the charge is positive. It is not yet known whether the proton is a combination of a neutron and a positron, or that the neutron is a combination of a proton and an electron.

The atom may be pictured as consisting of a central *nucleus* together with one or more electrons whirling around it in the same way that the planets revolve about the sun, most of the region "occupied" by the atom being empty space, as in the solar system. The simplest atom is that of hydrogen; it is visualized to have a single proton as its nucleus and one whirling electron, the two being held together by electrostatic attraction. Next in order of simplicity is the helium atom, composed of a nucleus and two electrons, the nucleus being regarded as a stable combination of two protons and two neutrons. The atoms of other elements have more and more protons and neutrons in the nucleus, with a corresponding increase of planetary electrons, the total amount of positive and negative charge being equal in any uncharged or *neutral* atom. The electrons are supposed to be arranged in *shells* around the nucleus, and there are particular limits to the number of electrons in each shell.

The hydrogen atom has its one electron in the first shell, and the helium atom has both its electrons in that shell. This shell accommodates only two electrons. The lithium atom, with a total of three planetary electrons, has two in the first shell and one in the second; beryllium with four electrons has two of them in the second shell. The structures of the four elements named are picture in Fig. 2. Continuing with the next few elements, boron has three electrons in the second shell, carbon four, nitrogen five, oxygen six, fluorine seven, and neon eight. The second shell accommodates eight electrons. Next in the order of elements comes the sodium atom with a total of eleven planetary electrons, of which two fill the first shell, eight fill the second shell, the remaining one being in a third shell. By continuing the foregoing process, and supposing the electrons to be arranged in shells of various sizes, it is possible to picture the atoms of all the known elements.

**4. Atomic Number and Atomic Weight.**—The number of positive charges (that is, protons) in the nucleus of each atom of an element is called the *atomic number* of that element. This number is equal to the number of planetary electrons of the particular atom when in an uncharged condition. Thus, the atomic number of hydrogen is 1; this means that the nucleus of the hydrogen atom has 1 proton and, when the atom is neutral, there is one electron rotating about the nucleus. The atomic number of helium is 2, that of lithium is 3, of beryllium 4, and so on.

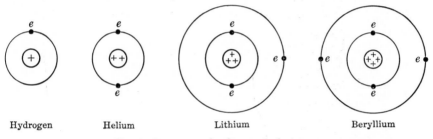

Hydrogen          Helium          Lithium          Beryllium

FIG. 2. Structure of a few neutral atoms

Each atom is pictured with a positive nucleus at the center and surrounded by whirling electrons *e* in one or more shells. Total positive charge equals total negative charge when atom is neutral.

Another important thing about atoms is their relative weights. The *average* weight of the atoms of any one element is always the same and is called its *atomic weight*. The atomic weight of oxygen is taken as 16, and the atomic weights of all the other elements are expressed relative to this value. For example, the atomic weight of hydrogen is 1.008 (roughly one-sixteenth as much as oxygen); that of helium is 4.003, of copper 63.57, and of silver 107.88.

Values of atomic number and atomic weight for the elements mentioned in this book are given in the accompanying table. In using this table, the atomic weights are not to be regarded as weights in pounds or in grams, but rather as the amount of the various elements that have a particular number of atoms. Thus, 1.008 grams of hydrogen, or 63.57 grams of copper, or 107.88 grams of silver, and so on, will all have the same number of atoms, and that number is 602 thousand billion billion, or $6.02 \times 10^{23}$.

This number has a theoretical significance and is called *Avogadro's constant;* it is named after the Italian physicist, Amadeo Avogadro (1776-1856).

SOME ELEMENTS AND THEIR CHARACTERISTICS

| Atomic Number | Element | Symbol | Atomic Weight | Atomic Number | Element | Symbol | Atomic Weight |
|---|---|---|---|---|---|---|---|
| 13 | Aluminum | Al | 26.97 | 80 | Mercury | | |
| 51 | Antimony (*Stibium*) | Sb | 121.76 | | (*Hydrargyrum*) | Hg | 200.61 |
| 18 | Argon | A | 39.94 | 42 | Molybdenum | Mo | 95.95 |
| 56 | Barium | Ba | 137.36 | 10 | Neon | Ne | 20.18 |
| 4 | Beryllium | Be | 9.02 | 28 | Nickel | Ni | 58.69 |
| 83 | Bismuth | Bi | 209.00 | 7 | Nitrogen | N | 14.008 |
| 5 | Boron | B | 10.82 | 8 | Oxygen | O | 16.000 |
| 48 | Cadmium | Cd | 112.41 | 15 | Phosphorus | P | 30.98 |
| 55 | Caesium | Cs | 132.91 | 78 | Platinum | Pt | 195.23 |
| 20 | Calcium | Ca | 40.08 | 19 | Potassium (*Kalium*) | K | 39.10 |
| 6 | Carbon | C | 12.01 | 88 | Radium | Ra | 226.05 |
| 17 | Chlorine | Cl | 35.46 | 45 | Rhodium | Rh | 102.91 |
| 24 | Chromium | Cr | 52.01 | 34 | Selenium | Se | 78.96 |
| 27 | Cobalt | Co | 58.94 | 14 | Silicon | Si | 28.06 |
| 29 | Copper (*Cuprum*) | Cu | 63.57 | 47 | Silver (*Argentum*) | Ag | 107.88 |
| 9 | Fluorine | F | 19.00 | 38 | Strontium | Sr | 87.63 |
| 79 | Gold (*Aurum*) | Au | 197.2 | 11 | Sodium (*Natrium*) | Na | 23.00 |
| 2 | Helium | He | 4.003 | 16 | Sulfur | S | 32.06 |
| 1 | Hydrogen | H | 1.008 | 90 | Thorium | Th | 232.12 |
| 26 | Iron (*Ferrum*) | Fe | 55.85 | 50 | Tin (*Stannum*) | Sn | 118.70 |
| 82 | Lead (*Plumbum*) | Pb | 207.21 | 74 | Tungsten | | |
| 3 | Lithium | Li | 6.94 | | (*Wolframium*) | W | 183.92 |
| 12 | Magnesium | Mg | 24.32 | 92 | Uranium | U | 238.07 |
| 25 | Manganese | Mn | 54.93 | 30 | Zinc | Zn | 65.38 |

**5. Characteristics of Atoms.**—Certain of the elements of matter do not combine readily with others. It is believed that this behavior indicates that their atomic structures are quite stable, and seems to imply that their electron shells are completely filled. The helium atom with its first shell complete, the neon atom with the first and second shells complete, and other atoms with similar structures, are chemically inactive.

The ability of atoms to combine and form molecules is determined by the planetary electrons, and the tendency in combining is apparently to form arrangements in which the electron shells are completely filled. A lithium or a sodium atom, with one electron in its outer shell, is in a condition that is favorable to the loss of this electron, while a fluorine or a chlorine atom, with one electron less than is needed to complete its outer shell, is in a condition which favors adding one. When sodium and chlorine are allowed to mingle, each sodium atom joins a chlorine atom, forming sodium chloride (NaCl), in which process the loosely held electron of the sodium atom is transferred to the chlorine atom, thus filling the electron shells of both atoms. The measure of the ability of atoms to form molecules by combining in this manner is known as *valence;* for example, sodium, which has one electron more than is needed to fill its second shell, is said to have a *valence number* of +1, and chlorine, which has one electron less than is needed to fill its outer shell, is said to have a valence number of −1. Silver and hydrogen have a valence number of +1, copper and zinc +2, oxygen −2, to mention but a few more.

The atoms of any one element are not all alike, for some are heavier than others. Elements containing atoms that have the same atomic number but different weights are called *isotopes,* the difference between them depending upon the number of neutrons in the atomic nucleus. Most elements consist of two or more isotopes. For example, chlorine has two isotopes, of weights 35 and 37, mixed in a proportion which yields an average atomic weight of 35.46; lithium has stable isotopes of weights 6 and 7, the average being 6.94. The isotopes of any element have substantially the same chemical properties but they show differences in the rate or extent to which they react with other elements in forming compounds. Isotopes are not given special names except in the case of hydrogen; its isotope of weight 2, with a nucleus composed of one proton and one neutron, is called deuterium. The combination of deuterium and oxygen is spoken of popularly as "heavy water."

**6. Insulators and Conductors.**—The process of charging a substance by rubbing it with another material may now be viewed as a stripping of electrons from some of its atoms at the contacting surface. Atoms of certain elements release electrons with comparative ease, and atoms of others acquire electrons readily. A neutral or uncharged body contains equal amounts of positive and negative electricity; when electrons are added it becomes negatively charged, and when electrons are removed it becomes positively charged. Applying this explanation, a hard-rubber rod, when brought into intimate contact with fur, gains electrons and becomes negative, at the same time the fur loses these electrons and becomes positive to an equal extent. A glass rod rubbed with silk loses electrons and becomes positive, while the silk gains these electrons and so becomes negative.

When electric charges are placed upon a variety of substances, it will be found that on some substances the charge will be localized while in others it will be distributed over the entire surface. In the first group the charge is confined to the immediate neighborhood of the point where it was applied; such substances are called *insulators*. In the other group the charge moves promptly from point to point and it then manifests itself everywhere on the surface; such substances are called *conductors* and the charge is said to be conducted from point to point. Glass, mica, rubber and dry silk are insulators; metals are conductors of electricity.

Consider a metal sphere hung from a dry silk thread or supported on props of mica or glass. If the sphere is touched with a charged rubber rod, some of the electrons will leave the rod at the point of contact because of their mutual repulsion and attach themselves to the sphere, making it negative also. The charge will remain on the sphere for a long time because charges are not conducted appreciably through the insulating materials which support it. If the sphere had been suspended by a metallic wire or mounted upon a metal support, practically all the electrons would have escaped, eventually reaching the earth. Insulating substances are not equally good in obstructing the transfer of electrons nor are conductors equally good in permitting electrons to flow. Many substances may be classed in an intermediate group as fair electrical conductors; damp wood, the human body, and the earth are examples.

The rubber tires of automobiles present an interesting illustration. When an automobile gets under way the contact between the tires and the roadway establishes a positive charge on the latter and a negative charge on the tires. Since rubber is a good insulator, the charge developed on the tires remains localized on the tread; in consequence, the neutral condition of the metal chassis and car body is disturbed and charges distribute themselves as shown in Fig. 3. However, after traveling but a short distance the tires become warm, and during this interval the steady accumulation of electrons goes on. Under these conditions rubber becomes more conducting, which means that electrons can pass through the tires more readily than before; as a result a considerable negative charge is developed on the car body by conduction. For this reason, in fueling an automobile, the metal nozzle of the hose should be put in contact with the filler opening before gasoline is pumped into the tank to avoid the possibility of a spark igniting the gasoline.

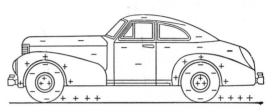

FIG. 3.　Normal distribution of charges on an automobile when starting

### 7. The Electroscope.—

An electric charge can be measured by means of an instrument called an *electroscope;* it consists of two thin leaves of gold or aluminum foil fastened to a metal rod as shown in Fig. 4. The rod protrudes through the top of a glass vessel, or of a wooden box with two glass sides, while the leaves are within the enclosure so that they may be protected against drafts. If a body carrying a small charge is brought in contact with the exposed knob of the electroscope,

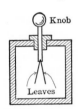

FIG. 4. Leaf electroscope and its housing

the rod and leaves will receive some of it and the leaves will separate because the charge on one leaf will repel that on the other. The amount of separation of the leaves is a measure of the charge. To avoid giving the instrument too large a charge, and thereby causing the leaves to repel each other so violently that they might be torn, it is better to use a *proof plane,* rather than making direct contact. This device is merely a small metal disk or coin fastened to the end of a glass rod; because of its small size, it can transfer only a little of the electricity from the charged body to the electroscope.

Suppose that a hard-rubber rod is electrified by stroking it with fur and that the amount of charge on both substances are to be compared. First use a proof plane to transfer some electricity from the rod to an electroscope. The instrument will become negatively charged and the leaves will separate to a certain extent. Then touch the knob of the electroscope with the finger to relieve the charge. Finally use the proof plane to transfer some electricity from the fur; the electroscope will be positively charged and the leaves will again repel each other. If the separations of the leaves first with negative charges and then with positive ones be compared, it will be possible to measure the relative amounts of charge on the rod and on the fur. Experiments such as these carried out with the greatest care show that in each case where electrification is developed *by contact* between two dissimilar substances, the charge produced on one substance is equal to that produced on the other, one being positive and the other negative.

**Experiment 2.**—Make an electroscope, using a wide-mouth bottle of clear glass and a metal rod for supporting the leaves. Because of the difficulty of cutting and fastening gold leaves, it is better to use aluminum foil; this can be cut readily with scissors when held between two sheets of paper. Make the leaves about 1¼ inches long and ¼ inch wide. Upon completion of the electroscope, show that when a hard-rubber rod is rubbed with wool, the wool becomes electrified as well as the rod, and that the charges are *unlike*. Repeat for glass rubbed with silk.

**8. Charging by Induction.**—In contrast with the method of charging an object from another initially charged body by contact,

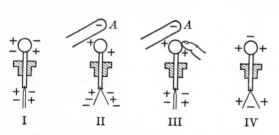

FIG. 5. Charging an electroscope by induction

as explained in the last section, there is another method which does not involve direct contact; it is called *electrostatic induction.* Consider an electroscope in an uncharged or neutral condition, or what is the same thing, consider it to have equal amounts of positive and negative electricity, as illustrated at I in Fig. 5. When an electrified rod is brought *near* it, the leaves of the electroscope will diverge showing that the neutral condition has been disturbed and that the two leaves have like charges. This condition is shown at II for a negative *inducing charge* on the rod *A;* some of the electrons on the electroscope have been repelled to the leaves and the knob becomes positive. If the electrified rod is then removed, the electrons will return and the electroscope will again be neutral, as shown at I. If, while the inducing rod $A$ is near the electroscope, the instrument is grounded by touching the knob momentarily with a finger, some of the negative electrons will escape to ground, as indicated at III. Upon removing the rod, the excess positive charge on the electroscope will cause the leaves to diverge, as shown at IV. In this way, a negative inducing charge places a positive charge on the electroscope. This result is characteristic of the charging of bodies by induction.

**Experiment 3.**—Charge an electroscope by induction in the manner described, using a hard-rubber rod as the inducing agent. To prove that the charge on the leaves is positive, bring a charged glass rod near the knob of the electroscope and note that the leaves diverge further. Repeat, using the glass rod as the inducing agent and the hard-rubber rod for testing the charge produced.

The process of induction is utilized in the generation of electric charges by means of an *electrophorus*. This device consists of a slab of hard rubber, rosin or sealing wax, $A$ in Fig. 6, and a separate metal disk $B$ fastened to an insulating handle $C$. The slab is first electrified by rubbing it with wool or fur, then the disk is held by its handle and placed upon the charged slab. Since contact is localized at only a few points, the disk does not take the negative charge off the slab but instead becomes charged by induction. The electrons of the neutral disk will be repelled to its upper surface and the lower surface will

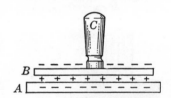

FIG. 6. Electrophorus and charges induced in it

be charged positively. The electrons are removed by touching the disk with a finger, and thereafter the disk may be raised by the handle to enable the positive charge to be used. The charge is often so great that sparks one-half inch long may be drawn from it. Since practically no charge is removed from the electrified plate, the process may be repeated many times before it is necessary to recharge it.

**Experiment 4.**—Charge a metal sphere that is supported on an insulating stand by contact with an electrified body; test the result by means of a charged pith ball. After relieving this charge, apply the method of induction to charge the sphere again, using the same electrified body. Show that the charges developed on the sphere in the two tests are of opposite sign. Try to charge a metal sphere which is not insulated from ground.

Place two metal spheres mounted on individual insulating supports in contact with each other. Bring a charged rubber rod near one of them, and separate the two spheres; then remove the rod. Test the charge on each sphere with a charged pith ball and show that one is positive and the other negative.

**9. Toepler-Holtz Generator.**—The production of substantial amounts of electric charge by means of induction is carried out in machines called *electrostatic generators.* In the Toepler-Holtz generator, a group of small disks is rotated near positive and negative electrified plates and the charges induced are collected on metal spheres. Fig. 7 illustrates a simple form of such a ma-

chine for demonstration purposes; it has a moving plate carrying six small disks of tinfoil, each with a metal contacting button, and a stationary plate supporting a positive and a negative inducing body in the form of tinfoil sectors. More powerful machines have several rotating plates and a corresponding number of stationary plates similarly equipped; these may be used to operate X-ray and other types of vacuum tubes.

The operation of the machine can be explained better with a diagram in which the flat circular plates of the actual machine are replaced by concentric cylinders, as shown in Fig. 8. The outer cylinder is stationary and supports the curved metal inducing bodies *A* and *B*, while the inner cylinder, carrying the disks *a* to *f*, is rotated clockwise. The metallic collecting combs *CC'*, neutralizing rod *N*, and replenishers *RR'* are stationary and make contact through brushes with the disks during their rotation.

To trace the operation, consider a single disk to make one revolution, starting at position *a,* just after leaving the brush on col-

Fig. 7.  Toepler-Holtz electrostatic generator
Machine with revolving plate 12 inches in diameter
yields sparks 4 to 6 inches long.

lector *C*. Here, in the presence of the positive inducing body *A*, a negative charge is induced on the outer surface of the disk and a positive one on the inner surface. Upon reaching position *b*, electrons are supplied by rod *N* to neutralize the positive charge on this inner surface, thus giving the disk an excess of negative charge. As the disk passes position *c*, some electrons are picked off by the replenisher *R* to keep inducing body *B* fully charged and compensate for possible leakage. At position *d*, the negative charge on the disk is strongly repelled by that on *B* and, therefore,

most of the electrons go to the collector *C'*. As this disk leaves position *d* it may be considered neutral momentarily, but since it is still under the influence of inducing body *B*, a negative charge will be induced on the inner surface of the disk and a positive one on the outside. At position *e*, electrons are picked off by the neutralizing rod (and transferred to another disk at *b*), leaving the disk under investigation charged positively. The actions of replenisher *R'* and collector *C* are the

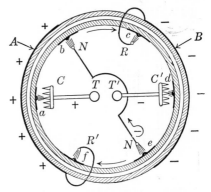

Fig. 8. Scheme of generating charges by induction

Cylinders are depicted instead of plates to simplify the explanation.

same respectively as of *R* and *C'* already described, except that the charge is now positive.

All six disks on the inner cylinder behave similarly to the one traced, and the continued motion of these carriers as the machine is driven builds up large positive and negative charges on collectors *C* and *C'* respectively. Presently a spark will pass in the air gap between the terminals *T* and *T'*, and their charges will be neutralized. In operation, the generator builds and then neutralizes these charges very rapidly, producing a steady stream of sparks between its terminals. The machine is self-exciting, that is, the charges *A* and *B* are established by the machine itself, beginning with the minute amounts that develop by the rubbing contact of the brushes on the disks as the machine starts rotating.

**10. Van de Graaff Generator.**—In the newer and more powerful Van de Graaff type of electrostatic generator the charges are transported on traveling belts. The machine consists essentially of a hollow metal terminal mounted on an insulating column within which a motor drives an endless belt of insulating material for conveying charges of electricity between the terminal and ground. The terminal may be made either positive or negative; the operation will be described for one having the latter polarity.

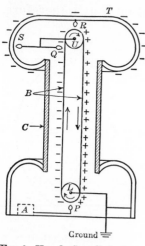

FIG. 9. Van de Graaff electro-static generator

Unit 4 feet high has rubber-fabric belt 10 inches wide driven at 5000 feet per minute.

A diagram of such a generator of recent design is shown in Fig. 9. The insulating belt $B$ travels around two metal pulleys, the lower one at $L$ is pivoted in the grounded base, and the upper one at $U$ is pivoted in the terminal $T$, supported on the base by the insulating column $C$. A row of metal points represented by $P$ is directed toward the lower metal pulley and receives continuously a supply of electrons from an auxiliary source $A$. These negative charges are repelled toward the pulley and deposited on the intervening belt. This neutralizes the positive charge that may be on the belt from its downward run and leaves a net negative charge to be carried to the terminal.

At the upper end, the collector $Q$ transfers this charge partly to the insulated pulley $U$ and partly to the point $S$ and thence to the terminal. The charges are so distributed as to make this pulley more negative than the terminal itself, and consequently the pointed collector $R$, connected to the terminal, may be regarded as positive with respect to the pulley. In consequence, electrons are drawn to this electrode and the belt becomes charged positively. Thus, as the machine is driven, there is a continuous transfer of negative charge up one side of the belt and positive charge down the other side, as a result of which the terminal acquires a large negative charge. Machines of this type are used for the production of X-rays of high penetration and for speeding up the charged particles needed for research on the atomic nucleus.

**11. Electric Current and Electron Flow.**—The transfer of electric charge within a substance, spoken of as conduction of electricity, takes place differently in solids and fluids. In solids, the atoms are relatively close to each other in contrast with their spacing in the other states of matter, particularly that in the gaseous state. The closeness of the atoms in solids makes it possible for the outer electron shells of neighboring atoms to overlap. Moreover, most conducting solids are metals in which the atom has only a few electrons in the outer shell, a condition which makes it easy to lose these electrons. Because of this, and possibly because some electrons serve in a double capacity in two adjoining atoms, it is believed that within metals a large number of electrons are comparatively free to move about; these are called *free electrons* to distinguish them from the electrons that are more definitely parts of atoms.

When one end of a conducting wire is maintained negative by supplying it with electrons and the other end is maintained positive by withdrawing electrons from it, the free electrons within the wire are repelled from the negative end and attracted toward the positive end. These electrons acquire a definite drift from atom to atom toward the positive end of the wire. It is this drift of electrons which constitutes an *electric current* in the wire. The positively charged atoms remain practically fixed in position and, therefore, the *current is attributed entirely to a movement of electrons.*

In insulating solids, the molecular structures are such that hardly any free electrons are available, yet electrons may be added to or removed from the surfaces of such insulators by intimate contact or rubbing with dissimilar materials. In conducting solids, the numbers of free electrons available differ with the different substances. For example, copper has more free electrons than iron; for this reason, copper is the better conductor of the two. The free electrons in a solid are also believed to assist in the conduction of heat, for it is well known that a good conductor of electricity is also a good conductor of heat.

An electric current in a metallic conductor is in reality, then, a drift of free electrons from the negative end of the conductor to its positive end. However, from the early days of electrical science an electric current has always been regarded as some kind of a flow in the opposite direction, that is from positive to negative, and this notion prevails still. Consequently, when it is necessary to designate the direction of flow, the term *current will be used to represent a flow from positive to negative,* and in contrast, *electron flow will be used to represent a drift of electrons from negative to positive.*

The expression "current flow" is often used in connection with electrical things, but it is, strictly speaking, a poor expression for the word "current" itself means flow. It is sufficient to say, for example, that "a current is established in a device by a dry battery," or that "the presence of a current in a conductor can be detected."

In the subject of *electrostatics,* which deals with electricity supposedly at rest, the primary consideration is the accumulation of electric charges for definite purposes. In establishing a negative charge on a body it acquires electrons, and in establishing a positive charge the body loses electrons; consequently, after sufficiently large charges have been built up, provision is made for a momentary transfer of electrons to re-establish the neutral condition of both bodies, and this transfer produces the effects desired. On the other hand, in the subject of *electrokinetics,* which deals with electricity in motion, the fundamental idea is the production of a continuous flow of electrons from one place to another to meet other objectives. This flow, or current, is utilized in a multitude of electrical applications in modern life.

## QUESTIONS

1. Does the negative charge on a piece of rosin attract or repel the charge on a piece of glass? Give explanation.
2. Make three sketches of two pith balls with different conditions of charge and indicate the forces on them by sloping their supporting threads appropriately.
3. State the law of electrostatic attraction and repulsion.
4. Explain the terms: element, compound, and mixture.
5. Nitric acid is written $HNO_3$. What elements are represented in this compound, and how many atoms of each are in one molecule of the acid?
6. Distinguish between a neutron and a proton.
7. In what two respects does an electron differ from a proton?
8. What do you mean by a neutral atom?

9. How is the structure of an atom pictured?
10. Make a sketch of a sodium atom and label its component parts and charges.
11. Distinguish between atomic weight and atomic number.
12. Explain the meaning of valence number.
13. What is an isotope of an element?
14. When a hard-rubber fountain pen is rubbed against a coat sleeve, there is a transfer of electrons. Do they travel toward the pen or toward the coat?
15. What distinguishes a conductor from an insulator?
16. Describe an electroscope.
17. Explain two methods of charging an electroscope.
18. A brass tube is mounted horizontally on an insulating support. Explain how you would give the tube a positive charge by induction.
19. Give a description of one form of electrostatic generator and explain how it operates.
20. When an electric current is established between the ends of a copper wire, do all the electrons of the copper atoms participate in this action? Do the electrons flow in the direction of the current? Explain.

# Lesson II

## MAGNETS AND MAGNETIC FIELDS

Magnets—Magnetic attraction and repulsion—Making a permanent magnet—Horseshoe magnets—Composition of permanent magnets—The electromagnet—The Earth as a magnet—Mariner's compass—Magnetic fields—Magnetic lines of force—Magnetic induction—Consequent poles—Theory of magnetism—Questions.

**12. Magnets.**—The ancients observed that some lead-colored stones, now known to be composed of an oxide of iron ($Fe_3O_4$), possessed the power of attracting small particles of iron or steel. The word *magnet* was applied to these stones, and the name was undoubtedly derived from Magnesia, a district in Asia Minor where such stones were plentiful. The ore constituting them is called *magnetite.* Later, the Chinese discovered that any piece of the ore, when freely suspended, would assume a position pointing north and south; hence, they gave it the name of *lodestone,* meaning leading stone. It was also observed many centuries ago that these characteristics could be imparted by lodestones to pieces of steel by stroking one against the other. The pieces of steel are then said to be *magnetized.* The properties possessed by a magnet are spoken of collectively as *magnetism.* Summing up, a magnet may be described as a piece of steel, or other magnetized substance, which possesses the properties of attracting pieces of steel or iron, of pointing in a north and south direction when freely suspended in a horizontal position, and of imparting similar properties to magnetizable substances.

The lodestone is called a *natural magnet,* since it possesses magnetism when found in the earth. A piece of soft iron or mild steel rubbed with lodestone, or magnetized in any other way, becomes an *artificial magnet*. Iron loses almost all its magnetism immediately after it is magnetized, while steel holds it for long periods of time. Thus, distinction is made between a *temporary magnet* made of iron and a *permanent magnet* made of steel. Magnets are extensively used in electrical devices, and are frequently designated by shape or form, such as *bar* magnet and *horseshoe* magnet.

Observations on a natural or an artificial magnet reveal that its magnetism is not uniform over the surface. This is easily shown by dipping the magnet into iron filings, for when the magnet is withdrawn, filings will cling to it at some places and none at others. Fig. 10 illustrates the result of such a test on a bar magnet and shows that the attraction of the magnet for the filings is greatest at both ends of the magnet, and that there

Fig. 10.  Magnetized steel bar attracting iron filings

is practically no attraction at the center. The ends of a magnet, where the attraction is strongest, are termed its *poles*.

The two poles of a bar magnet may be distinguished from each other by suspending or pivoting the magnet at its center so as to permit it to turn freely. The end which points in the general direction of the north pole of the earth is called the north-seeking pole, or more briefly the *north pole;* the magnet is usually marked on that end by an N or a line cut in the steel. The other end is naturally the *south pole* of the magnet; it is marked S or left unmarked. The term *polarity* is used to indicate the nature of the magnetism at the poles, whether north or south.

**13. Magnetic Attraction and Repulsion.**—It has been pointed out that a rod of magnetized steel, when pivoted so that it can move freely, will assume a definite direction pointing north and south. Thin pieces of magnetized steel, in the form of strips with pointed ends, are used to indicate this direction; such a pivoted strip is illustrated in Fig. 11 and constitutes a *horizontal magnetic needle*. When a small magnetic needle is poised on a jewel bearing above a graduated scale and these parts are mounted within a box having a glass cover, the device is termed a *compass*. Either a horizontal magnetic needle or a compass may be used for determining the polarity of magnets and for studying the force actions between magnetic poles.

FIG. 11. Horizontal magnetic needle

**Experiment 5.**—Bring the N-pole of a bar magnet near the N-pole of a magnetic needle, as shown at the left in Fig. 12; the needle will turn and soon come to rest with these poles farther apart. This action shows that the two N-poles *repel* each other. The same effect will take place if the two S-poles are brought near each other. If, however, the S-pole of the magnet is brought near the N-pole of the needle, each will *attract* the other and draw them closer together, as shown at the right in the figure.

The experiment shows that a N-pole repels a N-pole, a S-pole repels a S-pole, and a N-pole attracts a S-pole. These facts can be put together tersely by stating that *like magnetic poles repel each other, and unlike poles attract each other.* This is a law of great importance.

A magnet generally has two poles, although there may be more. Careful measurements of the strength of the forces exerted by them show that *the two poles have exactly the same strength.* A piece of lodestone has poles at a number of places on its surface, and a compass needle will reveal the location and polarity of these poles. It can be inferred that the total strength of the north poles of a lodestone is equal to the total strength of the south poles.

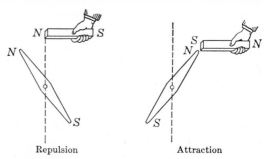

Repulsion                    Attraction

FIG. 12. Action of magnet on compass needle
Dotted lines show undisturbed position of needle.

Substances which a magnet can attract are called *magnetic substances;* such a substance can be attracted all over its surface. A piece of iron will attract a magnet, no matter what part of it approaches the magnet; it does not possess fixed poles like a magnet. The magnetic substances generally used are iron and steel. Besides these, the metallic elements of nickel, cobalt and chromium are attracted by a magnet, but only very feebly. There are also many alloys which are classified as magnetic substances. For practical purposes all other substances may be regarded as non-magnetic substances. Magnetic attraction or repulsion will, however, take place *through* these substances.

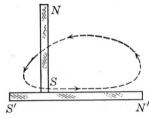

FIG. 13. Magnetizing a steel bar

Among the magnetic alloys, those containing nickel are particularly useful in telephone and radio communication. Alloys with from 30 to 90 per cent nickel and the rest iron are called *permalloys;* some have about 4 per cent of chromium or molybdenum to simplify the heat treatments in their preparation.

**14. Making a Permanent Magnet.**—Two simple procedures are employed for magnetizing a piece of steel by rubbing it with a permanent magnet. They are described in the following experiment:

**Experiment 6.**—Hold the steel bar to be magnetized on a table and, beginning at its unmarked end, stroke its entire length with the S-pole

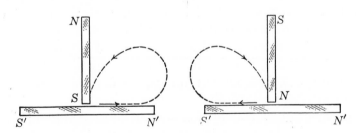

FIG. 14. Magnetizing a bar by halves separately

of a strong permanent magnet. Lift the magnet clear at the end and return again for a second stroke in the direction of the dotted line and the arrows in Fig. 13. Stroke both sides of the bar a number of times, and poles N' and S' of considerable strength will be produced in it.

Take another steel bar and magnetize each half separately, as illustrated in Fig. 14. Stroke one half of the bar with the S-pole, beginning at the center and following the direction of the dotted line at the left;

repeat this a number of times. Using the N-pole, stroke the other half of the bar in the same way. The action will develop poles N′ and S′ at the ends, as shown. After magnetizing the two bars, suspend each one at its middle point to swing horizontally and observe that as it comes to rest it will point in a' north-south direction.

In either method of magnetization the polarity produced in the steel bar is north at the end last touched by the S-pole of the magnetizing magnet. The latter method is the more effective in making a strong magnet.

**15. Horseshoe Magnets.**—When a straight bar of steel is bent into the form of a horseshoe, and then properly magnetized, the

end of one limb will be a N-pole and the other will be a S-pole of equal strength. By shaping the poles close together so that both can act on some object to be attracted, a greater force can be exerted by the magnet than the sum of the forces exerted by its poles separately; for this reason horseshoe magnets are more effective than bar magnets and find wider application in electrical apparatus.

FIG. 15. Permanent magnet used in electrical indicating instruments

Permanent magnets of modified horseshoe form are used in many electrical measuring instruments, telephone receivers, and magneto generators. Fig. 15 illustrates such a magnet that is used in portable ammeters and voltmeters for direct-current testing. The type of horseshoe magnet supplied for experimental use is equipped with a piece of soft iron, called a *keeper,* that is placed across the poles of the magnet when not in use; this tends to reduce the loss of magnetism.

It is quite important that permanent magnets used for the purposes mentioned should not change appreciably in strength over the years. In order to avoid loss of strength in service, magnets are often put through a process of aging during manufacture. In this process, a magnet is subjected to certain temperature changes and to vibration, treatments which have the effect of settling its strength at a value that will remain nearly permanent. Permanent magnets, or instruments containing them, should be handled with reasonable care as excessive heating and jarring reduce the magnetism.

**16. Composition of Permanent Magnets.**—The material originally used in making permanent magnets was ordinary high-
carbon steel, that is, iron containing 0.7 per cent of carbon. Much
greater strengths and more permanency of magnetization are
now available in special brands of steel containing tungsten,
chromium, cobalt, aluminum and nickel, to name them in the order
of development. Each brand is available in various compositions
and typical ranges are given below with the percentages of the
several elements that are added to the iron.

COMPOSITIONS OF PERMANENT MAGNETS

*Percentages of Elements Added to Iron*

*Tungsten Steel*

Tungsten .......5 to 6
Carbon ......... 0.7
Manganese ...... 0.3
Chromium ...... 0.3

*Cobalt Steel*

Cobalt .......3.5 to 8
Chromium ... 3 to 9
Tungsten .... 1 to 9
Carbon ...... 0.9
Manganese ...0.3 to 0.8

*Chromium Steel*

Chromium ... 1 to 6
Carbon ......0.6 to 1.0
Manganese ...0.2 to 0.6

*Alnico Alloys*

Aluminum ....10 to 12
Nickel ........17 to 28
Cobalt ........ 5 to 13

A pictorial comparison of the effectiveness of these materials
is given in Fig 16, which shows the relative sizes of permanent
horseshoe magnets having equal strength. Magnets made from
the alloys of aluminum, nickel, and cobalt (abbreviated alnico)
are observed to be the smallest. Tungsten and chromium steels
for magnets in shapes other than straight are formed to size
while hot and are then hardened at temperatures from 1450°
to 1700° F. by dipping them in cold water or oil. Magnets of
cobalt steel and alnico are cast in proper shape and then ground
to finished size, for they are too brittle and hard to be bent
or filed. The processing of alnico magnets involves heating to
temperatures in excess of 2000° F., rapid cooling in air or oil,
and then aging at temperatures about 1200° F.

Permanent magnets may also be made by compressing mixtures of metallic powders in suitable proportions in forms of proper shape, and then applying heat treatment. This procedure,

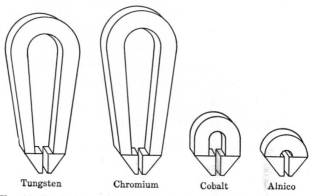

Tungsten        Chromium        Cobalt      Alnico

Fig. 16. Equivalent magnets of different brands of magnet steel

called powder metallurgy, has been utilized in manufacturing alnico magnets of small size, and the products have a fine grain structure free from impurities and blowholes; in consequence, they possess superior mechanical qualities.

Experiment 7.—Obtain a pair of cylindrical alnico magnets and place them on a smooth table several inches apart. The forces of attraction or repulsion between them will be found so great that the magnets will roll toward or away from each other over distances of several inches.

17. The Electromagnet.—Magnetism can also be produced by using electric currents, and this method is extensively used in electrical machinery and in all kinds of electrical devices. If a number of turns of insulated wire are wrapped around an iron bar as shown in Fig. 17, and a current is established in the coil so formed by connection of its terminals to an electric battery, the iron will be magnetized as long as the current is maintained. Such an arrangement of iron core and wire coil is called an *electromagnet*. If the battery is disconnected the iron will lose its magnetism, except for a small amount called *residual magnetism*.

Directing the electric current through the coil as shown by the arrows sets up a S-pole at the left end and a N-pole at the right end of the core. Reversing the current direction reverses the magnetism. If a larger number of turns is used, the electromagnet will be stronger with the same current. Powerful electro-magnets are made by using sizable cores wound with many turns, and having large currents through the windings.

If the iron core of an electromagnet is replaced by a bar of cold-rolled steel, and current is maintained through the coil for a few moments, the steel will become a permanent magnet. This means that the residual magnetism of this steel is larger than that of iron; naturally the residual magnetism of the various magnet

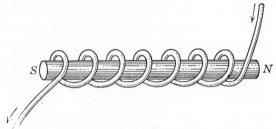

FIG. 17. Magnetization by an electric current

steels described in the last section is much larger still. Nowadays, practically all permanent magnets are magnetized with electro-magnets.

**Experiment 8.**—Wind a number of turns of insulated wire around a cardboard tube about ½ inch in diameter, insert an iron rod of sufficient length to protrude at each end of the tube, and connect the winding to a dry battery. Plunge the electromagnet so formed into iron filings and note that they are attracted at the ends; also that most of the filings drop off when the current is interrupted. Test the polarity of the rod with a compass, and then observe the effect of reversing the current. Finally, remove the rod and repeat the experiment with the coil alone. The behavior will be the same as before but the magnetism is much less.

**18. The Earth as a Magnet.**—Every magnet has two kinds of magnetic poles, one tending to point toward the general direction of the geographical north pole, and the other toward the general direction of the geographical south pole. This action takes place because the earth itself is magnetic. Since the north-seeking pole has been called the N-pole, the magnetism of the earth near the north geographical pole must be such as to attract the N-poles of all magnets. Similarly, the conditions of the earth's magnetism near the south pole are such that the S-poles of all magnets are attracted. Thus, a compass needle assumes a position pointing more or less north and south because the earth is virtually a magnet and possesses poles, and these exert forces upon the poles of the needle.

The magnetic poles of the earth are indicated by the terms north and south; the poles of all other magnets should, strictly speaking, be referred to as north-seeking and south-seeking, although they are generally styled N-pole and S-pole for short.

The earth's north magnetic pole is located in the northern hemisphere and its south magnetic pole is in the southern hemisphere. These poles are not coincident with the geographic poles; Fig. 18 shows the locations of the north magnetic and geographic poles. The region of the north magnetic pole was long believed to be on Boothia Peninsula, Canada (lat. 70° N., long. 96° W.). Explorations in 1947 indicated that this region possesses three poles, the major one on Prince of Wales Island and the others on Boothia Peninsula and on Bathurst Island. The south magnetic pole is in the Ross Sea, Antarctica (lat. 72° S., long. 157° E.).

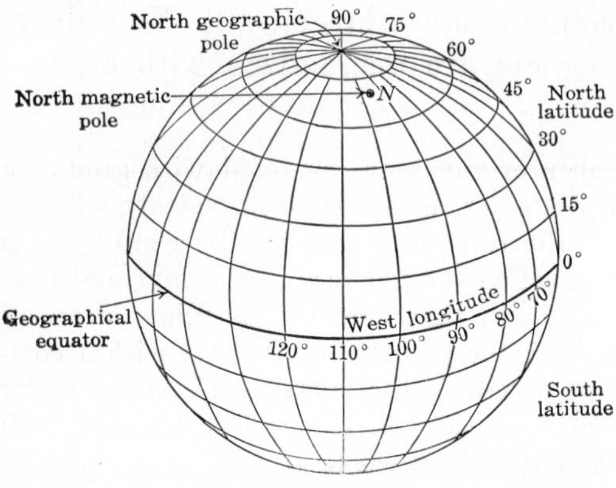

FIG. 18. Location of north magnetic pole of the earth

The two magnetic poles of the earth are not exactly opposite each other; a straight line connecting these poles would pass about 750 miles from the earth's center.

Wherever a compass needle may be placed, it comes to rest and the needle is then said to lie in the *magnetic meridian* of the earth at that place. In that position the needle generally shows a departure in direction from the true north-south line which passes through that place and through the geographic poles of the earth. This departure of the needle is known as *variation*, sometimes also as magnetic declination. Thus, the variation of a compass needle is the angle between the magnetic and geographic meridians and represents the angle that the needle points away from true north.

The variation of a compass needle, that is, its departure from true north, differs from place to place on the earth's surface or above it. For example, at New York City the magnetic variation is about 11° west, which means that a compass needle located there points about 11° west of the true north-south line. At Denver the variation is about 14° east of the true north-south line; at Savannah the variation happens to be 0°, and a compass needle there indicates true north. The variations for these places are indicated in Fig. 19, the dotted lines representing the true north-south direction.

In steering ships at sea or aircraft beyond the sight of land by the magnetic compass, it is necessary to know the amounts of variation at different localities. This information is given on charts prepared periodically by the United States Department of Commerce. Fig. 20 shows such a chart for the Americas and adjacent areas with lines, called *isogonic lines,* drawn on the map to connect places of equal magnetic variation.

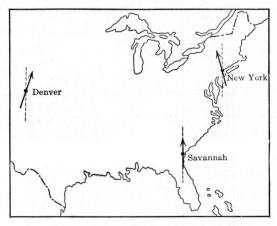

FIG. 19.  Magnetic variation pictured at Denver, New York, and Savannah

The variation at any place does not remain the same year after year, but changes somewhat over long periods of time. Besides these so-called *secular changes* which are quite definitely known, there are changes of small extent within the year as well as throughout the day. The magnetic variation is also subject to large erratic changes during *magnetic storms;* these storms usually accompany spurts of activity on the surface of the sun, commonly referred to as sun-spots.

If a steel knitting needle be carefully balanced and suspended by a silk thread, it will assume a horizontal position. When it is magnetized, its N-end will point directly toward the earth's magnetic north pole; since it is free to move in all directions, the needle will no longer be horizontal. The angle which the needle

makes with the horizontal is termed the *angle of dip*. This angle
increases in approaching either magnetic pole; at New York City
the N-pole points downward at an angle of 72° with the horizontal.
Fig. 21 illustrates a dipping needle for measuring the angle of

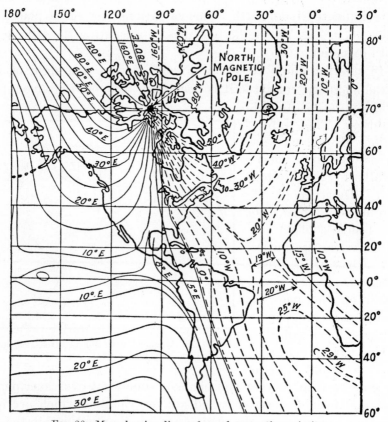

Fig. 20. Map showing lines of equal magnetic variation

Mercator projection of region between 30° E. and 180° W. meridians of longitude and between
60° S. and 80° N. parallels of latitude.

dip. It consists of a magnetic needle mounted on a horizontal
pin that is pivoted in a brass frame, together with a semicircular
scale divided into 180 degrees.

**19. Mariner's Compass.**—The familiar pocket compass is merely
a finely balanced and pivoted magnetic needle, contained in a
glass-covered brass case to exclude disturbing drafts of air, and

provided with a circular scale for indicating north, south, and intermediate points. In using this compass to determine direction, the needle is first allowed to come to rest so as to point magnetic north and south, and then the case is turned around until the point marked N on the scale is directly under the N-pole of the needle. The true geographical north will then be east or west of the position assumed by the N-pole of the needle, according to the amount of variation at the locality.

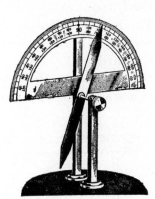

FIG. 21. Dipping needle
Central Scientific Company

The *mariner's magnetic compass* consists of a group of magnetized steel needles fastened to a circular graduated *card* that turns on a pivot. This pivot is mounted at the center of a bowl which is arranged mechanically to swing level, so that, no matter how much the ship may roll or lurch, the card will always be level. Magnetic compasses range in size from those having 4-inch cards to those used in the merchant marine service with cards 9 or 10 inches in diameter. The scale on the card is divided into 360 degrees numbered clockwise, and usually also into thirty-two "points of the compass," as shown

FIG. 22. Scale of the compass

in Fig. 22. The N-point on the scale always points to the north magnetic pole. A black line, termed the "lubber's line," is marked on the inside of the compass bowl, in line with the fore-aft direction of the ship. When it is desired to steer a ship in any particular direction, say northwest, the helm is turned until the point NW on the compass scale is at the lubber's line; correction must be made, of course, for the variation at the place where the ship is located.

Modern compasses are of the liquid-type, that is, the bowl is filled with liquid, about half alcohol and half distilled water, in order to hold the card steady in rough seas or during gunfire.

This type of compass allows the use of more powerful magnets, thereby giving the card greater directive force and sensitivity. A typical construction of the liquid-type of compass is shown in Fig. 23. The card is supported on a pivot mounted within the bowl, and it carries a spheroidal air vessel to buoy it in the liquid. The magnets consist of bundles of highly magnetized steel wires contained in four sealed cylindrical cases that are mounted below the card and parallel to its north and south line. Beneath the bowl is a self-adjusting expansion chamber of thin metal; it has two small holes to permit circulation of the liquid between the bowl and expansion chamber, thus keeping the bowl free from air bubbles. The bowl is of cast bronze, weighted with lead, and accurately balanced.

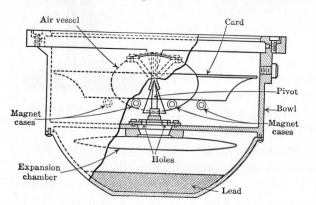

Fig. 23. Sectional view of a liquid-type magnetic compass

A compass on shipboard is affected by machinery and by electric light and power wires in its vicinity, as well as by the steel hull. Their combined influence on the compass is known as *deviation* and the amount varies with the heading of the ship. A number of movable magnets are kept in the binnacle near the compass to compensate for deviation, and these must be kept adjusted to assure accuracy of the compass.

There is another type of compass that is not dependent upon the earth's magnetism for the movement of the card; it is the "gyro-compass." The operation of this compass is based on the principle of the gyroscope, which consists essentially of a heavy rotating wheel, the shaft of which is free to turn in any direction. When the wheel of a gyro-compass is revolving at high speed, its shaft takes up a position parallel to the axis of the earth. The indication of a gyro-compass is true north.

The compensation of magnetic compasses on naval vessels is difficult because of the movements of great masses of steel in the turrets and guns, and the intermittent operation of large electrical equipments. The gyro-compass, being subject to no magnetic influence whatever, is particularly effective in battle. The magnetic compass, however, will always be retained as a check on the gyro-compass, and for use in case of damage to the latter.

There is still another type of compass which is used on aircraft; it is called an "earth-inductor" compass. Its operation is based on electromagnetic induction, §144, using the earth's magnetism to generate a current of electricity for deflecting an indicating instrument.

**20. Magnetic Fields.**—The region about a magnet where its influence can be detected is called a *magnetic field*. Throughout this region forces will act upon magnetic substances or magnet poles. The force that is experienced by any given pole within the field will not generally be the same at all points, but will vary in direction and in amount as that pole is moved about. This fact indicates that the magnetic field must have a certain direction and a particular intensity at every place. *The direction of a magnetic field at any point is the direction of the force acting upon an isolated N-pole placed at that point;* the idea of an isolated pole is a convenient one and implies that the companion pole of the magnet is too far away to affect the resulting action appreciably.

Experiment 9.—Use a compass to explore the magnetic field around a bar magnet. Place the magnet on a sheet of paper and shift the compass from place to place. At points equally distant from the two poles, the compass needle will assume positions parallel to the magnet. Move the compass toward either pole and observe that its needle points more directly toward it. For each location of the compass draw a line on the paper to show the direction of the needle.

The directions of the magnetic field around a bar magnet will be found approximately as illustrated in Fig. 24. Each arrow represents the direction that a compass needle will assume when placed there, the arrowhead indicating the N-pole of the compass. It is evident that the magnetic field has a definite direction at every point.

**21. Magnetic Lines of Force.**—Any magnetic field can be visualized as a whole by placing a sheet of glass or cardboard in the region to be observed and sprinkling it with iron filings. Upon tapping the sheet, the individual filings behave like tiny compasses and align themselves

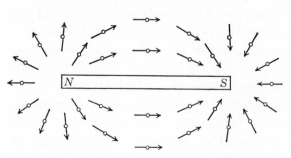

FIG. 24. Directions of magnetic field about a bar magnet explored by compass

with the field to form strings or chains; a few of these are represented by lines in Fig. 25 for the field existing around a bar magnet. Such tests indicate that the space around any magnet has a very definite magnetic orientation and reveal the character of magnetic strain throughout the region. The field is able to exert a force on any pole that is brought into it and the direction of the force will be along the direction of the lines representing the magnetic field. For this reason the lines are called *magnetic lines of force.* The iron filings in the test just described reveal the direction of such imaginary lines.

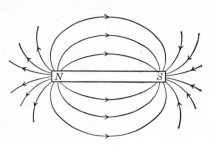

FIG. 25. Lines of force about a bar magnet

**Experiment 10.**—Place a piece of white cardboard upon a bar magnet and sprinkle fine iron filings over the card while tapping it gently. To avoid dropping large clusters of filings, it is desirable to put a small quantity in a fine wire sieve and shake this moderately a few inches above the card. A pattern similar to Fig. 25 will be produced.

It is assumed that the magnetic lines of force emerge from the N-pole of a magnet, pass through the surroundings, re-enter the S-pole, and complete the path from the S-pole to the N-pole through the magnet itself. *Every magnetic line of force forms a complete loop, each loop is independent of the others, and the lines never cross or merge into each other.*

The field within the magnet itself is more restricted in cross-sectional area than the external field and causes the magnetic lines of force to be more concentrated inside the magnet than in the surrounding air. Because of this concentration, the lines in the surrounding medium where they leave the magnet at the N-pole, and where they enter at the S-pole, are more crowded than elsewhere. The strong attraction at the poles is associated with the closeness of lines of force at those places. The more intense the magnetic field the closer will be its lines of force.

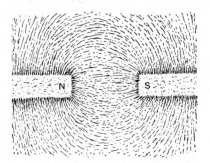

FIG. 26. Magnetic field between unlike poles

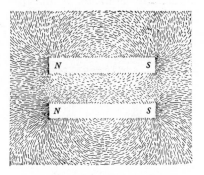

FIG. 27. Magnetic field about parallel bar magnets with their like poles adjacent

**Experiment 11.**—Make several patterns of magnetic fields by laying cardboard over some magnets placed in various positions and then sifting iron filings upon the cardboard. Figs. 26 to 28 suggest some of the arrangements and the student is urged to make up others to assure a thorough knowledge of the directions of magnetic fields. Permanent representations of these fields can be made by using glass plates coated with thin layers of paraffin; after the filings have been applied, the glass plate is heated so that the filings will stick to the paraffin.

It is found that tapping the cardboard in the foregoing experiment lessens the friction of the filings on

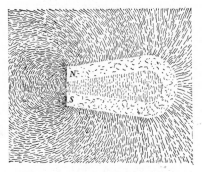

FIG. 28. Magnetic field around a horseshoe magnet

it and permits them to assume positions along lines of force more readily. During this agitation the strings of filings are observed to shorten themselves (like stretched rubber bands) and at the same time to keep away from each other as though they exerted a side-wise thrust upon one another. On the basis of this behavior, the attraction or repulsion between two magnets can be explained by the interaction between the lines of force in the space between their poles. The idea of lines of force has its chief value in directing attention to the part played by the medium that surrounds the magnet poles in determining their force actions.

**22. Magnetic Induction.**—A piece of soft iron, placed in the magnetic field of a magnet, also assumes the properties of a magnet. This phenomenon is known as *magnetic induction,* and

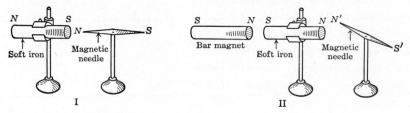

Fig. 29. Magnetic induction in a bar of iron

takes place whether contact is made with the magnet or not. Magnetic induction always precedes the attraction of a magnet for a magnetic substance, and can act through all non-magnetic substances.

**Experiment 12.**—Plunge a soft iron bar into iron filings and observe that no filings are attracted to it. Bring one pole of a magnet in contact with the iron bar and dip the end of the bar into filings; note that some are now attracted to it. Remove the magnet from contact with the soft iron; while most of the filings drop off, a few still cling to the iron. Separate the magnet from the iron bar by pieces of wood, brass, glass, etc., and apply the iron to the filings again. It will be observed that the iron becomes magnetized even though it does not touch the magnet.

**Experiment 13.**—Place a soft iron rod horizontally in line with a poised magnetic needle while pointing north and south, separating the two as shown at I in Fig. 29. The rod will be magnetized inductively by the needle, the N-pole of the needle inducing a S-pole in the end of the iron nearest to it, and a N-pole at the far end, as shown. Then bring a bar magnet near the iron rod and also in alignment with it, as illustrated at II in the figure. The bar magnet, being stronger than the needle, induces a S-pole in the end of the iron nearer to it and a N-pole in the other end, thus not only neutralizing the inductive effect of the needle but also remagnetizing the iron in the opposite direction. The iron rod now repels the needle to the position N'S'. When the magnet is removed the needle will assume its former position, provided the iron is very soft.

Explanation of magnetic induction is simplified by the idea of lines of force. It has been stated before that lines of force issue from a N-pole and enter at a S-pole; conversely, if lines of force enter a piece of iron at one place then a S-pole must be developed

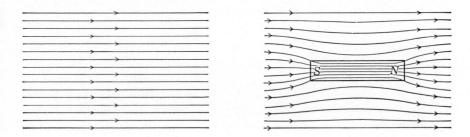

FIG. 30. Effect of introducing iron in a uniform magnetic field

there, and if lines of force leave the iron at another place a N-pole must be developed at that point. This induction of polarity is indicated in Fig. 30, which shows at the left a *uniform* magnetic field with the lines of force evenly spaced, and at the right a bar of iron in the field with a relatively larger number of lines threading through it. If the iron is removed from the field its magnetism is lost, except for a small amount of residual magnetism. Inserting a piece of steel in the field produces the same effect, but when it is removed, its residual magnetism will be much greater than for soft iron. The methods of magnetization described in §17 are based on magnetic induction.

Fig. 30 shows also the tendency of the magnetic lines of force to pass through a piece of iron located in the field rather than through the surrounding medium, because the iron is better able to accommodate magnetic lines of force than the medium. A piece of iron, so mounted as to permit free movement within a magnetic field, will turn and take up a position to allow the greatest number of lines to pass through it. The fundamental principle of many forms of electrical measuring instruments and electromechanical devices is that a magnetic substance, free to move under the influence of a magnetic field, will place itself in that field so that as many lines as possible will pass through the substance. If the substance is a magnet, it will move so that its own internal magnetic lines will be in the same direction as those of the field in which it is placed.

**23. Consequent Poles.**—Although the least number of poles a magnet can have is two, it may possess any number greater than two. Fig. 31 shows a bar magnet with four poles; the two intermediate ones are called *consequent poles.* The location of such poles may be readily shown by plunging the entire magnet into iron filings.

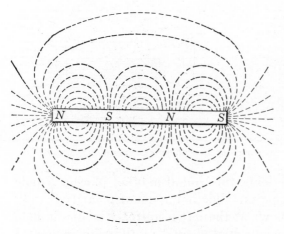

FIG. 31. Bar magnet with consequent poles

If the like-named poles of two magnets, one weak and the other strong, are brought near each other, repulsion will take place up to within a certain distance between the poles; at shorter distances attraction occurs because the inductive effect of the stronger magnet has neutralized the weaker one and has magnetized it with opposite polarity. Magnetic needles often have their polarity reversed by storing them near large magnets and sometimes consequent poles are produced in them. In making any tests with a magnetic needle, always check its polarity by noting the direction to which it points in the earth's field.

**24. Theory of Magnetism.**—An explanation of magnetism is suggested by a simple test which consists of breaking a magnet in two, then breaking one of these parts in two, and so on. As far as actual tests like this have been carried out, the parts of the original magnet were always found to be magnets themselves, so it is presumed that if the breaking process were continued until the parts became reduced to molecular sizes, each minute part would prove to be a magnet. The belief that a magnetic substance is composed of molecular magnets, although not necessarily that each individual molecule be a magnet, is called the *molecular theory of magnetism.*

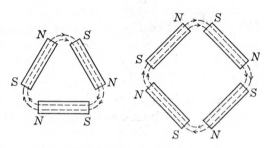

FIG. 32. Arrangements of molecular magnets within an unmagnetized bar

According to this theory, when a substance is unmagnetized its molecular magnets point in all conceivable directions and form small stable groups that exhibit no outside magnetism. Fig. 32 shows two such groups within a piece of iron portrayed by small bar magnets; the lines of force for each group form localized magnetic loops. When the iron is placed in a magnetic field and the intensity of the field is increased, the molecular magnets of the various groups align themselves more and more in a definite direction, an increasing number of the local magnetic loops are

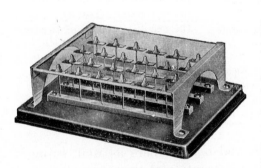

FIG. 33. Model of molecular magnets
W. M. Welch Scientific Company

broken up, and magnetic poles of increasing strength are produced at the ends of the piece of iron.

Fig. 33 shows a model of a magnet for demonstrating the molecular nature of magnetism. It consists of twenty-four bar magnets mounted on separate needle points to permit free turning. When placed near a large magnet the needles turn individually and the small groups give way to an aligned pattern, as shown. A cover plate of transparent material prevents the magnets coming off their pivots.

Hard steel requires a more intense field than soft iron to produce a given magnetization, because its molecular magnets turn with greater difficulty; for the same reason, upon removal from the field most of the molecular magnets of the steel retain their positions, while most of those of the iron again assume random groupings. This explains why steel has more residual magnetism than iron and accounts for its use in making permanent magnets.

**Experiment 14.**—Fill a glass tube with coarse steel filings, and insert a thin cork at each end, as shown in Fig. 34. Test each end of the tube of filings for magnetism by bringing it near a magnetic needle. Either end will attract the N-pole of the needle, proving that it is not magnetized; if the tube of filings were magnetized one end would repel this pole of the needle. Magnetize the tube of filings by any of the methods previously given, being careful not to shake it. Test again with the needle; one end of the tube will now repel one pole of the needle and attract the other.

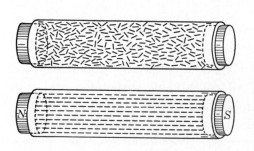

FIG. 34. Glass tube of steel filings before and after magnetization

Apparently, the filings were first located promiscuously, as shown at the top in the figure, and magnetization directed them more nearly in a straight line, as indicated at the bottom. Finally, shake the tube thoroughly and repeat the test; observe that the tube of filings is no longer a magnet.

The foregoing experiment, and many others as well, support the theory that a magnet is an aggregation of tiny magnets which are more or less properly directed. If a bar of unmagnetized steel is held in the direction of the earth's field and jarred by striking it repeatedly, some of its molecular magnets will align themselves with the field, and the bar will become permanently magnetized. Poles are induced in the bar so long as it remains in the field. It is because of these induced poles that a piece of unmagnetized iron is attracted by a magnet. Again, if a permanent magnet is heated to a dull red, the increased thermal agitation of the molecules will throw them out of alignment, and it will lose its magnetism.

**Experiment 15.**—Hold a small sheet of nickel edgewise up to the pole of a permanent magnet and make adjustments so that the magnet will just keep it attracted against the force of gravity. Apply a Bunsen flame to the nickel and observe that it falls off, showing that it loses its magnetic character when hot.

A more complete theory attributes magnetism to the motion of electrons within the atom. Each planetary electron not only revolves about the nucleus of the atom as pictured in Lesson I, but according to the present belief, based largely upon experiment, each electron also spins about an axis through its center. In highly magnetic substances, each atom is regarded to have more electrons spinning in one direction than in the other, and throughout a tiny region called a *domain*, these uncompensated spins have the same direction in all the atoms. The entire specimen is composed of a large number of such domains, each being highly magnetized but turned at random with respect to the others. When a small external magnetic field is applied, the directions of magnetization of the individual domains are shifted somewhat toward that of the field, and the specimen becomes slightly magnetized. Upon increasing the strength of the applied field, the domains themselves are rotated, one or more at a time, and the specimen experiences a series of minute jumps in magnetization. This process continues until the axes of magnetization of all the domains lie along the direction of the field, and the magnetization increases tremendously. Beyond this point, an increase in the applied field produces no further magnetic effect, and the specimen is said to be *saturated*.

## QUESTIONS

1. Distinguish between a natural magnet and an artificial magnet.
2. What important properties does a magnet possess?
3. What is polarity? How would you locate the poles on a magnet?
4. You are given two similar bars of steel, only one of which is magnetized. What tests would you apply to determine which is magnetized?
5. A small bar magnet is floated on a cork. What occurs when the S-pole of another magnet is brought near the S-pole of the floating magnet? What occurs when the N-pole is brought near the same end?
6. State the law regarding magnetic attraction and repulsion.
7. You are given a hard steel bar with a notch at one end. How would you magnetize it, by rubbing it only with the N-pole of a magnet, so that the notched end would become a N-pole?

8. How would you magnetize a steel sewing needle by magnetizing each half separately, so that the eye would become a N-pole? Illustrate with a sketch.

9. What kinds of steel are used for making good permanent magnets?

10. What is an electromagnet? Upon what does its strength depend?

11. Give a general classification of magnets, citing an example to illustrate each class.

12. What evidence can you give to show that the earth behaves as a magnet?

13. Show by means of a sketch how a compass needle would locate itself with respect to the true north-south meridian, at the point located at Latitude, 40° N.; Longitude, 120° W. *Ans.* 19° E.

14. Explain the terms variation, angle of dip, and isogonic line.

15. A compass on shipboard reads 25° at a place where the magnetic variation is 10° W. Allowing for a deviation of 1° W. due to ship's magnetism for the particular heading, find the true course of the ship. *Ans.* 14° east of north.

16. Explain why a pocket magnetic compass will probably yield incorrect indications when used casually in an automobile.

17. Describe the liquid-type of magnetic compass used in navigation.

18. Make a sketch of a bar magnet and locate somewhere around it two points where the directions of the magnetic field are parallel to the magnet. Locate a third point where the field is at right angles to the others.

19. How would you demonstrate that magnetic lines of force do not cross each other?

20. Two bar magnets are laid parallel to each other with unlike poles adjacent, and a horseshoe magnet is placed at one end so that its poles are directly opposite but a little distant from the poles of the bar magnets. Sketch the resultant magnetic field that you would expect. Repeat, interchanging the poles of the horseshoe magnet.

21. A steel ring is magnetized to have a N-pole diametrically opposite a S-pole. Make a sketch of the magnetic lines of force about the ring.

22. Cite and illustrate by sketches an experiment to demonstrate magnetic induction.

23. Upon testing a bar magnet with iron filings, it is found that the magnet attracts filings at the center and also at each end. How do you account for this? Make a sketch of the lines of force about the magnet to illustrate your answer.

24. How does the experiment of successively breaking up a bar magnet support the molecular theory of magnetism?

25. Explain what is meant by the molecular theory of magnetism.

26. Why is it that hard steel makes a better permanent magnet than soft iron?

27. Explain magnetic saturation by applying the molecular theory.

# Lesson III

## ELECTRIC CURRENT AND ELECTROLYSIS

Effects of electric current—Resistance of circuit—Electrolytic action—Electrolysis of hydrochloric acid—Decomposition of water—Electrolysis of copper sulfate—Electroplating—Electrotyping—Strength of current—Unit of current; the ampere—Unit of quantity of electricity; the coulomb—Faraday's Laws of Electrolysis—Measurements on a gas voltameter—Polarity indicators—Questions and Problems.

**25. Effects of Electric Current.**—The nature of an electric current has been described in §11 as a flow of electrons; the path through which the flow takes place is called an *electric circuit*. The electrons cannot be seen travelling along the circuit, but their presence can be detected by certain effects which the current produces. The principal effects of a current are *magnetism, heat,* and *electrolysis,* and examples of these effects are familiar to everyone. Thus, a current in a winding of wire around an iron core *magnetizes* the core and enables it to attract magnetic substances. A current in an electric lamp *heats* its filament to incandescence and provides illumination nearby. A current in acidulated water *electrolyzes* the liquid and liberates its components as hydrogen and oxygen gases. These effects in electric circuits form the basis of a great many applications of electricity.

There are several other effects of an electric current, and one of these demands particular caution, namely the *physiological effect.* Passing a current through the body produces muscular contractions, and care must be exercised to keep such currents to *very low* values to avoid interruption of heart action. Insulation or guards are expressly provided around electric circuits to prevent contact of persons with "live" conductors.

While the electric circuit is a conducting path for the transfer of electrons, it requires an agency like a battery to maintain a positive charge at one point in the circuit and a negative charge at another so that electrons will continue to flow between the two points. In other words, a battery is needed in the circuit and the circuit must be complete in order to maintain a current in it. A *switch* is a device for *closing* and *opening* an electric circuit conveniently; it consists of a metal strip or bar which can be moved to close or open a short air gap in the circuit.

**Experiment 16.**—Take apart a flashlight and connect the lamp bulb to the dry battery by means of copper wires and a switch. Set up the

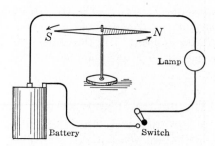

FIG. 35. Heating and magnetic effects of electric current

circuit near a poised magnetic needle as shown in Fig. 35, arranging one wire parallel to the needle after it has assumed the north-south direction. Close the switch and observe that the establishment of current in the circuit causes the lamp to glow (heating effect) and the needle to deflect (magnetic effect). Then insert pieces of tin, iron, brass, aluminum or other metals in the circuit and note that the same effects will be produced, although reduced in extent. Repeat with pieces of paper, glass, wood and mica forming part of the circuit; the heating and magnetic effects will cease because these insulating materials leave the circuit open and stop the current.

The deflection of the magnetic needle in this experiment shows that a magnetic field is produced around the wire when it carries a current. The effect can be enhanced by forming a coil around the needle as shown in Fig. 36, so that the direction of the current in all the turns is the same. This current sets

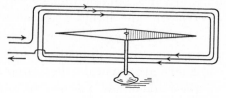

FIG. 36. Simple form of current detector

up a magnetic field directed at right angles to the turns of wire, and causes the needle to deflect away from its normal position pointing toward the north pole of the earth. The greater the current in the coil, the greater will be the deflection of the needle. Consequently, such an arrangement, called a *current detector,* serves not only to detect a current but also to give an idea of current strength.

It must be remarked, however, that the deflections of the needle reckoned in degrees are not proportional to the current strength; for example, if a certain current produces a deflection of 25 degrees, twice that current will *not* produce a deflection of 50 degrees.

FIG. 37. Coils of a current detector
Coil 1 has 100 turns of wire, coil 2 has 1 turn, and coil 3 has 25 turns.
Central Scientific Company

Fig. 37 shows a current detector of the form described with three separate coils but without the pocket compass which serves as the indicator. The compass is placed centrally under whichever coil is to be used.

**26. Resistance of Circuit.**—The experiment described in the last section shows that some substances conduct electricity and others do not; this difference has already been pointed out in Lesson I. The experiment shows also that the metallic conductors exhibit differences in their ability to conduct electricity, as evidenced by the different deflections of the needle when one after another of these metals was included in the circuit. Obviously the current is greater for a good conductor than for a poor one. Another way of stating this fact is to say that a good conductor presents less *resistance* to an electric current than a poor conductor.

**Experiment 17.**—Make up a rectangular coil formed of several turns of copper wire and line it up in a vertical plane with a poised magnetic needle to form a current detector. Place a circular scale under the needle to permit reading its deflections in degrees. An arrangement like that shown in Fig. 37 together with a pocket compass may be used instead. Procure several lengths of wire of different metals, preferably of the same size, and use these one at a time in connecting the detector to a dry battery. Read the deflection for each wire and record the values observed. Make up a list of the metals used and arrange them in accordance with their resistances, placing the metal of least resistance at the head of the list.

All conductors have resistance, and the amount possessed by any one conductor depends upon its size and upon the material of which it is made. For two wires of identical size, one of copper and the other of aluminum, the copper wire has only about *half as much resistance* as the aluminum wire. The same result can be expressed by saying that copper has almost *twice the conductivity* of aluminum. The difference is due to the presence of free electrons in the metal; copper has more free electrons than aluminum.

**27. Electrolytic Action.**—Liquids may be divided into three classes: (1) those which do not conduct electrons, such as petroleum and other organic compounds; (2) liquids which conduct like metals, such as mercury; and (3) liquids which transfer charged particles, such as solutions of acids and of metallic salts. The first class of liquids is widely used for insulating purposes, as in transformers and cables; the second is utilized in contacting devices, such as mercury switches; and the third class is extensively employed in electroplating and metal refining, as well as in batteries.

Liquids of the third class are of particular interest, inasmuch as electricity is transferred through the solutions by means of carriers called *ions*. Such a liquid is called an *electrolyte,* the process of transferring the ions through it is called *electrolysis,* and the apparatus used for the process is called an *electrolytic cell.*

Plates of carbon, lead, platinum, or other metals are used to conduct the current to and from the acid or salt solution; these plates are then designated *electrodes*. The plate at which the current *enters* the electrolyte is called the positive electrode or *anode,* and the plate by which it *leaves* the solution is called the negative electrode or *cathode,* as shown in Fig. 38. The direction of current in an electrolytic cell is from the Anode, through the electrolytic Bath, to the Cathode; that is, from $A$ to $B$ to $C$.

**Experiment 18.**—Connect a 110-volt incandescent lamp to the service mains and observe that the filament lights up. To demonstrate the difference between conducting and non-conducting liquids, cut one of the connecting wires to the lamp and dip the two ends into some water contained in a beaker. Note that the lamp goes out. Then pour a little sulfuric acid into the water and the lamp filament becomes bright again.

The behavior of any electrolytic cell, except for chemical actions which may occur, is based entirely upon the attraction of unlike charges and the repulsion of like charges. An electrolyte breaks up spontaneously because the electrostatic attraction between some of the atoms of the molecules present is greater than between others; this splitting up of an electrolyte is called *dissociation.* Thus, an acid or salt held in solution *dissociates into ions,* some with positive and others with negative charges. The usual solvent is water ($H_2O$), and this liquid will be assumed as the solvent when solutions are mentioned hereafter.

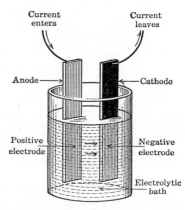

FIG. 38. Nomenclature of an electrolytic cell

In a solution of hydrochloric acid (HCl), for example, many molecules of the acid are dissociated; the H atom loses an electron and is, therefore, positively charged, while the Cl atom, with an extra electron, is negatively charged. The action is summarized by saying that hydrochloric acid dissociates into *positive hydrogen ions* and *negative chloride ions;* it is written as a chemical equation by representing the ions with appropriate + and − signs as follows:

$$HCl \rightleftharpoons H^+ + Cl^-$$

While in the ionic state, the substances do not have the same properties as the corresponding atoms. Thus, hydrogen ions are essentially different from hydrogen atoms, for a solution of hydrogen ions ($H^+$) affects such chemical indicators as litmus, while a solution of hydrogen gas ($H_2$) does not.

Recent evidence indicates that bare $H^+$ ions can hardly exist in water solutions; instead they are believed to occur in a hydrated form known as *hydronium ions* ($H_3O^+$), each being a combination of $H^+$ and $H_2O$. For simplicity, however, the hydrogen ion will be represented in this book by the simpler and more widely known notation, $H^+$.

The mechanism of electrical conduction through liquids will be illustrated by specific examples. In each case mention will be made of the behavior of the neutral atoms or groups of atoms at the electrodes after they have served in transferring charges. Such atoms may then be deposited on the electrodes, may pass off as gases, or may enter into chemical unions with other atoms.

### 28. Electrolysis of Hydrochloric Acid.

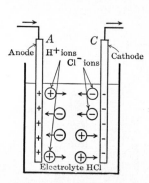

FIG. 39. Conduction in an electrolytic cell

—Suppose two platinum plates are dipped into a dilute solution of hydrochloric acid, and that current is directed through it from anode $A$ to cathode $C$ as shown in Fig. 39. The $H^+$ ions will be attracted by the negative plate $C$ and repelled by the positive plate $A$, and at the same time the $Cl^-$ ions will be attracted by the positive plate and repelled by the negative plate. The result will be a movement of ions in both directions through the liquid. Each $H^+$ ion upon reaching plate $C$ combines with an electron there, forming a hydrogen atom; this action may be written as

$$H^+ + e \rightarrow H$$

where $e$ represents the negative electronic charge. From these atoms hydrogen molecules are produced and pass off as gas. The $Cl^-$ ions upon reaching plate $A$ give up their electrons and become chlorine atoms; thus

$$Cl^- - e \rightarrow Cl$$

the atoms combining to form molecules of chlorine which will be liberated at this plate.

### 29. Decomposition of Water.

—As a typical illustration of the decomposition of water, consider the effect of a current through a dilute solution of sulfuric acid ($H_2SO_4$), using insoluble electrodes of platinum or carbon. The $H^+$ ions of the acid will be attracted by the negative plate and repelled by the positive plate, and the $SO_4^=$ ions, each with two electrons, will be attracted by the positive and repelled by the negative plate. The result will be a drifting of ions in both directions through the liquid. Each $H^+$ ion upon reaching the cathode combines with an electron there, forming a hydrogen atom, and the atoms combine into molecules and escape as gas; the composite equation is:

$$2H^+ + 2e \rightarrow H_2 \uparrow$$

where the arrow pointing up symbolizes the liberation of hydrogen gas. The $SO_4^=$ ions upon reaching the anode give up their electrons and combine with the water present to form more sulfuric acid, liberating oxygen as a gas; that is:

$$2SO_4^= - 4e + 2H_2O \rightarrow \underbrace{4H^+ + 2SO_4^=}_{2H_2SO_4} + O_2 \uparrow$$

Thus, hydrogen is produced at the cathode and oxygen at the anode, and just as much sulfuric acid is formed as was dissociated in the formation of ions. This shows that the net action is the *electrolysis of water* into its constituent elements, hydrogen and oxygen.

**Exeriment 19.** —Make up an electrolytic cell of the form shown in Fig. 40, and join it to a thistle tube by rubber hose. Add a few drops of sulfuric acid to some water and fill the U-tube with the solution. Put the corks holding the electrodes in place without entrapping air over the liquid columns. Connect the electrodes to a battery of several dry cells to establish current through the electrolyte. Observe that bubbles of gas will rise from the platinum electrodes and collect at the upper ends of the U-tube;

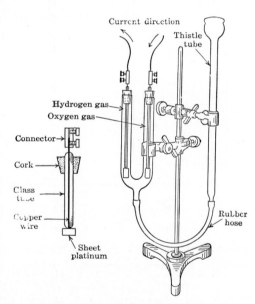

FIG. 40. Electrolytic cell formed of glass U-tube and simple electrodes

at the same time the solution will rise in the thistle tube. The oxygen collects in the column having the terminal where current enters the cell, and hydrogen collects in the column where it leaves. The volume of hydrogen collected in any given period of time will be twice that of the oxygen, showing that water is composed of two parts of hydrogen to one of oxygen, whence the designation of water as $H_2O$.

To test the gases collected, first remove the cork for an instant from the hydrogen column and quickly apply a lighted match at the opening; the hydrogen burns with a pale bluish flame. *Replace the cork quickly* so that the solution is not forced out of the U-tube. Then remove the cork from the oxygen column, extinguish the flame of the match, and quickly apply the glowing spark to the oxygen; the match immediately bursts into flame again. *Replace the cork quickly.* Oxygen gas does not burn, but supports combustion. If both gases were collected in a single tube and a lighted match were presented to the mouth of this tube, the hydrogen, instead of burning, would explode with a violent report, due to the presence of the oxygen.

**30. Electrolysis of Copper Sulfate.**—Consider next an electrolytic cell in which the electrolyte is a dilute copper sulfate solution, and suppose at first that the electrodes are inert, like platinum.

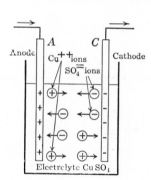

FIG. 41.  Copper plating cell

The copper sulfate ($CuSO_4$) is separated into copper ions carrying positive charge and *sulfate ions* carrying negative charge, each ion having two units of charge as indicated by the following equation representing the action:

$$CuSO_4 \rightleftharpoons Cu^{++} + SO_4^{=}$$

With current through the cell as shown in Fig. 41, the copper ions go toward the cathode or negative plate, while the sulfate ions combine with the water of the solution to form sulfuric acid ($H_2SO_4$) and liberate oxygen at the anode or positive plate. The reactions at the electrodes are:

At cathode $\qquad Cu^{++} + 2e \rightarrow Cu \downarrow$

At anode $\quad 2SO_4^{=} - 4e + 2H_2O \rightarrow \underbrace{4H^+ + 2SO_4^{=}}_{2H_2SO_4} + O_2 \uparrow$

where the arrow pointing down symbolizes that copper is plated upon the cathode, and the arrow pointing up indicates the liberation of oxygen. The equations show that the copper sulfate electrolyte gradually changes its composition to sulfuric acid; this would be observed experimentally by a change in color from a deep to a pale blue.

**Experiment 20.**—Prepare a solution of copper sulfate by dissolving some copper sulfate crystals (bluestone) in water, and insert two platinum electrodes. Connect the electrolytic cell so formed to a battery of several cells. Metallic copper is deposited upon the negative electrode, that is, this plate becomes copper-plated. Oxygen gas is liberated at the positive electrode and sulfuric acid is formed. Then reverse the current, making the copper-coated platinum plate the positive electrode, and the platinum plate the negative electrode. The latter will now have metallic copper deposited upon it, while the former will have its copper coating returned to the solution.

**Experiment 21.**—Substitute two copper plates for the platinum electrodes of Experiment 20 and repeat. Metallic copper is again deposited upon the negative electrode, but no gas is evolved from the positive electrode. The positive plate loses weight, while the negative electrode gains weight.

Just as much copper is thrown down into solution from the positive plate as is taken from the solution and deposited on the negative plate. The art of electroplating is based on the process just described.

**31. Electroplating.**—The deposition of a coating of metal upon any object with the aid of electricity is termed *electroplating*, and the process is based upon the principles of electrolysis already explained. Since the metallic ions are deposited on the object to be plated, it must be connected to form the cathode, while a plate of the metal from which the coating is derived, as nickel, copper, gold, or silver, is used as the anode.

In plating with silver or gold the electrolyte is usually an alkaline solution, generally of the cyanide of the metal to be deposited. To attain proper adherence of the deposit, articles of iron, steel, zinc, tin and lead to be silvered or gilded are first coated with a thin covering of copper. To plate an iron spoon with silver, for example, the iron is first cleansed to remove all dirt, rust and grease, and is then put in a copper plating bath to receive a deposit of copper. Afterward the spoon is transferred to a silver plating bath, and a coating of the desired thickness is deposited; finally the deposit is brightened on a buffing wheel.

Chromium plating presents more difficulty in practice than the plating of other metals, but is very popular on account of the hardness of the deposit and its resistance to corrosion. Chromium is usually deposited from a chromium sulfate bath, the anode material being lead or iron. The chromium content of the electrolyte is restored from time to time as the process continues.

Under certain conditions two substances can be deposited simultaneously in an electrolytic cell. For example, the use of a cyanide solution in which both zinc and copper are present makes it possible to obtain a simultaneous deposit of zinc and copper, that is, of brass. Non-conducting substances, such as wood, leather and ceramics, can be electroplated by first preparing the surface with a coating of powdered graphite, upon which metal can be deposited.

It is also possible to deposit rubber electrolytically from rubber latex (the milky juice of rubber trees), although the process differs from electroplating in that a migration of small particles rather than ions is involved. The latex is in suspension and the particles have negative charges, a frequent occurrence among colloids. Upon applying a high potential difference to the electrodes, the latex particles move to the anode, to which they become affixed. This process is known as *electrophoresis*.

**Experiment 22.**—Dissolve some crystals of zinc sulfate ($ZnSO_4$, white vitriol) in water and subject this solution to electrolysis. With platinum electrodes, metallic zinc is deposited upon the negative electrode and oxygen gas is evolved from the positive electrode. Upon reversing the current, the zinc previously deposited on the cathode goes back into solution, while the other electrode now receives a deposit of zinc. Oxygen gas is not evolved from the positive electrode until all of the zinc has been thrown down into solution. Repeat, using two zinc strips as electrodes, and note that the positive strip wastes away and the negative zinc strip gains in weight.

The action of the early *Edison electrolytic meter* for measuring current, made use of a cell with zinc electrodes and zinc sulfate solution, as in the foregoing experiment. The charge for electrical energy was determined by the gain in weight of one of the electrodes.

**Experiment 23.**—Prepare a solution of lead acetate, and pass it through filter paper to clear the solution. Place some in a small container and use platinum wires as electrodes. Upon establishing current through the cell, metallic lead is deposited at the negative plate and oxygen appears at the positive plate. When the current is quite low, the lead will be deposited in a beautiful tree-like form extending out into the solution from the negative plate. The solution becomes weaker as the extraction of metallic lead continues. When the current is reversed the former positive plate receives a lead deposit of the same form, but oxygen gas is not liberated from the positive plate until the lead previously deposited is dissolved in the solution. This experiment is also suitable for illustrating electrolysis to an audience by using a lantern projection cell and producing a large image of it upon a screen.

**32. Electrotyping.**—The preparation of plates from printers' type or artists' engravings is a branch of electroplating called *electrotyping*. Suppose it is desired to make a plate of a page of type. The type page is locked up in a chase; then impressed into wax which will take the impression. The surface of the wax impression is dusted over with powdered graphite to make it conducting. The mold is connected as the negative plate in a copper plating bath and receives a thin coating of metallic copper. After removal from the bath the copper deposit is removed from the mold and backed with lead alloy to about the depth of one-eighth inch. When cool, the back is planed smooth and trimmed to page size. It is now an *electrotype* and ready for use in printing. The copper mold is generally so thin that it is necessary to back it up with the lead alloy, owing to the pressure to which the electrotype is later subjected. In this manner the electrotypes for the pages of most books are made from type; they serve for printing thousands of copies.

**33. Strength of Current.**—The flow of water in a pipe is customarily expressed as some specified volume of water passing a given point of the pipe in a certain length of time; it would be expressed as so many cubic feet per second or as some number of gallons per minute. In the same way, the flow of electricity in a circuit could be expressed as a quantity of electric charge transferred in a certain length of time, and might be given in electrons per second. Water flow can, of course, be measured by collecting some in a suitable container for a definite period, but electron flow is not so tangible, for the electrons cannot be seen. The usual procedure in measuring an electric current is to rely upon the effects of the current and to measure them.

The three effects of an electric current in a circuit that were mentioned in §25, namely, the magnetic, the heating, and the chemical effects, serve very nicely to measure the *strength* or *intensity of current.* This is done by noting the amount of force exerted magnetically, or the amount of heat produced, or the amount of electrolysis observed, all in suitable parts of the circuit. Fig. 42 represents a circuit with such parts; it is made up of (1) an electromagnet comprising a number of turns of copper wire wound around a U-shaped iron core and having an iron armature, (2) a coil consisting of turns of fine wire wound around

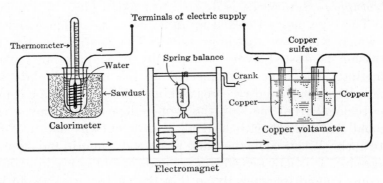

FIG. 42. The effects of electric current
Current is the same in all parts of this circuit.

the bulb of a thermometer and immersed in water contained in a vessel called a *calorimeter,* and (3) an electrolytic cell containing a solution of copper sulfate and electrodes of copper, called a *copper voltameter.* When a current is established in the circuit, the armature is attracted to the electromagnet by a force which can be read on the spring balance, heat is evolved in the coil and the temperature change can be read on the thermometer, and copper is deposited on one electrode of the voltameter and the amount can be determined by weighing. From such measurements an estimation can be obtained of the strength of current in the circuit.

Although the circuit is formed of several different parts, for the type of connection shown the intensity of current is the same in all of its parts, and therefore the three effects observed all correspond to that current intensity. As the current is increased, all three of the effects will become greater. To compare different current intensities some arbitrary standard must be adopted and called a *unit* of current strength. If the unit were defined as one in an electromagnet which would cause its armature to be attracted by a force, say of 5.4 pounds, it would be necessary to specify the size of the various parts of the magnetic structure and its material as well as the length of the air gap between core and armature. Again, if the unit of current strength were defined as one which would produce, say a 3.2° F. temperature elevation in 1 minute, it would be necessary to specify the size of the coil used, the quantity of water in the calorimeter, and the water equivalent of calorimeter and contents; besides the radiation losses would have to be known. These cumbersome specifications would make a unit defined in either way an impractical standard. Instead, the *unit of current is defined on the basis of electrolysis,* because the specifications do not involve dimensions of the apparatus used, and moreover, the amount of metal deposited (or gas liberated) is directly proportional to the current strength. Such proportionality does not hold for the magnetic effect nor for the heating effect of the current; for example, doubling the current quadruples the heat evolved by any given coil, §101. The magnetic and heating effects are employed in various practical measuring instruments, but they are standardized by comparison with devices utilizing the chemical effect of the current.

**34. Unit of Current; the Ampere.**—The amount of metal deposited, or gas produced, in an electrolytic cell is known to be directly proportional to the current through it and also proportional to the time the current is maintained. By international agreement, *the steady current which deposits silver at the rate of 0.001118 gram per second, from a solution of nitrate of silver in water, is taken as a unit of current and called one ampere.* The unit is named after the French scientist, André M. Ampère (1775-1836). It has been computed that one ampere of current corresponds to a flow of $6.25 \times 10^{18}$ electrons per second, that is, 6.25 billion billion electrons per second.

The character of metallic deposits by electrolysis depends upon the surface distribution or *density* of the current used, that is, the number of amperes per square foot of electrode surface. If electrolytic action takes place with too great a current density, the deposit will be soft, coarse-grained, and apt to prove unsatisfactory, while a small current density gives a good, hard, close-grained deposit.

The measurement of current on the basis of the definition of the ampere is made in a standardizing laboratory by means of a silver *voltameter*. This device consists of a platinum crucible holding a solution of 15 to 20 parts of silver nitrate to 100 parts of distilled water by weight, together with a piece of pure silver suspended in it. It is stipulated that the electrolyte should be not less than 6 cubic inches in volume, and that the current density over the electrode surfaces should not exceed 1.3 amperes per square inch at the silver anode and one-tenth that much at the platinum cathode.

Voltameters for student use may be constructed cheaply for the deposition of copper or zinc; they will serve very well for measuring current, although with somewhat less accuracy. One ampere will deposit in one second: 0.0003294 gram of copper in a copper voltameter, and 0.0003388 gram of zinc in a zinc voltameter. There are 453.6 grams in one pound.

**Problem 2.**—A piece of sheet-iron, 6 inches square, is to be plated on both sides in a copper voltameter. What current is required if its surface density is kept at 10 amperes per square foot?

Area of plate (both sides) = $6 \times 6 \times 2 = 72$ square inches = $72 \div 144$ or 0.5 square foot.

Current = 10 amperes per square foot $\times$ 0.5 square foot = 5 amperes

**35. Unit of Quantity of Electricity; The Coulomb.**—In the field of hydraulics, distinction must be made between the total quantity of water supplied and the rate of supply. The total quantity of water equals the rate of flow multiplied by the time of flow; thus, at a rate of 8 gallons per second and a time of flow of 60 seconds, the total quantity delivered would be $8 \times 60 = 480$ gallons. This same quantity could be delivered to a tank in one second if the rate were 480 gallons per second, or in one-half second if the rate were 960 gallons per second, or in 480 seconds if the rate were only one gallon per second.

In the field of electricity, distinction must also be made between total quantity of electricity and rate of transfer of electric charge. In this case the rate is expressed as the current in amperes. Consequently, *the unit quantity of electricity is the amount that passes any point in a circuit in one second when the current is one ampere, and this unit quantity is called the coulomb.* It is named after the French physicist, Charles A. Coulomb (1736-1806). If a current of 8 amperes is maintained for 60 seconds, then the quantity of electricity transferred is 480 coulombs of electricity. The same quantity would be transferred by a current of one ampere for 480 seconds.

To FIND THE QUANTITY OF ELECTRICITY PASSING THROUGH A CIRCUIT IN A GIVEN TIME WHEN THE CURRENT IS KNOWN:

*Multiply the current (expressed in amperes) by the time (expressed in seconds); the result will be in coulombs.*

That is

$$\text{quantity} = \text{current} \times \text{time}$$

or expressed in units

$$\text{coulombs} = \text{amperes} \times \text{seconds}$$

Let

$$I = \text{steady current in amperes,}$$
$$t = \text{current duration in seconds,}$$
$$Q = \text{total quantity in coulombs.}$$

Then in symbols

$$Q = I \times t \qquad\qquad 1$$

Formulas which will be used in the solution of problems are numbered at the right as indicated above; when they are employed in a solution their numbers will appear in parentheses at the left in line with the particular applications.

**Problem 3.**—An incandescent lamp requires a current of one-quarter ampere to maintain its rated output. If the lamp is illuminated for 2 hours, what quantity of electricity will pass through the lamp?

In this problem, the current is $I = 0.25$ ampere and the time interval is 2 hours or $t = 2 \times 60 \times 60 = 7200$ seconds; therefore, the quantity of electricity through the lamp is

(1) $\qquad Q = I \times t = 0.25 \times 7200 = 1800$ coulombs

To FIND THE AVERAGE CURRENT WHEN THE TIME OF FLOW AND THE QUANTITY OF ELECTRICITY ARE KNOWN:

*Divide the quantity (in coulombs) by the time (in seconds); the result will be in amperes.*

$$\text{current} = \frac{\text{quantity}}{\text{time}}$$

or

$$\text{amperes} = \frac{\text{coulombs}}{\text{seconds}}$$

$$I = \frac{Q}{t} \qquad\qquad\qquad 2$$

**Problem 4.**—What is the average current in an electromagnet if the quantity of electricity traversing it in 5 hours is 54,000 coulombs?

$$t = 5 \text{ hours} = 5 \times 60 \times 60 = 18{,}000 \text{ seconds}$$

(2) $$I = \frac{Q}{t} = \frac{54{,}000}{18{,}000} = 3 \text{ amperes}$$

To FIND THE TIME REQUIRED FOR A GIVEN QUANTITY OF ELECTRICITY TO PASS A POINT IN A CIRCUIT AT A UNIFORM RATE:

*Divide the quantity of electricity (in coulombs) by the current (in amperes); the result will be in seconds.*

$$\text{time} = \frac{\text{quantity}}{\text{current}}$$

or

$$\text{seconds} = \frac{\text{coulombs}}{\text{amperes}}$$

$$t = \frac{Q}{I} \qquad\qquad\qquad 3$$

**Problem 5.**—How long a time will be required to pass 18,000 coulombs through an electroplating bath if the average current is 6 amperes?

(3) $$t = \frac{Q}{I} = \frac{18{,}000}{6} = 3000 \text{ seconds} = \frac{3{,}000}{60} \text{ or 50 minutes}$$

The *coulomb* is found to be an unnecessarily small unit of quantity in many calculations, and for this reason a larger unit, the *ampere-hour,* is often used. One ampere-hour is the quantity of electricity that passes any point in a circuit in one hour when the current is one ampere. Obviously, one ampere-hour represents the same quantity of electricity as 2 amperes for one-half hour, or 4 amperes for one-quarter hour, or one-quarter ampere for 4 hours, and so on. One ampere-hour equals 3600 coulombs. The capacity of batteries is rated in ampere-hours.

**Problem 6.**—A current of 6.5 amperes was maintained by a particular battery for 4 hours. What quantity of electricity did the battery supply? Supposing the battery to have a capacity of 80 ampere-hours, how long could this current be maintained?

Using $t$ in hours and $Q$ in ampere-hours in the preceding formulas,

(1)      quantity = amperes $\times$ hours = $6.5 \times 4 = 26$ ampere-hours

(3)      $\text{time} = \dfrac{\text{ampere-hours}}{\text{amperes}} = \dfrac{80}{6.5} = 12.3$ hours

**36. Faraday's Laws of Electrolysis.**—Quantitative measurements in electrolytic cells are based on two laws due to the British chemist, Michael Faraday (1791-1867). They can be stated as follows:

1. *The amount of a substance liberated in an electrolytic cell is proportional to the quantity of electricity passing through the cell.*
2. *When the same quantity of electricity is passed through different electrolytic cells, the amounts of the substances liberated are proportional to their chemical equivalents.*

The *chemical equivalent* of an element is its chemical combining value; it is equal to its atomic weight divided by its valence number. In the case of ions composed of two or more elements, the chemical equivalent is the sum of the atomic weights of the component elements divided by the valence number of the ion. The atomic weights, valence numbers and chemical equivalents of a few elements are given below:

CHEMICAL EQUIVALENTS OF SOME ELEMENTS

| | Atomic Weight | Valence Number | Chemical Equivalent |
|---|---|---|---|
| Chlorine | 35.46 | —1 | 35.46 |
| Copper | 63.57 | 2 | 31.785 |
| Hydrogen | 1.008 | 1 | 1.008 |
| Nickel | 58.69 | 2 | 29.345 |
| Oxygen | 16.00 | —2 | 8.00 |
| Silver | 107.88 | 1 | 107.88 |
| Zinc | 65.38 | 2 | 32.69 |

In order to maintain any electrolytic process it is necessary to have an electric current in the circuit that includes the cell, because the external circuit must continuously supply electrons to the cathode and remove them from the anode. It appears that in forming a hydrogen or a silver atom, or any other element with valence number of 1, one electron is required, while for an atom of copper, or any other element with valence number of 2, two electrons are required, and so on. Since a flow of $6.25 \times 10^{18}$ electrons per second constitutes a current of one ampere, §34, it follows that in an electrolytic cell a current of 1 ampere maintained for 1 second (thereby transferring one coulomb of electricity) is capable of producing or depositing at the cathode $6.25 \times 10^{18}$ hydrogen or silver atoms, or half this number of copper atoms, and so on. A corresponding production or deposition of atoms will also occur at the anode of the cell.

In applying Faraday's laws of electrolysis, it is first desirable to find what quantity of electricity will liberate 1 chemical equivalent of a substance. This quantity is found by applying Avogadro's constant, §4, to any one of the elements; in silver, for example, there are $6.02 \times 10^{23}$ atoms in 107.88 grams of the element. Since 1 coulomb of electricity will deposit $6.25 \times 10^{18}$ atoms of silver, it will take $6.02 \times 10^{23} \div 6.25 \times 10^{18} = 0.965 \times 10^{5} = 96,500$ coulombs to deposit 107.88 grams of silver. It follows that *96,500 coulombs of electricity will deposit or produce the chemical equivalent of any substance in grams.* In consequence, the amount of an element in grams that is deposited by one coulomb will be the chemical equivalent of the element divided by 96,500, that is

$$\text{weight deposited per coulomb} = \frac{\text{chemical equivalent}}{96,500} = K \qquad 4$$

TO FIND THE WEIGHT OF ANY METAL THAT WILL BE DEPOSITED BY A GIVEN CURRENT IN A GIVEN TIME:

*Multiply the current (in amperes) by the time (in seconds) and by the weight deposited per coulomb, the result will be in grams.*

weight of deposit = current × time × weight deposited per coulomb

or expressed in units

grams = amperes × seconds × grams per coulomb

Let

> $I$ = current in amperes,
> $t$ = current duration in seconds,
> $K$ = weight deposited per coulomb = chemical equivalent ÷ 96,500,
> $W$ = weight of deposit in grams.

Then in symbols

$$W = I \times t \times K \qquad 5$$

**Problem 7.**—How many grams of zinc will be deposited in an electroplating bath by a current of 5 amperes in 45 minutes?

(4) $\qquad K$ for zinc $= \dfrac{32.69}{96,500} = 0.0003388$ gram per coulomb

$$t = 45 \text{ minutes} = 45 \times 60 \text{ or } 2700 \text{ seconds}$$

(5) $\qquad W = I \times t \times K = 5 \times 2700 \times 0.0003388 = 4.574$ grams

To FIND THE TIME REQUIRED TO ELECTROLYTICALLY DEPOSIT ANY GIVEN WEIGHT OF METAL WITH A GIVEN CURRENT:

*Divide the weight of deposit by the current, and also by the weight deposited per coulomb.*

$$\text{time} = \frac{\text{weight of deposit}}{\text{current} \times \text{weight deposited per coulomb}}$$

or

$$t = \frac{W}{I \times K} \qquad 6$$

**Problem 8.**—How long a time will be required to deposit 1.0 gram of silver on a teaspoon with a current of 0.2 ampere?

(4) $\qquad K$ for silver $= \dfrac{107.88}{96,500} = 0.001118$ gram per coulomb

(6) $\quad t = \dfrac{W}{I \times K} = \dfrac{1.0}{0.2 \times 0.001118} = 4472 \text{ seconds} = \dfrac{4472}{3600} \text{ or } 1.24 \text{ hours}$

The average rate of producing a deposit of metal in an electrolytic cell is the total amount of the deposit divided by the time required to produce it. Using the same symbols and units as before, the rate of deposit is merely $\dfrac{W}{t}$, and the result would be expressed in grams per second.

To CALCULATE THE CURRENT WHICH WILL DEPOSIT A METAL AT A DEFINITE RATE:

*Divide the weight of metal deposited per second by the weight deposited per coulomb.*

$$\text{current} = \frac{\text{weight deposited per second}}{\text{weight deposited per coulomb}}$$

or

$$I = \frac{\dfrac{W}{t}}{K} = \frac{W}{t \times K} \qquad\qquad 7$$

**Problem 9.**—The negative plate of a copper voltameter has increased in weight by 1.818 grams in 25 minutes. What was the average rate of depositing copper? What was the current?

The time interval was $t = 25$ minutes $= 25 \times 60$ or 1500 seconds. The average rate of depositing copper was

$$\text{weight deposited per second} = \frac{W}{t} = \frac{1.818}{1500} = 0.001212 \text{ gram per second}$$

(4)     $K$ for copper is $\dfrac{31.785}{96,500} = 0.0003294$ gram per coulomb

Therefore, the current was

(7)     $$I = \frac{1.818}{1500 \times 0.0003294} = 3.68 \text{ amperes}$$

**37. Measurements on a Gas Voltameter.**—The verification of Faraday's Laws as applied to gases is carried out experimentally in electrolytic cells which are arranged to collect the gases produced and to measure their volumes. Such a cell is called a *gas voltameter* and takes the form shown in Fig. 40. Since the volume occupied by a given weight of gas depends on its pressure and its temperature, these conditions of a gas in any test must be known. The so-called *standard conditions* are the pressure of the atmosphere at sea level (76 cm. of mercury) and the temperature of melting ice (32° F. or 0° C. or 273 centigrade degrees above absolute zero.) Under these standard conditions the volume of gas produced by one coulomb of electricity is, for example, 0.116 cubic centimeters for hydrogen, and 0.058 cubic centimeters for oxygen. There are 16.45 cubic centimeters in 1 cubic inch.

If the gas in a gas voltameter does not have standard conditions of pressure and temperature, the volume produced per coulomb of electricity can be determined by multiplying the volume produced per coulomb under standard conditions by the fraction

$$\frac{(273 + t) \times 76}{273 \times h}$$

where $t$ is the temperature of the gas in degrees centigrade and $h$ is the pressure of the gas in centimeters of mercury during the test. This product will be symbolized as $k$. Thus, $k$ for hydrogen collected at 10° C. and 80 cm. of mercury will be $(273 + 10) \times 76 \times 0.116 \div (273 \times 80) = 0.1142$ cubic centimeters per coulomb.

To FIND THE CURRENT WHICH YIELDS A DEFINITE VOLUME OF GAS IN A GIVEN TIME:

*Divide the volume of gas produced (in cubic centimeters) by the time of current duration (in seconds), and divide by the volume of gas produced per coulomb.*

$$\text{current} = \frac{\text{volume of gas produced}}{\text{time} \times \text{volume produced per coulomb}}$$

or

$$I = \frac{V}{t \times k} \qquad\qquad 8$$

**Problem 10.**—In an experiment the volume of oxygen produced in a gas voltameter in 500 seconds was found to be 20 cubic centimeters, its temperature being 15° C. The pressure of the atmosphere was equal to 75 centimeters of mercury and the pressure due to the hydrostatic head of the solution standing above the gas corresponded to 2 centimeters of mercury. What was the current?

The volume of oxygen produced per coulomb under the conditions stated is

$$k = \frac{(273 + 15) \times 76}{273 \times (75 + 2)} \times 0.058 = 0.0604$$

(8) $$I = \frac{20}{500 \times 0.0604} = 0.662 \text{ ampere}$$

Equation (8) can be transposed in the same way as in the section ahead to solve for the volume of gas produced by a given current in a given time, or for the time required to produce a definite quantity of gas with a given current.

**Problem 11.**—What volume of hydrogen would be produced in a gas voltameter in 10 minutes by a steady current of 0.5 ampere, supposing the temperature of the gas so produced to be 20° C. and its total pressure to be 77.5 centimeters of mercury?

The value of $k$ for hydrogen at 20° C. and 77.5 centimeters of mercury is

$$k = \frac{(273 + 20) \times 76}{273 \times 77.5} \times 0.116 = 0.122$$

Solving Formula (8) for the volume of gas liberated,

$$V = I \times t \times k = 0.5 \times 10 \times 60 \times 0.122 = 36.6 \text{ cubic centimeters}$$

**38. Polarity Indicators.**—The polarity of battery terminals or of electric service mains can be determined by dipping wires leading from them into some water, and noting the relative volumes of gas produced at the two wires. Care must be exercised not to touch the wires together. Since twice as much hydrogen is produced at the negative wire as oxygen at the positive wire, the polarity of the circuit is readily determined.

A solution of iodide of potassium, with a little starch added, is sometimes sealed in a glass tube with metallic terminals to form a polarity indicator. When current is established through the solution, iodine is liberated at the positive terminal and turns the starch blue around this terminal.

**Experiment 24.**—Place a solution of sodium alizarine sulfonate in a small glass cell, and provide two small electrodes of sheet platinum. A small current through the solution causes it to turn a deeper purple at one electrode and become yellow at the other. The liberation of sodium gives an alkaline reaction at the cathode (purple) and the sulfate ions form sulfuric acid at the anode (yellow). The experiment is very effective for class demonstration; it is best shown by using a parallel-sided cell in a lantern and projecting an enlarged image of the cell upon a screen.

## QUESTIONS

1. Name three effects of the electric current and give a commercial application of each.
2. What is meant by an open and by a closed circuit?
3. How could you determine by experiment whether a certain material is a conductor or an insulator?
4. Describe a simple detector of electric current.
5. How may liquids be classified according to their capabilities in conducting electric currents?

6. What is an electrolyte? What is electrolysis? What is an electrolytic cell?
7. Define the terms anode and cathode, and tell which electrode of an electrolytic cell is positive and which is negative.
8. Into what ions does hydrochloric acid dissociate? State the kind of charge on each.
9. Describe the action that takes place in an electrolytic cell containing a dilute solution of hydrochloric acid.
10. Explain the decomposition of water and describe an experiment to show that the products of dissociation are hydrogen and oxygen.
11. Give the electrolysis of copper sulfate, first with two platinum electrodes and then with a copper anode. Include the chemical equations in stating the results.
12. Plates of platinum and copper are dipped into a solution of zinc sulfate and current is directed from the copper to the platinum plate through the solution. How are the plates affected?
13. Describe how an electrotype is made.
14. What do you understand by current strength?
15. What experiments would you suggest to ascertain how the effects of a current vary with its strength?
16. Which effect of the current do you regard as most suitable for defining its strength? Give a reason for your answer.
17. Name and define the unit of current strength.
18. What do you understand by the statement that the current in a certain circuit is 5 amperes?
19. Distinguish between the terms current strength and quantity of electricity.
20. What is the strength of current through an electrical device if 5 coulombs pass through it every second?
21. State Faraday's Laws of electrolysis.
22. Give the meaning of chemical equivalent, and explain why the weights of substances deposited in electrolysis are proportional to their chemical equivalents.
23. Describe the appearance of a gas voltameter and explain how it works.
24. What is a polarity indicator, and how does it indicate?

## PROBLEMS

1. How many coulombs of electricity pass through an electrolytic cell in one-quarter of an hour if the current during this time is kept uniform at 10 amperes? *Ans.* 9000 coulombs.
2. A charge of 50 coulombs passes through a circuit in 0.5 second. What is the average current during this interval of time? *Ans.* 100 amperes.
3. How many ampere-hours of electricity will be delivered to a storage battery on charge which takes 160 amperes for 3 hours? *Ans.* 480 ampere-hours.

4. What quantities of electricity would be needed to deposit one gram of silver and one gram of copper? *Ans.* 894 and 3036 coulombs respectively.

5. How much silver will be deposited from a silver nitrate solution in an electrolytic cell by a current of 10 amperes maintained for 30 minutes? *Ans.* 20.12 grams.

6. The negative zinc plate of an Edison electrolytic meter increased in weight by 3.45 grams during a certain time. How much electricity passed through the meter? *Ans.* 10,180 coulombs.

7. What current is required to deposit 0.5 gram of copper upon an iron spoon in 35 minutes? *Ans.* 0.723 ampere.

8. Using a current density of 5 amperes per square foot, how much time is required to copper-plate both sides of a square iron plate measuring 4 feet along each edge, supposing sufficient thickness is attained when the coating weighs 4 grams per square foot? *Ans.* 40.5 minutes.

9. If 1000 coulombs of electricity produce a certain volume of hydrogen, how many coulombs will be required to produce the same volume of oxygen under the same conditions of temperature and pressure? *Ans.* 2000 coulombs.

10. What current would produce one liter (1000 cubic centimeters) of oxygen in one hour under standard conditions of temperature and pressure? *Ans.* 4.79 amperes.

# Lesson IV

## PRIMARY CELLS

Voltaic cells—Potential difference and electromotive force—Unit of potential difference; the volt—Voltaic action—Polarization—Local action—The electromotive series—Daniell and gravity cells—Leclanché cells—Dry cells—Standard cells—Questions and Problems.

**39. Voltaic Cells.**—When a metal plate is dipped into a solution of one of its salts, a contact is established between the metallic *atoms* of the plate and the positive metallic *ions* of the solution. As a result of this contact, either *metallic ions tend to acquire electrons and deposit themselves on the plate as atoms, or, the atoms of the plate tend to lose electrons and go into solution as ions.* For example, with a copper plate dipped in a copper sulfate solution, a few $Cu^{++}$ ions of the solution will take electrons from the plate and form atoms of copper, which deposit themselves upon the plate. The action will stop almost immediately, however, because the plate becomes positive by this loss of electrons, and repels the advance of further positive ions toward it. In contrast, with a zinc plate dipped in a zinc sulfate solution, a few atoms of the plate dissolve, leaving their electrons behind, and go into solution as $Zn^{++}$ ions. This effect is also of very slight magnitude because the plate becomes negative, and does not throw off further positive ions because of its electrostatic attraction for them. The mass of metal deposited or dissolved in these cases is very minute. The process could be made continuous, however, by removing the charges from the plates as fast as they are formed.

A combination of two *dissimilar* metal plates placed in separate but connecting solutions, or even in a single solution, permits the continual transfer of charges through any wire that may connect the two plates, and thus sets up a current in the wire. Such an electrolytic cell for establishing current in a circuit constitutes a *voltaic cell,* the name being derived from the Italian physicist, Alessandro Volta (1745-1827), who discovered the action in 1800. The term *battery* applies to a number of such cells connected together, although the name may also designate a single cell.

The term *primary cell* is generally used to signify any voltaic cell that generates an electric current directly from its constituent parts, that is, at the expense of the plates and the electrolyte. When the chemical energy of these parts is exhausted, they must be replaced by new plates and fresh electrolyte. There are other cells, classified as *secondary cells,* but generally called *storage cells,* which can be renewed without adding new materials; they are restored to their original condition by maintaining current from outside sources through them for appropriate periods in a direction opposite to the current supplied by the cell.

**40. Potential Difference and Electromotive Force.**—To appreciate the action of a battery in an electric circuit, consider first two vessels that are joined by a flexible tube and are partially filled with water. When the water is at the *same level* in both, there will be *no flow* from one to the other although the connecting tube is full of water, because the *pressure* at each end of the tube is the same. When one vessel is raised above the other, then there will be a *difference in pressure* between the two ends of the tube and *water will flow* from the higher to the lower level. This condition is shown in Fig. 43, where vessel *A* is higher than vessel *B;* the difference in water level, marked *H,* is called the *hydrostatic head.* To determine the amount of flow, it is not necessary to know the height of either vessel, but merely the difference of height between the two water levels, for this head determines the difference of pressure between them that causes the flow of water.

Just as a flow of water in a pipe is due to a difference of hydrostatic pressure, so a flow of electricity in a circuit is due to a *difference of electric potential.* The word potential as used in an electric sense is analogous to hydrostatic pressure in liquids; and it is also similar to temperature in the subject of heat. In the voltaic cell, then, there are two plates at different electric potentials, and the difference of potential between them is responsible for the current through the wire connecting the plates. Potential difference is abbreviated as p.d.

The ability of a battery, or other source of electricity, to produce a potential difference in an electric circuit is spoken of as its *electromotive force*. The abbreviation of this electrical term is e.m.f. When a source of electricity is connected to a conducting path, the action means that an e.m.f. is included in the electric circuit, and as a result differences of potential are established between points of the circuit. The current through any part of a circuit is due to the p.d. across that part, one end being positive with respect to the other. E.m.f. is the cause of electron flow in a circuit.

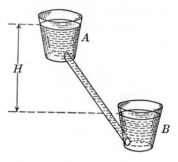

FIG. 43. Water analogy for potential difference

Care should be taken not to confuse e.m.f. or p.d. with current. The power house of an electricity supply system is equipped with machinery for generating e.m.f., and this maintains a definite p.d. across line wires that bring electric service to the home. The potential difference available at the lamp sockets and convenience outlets in the home is maintained substantially constant. If a number of lamps and appliances are connected to the service, each will take a definite current appropriate for the device. A large lamp will take more current than a small one, an electric iron will take more than a fan motor, and so on. The amount of current taken by a device is a measure of the flow of electricity through it, while the p.d. available at the mains or the e.m.f. generated at the power station is the agency which causes the flow.

**41. Unit of Potential Difference; the Volt.**—Energy is always involved in transferring electricity from one point in a circuit to another. Thus, when a primary cell supplies current to a circuit connected to it, the chemical energy of the materials of the cell is converted into electrical energy in the circuit. The amounts of energy are expressed in appropriate units, usually the *foot-pound* and the *joule*. The foot-pound is an amount of energy equivalent to the work done in lifting a 1-pound weight vertically a distance of 1 foot. The joule is named after the English experimenter, James P. Joule (1818-1889), and is a little smaller than the foot-pound; it takes 1.356 joules to make 1 foot-pound, §95. The joule is the unit of energy that is made use of in arriving at a measure of potential difference.

Potential difference is reckoned in terms of the energy needed to transfer a certain quantity of electricity. *If it takes exactly 1 joule of energy to transfer 1 coulomb from one point in a circuit to another, then the difference of potential between the two points is said to be 1 volt.* This unit of potential difference is named after Volta.

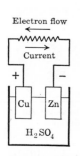

Electron flow

Current

+ | −

Cu | Zn

$H_2SO_4$

FIG. 44. Diagram of a voltaic cell

The sum of the potential differences measured around a complete circuit, for maintaining the current in it, is equal to the electromotive force of the battery or other agency which produces the current. Both potential difference and electromotive force are expressed in volts.

**42. Voltaic Action.**—A primary cell of elementary type is formed with electrodes of copper and zinc in a dilute sulfuric acid solution. Such a cell is indicated in Fig. 44 connected to a circuit denoted by a zigzag line.

The sulfuric acid dissociates into hydrogen ions carrying positive charges and sulfate ions carrying negative charges, as indicated below:

$$H_2SO_4 \rightleftarrows 2H^+ + SO_4^=$$

The action of the cell is explained by considering the behavior of the ions in the solution. At the copper plate, the $H^+$ ions receive electrons, thereby making that plate positive. At the other plate, the zinc atoms dissolve, throwing $Zn^{++}$ ions into solution and leaving electrons on the plate, thereby making the zinc plate negative. The electrons on the zinc plate repel one another along the connecting wire, and at the same time are being attracted by the positively charged copper plate; thus, a flow of electrons is established through the external circuit connecting the electrodes, and is directed from the zinc to the copper.

The $Zn^{++}$ and $SO_4^=$ ions remain in the solution, unless the latter is evaporated, in which case they unite to form zinc sulfate, as represented by the equation:

$$Zn^{++} + SO_4^= \to ZnSO_4$$

The action described continues as long as the circuit is closed, the zinc being dissolved gradually and the electrolyte changing from sulfuric acid to zinc sulfate.

Fig. 44 again calls attention to the distinction between flow of electrons and direction of current. Electrons flow from the negative to the positive terminals of the cell through the external circuit; current is directed in this circuit from the positive terminal to the negative terminal of the cell.

**Experiment 25.**—Place dilute sulfuric acid (one part acid to twenty parts water) in a tumbler and insert a strip of sheet zinc. Bubbles of gas immediately collect on the zinc, become larger, and rise to the surface of the liquid. The gas may be collected, by displacing water in an inverted test tube held over the rising bubbles, and tested as before. It burns with a pale bluish flame and is identified as hydrogen.

FIG. 45. Cell with copper and zinc electrodes

Insert a strip of copper in the acid solution, as before. No bubbles of gas will be seen rising from the copper. Bring the outer extremities of the copper and zinc strips into contact to form a circuit as shown in Fig. 45, and torrents of bubbles will rise from the copper as well as from the zinc strip as current is established. If collected and tested, the gas evolved from the copper proves to be hydrogen, the same as that rising from the zinc. If the action is continued, the zinc will waste away while the copper remains unchanged.

**43. Polarization.**—The current supplied by the simple voltaic cell just described is quickly reduced in value, during even a short period of use, because some of the hydrogen liberated clings to the positive plate. This action not only reduces the effective surface of that plate, but it practically alters the material of the electrode and thereby changes the e.m.f. which is available for supplying current to the external circuit. This effect, called *polarization,* is present in many types of cells.

Polarization of a voltaic cell is due primarily to the accumulation of hydrogen on its positive plate and to changes in concentration of its electrolyte. To correct these faults, some substance is usually added to combine chemically with the hydrogen gas as it forms. This substance is called a *depolarizer,* and may be either solid or liquid in form.

In the operation of electrolytic cells having like electrodes, it frequently happens that these electrodes become coated with dissimilar materials. Such a cell then acts like a voltaic cell, opposing the e.m.f. of the applied source of current. Thus, a cell with platinum electrodes in a solution of hydrochloric acid may cease to conduct current because hydrogen and chlorine accumulate on the electrodes and set up an e.m.f. of polarization opposing the outside source. So long as both electrodes of an electrolytic cell remain of the same substance, it is evident that whatever potential is developed at one of them will be neutralized by an equal and opposite potential at the other, supposing the electrolyte to be uniform throughout. The smallest p.d. applied to the cell will then set up a current in it.

**Experiment 26.**—Place sufficient mercury in a small battery jar to cover the bottom and suspend a piece of zinc from the top of the jar. Pour in a solution of ammonium chloride ($NH_4Cl$), commonly called sal-ammoniac, and make connection with the mercury by a piece of rubber-covered wire. Connect the cell to the bulb of a flashlight and note that the brilliancy of the light becomes steadily less, due to polarization of the cell. When the cell becomes sufficiently polarized, drop into the solution a piece of mercuric chloride ($HgCl_2$) about the size of a pin-head. The light from the bulb will instantly become brighter. The hydrogen has been removed by the chlorine in the mercuric chloride, which thus serves as a depolarizer. When the supply of chlorine becomes exhausted, polarization will set in again.

**44. Local Action.**—Ordinary commercial zinc contains many impurities, such as small particles of carbon, iron, tin or lead. When a rod of such zinc is placed in a cell, these foreign particles form a number of tiny voltaic cells on the surface of the zinc inside the cell, with the result that the zinc is continuously eaten away, whether the cell delivers current to the external circuit or not. Fig. 46 gives a magnified view of a particle of iron on a zinc rod, and indicates some local paths of current from the zinc to the iron through the solution, and from the iron to the zinc across the junction of the two metals. The effect of these currents is known as *local action.* In some cells local action is also caused by a difference in the *density* of the electrolyte at various parts of the cell, usually causing the zinc to dissolve more rapidly at the liquid surface.

Local action may be prevented by cleaning the zinc thoroughly with sandpaper, then immersing it in dilute sulfuric acid, and while still wet applying mercury by means of a cotton or cloth swab. This forms a bright amalgam over the surface of the zinc, and it is said to be *amalgamated.* The foreign particles in the zinc are apparently protected from the action of the acid by the amalgam, or else are carried down to the bottom of the cell. The mercury does not prevent the zinc from being dissolved during the operation of the cell, but continues to re-form an amalgam as the zinc wastes away. Zinc for battery plates is some-

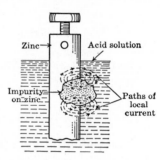

Fig. 46. Local action at an electrode

times cast with a small percentage of mercury in its composition in order to reduce local action.

**Experiment 27.**—Dip a strip of zinc momentarily into a weak solution of sulfuric acid and immediately rub over its surface a little mercury. Repeat Experiment 25 with this amalgamated zinc and note that now bubbles rise only from the copper plate when the ends of the two strips are brought together. Although there is no liberation of gas from the zinc plate, this plate still wastes away while current is maintained.

**45. The Electromotive Series.**—It has been pointed out that a voltaic cell must contain dissimilar electrodes in order to produce an electric current in a circuit connected to them. The electromotive force developed is an important factor in determining the amount of current produced, and this e.m.f. depends upon the materials of the cell. For example, a cell composed of zinc and lead plates, immersed in dilute sulfuric acid, will not generate as much e.m.f. as a cell with zinc and copper plates in the same electrolyte.

The relative chemical activites of electrode materials can be indicated by listing them in sequence to form an *electromotive series.* The table below indicates the more important electrode materials in such a series, and gives their normal potentials with respect to hydrogen. Each metal in the list displaces those toward the right from chemically equivalent solutions of their simple salts, and is itself displaced by those to its left, under ordinary conditions. The arrows indicate the direction of current through the internal and external circuits.

THE ELECTROMOTIVE SERIES

Direction of current through external circuit

←

| Zinc | Iron | Tin | Lead | Hydrogen | Copper | Oxygen | Mercury |
|------|------|-----|------|----------|--------|--------|---------|
| − 0.76 | 0.44 | 0.14 | 0.12 | 0 | 0.34 | 0.40 | 0.80 + |

⟶

Direction of current through solution

The potential values to the left of hydrogen are negative and those to the right are positive. Each represents the e.m.f. of a cell having a hydrogen electrode and an electrode of the metal referred to. The e.m.f. of a cell having any two electrodes in a uniform electrolyte can be predicted from the individual potential values.

**Problem 12.**—A cell is formed with an electrode of copper in copper sulfate and a zinc electrode in zinc sulfate, the solutions being kept apart by a porous partition which permits hydrogen ions to pass through. Find the e.m.f. of the cell and determine its polarity.

Referring to the electromotive series, the potential of copper is +0.34 volt and that of zinc is −0.76 volt, each with respect to hydrogen; consequently, the potential of copper is higher than that of zinc by the amount 0.34 + 0.76 or 1.10 volts. Therefore, the cell has an e.m.f. of 1.10 volts and its positive terminal is the one on the copper electrode.

The size of a cell does not affect its electromotive force, but does affect the current it can produce in a given circuit. A large cell has the *same e.m.f.* as a small one of the *same kind;* it is capable, however, of supplying a correspondingly larger current because of its greater electrode surfaces. Zinc is quite commonly used in primary cells; it is gradually dissolved as the cells are used. The amount of zinc dissolved in a voltaic cell is equal to the amount that would be deposited in an electrolytic cell under the same conditions of electrolyte, current, and time. The amount can be determined by applying Faraday's Laws exactly as with electro-lytic cells, §36.

**46. Daniell and Gravity Cells.**—A cell invented by J. F. Daniell comprises a copper electrode placed in a saturated copper sulfate solution ($CuSO_4$) and a zinc electrode in a dilute zinc sulfate solution ($ZnSO_4$), the latter containing a little sulfuric acid ($H_2SO_4$). The solutions are separated as shown in Fig. 47 by a cup of unglazed earthenware, which allows the passage of ions but prevents the solutions from dif-fusing. The so-called *gravity* cell employs the same materials, but a porous cup is not required. This cell is illustrated in Fig. 48; it shows the denser copper sulfate solution at the bottom of a jar and the lighter zinc sulfate solution above it. The electrodes are in their respective solutions and the wire leading to the copper elec-trode is insulated to prevent contact with the zinc sulfate solution.

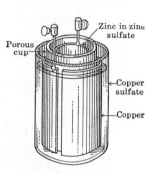

Fig. 47. Daniell cell

In either construction, the copper electrode is positive and the zinc elec-trode is negative, and the copper sul-fate solution surrounding the copper serves as the depolarizer. The sulfuric acid provides the $H^+$ and $SO_4^=$ ions of the solution. The zinc dissolves and displaces hydrogen from the sulfuric acid, leaving the electrode negative; while the copper receives a copper de-posit and becomes positive. When the electrodes are connected by an external circuit, a current is established and the following cell reactions occur:

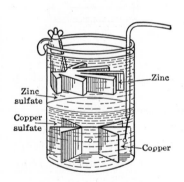

Fig. 48. Gravity cell

Zinc in dissolving leaves electrons on the plate and throws off $Zn^{++}$ ions; these combine with $SO_4^=$ ions to form zinc sulfate:

$$Zn \rightarrow Zn^{++} + 2e$$

$$Zn^{++} + SO_4^= \rightarrow ZnSO_4$$

The Cu$^{++}$ ions of the depolarizer take electrons from the copper plate, depositing metallic copper:

$$CuSO_4 \rightleftarrows Cu^{++} + SO_4^{=}$$

$$Cu^{++} + 2e \rightarrow Cu \downarrow$$

Hydrogen ions from the sulfuric acid combine with the $SO_4^{=}$ ions of the depolarizer, yielding sulfuric acid:

$$2H^+ + SO_4^{=} \rightarrow H_2SO_4$$

As the cell operates, the zinc electrode wears away and the copper electrode gains weight, while the concentration of the zinc

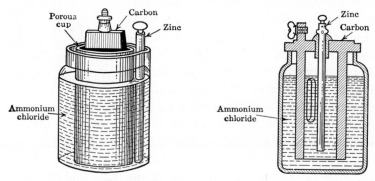

FIG. 49. Forms of Leclanché cells
Porous cup type at left and moulded carbon type at right.

sulfate solution increases and that of the copper sulfate solution diminishes. Some crystals of copper sulfate (bluestone) are added to the latter solution to maintain its concentration. The e.m.f. of the cell is about 1.09 volts. The gravity cell is best adapted to so-called *closed-circuit work* which demands a continuous current supply, because steady action helps to prevent the solutions from mixing by diffusion.

**47. Leclanché Cells.**—In the cell devised by Georges Leclanché the positive and negative electrodes are respectively a carbon slab and an amalgamated zinc rod; these are immersed in a solution of ammonium chloride ($NH_4Cl$). In the cell shown at the left in Fig. 49, a porous cup surrounds the carbon electrode and contains manganese dioxide ($MnO_2$) as a solid depolarizer; the cup is closed at the top by means of pitch, except for small holes that serve as gas vents. Another form of this cell is shown at the right in the figure; the carbon cylinder is moulded from a mixture of carbon and manganese dioxide. The zinc rod is hung from this cylinder but is insulated from it by a porcelain collar. The action in both types of cell is the same.

The solution of sal-ammoniac dissociates into ammonium positive ions and chlorine negative ions, as follows:

$$NH_4Cl \rightleftarrows NH_4^+ + Cl^-$$

When the cell delivers current, the zinc dissolves, leaving electrons behind, which repel one another along the external circuit to the carbon plate. The $Cl^-$ ions of the electrolyte migrate toward the $Zn^{++}$ ions near the zinc electrode, and the $NH_4^+$ ions migrate toward the carbon electrode and receive electrons from it. The formation of hydrogen gas at this electrode is prevented to a considerable extent by the manganese dioxide. The initial cell reactions are symbolized as follows:

Near negative electrode

$$Zn^{++} + 2Cl^- \rightarrow ZnCl_2$$

Near positive electrode

$$2NH_4^+ + 2e + MnO_2 + H_2O \rightarrow 2NH_4OH + MnO$$

Thus, during the operation of the cell, zinc chloride ($ZnCl_2$) is formed near the zinc, ammonium hydroxide ($NH_4OH$) is formed near the carbon electrode, and the depolarizing material, manganese dioxide, is changed to manganese monoxide ($MnO$).

This primary cell has an electromotive force ranging between 1.4 and 1.5 volts. The depolarizing action is somewhat imperfect and the e.m.f. falls off with continued use; however, the cell recuperates during periods of open circuit because the gas formed has an opportunity to escape. The cell is, therefore, best adapted to *open-circuit work,* that is, service in which the cell is called upon to deliver current only for short periods, its circuit at other times being open.

**48. Dry Cells.**—The familiar dry cell has the same constituents as the Leclanché cell, but is entirely enclosed so that externally the cell is dry. In the usual type the zinc is in the form of a cylindrical container, and this holds the other electrode (carbon rod), the electrolyte (ammonium chloride), and the depolarizer (manganese dioxide). The cell also contains a little zinc chloride to counteract polarization. Fig. 50 shows the internal construction; the electrolyte is a paste held or absorbed by a spongy gelatinous lining, and the region between the lining and the carbon rod is filled with a depolarizing material moistened with a solution of ammonium chloride and zinc chloride in water. The chemical reactions are the same as those in the Leclanché cell.

Dry cells, being portable, are very convenient for use and have practically superseded all other types of primary cells. The e.m.f. is about 1.5 volts. The most common standard size is 2½ inches in diameter and 6 inches high, known as No. 6, but many smaller standard sizes are made for use in flashlights, gas engine ignition, and radio receiving sets. For the latter purpose the dry cells are mounted in groups and connected together for operating vacuum tubes, §289-293, which rectify and amplify the radio impulses picked up by antennas. Those used for heating the filaments of such tubes are called "A" batteries, those employed in the plate circuits are called "B" batteries, and those used in making the grid potential negative are called "C" batteries.

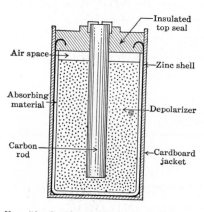

FIG. 50. Sectional diagram of dry cell

Batteries of dry cells are made up for supplying 3, 4½, 22½, 45 and other values of e.m.f., and this is done by joining two or more cells chain fashion with wires that connect the carbon electrode of one cell to the zinc electrode of the next. Such coupling of cells is called a *series connection,* and is illustrated at the left in Fig. 51; the three cells in series constitute a 4.5-volt battery. Another plan of connection is used when it is desired to divide the total current needed among several cells; the method of coupling the cells is then called the *parallel connection.* The two cells at the right in Fig. 51 are connected in parallel, the two zinc electrodes being connected to form one battery terminal and the carbon

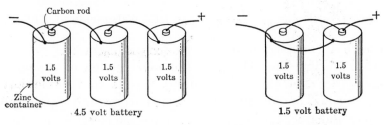

FIG. 51. Connection of dry cells in batteries
Series connection at left; parallel connection at right.

electrodes the other. In effect, the two cells behave together just like a single cell of double size; the e.m.f. of this battery is the same as that of one cell, namely 1.5 volts. Fig. 52 shows the construction of a 45-volt and a 1½-volt battery, both formed of cylindrical cells properly connected and sealed in cartons.

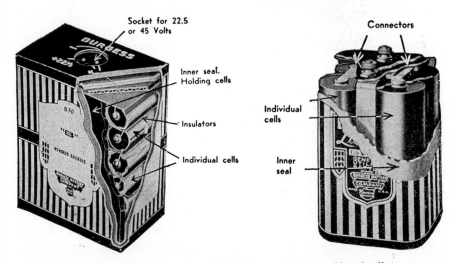

FIG. 52. Dry batteries partially opened to show assembly of cells
At left: 45-volt radio B battery with 30 cells in series. At right: 1½-volt general utility battery with 4 cells in parallel.

struction of a 45-volt and a 1½-volt battery, both formed of cylindrical cells properly connected and sealed in cartons.

**Problem 13.**—A dry cell of the size used in B batteries has 27.8 grams of zinc available for use. How long will the cell last with a current of 0.020 ampere drawn from it continuously?

The weight of zinc dissolved by 1 coulomb is equal to its chemical equivalent 32.69 divided by 96,500, which amounts to 0.0003388 gram. Using this value for $K$ in the formulas of §36, the life of the cell is:

$$(6) \quad t = \frac{W}{I \times K} = \frac{27.8}{0.020 \times 0.0003388} = 4,103,000 \text{ seconds} = 1140 \text{ hours}$$

A novel form of dry battery is made up of a stack of "Eveready Layerbilt" cells. Fig. 53 shows the construction of a single cell and also the manner of assembling 3 cells to form a battery having an e.m.f. of 4.5 volts. The electrodes are thin square plates of carbon and zinc, and between them are the electrolyte-saturated pad and the manganese dioxide cake; loss of moisture is prevented by an elastic seal snapped around the cell components as shown

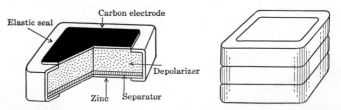

FIG. 53. Sectional view of a single "Layer-bilt" cell and assembly of a battery

at the left. A number of cells are stacked together, making automatic contact of the zinc of one cell with the carbon of the next, and each stack is then dipped into an insulating compound to provide complete sealing.

A dry battery deteriorates when in use because of polarization and because the zinc is gradually consumed. Examination of a cell which has failed shows that the zinc shell has become punctured and that its outside surface has become roughened, bulged, and covered with white pasty material from the electrolyte which has oozed through the openings. For this reason dry cells should always be removed from equipments in which they have been installed when such equipments are stored away for later use. Cells that are kept in stock also deteriorate but at a much slower rate; they should be stored in a cool, dry place and kept clean so that they will prove satisfactory when put in service.

**Experiment 28.**—Test the electromotive force of a No. 6 dry cell with a voltmeter and do the same for a small flashlight battery. Observe that the readings are the same, provided both cells are quite new. Connect the two cells in series and measure the total e.m.f.; repeat for the parallel connection.

**Experiment 29.**—Connect a dry cell to a resistor, a voltmeter, and a switch as indicated in Fig. 54. Use a 3-ohm resistor and a 1.5-volt voltmeter. Close the switch and measure the e.m.f. of the cell at two-minute intervals for a period of one hour; the switch should be opened for the brief intervals while the voltmeter is being read. Then open the switch and continue the readings at two-minute intervals for the subsequent half-hour. Plot the voltmeter readings on graph paper, and note the gradual falling off of e.m.f. while the cell delivers current to the resistor and its rapid recovery when the resistor is disconnected.

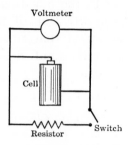

Fig. 54. Test of a dry cell

**49. Standard Cells.**—Voltaic cells of special form are used as *standards of e.m.f.* for measuring potential differences. These measurements are made under conditions such that the standard cell delivers only very small currents for brief periods of time. In the Weston standard cell, introduced in 1892, and widely used ever since, the electrodes are placed in the opposite sides of an

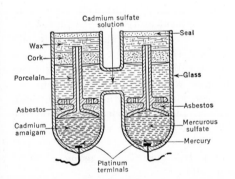

Fig. 55. Cross section and external view of Weston standard cell

H-shaped glass vessel which serves as a container for the electrolyte, as shown in Fig. 55. The positive electrode is mercury and the negative electrode is composed of cadmium amalgam (12.5 per cent Cd). The electrolyte is a solution of cadmium sulfate, and the depolarizer is mercurous sulfate. The saturated or *normal* cell has an excess of crystals of cadmium sulfate to keep the electrolyte saturated.

The e.m.f. of the saturated cell is 1.01830 volts at 20° C., and varies slightly but definitely with temperature changes. These cause slight variations in the amount of cadmium sulfate which dissolves in the solution, thus altering the concentration, and consequently affecting the e.m.f. of the cell to some extent.

In the unsaturated cell, temperature changes do not affect the concentration of the electrolyte, and their effect on the e.m.f. is so small that it is often neglected. Each unsaturated cell must have its e.m.f. determined by comparison with an e.m.f. of known value.

## QUESTIONS

1. Explain what is meant by the term ion. Name a few of them and state their polarities.
2. Distinguish between primary and secondary cells.
3. Explain difference of electric potential by analogy with difference of hydrostatic head.
4. What do you understand by electromotive force?
5. Define the foot-pound as a unit of energy. How many joules make a foot-pound?
6. Give the definition of the volt.
7. Since hydrogen gas is produced at the zinc when it is placed in dilute acid, how do you account for the fact that in a voltaic cell, when connected to a circuit, hydrogen gas is produced at the copper plate?
8. What is meant by polarization in a voltaic cell? How can it be reduced?
9. What is local action in a cell? How is it reduced?
10. Make a list of some materials used as cell electrodes, arranging them in the order of their potential difference with respect to hydrogen.
11. A cell is composed of copper and iron strips in dilute sulfuric acid. Draw a sketch indicating the + and − plates and electrodes, and the direction of current when the plates are connected externally to the cell.
12. Which is the negative electrode in a lead-copper cell using $H_2SO_4$? Which is the negative in a lead-iron cell?
13. Upon what factors does the e.m.f. of a cell depend?
14. Would you expect a very large cell to have the same e.m.f. as another of the same kind that is made up in a small test tube? Why?
15. Describe the Daniell cell and explain the chemical action that takes place in it.
16. Describe the Leclanché porous-cup type of cell, giving the chemical reactions.
17. Give an example of a cell with a solid and one with a liquid depolarizer, and state how the depolarizer acts in each.
18. Describe the construction of a dry cell.

19. Sketch the connections of a 3-volt battery formed of 4 dry cells.
20. What is the distinction between open- and closed-circuit cells?
21. What are standard cells and for what purpose are they used?
22. Describe the Weston standard cell.
23. Tabulate all the cells you know of, naming the + and − plates, electrolyte, depolarizer used if any, and type of cell (whether open- or closed-circuit) in the several columns of the table.

## PROBLEMS

1. What is the minimum amount of zinc which a dry cell should have to be able to supply 0.1 ampere for 1500 hours? *Ans.* 183 grams.
2. A test made on a large number of dry cells, measuring 1¼ inch in diameter and 3½ inches long, shows the following service life on the average when the cell supplies the stated currents continuously until the e.m.f. is reduced to 1.0 volt:

| Current | 0.5 | 0.2 | 0.1 | 0.05 | 0.02 | 0.01 | 0.005 | ampere |
|---------|-----|-----|-----|------|------|------|-------|--------|
| Life | 2.2 | 9.0 | 25 | 78 | 310 | 900 | 2000 | hours |

How many ampere-hours would a typical cell of this type deliver when currents of 1/2, 1/20 and 1/200 ampere are supplied continuously in dropping to 1 volt? *Ans.* 1.1, 3.9 and 10, respectively.
3. Plot a curve to show the effect of temperature changes on the e.m.f. of a normal standard cell, the data being as follows:

| Temperature | 10° | 15° | 20° | 25° | 30° | C. |
|-------------|-----|-----|-----|-----|-----|-----|
| Electromotive force | 1.01860 | 1.01848 | 1.01830 | 1.01807 | 1.01781 | volts |

Show degrees as abscissas and volts as ordinates, using 1.017 as the lowest ordinate and 1.019 as the highest.

# Lesson V

## STORAGE BATTERIES

Storage cells—Lead storage cell—Types of plates and their assembly—Electrolyte of a lead cell—Electrical characteristics of lead cells—Edison storage cell—Reactions and characteristics of Edison cells—Charging storage cells—Questions and Problems.

**50. Storage Cells.**—A storage or secondary cell is a voltaic cell consisting of two electrodes immersed in an electrolyte, the materials being so chosen that the cell, after supplying an electric current for a time, may be restored to its original condition by current from an outside source of electricity. While the cell supplies current to an external circuit it is *discharging,* and while the cell is being restored it is *charging.* The restoration of the storage cell is accomplished by electric current through it in a reversed direction, whereas in the primary cell it is done by adding new electrode material and fresh electrolyte.

The processes of charging and discharging are transformations of energy. When a storage cell is charged the electrical energy supplied to it from an outside source is converted into chemical energy which is then stored in the cell, and when the cell is discharged this chemical energy is transformed back again to electrical energy in maintaining a current through an external circuit. A *storage battery,* or *secondary battery,* is composed of one or more storage cells that are electrically connected to operate together.

The uses to which storage batteries may be put are many and varied. They are used principally in electrical power stations and isolated plants for emergency stand-by service or potential regulation, in telephone and telegraph service and railway signalling, in the operation of electric motor-driven vehicles and submarines, and in lighting steam railway cars. They are also used on automobiles and marine craft to furnish current for starting the gasoline engines and in connection with generators for ignition and lighting.

There are two kinds of storage batteries, namely: the lead-acid battery, and the nickel-alkaline battery.

**51. Lead Storage Cell.**—The more commonly used storage cell consists essentially of a positive plate of lead dioxide ($PbO_2$) and

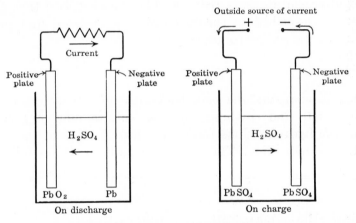

FIG. 56. Diagrams of lead storage battery

a negative plate of spongy lead (Pb), immersed in an electrolyte of sulfuric acid ($H_2SO_4$) in water. The two kinds of plates are readily distinguished by color, the positive is dark brown and the negative is light gray. As the cell discharges, the active materials of both plates change to lead sulfate ($PbSO_4$). Fig. 56 represents the battery on discharge and on charge.

**Experiment 30.**—Place two lead strips in a tumbler containing a solution of sulfuric acid in water, and connect the plates to a circuit that includes a lamp bulb or to a wire placed near a magnetic needle. No effect is observed. Now connect the plates to an outside source of electricity having a p.d. of about 3 volts. After maintaining a current for a short time, examine the plates and observe that one plate (the positive) has become brownish in color, while the other plate (the negative) has assumed a lighter shade of gray. Connect the plates to the current indicator as at first, and note that the lamp or the needle now reveals the presence of a current.

A repetition of the charging and discharging processes mentioned in Experiment 30 builds up substantial layers of lead dioxide and spongy lead on the plates and increases the ability of the cell to supply current. This procedure of *forming* the active material on lead plates was employed originally by Gaston Planté in 1859; nowadays the plates of storage cells are constructed of grids with the active materials pressed into them.

In explaining the chemical reactions occurring in the lead cell when discharging and when charging, it must be remembered that the electrolyte dissociates into positive hydrogen ions ($H^+$), and negative sulfate ions ($SO_4^=$). These ions travel through the solution as described in the two preceding lessons and produce reactions in the cell as follows:

## On Discharge

Upon discharging the cell, lead ions go into solution at the negative plate and combine with the sulfate ions to form lead sulfate; the hydrogen ions reduce the lead dioxide of the positive plate to lead monoxide. The chemical equations are as follows:

Negative plate $$Pb \rightarrow Pb^{++} + 2e$$

$$Pb^{++} + SO_4^= \rightarrow PbSO_4$$

Positive plate $$PbO_2 + 2H^+ + 2e \rightarrow PbO + H_2O$$

Lead dioxide ($PbO_2$) is inactive in the presence of sulfuric acid, but lead monoxide ($PbO$), which is formed at the positive plate on the reduction of the dioxide, reacts readily with sulfuric acid, thus:

$$PbO + H_2SO_4 \rightarrow PbSO_4 + H_2O$$

Consequently during discharge, both plates become coated with lead sulfate ($PbSO_4$), and the sulfuric acid is partly converted into water, thereby lowering the concentration of the electrolyte.

If both plates were reduced entirely to lead sulfate, the cell would no longer deliver current, for there would then be but one kind of electrode material present. In practice, the discharge of a lead cell is not continued until both plates are completely reduced to lead sulfate, because this material is bulkier than the active materials and, if excessive, would tend to buckle or warp the plates.

During discharge of the lead storage cell, the e.m.f. falls quickly from an initial value of approximately 2.1 volts and remains nearly constant at 2.0 volts throughout most of the discharge period. At the approach of complete discharge the e.m.f. falls rapidly from this value.

## On Charge

Upon charging the cell by current from an outside source, the lead sulfate on the negative plate is restored to lead and that on the positive plate to lead dioxide; the electrolyte returns to its original concentration. Thus:

Negative plate     $PbSO_4 + 2H^+ + 2e \rightarrow Pb + H_2SO_4$

Positive plate     $PbSO_4 + SO_4^= - 2e \rightarrow Pb(SO_4)_2$

The plumbic sulfate, $Pb(SO_4)_2$, formed at the positive plate is unstable in the presence of water, and breaks up as follows:

$$Pb(SO_4)_2 + 2H_2O \rightarrow PbO_2 + 2H_2SO_4$$

This action restores the lead storage cell to its original condition If the cell is overcharged, hydrogen and oxygen will be liberated profusely and the result will be the same as in the decomposition of water in an electrolytic cell. This effect is known as "gassing" and indicates the completion of charge. Charging or discharging at excessive rates also causes the rapid evolution of gases as well as unnecessary heating; these effects tend to loosen the active materials of the plates and produce such erosion as to shorten the useful life of the cell very materially.

**52. Types of Plates and Their Assembly.**—The active materials in lead storage batteries, lead dioxide at the positive plate and spongy lead at the negative plate, have no mechanical strength and, therefore, special construction is necessary to make them into suitable plates. In the early Planté type of plate, the layers of active materials were formed on the surfaces of lead plates by elec- trochemical means; they were relatively thin, and it was neces- sary to spread them over large areas in order to yield plates hav- ing sufficient material. The present types of plates support the active materials in frames or *grids*, usually made of lead-antimony alloy, which are immune to attack by the sulfuric acid solution which constitutes the electrolyte.

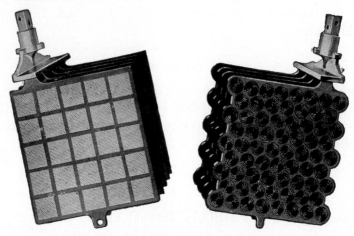

FIG. 57.  Plates of ''Exide-Chloride'' cell
Box-type negative plates at left and Manchester-type positive plates at right.

Fig. 57 shows the plates of one form of storage cell which bears the trade-name of ''Exide-Chloride'' cell, a name that extends back several decades to the time when chlorides were used in storage cells manufactured by The Electric Storage Battery Company and its foreign affiliates. The plates are arranged in groups and connected to common terminals, the left group is composed of five negative plates, and the right group of four positive plates. When these groups are mounted in the cell, the plates are interleaved so that each positive plate lies between two negative plates, the electrical separation of plates of opposite polarity being assured by thin board and dowel separators.

FIG. 58.  Construction of Manchester-type positive plate

The negative plate illustrated is of the so-called *Box-type;* it consists of a grid of horizontal and vertical ribs to provide rectangular pockets; these are filled with porous spongy lead and closed on both sides by sheets of perforated soft lead. The positive plate is of a kind styled *Manchester-type;* it consists of "buttons" formed of soft lead ribbon, corrugated crosswise and rolled into spirals, which are forced by hydraulic pressure into circular openings in the grid. The construction of the positive plate is illustrated in greater detail in Fig. 58. The buttons are electrolytically formed out of the metal itself by the Planté process, and provide collectively a large surface of lead dioxide to both sides of a plate. Fig. 59 shows an assembled view of an Exide cell.

FIG. 59. Cut-away view of "Exide" battery

The Electric Storage Battery Company

Another form of storage cell made by the same company bears the trade-name "Exide-Ironclad" cell to characterize its sturdy construction. The positive plate of this cell consists of a series of hollow tubes of finely slotted rubber, within which is packed the lead dioxide. A partial section of one of these tubes is shown at the right in Fig. 60 with the dioxide spread around a central metal core. Each plate is formed of a number of these tubes held in place vertically as shown in the assembly view at the left. The slots in the tubes

FIG. 60. Assembly of "Exide-Ironclad" cell with enlarged view of a positive tube

permit access of the electrolyte to the active material, but are so fine as practically to eliminate the washing out of this material. The negative plate is of the grid form with its rectangular pockets filled with spongy lead.

The construction of the so-called Floté grid used in Gould batteries is shown in Fig. 61. The grids are designed to lock the active materials firmly in place and to provide adequate cross section for the current from these materials to and from the battery terminals.

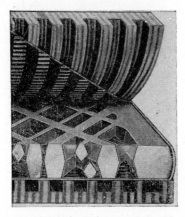

FIG. 61. Grid of Gould battery

Upper rubber retainer and wood separator are shown rolled up to reveal grid construction.

The positive and negative plates of a cell are separated by sheets of insulating material to keep the plates from touching each other and causing a "short circuit" between them. Wood separators are often used for this purpose; they are treated to be acid resisting yet sufficiently porous to let the ions through, and they are grooved vertically to allow the escape of gases liberated when the cell is charged. Separators are also made of slotted or perforated rubber and of spun glass. The rubber separators next to the grid in Fig. 61 serve as retainers in helping to keep the active materials in place.

The containers used for storage cells are made of glass, hard rubber, celluloid or lead-lined wood. They often have ribs across the bottom which serve to support the plates and provide spaces wherein the sediment from the active materials may settle without touching the plates. Stationary batteries usually have glass containers and are provided with glass or hard rubber covers.

Fig. 62 shows half of a battery for use on a mine locomotive. The assembly comprises four batteries of 5 cells each and two of 4 cells each.

**53. Electrolyte of a Lead Cell.**—The electrolyte in a lead storage cell is a solution of sulfuric acid in either distilled or rain water. The percentage of acid varies from 18 to 30 per cent by volume depending on the type of cell. The concentration of the electrolyte can best be determined from measurements of its *specific gravity*. The specific gravity of a substance is the ratio of the weight of that substance to the weight of an equal volume of pure water. Thus, water is regarded as the reference material and the specific gravity of water is taken as 1.000. The specific gravity of pure sulfuric acid is 1.835 (at 60° F.). Since the weight of 1 cubic foot

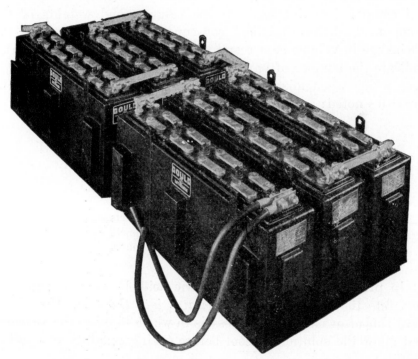

FIG. 62. Assembly of six batteries aggregating 28 cells

of water is 62.4 pounds, it follows that 1 cubic foot of pure sulfuric acid weighs 1.835 × 62.4 or 114.5 pounds.

The greater the proportion of acid in the electrolyte of a storage cell, the higher will be its specific gravity, and a typical value is 1.28 for a fully-charged cell. It is quite common in dealing with storage batteries to call the specific gravity of water 1000 rather than unity; on this basis the electrolyte mentioned would have a specific gravity of 1280. The concentration that would be appropriate for a cell depends somewhat upon its use; for example, the electrolyte of a cell under continuous operation may have a higher value than one which frequently stands unused for long intervals of time.

To make electrolytes of the proper concentration for use in lead storage batteries, tables are employed which give the proportions by volume of pure water and of acid having a specific gravity 1.835. The tables are prepared from experimental data and are not computed on the basis of the volumes and weights of the components before mixing; consequently, they allow for the shrinkage in volume as a result of mixing. The following entries indicate the number of parts of water to one part of acid *by volume* which when mixed will make solutions having the specific gravities noted:

### SULFURIC ACID BATTERY SOLUTIONS

| Specific Gravity | Water |
|---|---|
| 1200 | 4.4 parts |
| 1225 | 3.7 parts |
| 1250 | 3.2 parts |
| 1275 | 2.8 parts |
| 1300 | 2.5 parts |

In preparing solutions of sulfuric acid, be sure to pour the acid into the water, *never pour water into the acid.* Use glass, hard rubber or earthenware vessels in which to make the mixture, and allow the solution to cool before taking readings of specific gravity.

Temperature affects the specific gravity of the electrolyte; a change of 30 Fahrenheit degrees changes the specific gravity reading 10 points. For example, if a hydrometer reads 1270 in an electrolyte at 75° F., it would read 1280 at 45° F. and 1260 at 105° F.

A sufficient amount of electrolyte should be put in the storage cell to cover the plates and preferably the liquid surface should stand about one-half inch above them. Care should be taken with batteries in outdoor service to prevent freezing, particularly when in a discharged condition. The following table shows how the freezing point of the solution depends upon its concentration.

FREEZING TEMPERATURES OF ACID BATTERIES

| Specific Gravity | Degrees F. | Specific Gravity | Degrees F. |
|---|---|---|---|
| 1275 ........... | −85 | 1150 ........... | + 5 |
| 1250 ........... | −62 | 1125 ........... | +13 |
| 1225 ........... | −35 | 1100 ........... | +19 |
| 1200 ........... | −16 | 1050 ........... | +25 |
| 1175 ........... | − 4 | 1000 ........... | +32 |

The sulfuric acid solution of a lead storage cell becomes less dense during discharge of the cell, and more dense while the cell is being recharged. These facts are revealed by the equations of §51, since sulfuric acid is replaced by water during discharge, and water is replaced by acid during charge. When fully charged the electrolyte should have a specific gravity of from 1200 to 1300, according to the class of work for which the cell is intended. On discharge the specific gravity should not be allowed to fall below 1175.

The condition of a lead storage cell, with regard to charge or discharge, is readily ascertained by testing the specific gravity of its electrolyte with a *hydrometer*. This instrument consists of a long glass tube, near the bottom of which is a bulb loaded with mercury or "B-B" shot so as to make the instrument float in a vertical position when placed in the liquid, as shown in Fig. 63. There is a graduated scale placed inside the glass tube, and the divisions are evenly spaced. When lowered into a solution of acid and released, the hydrometer sinks to a certain depth, depending upon the specific gravity of the liquid. The reading of the hydrometer

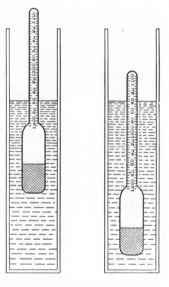

FIG. 63. Acid hydrometer showing difference in flotation levels in liquids of different specific gravities

scale at the surface of the solution gives its specific gravity; in the illustration, the specific gravity of the liquid in the left-hand container is 1260 and that in the other is 1140.

In the large storage batteries used in electric power stations there is sufficient room in the cells to float the hydrometer in their electrolytes, but this is not so in portable storage batteries. The form of instrument used in testing portable cells consists of a small hydrometer within a glass-barrel syringe that is fitted with a rubber bulb at its upper end for drawing enough liquid into the glass barrel to float the hydrometer.

The solution loses some of its water by charging the cell and by evaporation, but acid is not lost in these ways. Therefore, *only water should be added* if the level of the solution in the cell is too low.

**Experiment 31.**—To demonstrate the principle of the hydrometer, load a wooden dowel at one end with a piece of metal and mark off equal distances along the cylindrical surface. Place several liquids, such as water, alcohol, and carbon tetrachloride, in separate tall glass jars and place the dowel in in them successively. Note the scale divisions at which the dowel floats in the various liquids.

**54. Electrical Characteristics of Lead Cells.**—The electromotive force of a lead-acid storage cell does not depend upon the size of the cell, but it does depend upon the character of the plates and the concentration of the electrolyte. As previously stated, its value averages 2.0 volts. When the battery discharges from a fully charged condition the e.m.f. gradually decreases from about 2.1 to 1.7 volts. The fall in e.m.f. on discharge is due to a lowering of concentration of the electrolyte and to the changing of the active materials of both plates into lead sulfate; the formation of the latter also reduces the conductivity of the cell. The limiting e.m.f. beyond which discharge should not be carried depends upon the rapidity of discharge.

The *capacity* of a cell is the quantity of electricity that it will supply from a fully-charged condition, when discharging at constant current, for a prescribed time until its e.m.f. has fallen to a certain value. The capacity is determined by the size of the plates and by the rapidity of discharge, and is expressed in ampere-hours. The rating of a cell is frequently made in terms of several rates of discharge, one of them is usually the 8-hour rate to bring the e.m.f. down to a final value of 1.75 volts. For example, if a cell is rated as having a capacity of 200 ampere-hours, its 8-hour rate of discharge is determined by dividing 200 ampere-hours by 8 hours, giving 25 amperes as the steady current that can be taken from the cell over a period of 8 hours. Theoretically, it would seem that this cell should give a discharge of 50 amperes for 4 hours, or perhaps 200 amperes for 1 hour, since the product in both cases is 200 ampere-hours. But experience has shown that

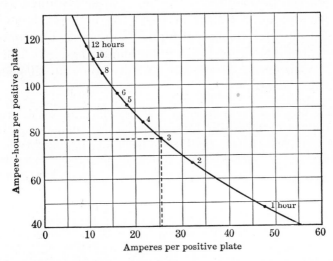

FIG. 64. Discharge characteristics of a typical storage cell

an increase in the rate of discharge of a cell decreases its ampere-hour capacity; thus, the foregoing cell may deliver only 100 amperes at the 1-hour rate. This reduction of capacity results from the inability of the solution to diffuse into the active material during quick discharges.

Specifically, a certain lead storage cell having 8 positive and 9 negative plates, each measuring 11 by 12 inches, has an 8-hour rating of 840 ampere-hours and a 3-hour rating of 616 ampere-hours, both to a final e.m.f. of 1.75 volts. Its 72-hour rating is 1330 ampere-hours to a final e.m.f. of 1.85 volts. This cell can supply for 1 minute either a current of 900 amperes to a final e.m.f. of 1.75 volts, or one of 1700 amperes to 1.50 volts.

The discharge characteristics of this make of storage cell are given in Fig. 64 on the basis of one positive plate measuring 11 by

12 inches. The numerals on the curve signify the duration of discharges to a final e.m.f. of 1.75 volts. Suppose it is desired to find the 3-hour rating of a storage cell of this type which has 8 positive and 9 negative plates. Referring to the figure, it will be observed that dotted lines are drawn parallel to the horizontal and vertical intersecting lines or coordinates at the point on the curve marked 3, signifying the 3-hour discharge rate; these lines give readings of 77 ampere-hours on the vertical scale and 25.6 amperes on the horizontal scale. Since these readings are based on 1 positive plate, it will be necessary to multiply them by 8 to obtain the values for the cell of 8 positive plates. The corresponding values are $8 \times 77$ or 616 ampere-hours, and $8 \times 25.6$ or 205 amperes. As a check, divide 616 ampere-hours by 205 amperes; the result is 3 hours.

**Problem 14.**—For the particular cell described above, determine the discharge current in amperes and the current density in amperes per square foot of positive plate surface (both sides included) for the 8-hour rate.

The ampere-hour capacity is stated as 840 ampere-hours at the 8-hour rate, therefore the discharge current over this period is $\dfrac{840 \text{ ampere-hours}}{8 \text{ hours}}$ or 105 amperes. This same result can be found from Fig. 64, which gives along the horizontal scale a current of 13.2 amperes per positive plate at the 8-hour rate. For 8 plates the current is $8 \times 13.2 = 105$ amperes.

The surface of each positive plate, measuring 11 by 12 inches, is $2 \times 11 \times 12$ or 264 square inches $= 264 \div 144$ or 1.83 square feet. The total positive plate surface is $8 \times 1.83$ or 14.6 square feet. Hence, the current density is $\dfrac{105 \text{ amperes}}{14.6 \text{ square feet}} = 7.2$ amperes per square foot.

**Problem 15.**—Determine the ampere-hour ratings of a lead cell having the discharge characteristics indicated in Fig. 64 for uniform discharges lasting 12 hours, 8 hours, and 1 hour, assuming the cell to have 6 positive plates.

The readings on the vertical scale corresponding to the dots on the curve carrying the notations "12 hours" down to "1 hour" give the ampere-hour ratings of the cell per positive plate for these discharge periods. The readings are 117 ampere-hours for a 12-hour rate, 105 for an 8-hour rate, 48 for a 1-hour rate. The corresponding ratings for a cell having 6 positive plates are six times these values, or 702 ampere-hours for 12 hours, 630 for 8 hours and 288 for 1 hour.

It will be noted from these problems that the discharge current and the capacity of a storage cell increase directly with the area of the plates exposed to the electrolyte. The capacity in practice is rated at from 40 to 60 ampere-hours (8-hour rate) per square foot of exposed positive plate surface.

**Problem 16.**—Allowing 45 ampere-hours per square foot of positive plate surface, what would be the capacity of a lead storage cell which has 12 positive and 13 negative plates, each measuring 10 inches square?

$$\text{Area of positive plate} = 12 \times 2 \times 10 \times 10 = 2400 \text{ square inches}$$
$$= 2400 \div 144 = 16.7 \text{ square feet}$$
$$\text{Capacity of cell} = 45 \times 16.7 = 750 \text{ ampere-hours}$$

An outstanding feature of the lead storage battery is its low internal resistance when fully charged. Because of this characteristic, such batteries are universally used to start the engines of gasoline-driven automobiles, a service which may require initial currents as high as 500 amperes in cold weather. The internal resistance, however, increases quite rapidly as the cell approaches the condition of full discharge, and the current may not then be sufficient to turn the engine.

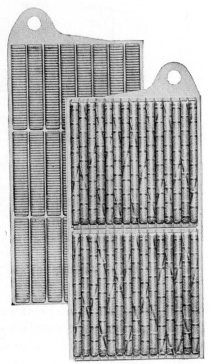

FIG. 65. Negative and positive plates of the Edison cell

**55. Edison Storage Cell.**—The nickel-alkaline storage cell was devised by Thomas A. Edison (1847-1931) and is different from the lead-acid cell in every particular. It employs a nickel oxide for the positive electrode and finely divided iron for the negative electrode, these materials being packed into pockets carried by steel grids. The electrolyte is a solution of potassium hydroxide, generally called caustic potash. As the cell discharges, the nickel oxide becomes reduced and the iron becomes oxidized, but the electrolyte remains unchanged in concentration.

The positive plate of the Edison cell consists of hollow perforated tubes formed of spirally-wound steel ribbon, as shown at
the right in Fig. 65. These tubes are filled with alternate layers of
nickel hydrate and pure nickel flake; the nickel hydrate is converted to nickel oxide on first charge and this becomes the active
material, while the nickel is introduced to increase the electrical
conductivity. The tubes are capped at each end, individually rein-

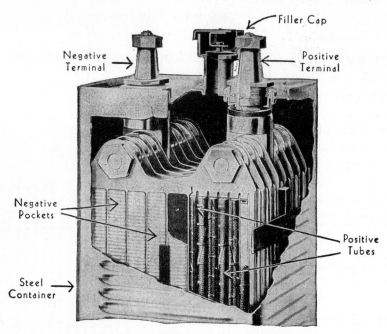

FIG. 66. Assembly of plates in the nickel-iron-alkaline cell
Thomas A. Edison, Inc.

forced by steel rings, and clamped into a steel supporting grid.

The negative plate consists of perforated rectangular, sheet-
steel pockets, which are loaded with iron oxide mixed with a little
mercury oxide to increase the conductivity. These pockets are
placed in the apertures of the steel supporting grid, as shown at
the left in the figure, and forced into good electrical contact under
hydraulic pressure.

Fig. 66 shows the plates assembled into a complete unit and
mounted in a heavily nickel-plated rectangular container of sheet
steel; Fig. 67 shows a 5-cell battery suitable for student use.

The electrolyte is a 21-per cent solution of caustic potash, to which is added a small amount of lithium hydroxide; the solution has a specific gravity from 1.20 to 1.23 and does not change through charging or discharging of the battery. This means that measurements of specific gravity with a hydrometer do not indicate the extent of charge or discharge. The e.m.f. of the Edison cell is about 1.2 volts when fully charged and about 0.9 when discharged. Consequently, its state of charge can be tested roughly by a voltmeter connected across its terminals.

Fig. 67. Portable Edison battery supplying 6 volts

### 56. Reactions and Characteristics of Edison Cells.—When current is supplied by an Edison cell, metallic iron at the negative plate is oxidized to form an iron oxide and the nickel oxide of the positive plate is reduced to a lower oxide. The reverse operations take place when current is supplied to the cell during the charging process. The electrolyte of potassium hydroxide (KOH) is dissociated into potassium positive ions and hydroxide negative ions, as indicated by the equation

$$2KOH = 2K^+ + 2OH^-$$

The reactions that actually occur in the cell on discharge and on charge are quite complicated, but the following equations represent the general behavior:

*Discharge*

| | |
|---|---|
| Negative plate | $Fe + 2OH^- - 2e \rightarrow FeO + H_2O$ |
| Positive plate | $NiO_2 + 2K^+ + H_2O + 2e \rightarrow NiO + 2KOH$ |

*Charge*

| | |
|---|---|
| Negative plate | $FeO + 2K^+ + H_2O + 2e \rightarrow Fe + 2KOH$ |
| Positive plate | $NiO + 2OH^- - 2e \rightarrow NiO_2 + H_2O$ |

In brief, the reactions may be viewed as a transfer of oxygen from positive to negative plates during discharge, and from negative to positive during charge. It is to be noted that just as much potassium hydroxide is formed in each process as is dissociated, consequently the concentration of the electrolyte remains unchanged.

The Edison cell costs more than the lead-acid cell, and its e.m.f. is less; however, it has less weight for the same capacity. It is rugged and reliable, and has a low maintenance cost, particularly in such service as electric-vehicle propulsion and train lighting. It will not be damaged through subjection to low temperatures or freezing. The plates of the Edison battery will not be injured if allowed to stand for long periods in the electrolyte in a discharged condition, in fact, complete discharge is recommended whenever the battery is to be withdrawn temporarily from service. Evaporation of the electrolyte is compensated for by the addition of distilled water. The battery may be charged at high rates without injury.

The ampere-hour ratings of Edison batteries are based on a 5-hour discharge period for most types and on a 3⅓-hour period for others, all to a final e.m.f. of 1.0 volt per cell.

A positive plate of a nickel-iron-alkaline cell designated as "Type B" consists of 15 cylindrical tubes, each 4.5 inches long and 0.25 inch in diameter, and a negative plate of this cell contains 16 pockets, each measuring 2.16 by 0.5 inches; the tubes and pockets are filled with the respective active materials. The positive plates of "Types A, C and D" cells consist respectively of 30, 45 and 60 tubes of the size above mentioned. The designations of the different cells are made by giving the types of plates and the number of positives; thus, a B-2 cell has 2 positive plates each with 15 tubes, and a D-10 cell has 10 positive plates each with 60 tubes, in all cases there is one more negative plate than positive. The ampere-hour rating of these types is 1.25 ampere-hours per positive tube based on the usual 5-hour discharge.

**Problem 17.**—Calculate the rating of an Edison cell per square foot of positive surface in contact with the electrolyte.

The contact surface of a single positive tube is 4.5 inches multiplied by the circumference of a circle ¼ inch in diameter; the latter is $\pi \times \frac{1}{4}$ inch, where the Greek letter $\pi$ represents 3.1416. Thus, the surface of one tube is $\dfrac{4.5 \times 3.1416}{4}$ = 3.53 square inches. The number of such tubes needed to yield 1 square foot of contact surface would be $144 \div 3.53 = 40.8$; each of these has a rating of 1.25 ampere-hours. Therefore, the desired rating is $40.8 \times 1.25$ or 51 ampere-hours per square foot of positive contact surface.

**57. Charging Storage Cells.**—The charging of storage batteries is usually accomplished by connecting them to the electricity supply circuits from local power companies, using current controlling or rectifying devices. Naturally only direct current can be used for charging purposes. Where alternating current is the only source available, it is necessary to convert the supply to direct current by means of a converter, motor-generator or rectifier. In order that the charging current shall be directed through the battery in the opposite direction to that produced by the battery on discharge, the *positive terminal of the battery must be connected to the positive conductor of the current supply source.*

The polarity of the current source may be determined by dipping into water a pair of wires leading from the service mains, exercising care not to touch the wires to each other. Since twice as much hydrogen gas is evolved at the negative wire as oxygen at the positive wire, the polarity of the circuit is readily determined. Another way of determining the direction of current is by use of some form of *polarity indicator,* §38. Voltmeters and neon glow tubes may also be used as polarity indicators.

The potential difference needed to charge a single lead storage cell is about 2.5 volts and to charge a single Edison cell is about 1.75 volts. If much more than these amounts are available per cell, use is made of controlling devices to keep the current to appropriate values. The method of charging varies with the type of service, and specific directions are supplied by the manufacturers.

Charging rates are usually higher than the rates of discharge. For example, the charging of a lead cell may be started with a current corresponding to the 3-hour discharge rate and finished with a current corresponding to the 8-hour rate. Charging should continue until the cell is gassing uniformly at both plates and until the specific gravity of the electrolyte stops rising. The number of ampere-hours supplied to a storage battery during charge is greater than the number delivered during its discharge, because of losses occurring in the battery.

The hydrogen and oxygen given off from a battery during charge or discharge, when not diluted with a large amount of air, form a combination that will explode violently if ignited by an open flame or an electric spark. If the battery is in a compartment, be sure to open or ventilate the compartment while the battery is charging, in order that these gases may be mixed with air and allowed to escape.

Failure of storage batteries is usually due to excess *sulfation*, that is, the production of too much lead sulfate. This material clogs the separators placed between the plates or causes the plates to buckle. Troubles may also arise due to broken separators or impurities in the electrolyte. The presence of oils or greases in the electrolyte, or the use of ordinary water containing mineral salts in making up for evaporation, result in a drop of capacity. The only method of purifying water for battery purposes is by *distillation;* use the condensed water vapor and not the boiled water itself.

## QUESTIONS

1. What is the difference between a primary cell and a storage cell?
2. What does a storage cell store?
3. To what uses are storage batteries put?
4. What are the active materials of a charged lead-acid storage cell?
5. Describe the chemical action taking place in a lead cell when it is discharging.
6. Describe the chemical action produced in a lead storage cell by the charging current.
7. Why is it inadvisable to discharge a storage cell beyond a certain point?
8. Describe the construction of a Manchester-type positive plate and of a box-type negative plate.
9. Define specific gravity of a substance.
10. What is a hydrometer and how is it used?
11. Mention typical values of specific gravity for the electrolyte of a lead storage cell when fully charged and discharged.
12. What should the gasoline station attendant add to the storage battery of an automobile when its electrolyte has dropped below the top of the plates?
13. How is the capacity of a storage cell rated and what factors does the capacity depend upon?

14. Does the ampere-hour rating increase or decrease with increase of discharge current? Why?
15. What is the average e.m.f. of a lead storage cell? of a nickel-alkaline cell?
16. Name the active materials that are used in the Edison storage cell.
17. Explain the actions that occur in the Edison cell during charge and discharge.
18. What are the advantages and disadvantages of the Edison storage cell over the lead cell?
19. How would you determine when a lead storage cell was fully charged, and how would you know when to stop its discharge?

### PROBLEMS

1. A certain lead storage battery for motor-coach service has a 20-hour rating of 200 ampere-hours, and a 4-hour rating of 145 ampere-hours. Determine the corresponding currents at uniform discharge. *Ans.* 10 and 36.3 amperes respectively.
2. Compute the ampere-hour ratings and the currents of a lead storage cell with 8 positive plates of the type having the discharge characteristic shown in Fig. 64 for uniform discharges (a) lasting 10 hours and (b) lasting 5 hours. *Ans.* (a) 888 ampere-hours and 88.8 amperes; (b) 728 ampere-hours and 145.6 amperes.
3. It is desired to provide a current of 150 amperes for 3 hours from a storage cell of the type having the discharge characteristic shown in Fig. 64. How many plates of each polarity should it have? *Ans.* 6 positive and 7 negative plates.
4. The rated capacity of a certain 11-plate lead storage cell is 200-ampere-hours for an 8-hour discharge and 156 ampere-hours for one of 3 hours. Each plate is square and measures 7¾ inches on a side. (a) What are the discharge currents in amperes at these rates? (b) What are the corresponding current densities in amperes per square foot of positive plate surface. *Ans.* (a) 25 and 52 amperes respectively; (b) 6.0 and 12.5 amperes per square foot respectively.
5. A 37.5-ampere-hour Edison cell has 2 positive and 3 negative plates, each grid measuring 4.5 by 4.25 inches. Calculate the rating per unit of positive grid surface. *Ans.* 71 ampere-hours per square foot.
6. Determine the ratings of the A-12, C-8 and D-6 Edison cells on the usual 5-hour basis. *Ans.* 450 ampere-hours each.

# Lesson VI

## RESISTANCE

Resistance of conductors—Unit of resistance; the ohm—Prefixes used with electrical units—Factors affecting resistance—The circular mil—Resistivities of materials—Calculation of resistance—Wire gage sizes—Heat and temperature—Dependence of resistance upon temperature—Super-conductivity—Rheostats and resistance boxes—Resistance of connections—Questions and Problems.

**58. Resistance of Conductors.**—Water flowing through pipes encounters some opposition because of the friction between the running water and the inner surfaces of the pipes. Because of this mechanical friction, the water loses a certain amount of its energy of motion and that amount is converted into heat energy, §101. Similarly, electricity flowing through conductors encounters an opposition analogous to friction, and some of the energy of the electric current is converted into heat. *The opposition in an electric circuit which causes heat to be produced in it by a current is called resistance.* It may be looked upon as the opposition experienced by the electrons in weaving their way among the atoms of the conductors of the circuit.

All conductors of electricity possess resistance, some more than others; a good conductor has less resistance than a poor conductor. Another term is used in contrast with resistance; it is called *conductivity*. The greater the resistance of a substance the lower will be its conductivity. Insulators have a very high resistance and consequently their conductivity is very low. Metals and alloys have relatively low resistances and these substances are rated high in conductivity. Both conductors and insulators are necessary in all electrical devices and circuits; the conductor provides the current path and the insulator prevents leakage of current from that path.

Fundamentally, the conductivity of a substance depends on the relative number of free electrons in it. If there are many free electrons per unit of volume, the substance is a good conductor; if there are very few, it is a poor conductor or a good insulator.

**59. Unit of Resistance; the Ohm.**—The amount of resistance possessed by a conductor is expressed in terms of a unit called the *ohm,* named after the German physicist, Georg S. Ohm (1787-1854). Through international agreement, the ohm is the resistance offered to an unvarying electric current by a column of mercury 106.3 centimeters long, weighing 14.4521 grams and having a uniform cross-sectional area, at a temperature of 0° C. (or 32° F.).

It will be developed later that heat will be produced at a particular rate in a circuit of 1 ohm resistance when the current in it is 1 ampere. Every second the amount of heat produced, expressed in energy units, is exactly one joule, §41. Thus, the basic definition of the ohm is the resistance which will produce 1 joule of heat per second when the current through it is 1 ampere. It is understandable now why the specification of the international ohm should involve such singular numbers as given above for the length and weight of a mercury column.

A few samples will serve to give an approximate idea of the unit of resistance. A copper wire 1000 feet long and 0.1 inch in diameter has a resistance of 1 ohm, and one 2.4 feet long and 0.005 inch in diameter has the same resistance. An overhead trolley wire of copper 3 miles long has a resistance of about 1 ohm.

**60. Prefixes Used with Electrical Units.**—For convenience in expressing a wide range of mechanical and electrical values, certain multiples and submultiples of units have come into wide use, and these carry the basic unit names with prefixes. The principle prefixes have the following meaning:

*Significance of Prefixes*

| micro | one millionth | 0.000001 | $10^{-6}$ |
|-------|---------------|----------|-----------|
| milli | one thousandth | 0.001 | $10^{-3}$ |
| centi | one hundredth | 0.01 | $10^{-2}$ |
| kilo | one thousand | 1000. | $10^{3}$ |
| meg(a) | one million | 1,000,000. | $10^{6}$ |

Thus, 1 microcoulomb = 0.000001 coulomb, 1 milliampere = 0.001 ampere, 1 centimeter = 0.01 meter, 1 kilovolt = 1000 volts, and 1 megohm = 1,000,000 ohms.

**Problem 18.**—What is the equivalent resistance (a) of 47,500,000 ohms in megohms? (b) of 0.000385 ohm in microhms?

Since 1,000,000 ohms constitute 1 megohm, the larger resistance mentioned is

$$47,500,000 \div 10^6 = 47.5 \text{ megohms} \tag{a}$$

Since 0.000,001 ohm is 1 microhm, the smaller resistance is

$$0.000385 \times 10^6 = 385 \text{ microhms} \tag{b}$$

**61. Factors Affecting Resistance.**—The resistance of a conductor depends primarily upon its size and the material of which it is made; it is also affected by temperature. The manner in which these factors influence the resistance of a conductor is considered below with numerical illustrations:

I. *The resistance of a conductor is directly proportional to its length.* A length of 1000 feet of copper wire 0.1 inch in diameter has a resistance of 1 ohm; consequently, a piece of it 500 feet long will have a resistance of 0.5 ohm. Similarly, 2000 feet of this wire will have 2 ohms resistance; 10,000 feet, 10 ohms; and so on. To generalize, if $R_1$ be the resistance of a wire of length $l_1$, and $R_2$ the resistance of a length $l_2$ of the same wire, then by proportion

$$R_1 : R_2 = l_1 : l_2$$

II. *The resistance of a conductor is inversely proportional to its cross-sectional area.* Since a length of 1000 feet of copper wire 0.1 inch in diameter has 1 ohm resistance, the same length of copper wire with twice that cross section will have ½ ohm resistance, and another wire of one-quarter of the original cross section will have 4 ohms resistance. To generalize, if $R_1$ be the resistance of a conductor of sectional area $A_1$, and $R_2$ the resistance of an equally long one of sectional area $A_2$, then for conductors of the same material

$$R_1:R_2 = A_2:A_1$$

The cross-sectional area of a round wire is directly proportional to the square of its diameter, that is to the diameter multiplied by itself. Thus, a wire that has half the diameter of another will have one-quarter of its sectional area; consequently, its resistance will be four times as much. A copper wire 1000 feet long and 0.05 inch in diameter will have 4 ohms resistance. To generalize, if $R_1$ be the resistance of a wire of diameter $d_1$, and $R_2$ the resistance of an equally long wire of diameter $d_2$, then for wires of the same material

$$R_1:R_2 = d_2{}^2:d_1{}^2$$

III. *The resistance of a conductor of given length and cross section depends upon the material of which it is made.* For example, the resistance of 1000 feet of copper wire 0.1 inch in diameter is 1 ohm, as mentioned before, while the resistance of a piece of iron wire of the same length and cross section is about 6 ohms. A similar piece of aluminum wire has almost 2 ohms, and of manganin about 25 ohms of resistance. The materials which have relatively high resistances are used in wire or rod form to make convenient control devices called *resistors.*

IV. *The resistance of a conductor depends upon the temperature.* All pure metals exhibit an increase of resistance with a rise of temperature. The resistance of copper increases about one-fifth of one per cent for each degree Fahrenheit rise of temperature around ordinary room temperature. The increase is given more accurately by the figure 0.0022 per ohm per degree Fahrenheit. For the 1-ohm copper wire referred to repeatedly, a 25-degree change of temperature produces a change of resistance of 25 × 0.0022 = 0.055 ohm. Some alloys, like manganin, experience very slight changes of resistance with temperature, and find application in electrical measuring devices for that reason.

In summary, the resistance of a conductor varies directly as the length and inversely as the cross-sectional area; it also depends on the material and temperature of the conductor. These conclusions are brought out pictorially in Fig. 68 in which the 1-ohm conductor that serves as the reference standard appears first under each factor and the others are stipulated in the foregoing paragraphs bearing like Roman numerals.

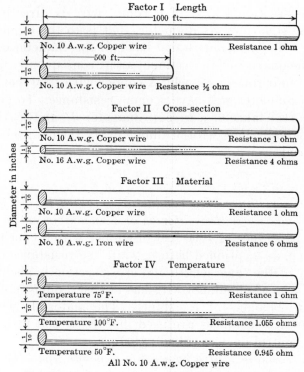

FIG. 68. Resistance of some electrical conductors

**Experiment 32.**—Make up four different resistance coils by winding insulated wire upon wooden spools, and connect them separately to a dry

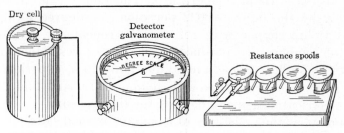

FIG. 69. Apparatus for revealing the factors affecting resistance

cell with a detector galvanometer included in the circuit, as shown in Fig. 69. The following windings are suggested to gain an appreciation of the correctness of the foregoing statements: Spool 1 contains 100 feet of No. 24 A.w.g. copper wire, diameter 0.0201 inch; Spool 2, 200 feet of the same size copper wire; Spool 3, 100 feet of No. 18 A.w.g. copper wire, diameter 0.0403 inch; Spool 4, 100 feet of No. 24 A.w.g. manganin wire.

Connecting these spools to the circuit one at a time, observe that with Spool 2 the deflection of the needle is smaller than with Spool 1 (Factor I); with Spool 3 the deflection is larger than with Spool 1 (Factor II); and with Spool 4 the deflection is the smallest of all (Factor III). Finally, using Spool 1, continue the current for a little while and note that as the winding becomes warm the deflection becomes slightly less (Factor IV).

## 62. The Circular Mil.

In calculating the electrical resistance of round wires, it is customary to use a *circular measure* to express cross-sectional areas. The unit of this measure is called the *circular* mil. The term *mil* alone means one one-thousandth of an inch (that is, 0.001 inch), and consequently, *one circular mil is the area of a circle having a diameter of one mil*. The circular mil is abbreviated as CM.

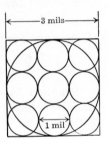

FIG. 70. Illustrating circular mil areas

Area of large circle equals that of the nine small circles.

If the diameter of a wire measures 2 thousandths of an inch (0.002 inch or 2 mils), then it has a sectional area of $2 \times 2 = 4$ circular mils. Again, a wire having a diameter of 3 mils has a sectional area of $3 \times 3 = 9$ circular mils; another with a diameter of 10 mils has a sectional area of $10 \times 10 = 100$ circular mils. Therefore, to determine the area of a wire in circular mils, express the diameter in mils and square this number.

To visualize these results, consider the circle inscribed in the square shown in Fig. 70 to have a diameter of 3 mils. Nine circles each 1 mil in diameter can be placed side by side within this square, and the sum of the areas of these small circles equals the area of the large circle. This is evident from the following, taking the diameter of the small circles as unity or 1 and that of the large circle as three (3). Since the area of a circle is $\pi/4$ or 0.7854 times the square of its diameter, the area of each of the small circles equals $0.7854 \times 1^2 = 0.7854$ and the area of nine of them will be $9 \times 0.7854 = 7.0686$. The area of the large circle equals $0.7854 \times 3^2 = 0.7854 \times 9 = 7.0686$. Therefore, the area of the large circle equals the sum of the areas of the nine small circles.

To FIND THE SECTIONAL AREA OF A ROUND WIRE IN CIRCULAR MILS WHEN ITS DIAMETER IS KNOWN:

*Express the diameter in mils and square it.*

Let

$$d = \text{diameter of wire in mils,}$$
$$CM = \text{sectional area in circular mils.}$$

Then the circular mil area is

$$CM = d^2 \qquad\qquad 9$$

To FIND THE DIAMETER OF A WIRE WHEN ITS SECTIONAL AREA IS KNOWN:

*Extract the square root of the circular mil area; the result will be in mils.* This rule is derived from Formula (9) by extracting the square root of both sides; thus,

$$d = \sqrt{CM} \qquad\qquad 10$$

**Problem 19.**—What is the sectional area of a metal rod $\frac{1}{4}$ inch in diameter? Since 1 inch = 1000 mils, it follows that $\frac{1}{4}$ inch = $\frac{1}{4} \times 1000$ or 250 mils = $d$.

(9) $\qquad CM = d^2 = 250 \times 250 = 62,500$ circular mils

**Problem 20.**—What is the diameter of a wire having a sectional area of 26,250 circular mils?

Since the square of the diameter in mils is the sectional area in circular mils, it follows that the square root of the sectional area in circular mils is the diameter in mils, therefore

(10) $\qquad d = \sqrt{CM} = \sqrt{26,250} = 162\,\text{mils} = 0.162\,\text{inch}$

**63. Resistivities of Materials.**—It has been stated ahead that two conductors of the same dimensions have different resistances if they are of different substances. This fact is attributed to differences in the numbers of free electrons present in these substances. To take these differences into account use is made of the term *resistivity*, which is the resistance of a sample of the substance having dimensions with specified unit values.

In scientific writings, the resistivity of a material is the resistance of a cube of it when measured between opposite faces, the size of the cube being either 1 centimeter or 1 inch along each edge. Since most conductors have circular sections, it is convenient also to define resistivity as the resistance of a round wire of the material 1 foot long and 1 mil in diameter. For example, copper has a resistivity of 1.72 microhm-centimeters, and this means that a specimen of copper 1 centimeter long and 1 square centimeter in cross section will have a resistance of $1.72 \times 10^{-6}$ ohms between opposite faces of the cube. For a 1-inch cube of copper the resistivity is 0.68 microhm-inch. The same material has a resistivity of 10.4 ohm-CM per foot, meaning that a specimen 1 foot long and 1 CM in cross section (diameter of round wire being 1 mil) will have a resistance of 10.4 ohms.

The following table gives the resistivities of a number of metals and alloys used in electrical work. The resistivity of a substance is affected somewhat by temperature changes, and the values listed are those which apply to a temperature of 20° C. or 68° F. The symbol used for resistivity is $\rho$, the Greek letter rho.

RESISTIVITIES OF CONDUCTORS

| Substance | Microhms | | Ohm-CM per Foot |
| --- | --- | --- | --- |
| | Centimeter Cube | Inch Cube | |
| Aluminum ......................... | 2.83 | 1.11 | 17.0 |
| Carbon (Graphite) ...............about | 700. | 275. | 4210. |
| Constantan (Cu 60%, Ni 40%)......... | 49. | 19.3 | 295. |
| Copper (annealed) ................... | 1.72 | 0.68 | 10.4 |
| Iron (99.98% pure) ................. | 10. | 3.94 | 60.2 |
| Lead ............................... | 22. | 8.66 | 132. |
| Manganin (Cu 84%, Ni 4%, Mn 12%).... | 44. | 17.3 | 264. |
| Mercury ........................... | 95.78 | 37.7 | 576. |
| Nichrome (Ni 60%, Cr 12%, Fe 26% Mn 2%) ........................... | 110. | 43. | 660. |
| Platinum ........................... | 9.9 | 3.9 | 59.5 |
| Silver ............................. | 1.65 | 0.65 | 9.9 |
| Tungsten ........................... | 5.5 | 2.17 | 33.1 |
| Zinc ............................... | 6.1 | 2.4 | 36.7 |

Low resistivity is necessary for wires that are used for transmitting electricity efficiently from place to place. On the other hand, conductors of moderately high resistivity are used in devices when the primary purpose of the current is the production of heat. Thus, electric heaters are wound with wire of nichrome, or similar alloys, and lamp filaments are made of tungsten. Insulators have much greater resistivities than those tabulated ahead for conductors; for example, the resistivity of gutta percha is $2 \times 10^9$ and that of mica is $9 \times 10^{15}$, both in ohm-centimeters.

**64. Calculation of Resistance.**—In calculating the resistance of metal conductors, the resistivity of the particular metal is taken as a constant and applied to conductors of the same material but of correspondingly greater or lesser length and sectional area. Values of this constant for a number of materials are listed in the table of the preceding section, and three numerical values are given for each material to suit the usual units in which the dimensions of conductors are generally stated.

The resistance of a conductor can be calculated when its dimensions and its resistivity are known. The computation is based upon the facts that the resistance varies directly with the length of the conductor and inversely with its cross-sectional area. Consequently, a conductor having a length $L$, a sectional area $A$, and a resistivity $\rho$, will have a resistance expressed by

$$R = \frac{\rho \times L}{A} \qquad \qquad 11$$

The units of the quantities represented by the letters in this formula must be consistent. For example, if the length of the conductor is expressed as $L$ feet, the sectional area as $A$ circular mils, then $\rho$ must be in ohm-CM per foot as given in the last column of the table. These are the units generally used for round wires.

To CALCULATE THE RESISTANCE OF A WIRE OF GIVEN LENGTH AND SECTIONAL AREA:

*Multiply the resistivity of the material by the length of the wire and divide by its sectional area.*

Let

$\rho$ = resistivity in ohm-CM per foot,
$L$ = length of the conductor in feet,
CM = sectional area in circular mils.

Then the resistance of the conductor is

$$R = \frac{\rho \times L}{CM} \qquad \qquad 12$$

**Problem 21.**—Find the resistance of 1000 feet of copper wire having a cross-sectional area of 10,000 CM.

Since $\rho$ for copper $= 10.4$ in the units mentioned, it follows that the resistance of the wire is

(12) $$R = \frac{\rho \times L}{CM} = \frac{10.4 \times 1000}{10,000} = 1.04 \text{ ohms}$$

TO FIND THE LENGTH OF A WIRE OF GIVEN RESISTANCE AND SECTIONAL AREA:

*Multiply the resistance of the wire by its sectional area and divide this product by the resistivity of the material.*

$$L = \frac{R \times CM}{\rho} \qquad 13$$

**Problem 22.**—What is the length of manganin wire wound on a resistance spool, if its resistance is 500 ohms and the wire has a diameter of 20 mils?

The sectional area of the wire is

(9) $$CM = d^2 = 20 \times 20 = 400 \text{ circular mils}$$

The resistivity of manganin is $\rho = 264$ ohm-CM per foot; hence the length of the wire is

(13) $$L = \frac{R \times CM}{\rho} = \frac{500 \times 400}{264} = 757 \text{ feet}$$

TO FIND THE CROSS-SECTION OF A WIRE OF GIVEN LENGTH AND RESISTANCE:

*Multiply the length of the wire by the resistivity of the material and divide this product by the resistance.*

$$CM = \frac{L \times \rho}{R} \qquad 14$$

**Problem 23.**—What is the sectional area of 1000 feet of a certain iron wire, if its resistance is 23.3 ohms?

Since $\rho$ for iron is 60.2 ohm-CM per foot, the area of the wire is

(14) $$CM = \frac{L \times \rho}{R} = \frac{1000 \times 60.2}{23.3} = 2580 \text{ circular mils}$$

For conductors of rectangular section, the areas can be reckoned in square centimeters or square inches and the resistances can be computed by using the resistivities per centimeter cube or per inch cube respectively.

**Problem 24.**—Find the resistance of a copper bar 16 feet long that measures 2 inches by ¼ inch.

The resistivity of copper is 0.68 microhm-inch, which means that the resistance of a cube of this metal measuring 1 inch on each edge is 0.68 microhm or $0.68 \times 10^{-6}$ ohm. The length of the conductor is $16 \times 12$ or 192 inches, and its sectional area is $2 \times \frac{1}{4}$ or 0.5 square inch. Consequently, the resistance of the bar between its ends is

$$(11) \quad R = \frac{\rho \times L}{A} = \frac{0.68 \times 10^{-6} \times 192}{0.5} = 0.000261 \text{ ohm or 261 microhms}$$

**65. Wire Gage Sizes.**—The diameters of round wires are commonly given by the numbers of a *gage*. There are several wire gages, originated by different manufacturers, but the one generally used in this country is the *American Wire Gage* (A.w.g.), also called the Brown & Sharpe (B. & S.) gage. The numbers on this gage range from four naughts to forty, that is, from No. 0000 wire (460 mils in diameter) to No. 40 wire (about 3 mils in diameter), the sizes decreasing as the gage numbers increase. The cross-sectional areas of wires on this gage increase to double value in lowering the gage size by three numbers. The ratio of the areas for two successive gage numbers is 1.26. The weights of wires vary in the same ratio and their resistances vary in the inverse ratio.

The following table lists the diameters and sectional areas of the various gage numbers and gives the resistance characteristics of annealed copper wire. The data involving weights are based on a specific gravity of 8.89 for copper. This table is intended for ultimate reference purposes and is computed to a greater precision than is necessary in practice.

Experiment 33.—You are given a wire gage and a number of copper wires of different diameters. Measure each wire and express its size by diameter and gage number. Refer to the wire table on next page and report the resistance and weight, both per 1000 feet of length, for each size of wire measured. Also compute the sectional area in circular mils of each wire.

**66. Heat and Temperature.**—It has been known for many years that heat is a form of energy, and that this energy can be transferred from place to place in several ways. Energy from the sun reaches the earth by radiation of heat and light; heat from a

## COPPER WIRE TABLE

*Standard Annealed Copper (A.w.g.)*

| Gage No. | Diameter in Mils | Cross-sectional Area | | Ohms per 1000 Feet | | Pounds per 1000 Feet |
|---|---|---|---|---|---|---|
| | | Circular Mils | Square Inch | 25° C. (77° F.) | 65° C. (149° F.) | |
| 0000 | 460. | 212 000. | 0.166 | 0.0500 | 0.0577 | 641. |
| 000 | 410. | 168 000. | .132 | .0630 | .0727 | 508. |
| 00 | 365. | 133 000. | .105 | .0795 | .0917 | 403. |
| 0 | 325. | 106 000. | .0829 | .100 | .116 | 319. |
| 1 | 289. | 83 700. | .0657 | .126 | .146 | 253. |
| 2 | 258. | 66 400. | .0521 | .159 | .184 | 201. |
| 3 | 229. | 52 600. | .0413 | .201 | .232 | 159. |
| 4 | 204. | 41 700. | .0328 | .253 | .292 | 126. |
| 5 | 182. | 33 100. | .0260 | .319 | .369 | 100. |
| 6 | 162. | 26 300. | .0206 | .403 | .465 | 79.5 |
| 7 | 144. | 20 800. | .0164 | .508 | .586 | 63.0 |
| 8 | 128. | 16 500. | .0130 | .641 | .739 | 50.0 |
| 9 | 114. | 13 100. | .0103 | .808 | .932 | 39.6 |
| 10 | 102. | 10 400. | .008 15 | 1.02 | 1.18 | 31.4 |
| 11 | 91. | 8230. | .006 47 | 1.28 | 1.48 | 24.9 |
| 12 | 81. | 6530. | .005 13 | 1.62 | 1.87 | 19.8 |
| 13 | 72. | 5180. | .004 07 | 2.04 | 2.36 | 15.7 |
| 14 | 64. | 4110. | .003 23 | 2.58 | 2.97 | 12.4 |
| 15 | 57. | 3260. | .002 56 | 3.25 | 3.75 | 9.86 |
| 16 | 51. | 2580. | .002 03 | 4.09 | 4.73 | 7.82 |
| 17 | 45. | 2050. | .001 61 | 5.16 | 5.96 | 6.20 |
| 18 | 40.3 | 1620. | .001 28 | 6.51 | 7.51 | 4.92 |
| 19 | 35.9 | 1290. | .001 01 | 8.21 | 9.48 | 3.90 |
| 20 | 31.9 | 1020. | .000 802 | 10.4 | 11.9 | 3.09 |
| 21 | 28.5 | 810. | .000 636 | 13.1 | 15.1 | 2.45 |
| 22 | 25.3 | 642. | .000 505 | 16.5 | 19.0 | 1.94 |
| 23 | 22.6 | 509. | .000 400 | 20.8 | 24.0 | 1.54 |
| 24 | 20.1 | 404. | .000 317 | 26.2 | 30.2 | 1.22 |
| 25 | 17.9 | 320. | .000 252 | 33.0 | 38.1 | 0.970 |
| 26 | 15.9 | 254. | .000 200 | 41.6 | 48.0 | .769 |
| 27 | 14.2 | 202. | .000 158 | 52.5 | 60.6 | .610 |
| 28 | 12.6 | 160. | .000 126 | 66.2 | 76.4 | .484 |
| 29 | 11.3 | 127. | .000 099 5 | 83.4 | 96.3 | .384 |
| 30 | 10.0 | 101. | .000 078 9 | 105. | 121. | .304 |
| 31 | 8.9 | 79.7 | .000 062 6 | 133. | 153. | .241 |
| 32 | 8.0 | 63.2 | .000 049 6 | 167. | 193. | .191 |
| 33 | 7.1 | 50.1 | .000 039 4 | 211. | 243. | .152 |
| 34 | 6.3 | 39.8 | .000 031 2 | 266. | 307. | .120 |
| 35 | 5.6 | 31.5 | .000 024 8 | 335. | 387. | .0954 |
| 36 | 5.0 | 25.0 | .000 019 6 | 423. | 488. | .0757 |
| 37 | 4.5 | 19.8 | .000 015 6 | 533. | 616. | .0600 |
| 38 | 4.0 | 15.7 | .000 012 3 | 673. | 776. | .0476 |
| 39 | 3.5 | 12.5 | .000 009 8 | 848. | 979. | .0377 |
| 40 | 3.1 | 9.9 | .000 007 8 | 1070. | 1230. | .0299 |

stove warms a room by convection currents in the air; a metal rod with one end placed in a fire becomes warmer throughout as heat is gradually conducted along it. The latter process is explained by supposing that the molecules of the metal in the fire are set into rapid vibration and that these in striking neighboring molecules of the rod impart kinetic energy to them, and this action takes place progressively throughout the rod.

FIG. 71. Fahrenheit and Centigrade scales between freezing and boiling points of water

The application of heat to an object sets up a thermal agitation of its molecules and usually produces an increase in *temperature*. This term is used to express how hot or how cold the object is; a statement of its temperature means that the molecules possess a particular amount of kinetic energy due to thermal agitation. To express temperatures definitely it is necessary to have one or more scales; these are usually called *thermometric scales*. Such a scale is constructed by choosing two standard temperatures, called fixed points, that can be reproduced easily; next, assigning arbitrary numbers to these temperatures; and finally, dividing the interval between them into a convenient number of equal parts. The divisions are extended above and below the fixed points, and a unit division is called a *degree* (°).

Two such temperature scales are in common use, and the relation between them is indicated in Fig. 71. The fixed points are taken as the melting point of ice and the boiling point of water, both at standard atmospheric pressure. The *Fahrenheit scale* was named after the German physicist, Gabriel D. Fahrenheit (1686-1736), who made the first thermometer with mercury in glass. The *centigrade scale* is due to the Swedish astronomer, Anders Celcius (1701-1744). The Fahrenheit scale is used largely for engineering and household purposes and the centigrade scale is used generally for scientific measurements.

On the Fahrenheit scale the melting point of ice is placed at 32° and the boiling point of water at 212°, while on the centigrade scale the melting point is placed at 0° and the boiling point at 100°

Hence, 100 centigrade degrees $= 212 - 32 = 180$ Fahrenheit degrees, or the ratio of a degree centigrade to a degree Fahrenheit is as 9 is to 5. In converting a centigrade reading into a Fahrenheit reading 32 must be added *after* multiplying by 9/5; in converting a Fahrenheit reading to a centigrade reading 32 must be subtracted *before* multiplying by 5/9.

To CONVERT A READING FROM THE CENTIGRADE TO THE FAHRENHEIT SCALE:

*Multiply by 9 and divide by 5; then add 32.*

Represent the readings on the centigrade and Fahrenheit scales by $C$ and $F$ respectively; then

$$F = \frac{C \times 9}{5} + 32 \qquad\qquad 15$$

**Problem 25.**—A field-magnet spool is said to have a certain resistance at 15.5° C. Express this temperature in degrees Fahrenheit.

$$(15) \qquad F = \frac{C \times 9}{5} + 32 = \frac{15.5 \times 9}{5} + 32 = 59.9° \text{ F.}$$

To CONVERT A READING FROM THE FAHRENHEIT TO THE CENTIGRADE SCALE:

*Subtract 32; then multiply by 5 and divide by 9.*

$$C = (F - 32) \times \frac{5}{9} \qquad\qquad 16$$

**Problem 26.**—The temperature of a certain kind of insulating material should not exceed 180° F. What is the corresponding temperature on the centigrade scale?

$$(16) \qquad C = (F - 32) \times \frac{5}{9} = \frac{(180 - 32) \times 5}{9} = 82.2° \text{ C.}$$

The lowest possible temperature is −273.1° C. or −459.6° F., and is called the absolute zero of temperature. It has been approached experimentally to within a small fraction of 1 degree.

**67. Dependence of Resistance upon Temperature.**—As already indicated, the resistance of all pure metals increases with rising temperature. The *proportional* change in resistance with a unit change in temperature is known as the *temperature coefficient of* *resistance;* numerically it is the increase in resistance of 1 ohm for each degree rise in temperature.

The temperature coefficients for the different metals are determined experimentally and their value depends somewhat upon the temperature that is taken as the standard or initial temperature. The following table lists the values of the temperature coefficients for a number of materials commonly used, and applies to initial temperatures around 20° C. or 68° F.

TEMPERATURE COEFFICIENTS OF RESISTANCE

| Material | Per Centigrade Degree | Per Fahrenheit Degree |
|---|---|---|
| Aluminum | 0.0038 | 0.0021 |
| Carbon (0 to 1850° C.) | —0.00025 | —0.00014 |
| Constantan (0 to 100° C.) | negligible | negligible |
| Copper (at 20° C.) | 0.00393 | 0.00218 |
| Iron | 0.0050 | 0.0028 |
| Lead | 0.0043 | 0.0024 |
| Manganin (0 to 100° C.) | negligible | negligible |
| Mercury | 0.00090 | 0.00050 |
| Nichrome | 0.00018 | 0.00010 |
| Platinum | 0.0038 | 0.0021 |
| Silver | 0.0040 | 0.0022 |
| Tungsten | 0.0045 | 0.0025 |
| Zinc | 0.0037 | 0.0021 |

The figures give the amount that 1 ohm would increase or decrease in resistance when subjected to a rise or fall of one degree C. or F. A negative value signifies a decrease in resistance with increase of temperature.

The temperature coefficient is positive for metallic conductors, and usually negative for non-metallic substances, including carbon, liquids, and insulating materials. Certain alloys have been developed in which the temperature coefficient is very small; these materials are useful for the windings in resistance boxes and other measuring instruments in which constancy of resistance is desired.

**Experiment 34.**—Wind a length of iron wire into a' small helix and connect it in series with a 110-volt incandescent lamp across the service mains. Apply a Bunsen flame to the helix in order to show that the resistance of a wire depends upon its temperature. The fact that the lamp becomes dim shows that the iron wire has more resistance when hot.

The change in the resistance of electrical conductors and windings due to temperature changes is often of importance in electrical calculations and measurements.

To CALCULATE THE CHANGE OF RESISTANCE DUE TO A DEFINITE CHANGE OF TEMPERATURE:

*Multiply the resistance at the reference temperature by the temperature coefficient of resistance and by the change in temperature.*

Let

    $R_1$ = resistance of a conductor at the reference temperature,
    $R_2$ = resistance after a change in temperature,
    $t$ = temperature rise in degrees,
    $a$ = temperature coefficient of resistance, or the change of resistance per ohm per degree.

Then the change of resistance is

$$R_2 - R_1 = R_1 \times a \times t \qquad\qquad 17$$

For a drop in temperature the value of $t$ is taken as negative.

When the temperature change is expressed in centigrade degrees the value of the temperature coefficient must be for that scale; similarly for Fahrenheit temperatures.

**Problem 27.**—The resistance of the field magnets of a dynamo is 55 ohms at 68° F. After a ten-hour run the temperature of these copper windings became 160° F., as indicated by a thermometer placed against them. (a) What is the resistance of the field magnets at this temperature? (b) What would be the resistance at 32° F.?

The temperature coefficient for copper is 0.00218 per Fahrenheit degree, and the temperature rise is $160 - 68 = 92$ Fahrenheit degrees. Consequently, the increase of resistance is

(17)    $R_2 - R_1 = R_1 \times a \times t = 55 \times 0.00218 \times 92 = 11.0 \text{ ohms}$

and the resistance at the higher temperature is

$$R_2 = R_1 + R_1 \times a \times t = 55 + 11 = 66 \text{ ohms} \qquad\qquad \text{(a)}$$

For a temperature drop from 68° to 32° F., $t = -36$ degrees and the change of resistance would be

(17)    $R_2 - R_1 = 55 \times 0.00218 \times (-36) = -4.3 \text{ ohms}$

Hence, the resistance of the windings at 32° F. would be

$$R_2 = 55 - 4.3 = 50.7 \text{ ohms} \qquad\qquad \text{(b)}$$

For practical purposes, where the temperature change involved is small, the temperature coefficient of a substance is usually considered as remaining constant at the value which it has at the reference temperature; actually it varies somewhat with the temperature and for accurate calculations it may be necessary to use the average value for the temperature range involved.

**68. Super-Conductivity.**—Certain metals are found to exhibit a remarkable drop in resistance at very low temperatures; this effect is known as *super-conductivity*. As the temperature is lowered, the resistance of the specimen is observed to decrease in the manner to be expected from Formula (17), but at a certain temperature, which seems to have a characteristic value for each material, and which is only a few degrees above absolute zero, the resistance drops abruptly to an extremely low value. The resistance of lead, for instance, falls at a temperature of $-266°$ C. to less than $10^{-12}$ of its value at $20°$ C.

This effect was discovered by the Dutch physicist, H. Kamerlingh Onnes (1853-1926), and is important from a theoretical viewpoint. As early as 1914, he reported a 1-hour test, in which current was produced in a lead ring at a very low temperature and the source of electromotive force was removed, nevertheless the current in the closed ring persisted without appreciable reduction throughout the test. Super-conductivity has been observed in seventeen metallic elements as well as in a large number of alloys.

**69. Rheostats and Resistance Boxes.**—The usual method of regulating and controlling the current required for various electrical purposes is by varying the resistance of a circuit. An adjustable resistor for changing the resistance without opening the circuit is called a *rheostat*. The function of a rheostat is to absorb electrical energy, and this energy, which appears as heat, is wasted instead of performing useful work in the circuit. Rheostats may be constructed of coils or grids from a variety of metals and alloys; they may also be made of carbon, either pulverized and held in tubes or in the form of solid rods or disks. The cross-sectional area of the material must be sufficient to carry the current intended without excessive heating. In rheostats used for regulating current, the resistors do not usually require accurate calibration of resistance. Fig. 72 shows two forms of the slide-wire type of rheostat and Fig. 308 shows a motor starting and field regulating rheostat.

FIG. 72. Slide-wire rheostats
Linear type—Rex Rheostat Company.  Rotary type—Ohmite Manufacturing Company.

Accurately standardized resistance boxes are used in making electrical measurements of all sorts. They consist of coils of wire having definitely known resistances which can be grouped together

FIG. 73. Resistance box of four decades and its interior construction
General Radio Company

to make up any desired amount between the terminals. The current through these boxes is very small so that the wire need not be of large size, yet it must be large enough to accommodate the current with little heating. The material of the wire is an alloy, such as manganin, which has a low temperature coefficient of resistance, and the winding is made non-inductive, §157. Fig. 73 shows a four-decade resistance box having a group of nine 1000-ohm coils, and similar groups of 100-ohm, 10-ohm and 1-ohm coils; each group has a 10-point switch so that from 0 to 9 coils can be put in series progressively. The total resistance included in the circuit is found by noting the digits indicated by the switch dials.

**70. Resistance of Connections.**—When two metallic surfaces are pressed together *lightly* the resistance of the contact is much greater than when the surfaces are pressed together firmly. This difference is due to irregularities or unevennesses of the surfaces as well as to oxidation or corrosion of the metals themselves. To make sure that such contact resistances are kept to low values, all binding screw contacts should be thoroughly cleaned to a bright metallic lustre and screwed down so as to clamp the wires firmly. Joints in electrical conducting systems are usually soldered in order to attain low contact resistances and to keep them so over long periods of time.

### QUESTIONS

1. What is electrical resistance and what is the unit of resistance?
2. Name four prefixes that are used with electrical units.
3. Name the factors which affect the resistance of a conductor, and state how each factor influences it.
4. A voltaic cell supplies a certain current through a piece of copper wire. Would the same cell supply more or less current through another piece of copper wire twice as long but of double the sectional area of the first piece?
5. If the second wire in Question 4 had twice the length and twice the diameter of the first wire, what would the answer be?
6. Current from a cell through a piece of iron wire deflects a galvanometer needle 15 degrees. When a piece of aluminum having the same dimensions as those of the iron is substituted, the deflection is found to be 50 degrees. How do you account for this?
7. Define the unit of area that is called the circular mil.
8. State what is meant by resistivity.
9. The resistivity of aluminum is tabulated in three ways—namely, 2.83 microhm-centimeters, 1.11 microhm-inches, and 17.0 ohm-CM per foot.

Make a sketch showing the shapes and sizes of this material that have these values of resistance.

10. What size wire on the A.w.g. would have twice the sectional area of a No. 30 wire? Which size would have four times that area?

11. If a change in the weather brings about a temperature drop of 20 Fahrenheit degrees, would this drop be expressed by a larger or a smaller number of centigrade degrees?

12. Which represents the higher temperature, 20° F. or 20° C.?

13. Explain what is meant by the term: temperature coefficient of resistance.

14. What is the function of a rheostat? How can its resistance be varied?

15. State what is meant by super-conductivity.

## PROBLEMS

1. The resistance of the field coil of a particular dynamo is 0.0065 ohm. Express its resistance in microhms. *Ans.* 6500 microhms.

2. The insulation around a certain piece of wire measures 16.75 megohms. What is its resistance in ohms? *Ans.* 16,750,000 ohms.

3. How many circular mils of area are in a circle having a diameter of 1 inch? *Ans.* 1,000,000 CM.

4. What is the circular mil area of a wire that is ½ inch in diameter? *Ans.* 250,000 CM.

5. The sectional area of a wire is 5625 CM. What is its diameter? *Ans.* 75 mils.

6. How many circular mils are in a square measuring 1 inch on a side? *Ans.* 1,273,240 CM.

7. An armature is wound with copper strip measuring ½ by ⅛ inch. What is its equivalent area in circular mils? *Ans.* 79,578 CM.

8. A tungsten lamp filament is 1 foot long and 1.5 mils in diameter. What is its resistance? *Ans.* 14.7 ohms.

9. Calculate the resistance of 1000 feet of copper wire that has a diameter of 0.162 inch. *Ans.* 0.397 ohm.

10. A resistor is to be wound with manganin wire 0.02 inch in diameter. What length of wire will be needed for a 20-ohm coil? *Ans.* 30.3 feet.

11. A platinum wire 10 feet long has a resistance of 23.8 ohms. Compute its diameter. *Ans.* 5.0 mils.

12. What is the resistance of 500 feet of stranded copper wire, made of 17 strands, each 0.032 inch in diameter? *Ans.* 0.299 ohm.

13. Taking the resistivity of steel as 5 microhm-inches, compute the resistance of a length of track rail 30 feet long and 7 square inches in sectional area. *Ans.* 257 microhms.

14. Calculate the resistance of 2000 feet of No. 6 A.w.g. copper wire. *Ans.* 0.792 ohm.

15. A resistor is constructed of No. 12 A.w.g. nichrome wire and has a resistance of 10 ohms. What length of wire was required. *Ans.* 99 feet.

16. Express the following temperatures on the other scale: 50° C., 50° F., 200° C., and −40° F. *Ans.* 122° F., 10° C., 392° F. and −40° C., respectively.

17. A copper wire is used as a' resistance thermometer for measuring temperatures around 20° C., its resistance being 40 ohms at this temperature. How much will its resistance increase for a temperature rise of 1 centigrade degree? *Ans.* 0.157 ohm.

18. A field winding on a motor consists of a copper coil having a resistance of 270 ohms at 20° C. What will be its resistance if the temperature rises 40 centigrade degrees? *Ans.* 312.4 ohms.

# Lesson VII

---

## OHM'S LAW

---

**71. Current, Electromotive Force and Resistance.**—In the last few lessons three important electrical quantities were considered in detail; these are current, e.m.f., and resistance. The meaning of these quantities and the definition of their units will be reviewed in order to afford a better understanding of the relationship between them in a direct-current circuit.

An electric current is a drift of electrons carrying negative charges from one point in a circuit to another. The ampere is a current in which $6.25 \times 10^{18}$ electrons pass any point of the circuit per second; a current of this intensity will deposit silver from a solution of silver nitrate at the rate of 0.001118 gram per second.

Electric charges are attracted by others of opposite sign and repelled by those of like sign. Because of this action free electrons within a conductor will move when one part of it is charged positively and another part negatively, and their motion will be directed from the negative to the positive parts. Long before the existence of electrons was known, an electric current was assumed to be a flow of some sort around a circuit from the positive to the negative terminals of a voltaic cell or generator. This direction of current is still recognized; and it must be remembered that this direction is opposite to the motion of the electrons in a circuit.

The purpose of a voltaic cell or an electric generator is to provide an electromotive force (e.m.f.), which can establish a differ-

125

ence of potential (p.d.) between points in an electric circuit, maintaining the potential at one point positive with respect to that at another. Thus, e.m.f. is the primary cause of electron flow in a circuit. The volt is that e.m.f. which in transferring $6.25 \times 10^{18}$ electrons (a quantity of electricity called a coulomb) represents the expenditure of 1 joule of work, §95. A dry cell has an e.m.f. of about 1.5 volts.

Conductors having few free electrons are said to present much resistance to the establishment of current in a circuit, while those with many free electrons present little resistance. The ohm is the unit of resistance, and conductors of various materials can be made up of appropriate size and form so as to have just one ohm of resistance. Such a conductor would produce 1 joule of heat energy during every second that a current of one ampere is maintained in it. Resistance is aptly spoken of as the property of an electric circuit which causes heat to be produced when there is current in the circuit; resistance of a circuit is analogous to friction in a pipe through which water is flowing.

**72. Hydraulic Analogy.**—When the water pressure in a pipe is the same at both ends, there will be no flow of water in the pipe. To establish a flow, the pressure at one end must be made greater than that at the other; a difference of pressure can be produced by a difference in level or developed by a hydraulic pump. Similarly, when the electric potential of a conductor is the same at both ends, there will be no current in the conductor. To establish a current, the potential at one end must be higher than that at the other; a difference of potential can be developed by a voltaic cell or by an electric generator. In the hydraulic analogy of an electric circuit, there might be a difference of pressure between points along a pipe and yet no flow of water between them; this would be true if the pipe were clogged or a valve in it were left closed. Similarly, there might be a difference of potential between points along an electric circuit and yet no current, for a switch in the circuit might be open.

The flow of water established in a pipe depends upon the difference of pressure maintained across its ends and also upon the resistance to water flow presented by the pipe. The greater the pressure difference or head of water, and the lower the resistance of the pipe, the more water will be transferred in a given time. Similarly, in an electrical conductor, the strength of the current depends on the difference of potential between its ends and also upon the resistance of the conductor. The larger the potential difference and the lower the resistance of the conductor, the greater will be the current. Both the mechanical resistance of a pipe to water flow and the electrical resistance of a conductor to an electric current depend upon the length and area of the path.

**73. Ohm's Law.**—Experience with direct-current circuits shows that the current established in closed metallic paths is directly proportional to the e.m.f. of the source of electricity in the circuit and inversely proportional to the resistance of the path. These facts were first expressed by Ohm, and the relation between the three factors involved is known as Ohm's Law. Since its first phrasing in 1827, this law has been of outstanding importance in electrical calculations.

*Ohm's Law states that the current in a metallic circuit is equal to the e.m.f available in the circuit divided by the resistance of that circuit.* In order to write the formula for this law, let

$I$ = current maintained in the circuit,
$E$ = e.m.f. of the source of electricity included in the circuit,
$R$ = total resistance of the circuit, including the internal resistance of the source.

Then, by the foregoing statement of Ohm's Law,

$$\text{current} = \frac{\text{e.m.f.}}{\text{resistance}}$$

The value of any one of the three factors can be calculated when the values of the other two are known.

To find the current in a circuit when the e.m.f. and resistance are known:

*Divide the e.m.f. by the resistance.*

$$I = \frac{E}{R}$$

**18**

Introducing the units in Ohm's Law, ampere for current, volt for e.m.f., and ohm for resistance, it follows that in a metallic circuit

$$\text{amperes} = \frac{\text{volts}}{\text{ohms}}$$

**Problem 28.**—A particular incandescent lamp is connected to an electric generator which develops an e.m.f. of 110 volts; under these conditions the lamp has a resistance of 275 oh.ns. What current will the lamp take?

The current is given by Ohm's Law as

(18) $$I = \frac{E}{R} = \frac{110}{275} = 0.40 \text{ ampere}$$

**Problem 29.**—An electric heater has a resistance of 20 ohms and another has a resistance of 40 ohms. Two sources of e.m.f. are available, one of 240 volts and the other of 120 volts. Find how much current each heater will take when connected with each source.

Formula (18) is used to compute the results desired; first, take $R = 20$ ohms with $E = 240$ and then $E = 120$ volts, and second, take $R = 40$ ohms with $E = 240$ and then $E = 120$ volts.

For the 20-ohm heater operating on 240 volts

$$I = \frac{240}{20} = 12 \text{ amperes} \tag{a}$$

and on 120 volts

$$I = \frac{120}{20} = 6 \text{ amperes} \tag{b}$$

For the 40-ohm heater operating on 240 volts

$$I = \frac{240}{40} = 6 \text{ amperes} \tag{c}$$

and on 120 volts

$$I = \frac{120}{40} = 3 \text{ amperes} \tag{d}$$

The latter problem shows the effect of changing the available e.m.f. or of changing the resistance. Halving the e.m.f. reduces the current to one-half, as indicated by results *a* and *b,* or by *c* and *d.* Doubling the resistance also reduces the current to one-half, as indicated by results *a* and *c,* or by *b* and *d.* These numerical results illustrate the statement of Ohm's Law that the current varies directly with the e.m.f. and inversely with the resistance.

**Experiment 35.**—A number of coils of known resistance, a 1.5-volt dry cell, and either an ammeter or a milliammeter are provided for verifying Ohm's Law. Connect one of the coils in series with the meter and the cell, and read the deflection of the pointer. Compare the reading with the value of the current as determined by the quotient of 1.5 volts and the known resistance of the coil. Repeat for the other coils.

TO FIND THE RESISTANCE OF A CIRCUIT WHEN THE E.M.F. AND CURRENT ARE KNOWN:

*Divide the e.m.f. by the current.*

Formula (18) can be solved for the resistance, thus

$$R = \frac{E}{I} \qquad \qquad 19$$

$$\text{ohms} = \frac{\text{volts}}{\text{amperes}}$$

**Problem 30.**—What is the resistance of the heater in an electric iron that takes 5.7 amperes when operated at 115 volts?

Ohm's Law gives the resistance of the heater as

(19) $$R = \frac{E}{I} = \frac{115}{5.7} = 20.2 \text{ ohms}$$

**Problem 31.**—A 240-volt rheostat has two resistors and each is equipped with a switch so that one or both of them may be placed in circuit. When one switch is closed the current in the circuit is 5 amperes, when the other is closed the current is 10 amperes, and when both switches are closed the current is 15 amperes. Find the resistance of the rheostat under each of these conditions.

Formula (19) gives the resistance of the rheostat for any switching arrangement. With the first switch closed, its resistance is

$$R = \frac{E}{I} = \frac{240}{5} = 48 \text{ ohms}$$

With the second switch closed the resistance is $\frac{240}{10} = 24$ ohms, and with both switches closed the resistance is $\frac{240}{15} = 16$ ohms.

TO FIND THE E.M.F. NEEDED TO MAINTAIN A CERTAIN CURRENT IN A CIRCUIT OF KNOWN RESISTANCE:

*Multiply the current by the resistance.*

Solving Formula (18) again, this time for the e.m.f.,

$$E = I \times R \qquad \qquad 20$$
$$\text{volts} = \text{amperes} \times \text{ohms}$$

**Problem 32.**—A telegraph sounder requires a current of 0.2 ampere to operate it satisfactorily. If the sounder circuit has a total resistance of 40 ohms, what e.m.f. must be supplied to the circuit?

The answer is given by Ohm's Law as

(20) $$E = I \times R = 0.2 \times 40 = 8 \text{ volts}$$

All three forms of the equation that represent Ohm's Law can be visualized by the fraction

$$\frac{E}{I \times R}$$

If a problem seeks the value of the current $I$, cover $I$ in this fraction with a pencil and the uncovered part shows that $I$ is given by $\frac{E}{R}$ (Formula 18). Again, if a problem calls for the resistance $R$, cover $R$ and the visible part of the fraction is $\frac{E}{I}$ (Formula 19). Lastly, if the e.m.f. $E$ is sought, cover $E$ and the result is $I \times R$ (Formula 20).

Most electrical appliances are designed for operation on 110- to 120-volt service mains; that is, they will take the proper amount of current when connected to such mains. If an appliance takes just 4 amperes on 120 volts, Ohm's Law indicates that its resistance must be $120 \div 4 = 30$ ohms. Connecting it to 110-volt mains means that it will receive $110 \div 30 = 3.67$ amperes; the reduction from 4.0 amperes will generally not interfere with its proper functioning. It should be remembered that the resistance of the appliance is fixed (neglecting the effect of temperature changes) and that, therefore, a definite e.m.f. is needed to provide its appropriate operating current, as specified by the formulas. If the available e.m.f. is too low, the appliance will receive too little current and it will not function properly; if the e.m.f is too high, it will receive too much current and there is danger that its electrical circuit may burn out through excessive heating.

**74. Application of Ohm's Law to Parts of Circuits.**—Ohm's Law applies equally well to a part of a circuit as to an entire circuit, but care must be exercised to have all quantities apply to the part involved. Fig. 74 shows a circuit with several resistors, one of them marked $R_1$, connected to a battery marked $B$. The usual representation of a battery is a group of parallel lines alternately long and short, as indicated.

Let
$R_1$ = resistance of *one part* of a circuit,
$I$ = current in *that part* of the circuit,
$E_1$ = potential difference across the *same part* of the circuit.

Then by Ohm's Law:

$$I = \frac{E_1}{R_1} \qquad\qquad 21$$

It should be noted particularly that the numerator in this equation is the *difference of potential* across a part of a circuit, whereas in Formula (18) the numerator is the *electromotive force* supplied by the source of electricity to the entire circuit.

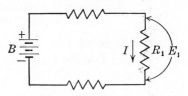

Formula (21) can be transposed so that it may be used in solving problems in which it is desired to compute the resistance or the potential differ-

FIG. 74. Application of Ohm's Law to part of a circuit

ence. The equations will be like Formulas (19) and (20), except that the e.m.f. $E$ will be replaced by the potential difference $E_1$. For example, to determine the p.d. necessary to establish a current through any part of a circuit, the current through it is multiplied by the resistance of that part of the circuit; that is

$$E_1 = I \times R_1 \qquad\qquad 22$$

To find the drop in potential across a resistor carrying current:

*Multiply the current by the resistance of the resistor.*

**Problem 33.**—Among the devices connected to a source of electricity in the manner indicated in Fig. 74 is a resistor having a resistance of 3 ohms. What p.d. will there be at the terminals of this resistor when the current in it is 8 amperes?

(22)               $E_1 = I \times R_1 = 8 \times 3 = 24$ volts

Naturally, if the e.m.f. available for the circuit is changed, or if the resistance of the other devices is altered, the current through resistor $R_1$ will be different and, in consequence, the potential difference across it will change accordingly.

**75. Effect of Internal Resistance of Source.**—All sources of electricity possess some resistance, even though they are designed to have very little, and as a result some difference of potential must be involved in establishing current through these sources themselves. Because of this, not all of the e.m.f. of a source is available for use in its external circuit, and the loss is spoken of as the *drop in potential due to internal resistance.*

Let

$R$ = total external resistance of the circuit,
$r$ = internal resistance of the battery or generator,
$E_d$ = drop in potential across either source of electricity.

Then the total resistance of the circuit (external + internal) is $R + r,$ and Ohm's Law becomes,

$$I = \frac{E}{R + r} \qquad\qquad 23$$

This current multiplied by the internal resistance gives the potential drop in the source, or

$$E_d = I \times r \qquad\qquad 24$$

This result is obtained from Formula (22) by using the internal resistance $r$ instead of the total resistance $R$.

To find the drop in potential due to the current through the source of electricity:

*Multiply the current by the internal resistance of the source.*

**Problem 34.**—A storage battery, having an e.m.f. of 2.0 volts and an internal resistance of 0.05 ohm, is connected to an electromagnet which has a resistance of 0.35 ohm. How much of the e.m.f. is used in establishing current through the battery? and what is the p.d. available for supplying current to the electromagnet?

The total resistance of the circuit is the sum of the internal resistance of the battery and the resistance external to it, that is $R + r = 0.35 + 0.05 = 0.40$ ohm. The current in the circuit is

$$(23) \qquad I = \frac{E}{R + r} = \frac{2.0}{0.35 + 0.05} = 5 \text{ amperes}$$

This current through the internal resistance of the battery produces a drop of potential amounting to

(24)                $E_d = I \times r = 5 \times 0.05 = 0.25$ volt

Therefore, the potential difference available at the electromagnet is $2.00 - 0.25 = 1.75$ volts.

**Problem 35.**—An Edison cell has an e.m.f. of 1.20 volts as measured across its terminals on open circuit, and a p.d. of 1.10 volts across these terminals when it delivers 10 amperes. What is its internal resistance? What would the p.d. across its terminals be when delivering 4 amperes?

When the current is 10 amperes, the potential drop due to the internal resistance of the battery is $1.20 - 1.10 = 0.10$ volt. Since $E_d = 0.10$ volt when $I = 10$ amperes, the internal resistance of the battery is obtained from Formula (24) as

$$r = \frac{E_d}{I} = \frac{0.10}{10} = 0.01 \text{ ohm}$$

When the current is reduced to 4 amperes, the potential drop in the battery is $E_d = I \times r = 4 \times 0.01 = 0.04$ volt; consequently the p.d. of the cell will then be $1.20 - 0.04 = 1.16$ volts.

Formula (23) may also be expressed in other forms following the procedure of the two foregoing sections. The results are

$$E = I \times (R + r)$$

$$R = \frac{E}{I} - r$$

and                $$r = \frac{E}{I} - R$$

*Note.* The student in reaching this part of the text will have gained facility in transposing equations so that he can solve them directly for any one of the quantities represented therein if the others are known. Henceforth only one form of an equation will be given and numbered.

**Problem 36.**—A cell with an internal resistance of 0.4 ohm supplies a current of 84 milliamperes to the electromagnet of a bell having a resistance of 12 ohms. What is the e.m.f. of this cell?

(23)        $E = I \times (R + r) = 0.084 \times (12.0 + 0.4) = 1.042$ volts

**Problem 37.**—A current of 0.25 ampere is maintained through a circuit by a cell having an e.m.f. of 2 volts; its internal resistance is 0.1 ohm. What is the value of the external resistance?

(23)                $$R = \frac{E}{I} - r = \frac{2}{0.25} - 0.1 = 7.9 \text{ ohms}$$

**Experiment 36.**—Connect a dry cell to a 3-ohm resistor and a 1.5-volt voltmeter as shown in Fig. 54. At intervals of five minutes over a discharge period of one hour take a reading of the meter and then open the switch just long enough to take another reading. The first of each pair of readings is the terminal p.d. at the cell and the second is its e.m.f. Calculate the resistance of the cell from each pair of readings and plot a curve of cell resistance against time. Usually this curve rises at first and then gradually falls.

**76. Drop of Potential in Circuits.**—It has been explained in the last section that in operating an electrical device a small part of the e.m.f. of the source of electricity is generally needed to take care of the potential drop within itself, and the amount of this drop is the product of the current and the internal resistance of the source. Often the device is located some distance away from the source, and *line wires* are needed to conduct the current to and from the device; these lines wires also introduce a drop of potential due to their resistance.

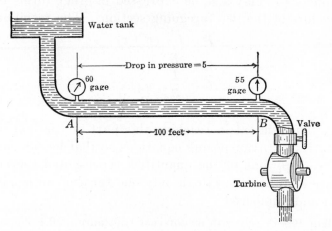

FIG. 75. Drop in pressure in a pipe line

The hydraulic analogy given earlier in this lesson will assist in clarifying the idea of potential drop in an electric circuit. In Fig. 75 an elevated water tank is connected by a horizontal pipe *AB* to a water turbine, and gages are shown at each end of this pipe. With the valve near *B* closed and the pipe full of water, the pressure would be the same at both gages; but with the valve open, the gage at *B* would indicate less pressure than that at *A*. The difference is the hydrostatic pressure necessary to overcome the friction between the flowing water and the inside surface of the pipe.

To make the idea of pressure drop more definite, assume the tank to be at such elevation as to provide a pressure of 60 pounds per square inch at *A,* and that, under a certain water flow controlled by the valve, the pressure at *B,* say 100 feet away from *A,* is 55 pounds per square inch, as indicated in the figure. The latter value is the water pressure available to operate the turbine. If the pipe is uniform in sectional area, the difference in pressure of 5 pounds per square inch would be spread uniformly over the pipe length of 100 feet. Next, assume that the valve is opened further so that twice as much water flows per second as before. Under these conditions the gage at *B* would read 50 pounds per square inch, assuming the gage at *A* to remain unchanged. The pressure difference of 10 pounds per square inch would also be spread uniformly over the length of pipe. Thus the drop in pressure or "loss of head" depends upon the flow of water; the greater the flow the greater the drop in pressure.

If the pipe under consideration is replaced by another of larger diameter, the friction between water and pipe will be less and the drop in pressure will be correspondingly reduced. Conversely, with a smaller pipe, the pressure drop will be increased. The aim in the hydraulic calculation is to supply water at a certain rate and under a certain pressure to the turbine so that it can deliver its rated output, and the pipe line from the source is designed for a definite drop in pressure. Similar considerations are involved in the design of electric circuits for supplying power and light.

Assume that an electric motor is to be operated at a distance from electric service mains and that two line wires connect it to the mains as illustrated in Fig. 76. When the motor is operated, the potential difference available at the motor will be less than that at the service mains because of the potential drop in the line wires. If, for example, the p.d. across the mains is kept constant at 120 volts, and if the p.d. across the motor terminals when the machine is operating at a certain load is 115 volts, then the potential drop in the line wires under the condition stated is 5 volts. Supposing these wires to be uniform in sectional area and of the same material, this drop will be spread uniformly over the 100 feet separating the motor from the mains, or spread uniformly over the 200 feet length of connecting wire. If the motor is more heavily loaded, it would take more current, and the potential drop in the line wires would increase. Doubling the current to the motor would cause the drop in potential in the line wires to be twice as much; a 10-volt drop means that only 110 volts would be available at the motor. Thus, the potential drop in a wire depends on the current in it.

If the line wires under consideration are replaced by others of larger diameter, the resistance will be less and the drop in

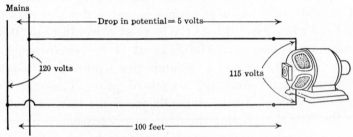

FIG. 76. Drop in potential in electric circuit

potential will be correspondingly reduced; on the other hand, smaller conductors will increase the potential drop. Summing up, the potential drop in a conductor depends upon its resistance and upon the current in it; numerically the drop is the product of these factors and is expressed by Formula (24).

**77. Wiring Calculations.**—The determination of the size of wire required to conduct current from generators or service mains to lamps, motors or other electrical devices is of frequent occurrence in electrical calculations. It is, of course, desirable to keep such line wires as small as possible for the sake of economy; but if they are too small, their resistances will be unduly high and the potential drop along the lines will be excessive. As a result, the potential difference available at the devices may be too low to operate them satisfactorily, or when lamps are turned on and off the light from the lamps still in circuit will fluctuate. It is common practice to restrict the potential drop along the line wires to less than 3 per cent on lighting circuits and to from 5 to 10 per cent on power circuits.

A second objection to undersized line wires is the excessive heating which the current would produce in them, as well as the damage that might occur to the insulation surrounding the wires as a result of heating. For safe operation the current should not exceed the values given in the following table from the National Electric Code.

ALLOWABLE CURRENT-CARRYING CAPACITIES OF CONDUCTORS

Not More Than Three Conductors in Raceway, Conduit or Cable

*Based on Room Temperature of 30° C. or 86° F.*

AMPERES

| Wire Size A.w.g. | Rubber Types RW, R | Synthetic Type SN / Type RU / Rubber Types RPT, RP | Rubber Types RHT, RH | Paper / Synthetic Type SNA / Asbestos Varnished-Cambric Type AVB / Varnished-Cambric Type V | Asbestos Varnished-Cambric Types AVA, AVL | Impregnated Asbestos Type AI | Asbestos Type A |
|---|---|---|---|---|---|---|---|
| 14 | 15 | 18 | 22 | 23 | 28 | 29 | 32 |
| 12 | 20 | 23 | 27 | 29 | 36 | 38 | 42 |
| 10 | 25 | 31 | 37 | 38 | 47 | 49 | 54 |
| 8 | 35 | 41 | 49 | 50 | 60 | 63 | 71 |
| 6 | 45 | 54 | 65 | 68 | 80 | 85 | 95 |
| 5 | 52 | 63 | 75 | 78 | 94 | 99 | 110 |
| 4 | 60 | 72 | 86 | 88 | 107 | 114 | 122 |
| 3 | 69 | 83 | 99 | 104 | 121 | 131 | 145 |
| 2 | 80 | 96 | 115 | 118 | 137 | 147 | 163 |
| 1 | 91 | 110 | 131 | 138 | 161 | 172 | 188 |
| 0 | 105 | 127 | 151 | 157 | 190 | 202 | 223 |
| 00 | 120 | 145 | 173 | 184 | 217 | 230 | 249 |
| 000 | 138 | 166 | 199 | 209 | 243 | 265 | 284 |
| 0000 | 160 | 193 | 230 | 237 | 275 | 308 | 340 |

For example, a No. 10 rubber-insulated wire may be limited to 25 amperes, whereas the same size of conductor insulated with asbestos may carry as many as 54 amperes. The reason for this difference is that rubber insulation deteriorates rapidly when heated while asbestos and its binder remains unaffected at relatively high temperatures. Therefore, the particular insulation used on a wire must be considered in selecting the size.

The first step in a calculation for wire size is to determine the permissible potential drop and the current to be supplied; from these facts the resistance of the line wires can be calculated. The second step is to ascertain the size of copper wire of appropriate length which will have the desired resistance. The final step is to check this computed wire size with the foregoing table of safe current values so that there will be no over-heating. To make the procedure definite, let

$R$ = total resistance of both line wires in ohms,
$E_d$ = allowable potential drop in the line wires in volts,
$I$ = current in the line wires in amperes,
CM = cross-sectional area of the line wire in circular mils,
$L$ = total length of both line wires in feet,
$\rho$ = resistivity of the wire material in ohm-CM per foot.

Then, from Formulas (24) and (14), the resistance and sectional area of the line wires are given respectively by:

$$R = \frac{E_d}{I}$$

$$CM = \frac{L \times \rho}{R}$$

These equations will be merged, by eliminating $R$, to enable the sectional area of the wires to be computed directly.

To FIND THE SECTIONAL AREA OF LINE WIRES OF GIVEN LENGTH, WHEN THE LINE CURRENT AND POTENTIAL DROP ARE KNOWN:

*Multiply the total length of the lines (in feet) by the resistivity of the line material (in ohm-CM per foot) and by the current (in amperes); then divide by the permitted potential drop (in volts).*

$$CM = \frac{L \times \rho \times I}{E_d} \qquad\qquad 25$$

The result gives the desired wire size on the basis of a limiting potential drop; it should be checked for current-carrying capacity with the table ahead.

**Problem 38.**—Lamps are to be installed in a room 200 feet away from service mains across which the p.d. is maintained at 120 volts. The lamps require a total current of 30 amperes. What is the smallest size of rubber-insulated copper wire that can be used for the line wires to connect the generator with the lamps, if a potential drop of 2½ per cent is allowed on the lines?

This problem will be solved from fundamentals; the result may be checked by applying Formula (25). A 2½ per cent potential drop amounts to $0.025 \times 120$ or 3 volts across the two line wires, leaving 117 volts available for illuminating the lamps. The resistance of the line should be such as to give a 3-volt drop with a current of 30 amperes; this resistance would be $R = \dfrac{E_d}{I} = \dfrac{3}{30} = 0.10$ ohm. Hence, the required cross section of the copper wires, each 200 feet long, is

$$CM = \frac{L \times \rho}{R} = \frac{400 \times 10.4}{0.10} = 41,600 \text{ CM}$$

Referring to the table of copper wire sizes, §65, the next larger standard size is found to be 41,700 circular mils or No. 4 A.w.g.; this is the desired wire size as determined by potential-drop considerations. Before adopting this size, the allowable current-carrying capacity of the wire should be found by referring to the table in this section. It is seen that a rubber-insulated wire of this size is rated at 60 amperes; since the line current is only 30 amperes, a' No. 4 wire will be satisfactory for the proposed installation.

**78. Measurement of Current and Potential.**—Instruments for measuring current and potential difference are equipped with pointers that move over suitable scales, and the deflections indicate the values sought. An instrument calibrated to measure current is called an *ammeter* (contraction of ampere-meter) and one calibrated to measure potential differences is called a *volt-meter*.

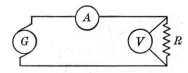

Fig. 77. Connection of ammeter and voltmeter to a circuit

The construction and operation of these instruments is described in Lesson XI.

There is no structural difference between an ammeter and a voltmeter, and both deflect in proportion to the current through the instrument. The difference between them is only in electrical resistance; the instruments are designed in this respect so that their introduction into the circuit for purposes of measurement will not change the quantities they are intended to measure. The ammeter has a very low resistance and the voltmeter has a very high resistance.

The connections of an ammeter and a voltmeter are illustrated in Fig. 77, which shows a generator $G$ supplying current to a resistor marked *R*. The ammeter *A* is connected *in the line* and the voltmeter *V* is connected *across the resistor*. Since practically all of the current in the line passes through this resistor, the ammeter reading gives substantially the current in it. The voltmeter reading gives the potential difference across the resistor. If the readings of both instruments are known it is a simple matter to calculate the resistance of the resistor by Ohm's Law. Taking the ammeter and voltmeter readings as *I* and *E* respectively, the resistance is given by Formula (19) as $R = \dfrac{E}{I}$.

Always be sure to connect the ammeter in the line circuit and never across the line wires; it would burn out immediately if connected from one generator terminal to the other, and probably also if it were connected across the resistor.

**Experiment 37.**—Stretch a fine manganin wire on a board between screws or binding posts and place a yardstick alongside it, as depicted in

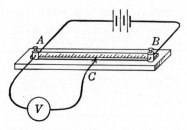

FIG. 78. Demonstrating fall of potential along a wire

Fig. 78. Connect leads from a battery to the posts *A* and *B* in order to establish current in the wire. Then connect one terminal of a voltmeter to post *A* and touch the other terminal to some point *C* on the wire. The voltmeter will read the difference of potential on the length of wire between points *A* and *C*. As the contact *C* is moved gradually along the wire toward *B*, the deflection of the voltmeter will increase. Show experimentally that the potential drop on the wire increases proportionately to the length included; this verifies the fact that the resistance of a wire varies as its length. Repeat with a thicker manganin wire or with a wire of another material.

**Experiment 38.**—Make up a circuit of four lamps connected as shown in Fig. 79 through separate switches to two line wires, and join these through a main switch to electric service mains. The lamps may be of any size and the line wires may have any resistance, but in describing the experiment it will be assumed that each lamp takes 2 amperes and that lines *BC* and *B'C'* each have 1 ohm resistance. An ammeter *A* of 10-ampere range and a voltmeter *V* of 150-volt range are included in the circuit as shown, the latter instrument being connected either across *BB'* or across *CC'*.

Close only main switch $M$ and read the instruments; the ammeter will indicate zero and the voltmeter in either position will indicate 120 volts. Now close switch $S$ to put lamp $L$ in circuit; the ammeter will read 2 amperes, and the voltmeter will read 120 volts across $BB'$ and only 116 volts across the lamps at $CC'$. The difference of 4 volts is the potential drop

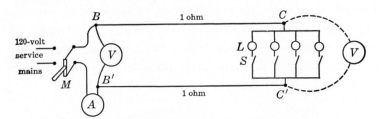

FIG. 79. Illustrating potential drop on line wires

on the line wires of 2 ohms resistance that carry 2 amperes. Continue the experiment by closing switches to include more lamps in the circuit, and observe the successive lowering of p.d. across the lamps as the current supplied to them is increased.

The values of the units used in electrical science were adopted by the International Electrical Congress in 1893 and are called *international* units. While they have been modified in various particulars since that time, they have been consistently defined by reference to three physical standards, the ampere by the silver voltameter, the ohm by a specified mercury column, and the volt by a standard cell (1.0183 volts for a Weston cell), as explained ahead. It is now proposed to modify these units in accordance with the decision of the International Committee on Weights and Measures to have them agree with the fundamental units of the metric system. The new electrical units will be called *absolute units* and will begin to be used in 1948.

While the change affects the methods of fixing the magnitudes of the units, it affects the magnitudes themselves so little that differences are appreciable only in measurements of high precision. The change is most simply represented by the relative magnitudes of the ohms and the volts in the two systems. The relations are:

1 international ohm = 1.00049 absolute ohms
1 international volt = 1.00034 absolute volts

Other electrical units will be changed by amounts derived from these two basic units; for example, the joule and the watt will be reduced by one-sixtieth of one per cent.

For years the international units have been maintained in national standardizing laboratories of several countries by groups of wire resistors for the ohm and of Weston cells for the volt, although occasional determinations by means of mercury columns and silver voltameters were made for checking purposes. The new absolute units will be similarly maintained in accordance with the relations given above.

## QUESTIONS

1. Name and define the units of current, e.m.f., and resistance.
2. State Ohm's Law and explain its application to a circuit by using the hydraulic analogy.
3. An electromagnet that is connected to a small lead storage cell attracts more iron filings than when it is connected to a large dry cell. Explain.
4. Two electromagnets are connected to separate 6-volt storage batteries, and it is found that one electromagnet takes 50 per cent more current than the other. Explain.
5. An incandescent lamp receives a current which is insufficient to illuminate it properly. What could be done to make the lamp yield its rated candlepower?
6. Distinguish between e.m.f. and p.d.
7. The temperature coefficient of resistance is positive for tungsten and negative for carbon, §67. Contrast the behavior of lamps with filaments of these materials at the moment of connection to electric service mains, particularly the variation of current while the operating temperature is being reached.
8. With a constant potential difference applied to a part of a circuit, how will the current in that part vary with its resistance?
9. What do you understand by the term "drop of potential"?
10. The e.m.f. of a cell as measured by a voltmeter is 2.0 volts. When the cell is connected to a spool of wire, the voltmeter across the battery terminals indicates only 1.7 volts. Explain the difference.
11. Outline the procedure in determining the size of wire to be used in connecting a certain electrical device to service mains that are located some distance from that device.
12. Make a sketch of an electric circuit, showing how you would connect in the circuit an ammeter to measure the current and a voltmeter to measure the p.d. at the device to be operated.

## PROBLEMS

1. How much current will a 30-ohm electric iron take when operated on 115-volt service mains? *Ans.* 3.83 amperes.

2. What is the resistance of a heating coil that draws a current of 5.8 amperes when connected across 118-volt service mains? *Ans.* 20.4 ohms.

3. What potential difference must be applied to an incandescent lamp if it has a resistance of 46 ohms and requires 2.5 amperes? *Ans.* 115 volts.

4. The current through the field magnets of a dynamo is 1.8 amperes when the applied potential difference is 117 volts. What is the resistance of the field magnets? *Ans.* 65 ohms.

5. Accidental contact by a person with the third rail of an electric railway operated at 550 volts usually proves fatal because of the relatively large current through the body. Assuming the resistance of the body between the contacting points to be 3500 ohms, what would the current be? *Ans.* 0.157 ampere.

6. The field coils of an electric motor take 1.6 amperes at 220 volts. Determine the resistance of these coils. *Ans.* 137.5 ohms.

7. What is the potential difference across a bank of lamps having an equivalent resistance of 8.2 ohms and in which the current is 15 amperes? *Ans.* 123 volts.

8. A slidewire resistance has 250 turns wound on an insulating cylinder. A current of 2.3 amperes traverses the entire length of the wire, which has a resistance of 40 ohms. What is the potential difference between adjacent turns of the winding? *Ans.* 0.368 volt.

9. What current will be established in a resistor of 0.1 ohm resistance by a Leclanché cell of 1.4 volts e.m.f., if it has an internal resistance of 0.4 ohm? *Ans.* 2.8 amperes.

10. The e.m.f. of a certain cell is 1.44 volts, its internal resistance is 0.16 ohm, and it is connected to an external circuit of 0.4 ohm resistance. What is the drop in potential through the cell? *Ans.* 0.41 volt.

11. A voltaic cell, having an e.m.f. of 1.56 volts and an internal resistance of 0.4 ohm, is connected to an external circuit of 10 ohms resistance. Calculate the current in the circuit, and the potential difference across the terminals of the cell. *Ans.* 0.15 ampere; 1.50 volts.

12. A battery having an e.m.f. of 6.4 volts and an internal resistance of 0.25 ohm supplies a current of 2 amperes to a group of lamps. Find the p.d. across the terminals of the battery and also the equivalent resistance of the lamps. *Ans.* 5.9 volts; 2.95 ohms.

13. A storage battery has an e.m.f. of 6 volts and an internal resistance of 0.1 ohm. Find the potential difference across the terminals of this battery (a) when it is delivering 8 amperes and (b) when it is being charged with 8 amperes. *Ans.* (a) 5.2 volts; (b) 6.8 volts.

14. A dry cell has a p.d. of 1.476 volts across its terminals when on open circuit; this is lowered to 1.435 volts when the cell delivers current to an external circuit of 2.5 ohms resistance. Calculate the internal resistance of the cell. *Ans.* 0.0714 ohm.

15. A Daniell cell is found to establish a current of 0.095 ampere in an external circuit of 10 ohms resistance. The current increases to 0.170 ampere when the resistance of the external circuit is reduced to 5 ohms. Compute the e.m.f. of the cell and also its internal resistance. *Ans.* 1.077 volts; 1.33 ohms.

16. A gravity cell has an e.m.f. of 1 volt and an internal resistance of 0.63 ohm. What current will it establish through an electromagnet wound with 150 feet of No. 18 A.w.g. copper wire? *Ans.* 0.623 ampere.

17. The resistance of the armature of a certain generator is 0.05 ohm. (a) What is the drop of potential in the armature when it carries a current of 12 amperes? (b) What is the e.m.f. generated in the machine when the potential difference across the armature is 115 volts with the current stated? *Ans.* (a) 0.60 volt; (b) 115.6 volts.

18. A farm-lighting plant includes a storage battery having 32 volts across its terminals. From the battery a pair of No. 12 A.w.g. copper line wires extend to a point 60 feet away, where a load drawing a current of 11 amperes is connected. Compute the p.d. across the load. *Ans.* 29.86 volts.

19. A group of flood lamps which takes a current of 45 amperes is located at a distance of 250 feet from a generator which maintains 120 volts across its terminals. What gage rubber-insulated copper wires are needed for the line connecting the lamps to the generator, if the allowable potential drop is 3 per cent? *Ans.* No. 2 A.w.g.

# Lesson VIII

## SERIES AND PARALLEL CIRCUITS

Methods of connection—Series connection—Parallel connection—Two resistors in parallel—Series-parallel arrangements—Wye-delta equivalents —Division of current in parallel circuits—Current and potential distribution in networks—Cells in series and in parallel—Connections of cells for maximum current—Cells in opposition—Battery charging circuits— Questions and Problems.

**79. Methods of Connection.**—There are two simple ways of connecting electrical devices in a circuit. When they are joined in the manner shown by resistors $R_1$ and $R_2$ in Fig. 80 they are said to be *connected in series,* and when joined in the manner shown in Fig. 81 they are said to be *connected in parallel.* Multiple and shunt are other names for the parallel connection. Com-

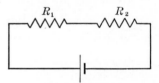

Fig. 80. Two resistors in series

binations of these methods of connection may also exist in the same circuit.

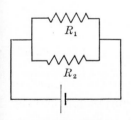

Fig. 81. Two resistors in parallel

In the series arrangement, the current has the same value throughout the circuit; in Fig. 80 the current is the same in the battery, in resistor $R_1$ and in resistor $R_2$, no matter what their individual resistances may be. The sum of the potential drops in a series circuit will be equal to the potential difference made available by the source; in the figure the p.d. across $R_1$ plus that across $R_2$ will equal the p.d. across the battery. To summarize, *in a series circuit the current is the same throughout,* and all the potential drops add up to the value of the e.m.f. acting in the circuit.

145

In the parallel arrangement, the current supplied by the source will divide between the branches, and the current in each one will be determined by its particular resistance. In Fig. 81 the potential difference between the terminals of resistor $R_1$ will be the same as that for resistor $R_2$. Thus, *in a parallel circuit the potential drop is the same across all branches,* and the currents in the branches add up to the value of the main current.

It is often desired to find the effect of the grouping of resistors in series or in parallel upon the total resistance of the circuit. To do this, imagine several resistors, $R_1$, $R_2$, $R_3$ . . . to be combined in either manner; then let $I_1$, $I_2$, $I_3$, . . . be the respective currents in them and let $E_1$, $E_2$, $E_3$, . . . be the respective potential drops across them. Then Ohm's Law applied to each of the resistors gives their resistances as

$$R_1 = \frac{E_1}{I_1} \qquad R_2 = \frac{E_2}{I_2} \qquad R_3 = \frac{E_3}{I_3} \qquad\qquad 26$$

By applying these equations to the principles of series and of parallel circuits stated above, it is possible to find the equivalent resistance of any circuit, as explained in the following sections.

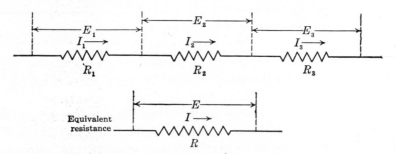

Fig. 82. Resistors connected in series

**80. Series Connection.**—Fig. 82 shows at the top the connection of several resistors in series; each one of them is marked by symbols $I$, $R$ and $E$ with appropriate subscript to designate the current in the resistor, its resistance, and the potential drop across it, respectively. The entire group may be replaced by a single *equivalent resistance* $R$ shown at the bottom of the figure, if the current $I$ supplied to it is the same as the current supplied to the upper group and if the potential drop $E$ across $R$ is the same as the potential drop across the entire upper group. It is the purpose of the demonstration which follows to find the equivalent or joint resistance of the group of resistors connected in series.

Since the resistors $R_1$, $R_2$ and $R_3$ are connected in series, the current is the same in all, and the total available potential difference is the sum of the individual potential drops. Expressing these facts by symbols,

$$I = I_1 = I_2 = I_3 = \ldots$$

and

$$E = E_1 + E_2 + E_3 + \ldots$$

Dividing the second equation by the first,

$$\frac{E}{I} = \frac{E_1 + E_2 + E_3 + \ldots}{I} = \frac{E_1}{I} + \frac{E_2}{I} + \frac{E_3}{I} + \ldots$$

Since $E \div I$ represents the equivalent resistance $R$, its value is

$$R = \frac{E_1}{I_1} + \frac{E_2}{I_2} + \frac{E_3}{I_3} + \ldots$$

where the subscripts of the common current $I$ are matched with those of p.d.'s in the numerators. Applying Formulas (26), the joint resistance of the group becomes

$$R = R_1 + R_2 + R_3 + \ldots \qquad 27$$

This formula shows that the equivalent resistance of several resistors connected in series is equal to the sum of their individual resistances. This result could be anticipated from an understanding of the factors affecting resistance, for connecting resistors in series is equivalent to lengthening the wire on one of them proportionately, and this means a corresponding increase of resistance.

To FIND THE JOINT RESISTANCE OF A NUMBER OF DEVICES CONNECTED IN SERIES:

*Add the individual resistances of the devices connected to the circuit.*

Problem 39.—An electric bell is operated by a dry battery and controlled by a push-button some distance away. The resistances of the parts of the circuit are as follows: bell 5.1 ohms, connecting wires 1.4 ohms, battery 0.3 ohm. What current is supplied by the 1.5-volt battery?

The total resistance of the circuit is

(27)          $R = R_1 + R_2 + R_3 = 5.1 + 1.4 + 0.3 = 6.8$ ohms

and the current is

(18)          $I = \dfrac{E}{R} = \dfrac{1.5}{6.8} = 0.22$ ampere

**81. Parallel Connection.**—Fig. 83 shows at the left several resistors connected in parallel, marked as in the previous section. The equivalent resistance $R$ of this group of resistors is shown at the right and its value can be calculated as follows:

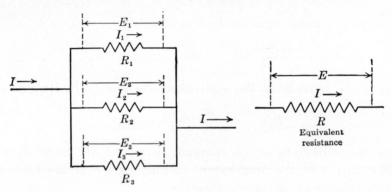

FIG. 83. Resistors connected in parallel

The current supplied by the source divides between the resistors, and the potential difference across them is the same for all. This statement can be expressed as

$$I = I_1 + I_2 + I_3 + \ldots$$

and          $$E = E_1 = E_2 = E_3 = \ldots$$

The equivalent resistance $R$ is found by dividing the second equation by the first, whence

$$R = \frac{E}{I} = \frac{E}{I_1 + I_2 + I_3 + \ldots}$$

This can be simplified by taking reciprocals of the outer members of the last equation, expanding the result, and matching subscripts; thus

$$\frac{1}{R} = \frac{I_1 + I_2 + I_3 + \ldots}{E} = \frac{I_1}{E_1} + \frac{I_2}{E_2} + \frac{I_3}{E_3} + \ldots$$

Applying Equations (26),

$$\frac{1}{R} = \frac{1}{R_1} + \frac{1}{R_2} + \frac{1}{R_3} + \ldots \qquad 28$$

This formula shows the relation in the parallel connection between the individual resistance $R_1$, $R_2$, $R_3$ ... of the resistors and their equivalent resistance $R$.

In direct-current circuits the reciprocal of resistance is called *conductance*, and the symbol for this quantity is $G$. Conversely, in such a circuit the resistance is the reciprocal of its conductance. Thus,

$$G = \frac{1}{R} \quad \text{and} \quad R = \frac{1}{G} \qquad 29$$

The term *mho* (ohm spelled backward) is sometimes used as the unit of conductance. A wire of 1 ohm resistance has a conductance of 1 mho; one of 2 ohms resistance has a conductance of ½ mho; one of ⅔ ohm resistance, 3/2 or 1½ mhos. Conversely a wire of 3 mhos conductance has a resistance of ⅓ ohm; one of ⅛ mho conductance 8 ohms.

Using the idea of conductance, it is possible to express Formula (28) in simpler shape by replacing the fractions by conductances. Thus substituting $G$ for the fraction $\frac{1}{R}$,

$$G = \frac{1}{R_1} + \frac{1}{R_2} + \frac{1}{R_3} + \ldots$$

Doing the same for the other fractions, the conductance of a number of resistors connected in parallel becomes the sum of the conductances of the individual resistors, or

$$G = G_1 + G_2 + G_3 + \ldots \qquad 30$$

To FIND THE JOINT RESISTANCE OF ANY NUMBER OF RESISTORS CONNECTED IN PARALLEL:

*Find the sum of the conductances of the individual resistors and take the reciprocal of this sum.*

**Problem 40.**—Determine the joint resistance of three resistors, of 2, 4 and 8 ohms resistance, connected in parallel.

The conductances of the resistors are given by Formula (29) as ½, ¼ and ⅛ mho respectively. Therefore, the sum of the conductances is

$$(30) \quad G = G_1 + G_2 + G_3 = \frac{1}{2} + \frac{1}{4} + \frac{1}{8} = \frac{4+2+1}{8} = \frac{7}{8} \text{ mho}$$

or in decimals is

$$G = 0.500 + 0.250 + 0.125 = 0.875 \text{ mho}$$

Consequently, the total resistance is the reciprocal of $\frac{7}{8}$ or of 0.875 mho, namely $\frac{8}{7}$ or 1.143 ohms.

The total resistance of any number of resistors connected in parallel will always be less than that of the resistor having the lowest resistance. This is a natural result, for the parallel connection virtually means that the sectional area of one path has been increased by the presence of the others, and an increase of sectional area between two points in a circuit means a lowering of its resistance.

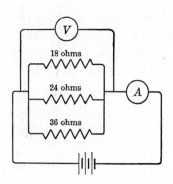

FIG. 84. Experiment on resistors in parallel

**Experiment 39.**—Make up three resistors of different resistance and measure their resistances separately. Connect them in parallel and measure their joint resistance to verify the statements in this section. The resistance in each case may be determined by connection to a source of electricity, measuring both current and p.d., and then applying Ohm's Law. Fig. 84 shows the connection arrangement on the supposition that the resistors are of 18, 24 and 36 ohms. With a voltmeter bridged across the parallel group and also an ammeter in series with it, show by test that the joint resistance is 8 ohms.

To FIND THE JOINT RESISTANCE OF ANY NUMBER OF LIKE RESISTORS CONNECTED IN PARALLEL:

*Divide the resistance of one resistor by the number connected in parallel.*

Let

    $R'$ = resistance of each resistor,
    $n$ = number of resistors of equal resistance connected in parallel,
    $R$ = joint resistance of the group of resistors.

Then

$$R = \frac{R'}{n}$$
                                                                    31

**Problem 41.**—Six incandescent lamps, all alike, are connected in parallel as shown in Fig. 85. Assume each lamp to have a constant resistance of 360 ohms. What is the total resistance of the group of lamps?

(31)                   $R = \dfrac{R'}{n} = \dfrac{360}{6} = 60$ ohms

**82. Two Resistors in Parallel.**—The connection of *only two* resistors in parallel is of frequent occurrence in electrical circuits, and it is fortunate that a simple formula exists which gives the total resistance of the pair. For the two resistors of resistance $R_1$ and $R_2$, Formula (28) becomes

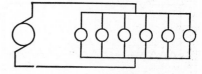

FIG. 85.  Lamps connected in parallel to a generator

$$\frac{1}{R} = \frac{1}{R_1} + \frac{1}{R_2} = \frac{R_1 + R_2}{R_1 \times R_2}$$

from which the total resistance is found by taking reciprocals, or

$$R = \frac{R_1 \times R_2}{R_1 + R_2}$$
                                                                    32

and naturally this total will be less than the resistance of either resistor.

To find the total resistance of two resistors connected in parallel:

*Divide the product of their resistances by their sum.* This rule does not apply to the connection of more than two resistors in parallel.

**Problem 42.**—Calculate the total resistance of two coils joined in parallel, one having a resistance of 3 and the other of 7 ohms.

(32)                $R = \dfrac{R_1 \times R_2}{R_1 + R_2} = \dfrac{3 \times 7}{3 + 7} = 2.1$ ohms

**83. Series-Parallel Arrangements.**—Combinations of the series connection and parallel connection can be formed in great profusion; Figs. 86 and 87 indicate two of the simplest cases. In the first circuit resistors $R_1$ and $R_2$ are connected in series, and again resistors $R_3$, $R_4$, and $R_5$ are connected in series; these two groups are then connected in parallel. In Fig. 87, resistors $R_1$ and $R_2$ are connected in parallel, and again resistors $R_3$, $R_4$, and $R_5$ are connected in parallel; these two groups are then connected in series. The total resistance for either circuit can be worked out when the resistances of the individual resistors are given.

**Problem 43.**—Compute the total resistance for the grouping shown in Fig. 86, assuming the resistors to have the following resistances: $R_1 = 6$ ohms, $R_2 = 24$ ohms, $R_3 = 3$ ohms, $R_4 = 9$ ohms, and $R_5 = 18$ ohms.

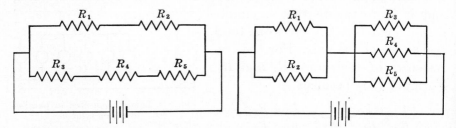

FIG. 86. Series-parallel connection        FIG. 87. Series-parallel connection

The upper series group has a resistance of $6 + 24$ or 30 ohms, and the lower series group has a resistance of $3 + 9 + 18$ or 30 ohms, both determined by Formula (27). The total resistance of the two groups in parallel, each of 30 ohms, is given by Formula (31) as $30 \div 2$ or 15 ohms.

**Problem 44.**—Determine the total resistance for the grouping of resistors shown in Fig. 87, assuming the same resistance values as in Problem 43.

The left-hand parallel group has a resistance of

$$(32) \qquad R = \frac{R_1 \times R_2}{R_1 + R_2} = \frac{6 \times 24}{6 + 24} = 4.8 \text{ ohms}$$

while the right-hand parallel group has a conductance of

$$(30) \qquad G = G_3 + G_4 + G_5 = \frac{1}{3} + \frac{1}{9} + \frac{1}{18} = \frac{6 + 2 + 1}{18} = \frac{1}{2} \text{ mho}$$

making $R = 2$ ohms. The total resistance of the two groups in series is $4.8 + 2 = 6.8$ ohms.

**84. Wye-Delta Equivalents.**—There are some electrical networks which cannot be reduced to simple series or parallel groupings such as those described, and the calculations are often quite involved. A scheme for simplifying such calculations makes use of two groups of three resistors each group having three exposed terminals. Fig. 88 shows the two groups of resistors, each with terminals $M, N, P$; those at the left are connected to resemble the letter $Y$ (wye), and those at the right are joined to form the Greek letter $\Delta$ (delta). By a proper choice of their resistances one group may be made equivalent to the other so far as external connections to the three terminals are concerned.

The component resistors are marked $a, b,$ and $c$ in the $Y$-group, and $A, B,$ and $C$ in the $\Delta$ group; these letters will be used also to represent their resistances in order to simplify the derivation to follow. The letters are assigned in a definite order to make $A$ opposite to $a$, $B$ opposite to $b$, and $C$ opposite to $c$; this selection will help in applying the results.

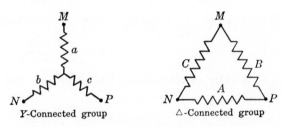

Y-Connected group        $\Delta$-Connected group

Fig. 88.  Equivalence between $Y$-connected and $\Delta$-connected resistors

In order that the two connection groups may be equivalent electrically, the resistance must be the same between like-marked terminals. Between terminals $M$ and $N$ of the $Y$ group, resistors $a$ and $b$ are in series and resistor $c$ is not involved, consequently the total resistance is $a + b$. Between the same terminals of the $\Delta$ group, resistors $A$ and $B$ are in series and this pair is in parallel with resistor $C$; applying Formula (32) to the two resistors in parallel, one $(A + B)$ and the other $C$, gives the total resistance as $\dfrac{(A + B) \times C}{A + B + C}$. Continuing this procedure and collecting the results, it is clear that for equivalence of the two groups

| Between terminals | Y group | | $\Delta$ group |
|---|---|---|---|
| $M$ and $N$ | $a + b$ | $=$ | $\dfrac{(A + B) \times C}{A + B + C}$ |
| $N$ and $P$ | $b + c$ | $=$ | $\dfrac{(B + C) \times A}{A + B + C}$ |
| $P$ and $M$ | $c + a$ | $=$ | $\dfrac{(A + C) \times B}{A + B + C}$ |

Adding all the left members and all the right members of these equations separately and then dividing each member of the resulting equation by 2, the following expression is obtained:

$$a + b + c = \frac{(A \times B) + (B \times C) + (C \times A)}{A + B + C}$$

Subtracting therefrom successively each one of the three foregoing equations gives the results sought for. First, subtracting the equation for the resistance between $N$ and $P$,

$$a = \frac{B \times C}{A + B + C} \qquad\qquad \text{33a}$$

Then, subtracting the equation for the resistance between $P$ and $M$,

$$b = \frac{C \times A}{A + B + C} \qquad\qquad \text{33b}$$

and finally, subtracting the equation for the resistance between $M$ and $N$,

$$c = \frac{A \times B}{A + B + C} \qquad\qquad \text{33c}$$

These results can be summarized by stating that *the resistance of any arm of an equivalent Y circuit is equal to the product of the resistances of the adjacent arms of the $\Delta$ circuit, divided by the sum of the three delta resistances.* Formulas (33) permit the calculation of an equivalent $Y$ circuit for any trio of resistors forming a $\Delta$ circuit.

**Experiment 40.**—Connect in the form of a $Y$ three resistors of equal resistance; also connect in the form of a $\Delta$ three resistors each having three times the resistance of one of the $Y$ group. Measure the resistance between any pair of terminals of the $Y$ and also of the $\Delta$; show that the resistance is the same. The resistance may be measured by utilizing Ohm's Law as in Experiment 39.

It is also possible to derive the values of the resistances of a $\Delta$ circuit that shall be equivalent to a given $Y$ circuit. To proceed, divide Equation (33a) by Equation (33b) to get

$$\frac{a}{b} = \frac{B}{A}$$

and divide Formula (33b) by Formula (33c) to get

$$\frac{b}{c} = \frac{C}{B}$$

By combining these results the basic requirement for the equivalence between the $Y$ and $\Delta$ circuits is found to be

$$a \times A = b \times B = c \times C$$

Further manipulation of the numbered equations gives the resistance of $A$ as

$$A = \frac{(a \times b) + (b \times c) + (c \times a)}{a} \qquad \textbf{34}$$

Similarly, the expression for resistance $B$ has the same numerator but the denominator is $b$, and that for resistance $C$ has the same numerator but the denominator is $c$.

**Problem 45.**—Five resistors are included in a circuit with four of them connected in the form of a square and the fifth joined to opposite corners, as shown at the left in Fig. 89. The resistances of these resistors are given in ohms. It is desired to find the total resistance of the circuit between the top and bottom terminals.

Replace the $\Delta$ group formed of the 10-, 30- and 60-ohm resistors by a $Y$ group. In the foregoing analysis let $A = 60$ ohms, $B = 30$ ohms, and $C = 10$ ohms; thus $A + B + C = 100$ ohms.

The application of Formulas (33) gives the resistances of the equivalent $Y$ circuit as

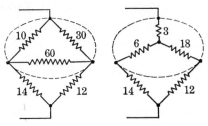

Fig. 89. Application of $\Delta$ to $Y$ transformation

$$a = \frac{30 \times 10}{100} = 3 \text{ ohms}, \ b = \frac{10 \times 60}{100} = 6 \text{ ohms, and } c = \frac{60 \times 30}{100} = 18 \text{ ohms}$$

The replacement of the upper trio of resistors is indicated at the right of the figure and the other two resistors of 14 and 12 ohms resistance are brought over. A series-parallel grouping has now been formed with a series pair aggregating 20 ohms on the left and another aggregating 30 ohms on the right. These groups in parallel give a combined resistance of $\frac{20 \times 30}{20 + 30} = \frac{600}{50} = 12$ ohms. Hence, the desired total resistance between top and bottom terminals of the circuit is $3 + 12 = 15$ ohms.

**Problem 46.**—A certain wye ($Y$) circuit consists of a 10-ohm, a 20-ohm and a 40-ohm branch. Calculate the delta circuit which will be equivalent to the circuit given.

Referring to Fig. 88, let $a = 10$, $b = 20$ and $c = 40$ ohms. By Formula (34)

$$A = \frac{(10 \times 20) + (20 \times 40) + (40 \times 10)}{10} = \frac{1400}{10} = 140 \text{ ohms}$$

Similarly $B = \dfrac{1400}{20} = 70 \text{ ohms}$, and $C = \dfrac{1400}{40} = 35 \text{ ohms}$

**85. Division of Current in Parallel Circuit.**—The current in the several paths of a divided circuit can be obtained by applying Ohm's Law to each path. Since the p.d. is the same across paths that are in parallel, the currents in these paths of resistance $R_1, R_2, R_3 \ldots$ as shown in Fig. 83 are respectively

$$I_1 = \frac{E}{R_1} \qquad I_2 = \frac{E}{R_2} \qquad I_3 = \frac{E}{R_3} \ldots$$

where $E$ is the potential difference common to all. Using corresponding conductances for the resistances of the paths, the currents become

$$I_1 = E \times G_1 \qquad I_2 = E \times G_2 \qquad I_3 = E \times G_3$$

The first line of equations shows that the *current in each of the parallel paths is inversely proportional to its resistance,* and the second line shows that *the current in each path is directly proportional to its conductance.*

The total current in the circuit is given by $I = \dfrac{E}{R}$, where $R$ is the joint resistance of the several paths, or by $I = I_1 + I_2 + I_3 + \ldots$. If the common p.d. $E$ is eliminated from the equations involving resistance, they can be put together as follows:

$$I \times R = I_1 \times R_1 = I_2 \times R_2 = I_3 \times R_3 = \ldots \qquad \textbf{35}$$

which states that the p.d. across all resistors is the same.

**Experiment 41.**—Connect three resistors in parallel to a battery as shown in Fig. 84 for resistors of 18, 24, and 36 ohms. Read on the ammeter the total current taken by the group. Then remove the ammeter from its position in the figure and place it in series with the 18-ohm resistor so as to measure the current in it. Do this also for the 24-ohm and the 36-ohm resistors. Show by test that the result of the first current measurement is equal to the sum of the other three. Also show that the respective currents in the resistors are 4/9, 3/9, and 2/9 of the total current.

In the case of just two resistors in parallel, the current in one branch can be expressed in terms of the current in the other branch as

$$I_1 = I_2 \times \frac{R_2}{R_1}$$
35a

or in terms of the total current as

$$I_1 = I \times \frac{R}{R_1}$$
35b

Both of these equations come from Formula (35).

For example, if two resistors of equal resistance are connected in parallel, the total current of the circuit will divide equally through them. If one resistor of a pair connected in parallel has a higher resistance than the other, the greater part of the current will be through the one of lower resistance.

Assuming $R_1$ to be 6 ohms and $R_2$ to be 12 ohms, then from Formula (35a) there will be twice as much current in $R_1$ as in $R_2$. By dividing the total current into three equal parts, it is evident that two parts will pass through $R_1$ and one part through $R_2$. Should the total current be 24 amperes then there would be 16 amperes in $R_1$ and 8 in $R_2$.

If $R_1$ be 6 ohms and $R_2$ be 12 ohms, as before, their joint resistance when connected in parallel would be $R = \dfrac{6 \times 12}{6 + 12} = 4$ ohms, by Formula (32). Again taking 24 amperes as the total current, the current in $R_1$ would be given by Formula (35b) as 4/6 of the total current, or $4/6 \times 24 = 16$ amperes. Similarly $I_2$ would be $4/12 \times 24 = 8$ amperes.

**Problem 47.**—A current of 39 amperes is supplied to a circuit having three coils of wire joined in multiple. The resistances of these coils are $A = 8$, $B = 12$, and $C = 16$ ohms. What will the current be in each coil? What will be the p.d. across each?

The conductance of $A$ is 1/8 mho, of $B$ is 1/12 mho, and of $C$ is 1/16 mho; the total conductance = $1/8 + 1/12 + 1/16 = 6/48 + 4/48 + 3/48 = 13/48$ mho. Consider the total current divided into 13 parts, then 6 parts will pass through $A$, 4 through $B$, and 3 through $C$, or directly as their conductances. Consequently, the currents in the various coils will be $A = 6/13 \times 39 = 18$ amperes, $B = 4/13 \times 39 = 12$ amperes, and $C = 3/13 \times 39 = 9$ amperes, making a total of 39 amperes.

Since the conductance of the group of coils is 13/48 mho, its resistance is 48/13 ohms. With a total current of 39 amperes, the potential drop across each coil will be

(22) $$E = I \times R = 39 \times \frac{48}{13} = 144 \text{ volts}$$

The current can now be determined for each coil by applying Ohm's Law directly; for example, the current in coil $A$ is $144 \div 8 = 18$ amperes.

## 86. Current and Potential Distribution in Networks.—A circuit formed of a number of resistors in series and parallel groupings, and sometimes with delta groups as well, is called a *network*. It is often desired to determine the current and potential distributions in such a network, and this can be done by applying to its various parts the principles discussed in this lesson.

RESULTS OF CALCULATIONS

| Resistor Ohms | Current Amperes | Potential Difference Volts |
|:---:|:---:|:---:|
| 6 | 3.0 | 18 |
| 8 | 1.5 | 12 |
| 10 | 3.0 | 30 |
| 12 | 1.0 | 12 |
| 15 | 6.0 | 90 |
| 24 | 0.5 | 12 |

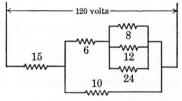

Fig. 90. A series-parallel network

**Problem 48.**—Fig. 90 shows a simple network comprising six resistors, with the resistance value in ohms indicated on each. With 120 volts impressed on the network, compute the current in each of the resistors and the potential difference across each.

The parallel grouping of the 8-, 12-, and 24-ohm resistors has a conductance of $1/8 + 1/12 + 1/24 = 6/24$ mho, and the joint resistance is $24/6 = 4$ ohms. The resistance of the upper branch is then $6 + 4 = 10$ ohms. The two 10-ohm branches in parallel have a joint resistance of $10/2 = 5$ ohms, and consequently the aggregate resistance of the network is $15 + 5 = 20$ ohms.

The total current supplied to the network is $120/20 = 6$ amperes, and this is the current in the 15-ohm resistor. The p.d. across this resistor is $6 \times 15 = 90$ volts, and that across the remainder of the network is $6 \times 5 = 30$ volts. The main current divides equally between the upper and lower branches. With 3 amperes in the 6-ohm resistor, the p.d. across it is $3 \times 6 = 18$ volts; the p.d. across the parallel group of the three resistors is $3 \times 4 = 12$ volts. The current in each of these is determined by Ohm's Law. The summary of current and potential values appears alongside the figure.

**87. Cells in Series and in Parallel.**—Voltaic cells are frequently connected in series in order to obtain an increased e.m.f. They are sometimes connected in parallel in order that jointly they may supply a large current to a low-resistance device without demanding an excessive current from any single cell. These methods of connection were mentioned earlier and illustrated in Fig. 51.

When a number of cells are connected in series, the combined e.m.f. of the battery is the sum of the e.m.f.'s of the individual cells. The internal resistance of the battery is the sum of the internal resistances of the several cells.

When a number of cells having equal e.m.f.'s are connected in parallel, the e.m.f. of the combination is the same as that of any individual cell. The effect of connecting cells in parallel is the same as increasing the size of a single cell, the areas of both electrodes and of the electrolyte being correspondingly enlarged. Since the size of a cell does not affect its e.m.f., §45, the parallel connection of cells will not yield an increase of e.m.f for the combination. However, the increase in the effective area of the electrolyte brought about by the parallel connection lessens the internal resistance of the combination of cells and the current supplied will be correspondingly large. If $n$ cells are connected in parallel and each has an internal resistance $r$, then the internal resistance of the combination is $r/n$, just as in a parallel grouping of resistors given by Formula (31).

**Problem 49.**—Ten dry cells, each having an e.m.f. of 1.5 volts and a resistance of 0.06 ohm, are connected first in series and then in parallel. What is the total e.m.f. available and the total internal resistance of the cells for each method of connection?

For the series connection, the e.m.f. is $1.5 \times 10 = 15$ volts, and the internal resistance is $0.06 \times 10 = 0.6$ ohm. For the parallel connection, the e.m.f. is 1.5 volts, and the internal resistance is $0.06 \div 10 = 0.006$ ohm.

**88. Connection of Cells for Maximum Current.**—The question is frequently raised whether the parallel or the series connection of a certain number of identical cells will provide the greater current in an electrical device connected to the battery. The answer depends entirely upon the relative resistances of the battery and of the device to be operated. To investigate the question, let

> $n$ = number of like cells to be connected,
> $E$ = e.m.f. of each cell,
> $r$ = internal resistance of each cell,
> $R$ = resistance of the electrical device or external circuit;

then consider the cells first joined in series and later in parallel, and compute the current for each connection scheme.

In the series connection shown at the left in Fig. 91, the total e.m.f. available in the circuit is $n \times E$, and the total resistance is

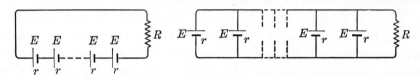

FIG. 91. Series and parallel connections of cells to operate device $R$

$R + (n \times r)$; then by Ohm's Law the current in every part of the circuit will be

$$I_s = \frac{n \times E}{R + (n \times r)} \qquad\qquad 36$$

where the subscript $s$ indicates the series connection. In the parallel connection depicted at the right, the total e.m.f. available in the circuit is that of only one cell, namely $E$, and the total resistance of the circuit is $R + \dfrac{r}{n}$; consequently, the current in the device will be

$$I_p = \frac{E}{R + \dfrac{r}{n}} = \frac{n \times E}{(n \times R) + r} \qquad\qquad 37$$

where the subscript $p$ indicates the parallel connection, and the current in any cell will be $\dfrac{I_p}{n}$.

To determine the conditions of the circuit which will make the current through $R$ for the series connection equal to the current for the parallel connection, equate Formulas (36) and (37). Since their numerators are the same, namely, $n \times E$, the result will be

$$R + (n \times r) = (n \times R) + r$$

or
$$r \times (n - 1) = R \times (n - 1)$$

which means that $R = r$. Thus, when the external resistance is equal to the internal resistance of one cell, it will be immaterial whether the cells are connected in series or in parallel for the current through the device will be the same for either connection.

Suppose, next, that the external resistance $R$ is varied and that its ratio to the cell resistance $r$ is taken as $m$; that is $\dfrac{R}{r} = m$, where $m$ may have any value larger or smaller than unity. Substituting $m \times r$ for $R$ in Formulas (36) and (37), and then dividing the first by the second, there results

$$\frac{I_s}{I_p} = \frac{(m \times n) + 1}{m + n} \qquad \textbf{38}$$

The number of cells $n$ will necessarily be an integer beginning with 2. Trying out different numerical values for the ratio $m$ in Formula (38), it will be found that $I_s$ will be greater than $I_p$ for all values of $m$ greater than 1, and vice versa. Consequently, the series connection of cells will yield a larger current in the external circuit than the parallel connection whenever that circuit has a resistance *greater* than the internal resistance of one of the cells, otherwise the parallel connection will afford the larger current.

**Problem 50.**—Six gravity cells are joined to a coil of wire having a resistance of 7 ohms. The e.m.f. of each cell is 1.0 volt, and the internal resistance of each is 0.5 ohm. What current will be established in the coil when the cells are connected in series? and when connected in parallel?

The current for the series connection of the cells is

$$(36) \qquad I_s = \frac{n \times E}{R + (n \times r)} = \frac{6 \times 1.0}{7 + (6 \times 0.5)} = 0.60 \text{ ampere}$$

and the current for the parallel connection is

$$(37) \qquad I_p = \frac{E}{R + \dfrac{r}{n}} = \frac{1.0}{7 + \dfrac{0.5}{6}} = \frac{1.0}{7.083} = 0.141 \text{ ampere}$$

Over four times as much current is obtained with a series connection of the cells to this particular coil as with the parallel connection.

**Problem 51.**—The six cells of Problem 50 are connected to a coil of 0.3-ohm resistance. Calculate the current in the coil for the two methods of connection.

The currents for the series and the parallel connection are respectively

$$(36) \qquad I_s = \frac{6 \times 1.0}{0.3 + (6 \times 0.5)} = 1.82 \text{ amperes}$$

$$(37) \qquad I_p = \frac{1.0}{0.3 + \dfrac{0.5}{6}} = \frac{1.0}{0.383} = 2.61 \text{ amperes}$$

Thus, the parallel connection of the cells yields a larger current through the 0.3-ohm coil than the series connection. However, both currents are considerably larger than in Problem 50, wherein the coil had much more resistance.

**Problem 52.**—Find the current through an electrical device having a resistance of 1 ohm, when connected to a battery of 24 cells, arranged 4 cells in a series group and 6 such groups in parallel. Each cell has an e.m.f. of 2 volts and an internal resistance of 0.3 ohm.

The e.m.f. available will be $4 \times 2 = 8$ volts. The internal resistance of the 24 cells in series-parallel will be $\dfrac{0.3 \times 4}{6} = 0.2$ ohm. Consequently, Ohm's Law gives the current through the device as

$$I = \frac{8}{1 + 0.2} = 6.67 \text{ amperes}$$

**89. Cells in Opposition.**—When two cells are included in a circuit with like electrodes connected, their e.m.f.'s will be in opposition and each one will tend to establish current through the other. If the two e.m.f.'s are equal, then there will be no current in the connecting wires. When two cells of unequal e.m.f.'s are connected in opposition, there will be a current through the connecting wires in the direction dictated by the higher e.m.f.

To find the current in a series circuit when it has two e.m.f.'s in opposition to each other:

*Divide the difference between the e.m.f's by the total resistance of the current path.*

In the circuit of Fig. 92, showing two cells in parallel, the switch $S$ is open and no current will be supplied to the device $R$; nevertheless the two cells are joined in a closed loop, and there will be current in it unless their e.m.f.'s $E_1$ and $E_2$ are equal.

Take $r_1$ and $r_2$ as the respective internal resistances of the cells; then the current in the connecting loop will be

$$I = \frac{E_1 - E_2}{r_1 + r_2}$$

**39**

disregarding the resistance of the connecting wires themselves. In practice, cells having appreciably different e.m.f.'s would not be connected in parallel, because wasteful circulating currents would be set up in the cells themselves, even when the external circuit is open.

**Problem 52.**—Two storage cells connected in parallel supply jointly a current of 20 amperes to an external circuit. The cells have e.m.f.'s of 2.1 volts and 2.0 volts, and each has an internal resistance of 0.025 ohm. Find the circulating current when the external circuit is open, and the current supplied by each cell when that circuit is closed.

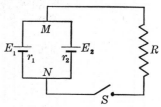

Fig. 92. Two cells of unequal e.m.f.'s in parallel

The connections are the same as those of Fig. 92, and the circulating current in the loop is

(39)     $$I = \frac{E_1 - E_2}{r_1 + r_2} = \frac{2.1 - 2.0}{0.025 + 0.025} = \frac{0.1}{0.05} = 2 \text{ amperes}$$

The potential difference maintained between points $M$ and $N$ by the left-hand cell is $E_1 - I_1 \times r_1$ and that by the right-hand cell is $E_2 - I_2 \times r_2$, where $I_1$ and $I_2$ are the respective currents supplied by the cells of e.m.f. $E_1$ and $E_2$. These potential differences must be equal since the paths are in parallel, and therefore,

$$E_1 - I_1 \times r_1 = E_2 - I_2 \times r_2$$

or          $$2.1 - 0.025\,I_1 = 2.0 - 0.025\,I_2$$

which reduces to $I_1 - I_2 = 4$. Further, the two currents together make up 20 amperes, consequently $I_1 + I_2 = 20$ amperes. Adding the two current equations, $I_1$ is found to be 12 amperes, and subtracting one of them from the other, $I_2$ is found to be 8 amperes. The difference of potential across $M$ and $N$ is found to be 1.8 volts and the external resistance to be 0.09 ohm.

**90. Battery Charging Circuits.** —It is often necessary to charge storage batteries from direct-current lighting circuits of much higher p.d. than the e.m.f. of the batteries. In such cases it is necessary to insert a resistor of appropriate resistance in the charging circuit, or else use a rheostat which can be adjusted for obtaining a suitable charging current. Fig. 93 shows the connections of the battery to 110-volt service mains, using a resistor of incandescent lamps in the diagram at the left and a rheostat in the diagram at the right. Note that the + terminal of the battery is connected to the + terminal of the mains, in order to have the charging current opposite in direction to the battery current on discharge.

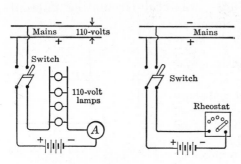

FIG. 93. Connections for charging storage batteries

**Problem 54.**—How much resistance must a rheostat have for use in charging a lead battery of 10 series-connected cells from a 110-volt circuit, if the charging current is to be 5 amperes and the p.d. across each cell is to be 2.4 volts at the beginning of charge?

Charging potential = $10 \times 2.4 = 24$ volts. Consequently, the resistance of the rheostat is $R = \dfrac{110 - 24}{5} = 17.2$ ohms.

The charging of storage batteries from alternating-current supply circuits will be considered in Lesson XXIII.

## QUESTIONS

1. State the result of connecting several resistors in series, with respect to current, potential difference, and resistance.
2. Explain how the formula is derived for the total resistance of a number of resistors connected in series.
3. What do you understand by the term conductance? What is the name of the unit that is sometimes used for conductance?
4. How would you find the total resistance of a number of resistors connected in parallel (a) when they are all alike? and (b) when they have different resistances?
5. Give the rule for finding the combined resistance of two resistors connected in parallel.
6. Derive Formula (31) for the total resistance of a number of like resistors connected in parallel.
7. A 2-ohm coil is connected in parallel with a 5-ohm coil. Is the combined resistance less than 2 ohms, between 2 and 5 ohms, or more than 5 ohms?

Does the 2-ohm coil take more or less than the current taken by the 5-ohm coil?

8. A number of incandescent lamps are connected in multiple to a generator. How will the total resistance of the circuit be affected if some lamps are turned off?

9. An electric heater is joined in parallel with an incandescent lamp to service mains. The heater takes a current of 2.5 amperes, while the lamp takes 1 ampere. Which device has the higher resistance? Explain.

10. Make a sketch showing five different ways in which four resistors can be connected into a circuit.

11. What do you mean by the equivalent wye of a delta-connected group of three resistors?

12. Explain how the current divides between the branches of a parallel circuit.

13. Why are cells connected in series? why in parallel?

14. Would you connect two cells in series if one has an e.m.f. of 1.0 volt and the other of 2.1 volts? Would you connect these cells in parallel? Give reasons for your answers.

15. How would the internal resistance of a battery, having four cells connected in series, compare with the resistance of the battery if the four cells were connected in parallel?

16. How should the cells of a battery be connected to provide the largest possible current through a device that is supplied by that battery? What are the conditions involved in your answer?

17. Two dry cells, each having an e.m.f. of 1.5 volts and an internal resistance of 0.6 ohm, are to be connected in such a manner as to supply as large a current as possible to an external circuit. Should the cells be connected in series or in parallel (a) if the external circuit has a resistance of 0.5 ohm, (b) if the external circuit has a resistance of 5.0 ohms?

18. What circuit arrangement could be made to charge an 80-cell lead storage battery from 120-volt service mains?

## PROBLEMS

1. It is desired to operate a motor, requiring 1 ampere at 6 volts, from a 32-volt supply circuit. How much resistance must be added in series with the motor? *Ans.* 26 ohms.

2. Four spools of wire are connected in series to a battery of 30 volts and of negligible internal resistance. The spools have resistances of 2, 3, 4 and 6 ohms. (a) What is the total resistance of the circuit? (b) What is the potential drop across each spool? *Ans.* (a) 15 ohms; (b) 4, 6, 8 and 12 volts respectively.

3. Three resistors are connected in parallel, one has 10 ohms resistance, another 30 ohms, and the third 60 ohms. What is the combined resistance? *Ans.* 6.67 ohms.

4. One hundred incandescent lamps are connected in parallel to a generator circuit. The resistance of the line wires is 0.05 ohm and the resistance of each lamp is 240 ohms. The potential difference at the generator terminals is 112 volts. What is the current in the circuit? *Ans.* 45.7 amperes.

5. Two resistors are connected in parallel, one of 3 ohms and the other of 8 ohms resistance. What is their combined resistance? *Ans.* 2.18 ohms.

6. In a trolley car, five lamps, each requiring 0.4 ampere at 110 volts, are connected in series between the line and track across which a p.d. of 550 volts is maintained. If there are 6 such groups, what would be the total resistance of the lamp circuit and how much current would it take? *Ans.* 229 ohms; 2.4 amperes.

7. What p.d. must be maintained at the terminals of a generator so that 150 lamps, connected in parallel, each requiring 0.3 ampere at 110 volts, will receive their proper current? Resistance of leads is 0.04 ohm. *Ans.* 111.8 volts.

8. Find the size of wire required to conduct current to eighty-five 300-ohm lamps in parallel, located at a distance of 125 feet from the generator, which maintains a p.d. of 112 volts at its terminals. The lamps should receive 110 volts. *Ans.* No. 4 A.w.g.

9. Three 12-ohm resistors are connected in delta. What is the resistance of each arm of the equivalent wye circuit? *Ans.* 4.0 ohms.

10. Resistors are connected between terminals *M, N* and *P* as shown in Fig. 88 so that the resistance of either group as measured across *MN* is 5 ohms, across *NP* is 3 ohms, and across *PM* is 7 ohms. Find the resistances *a, b* and *c* of the *Y* group and *A, B* and *C* of the Δ group. *Ans.* $a = 4.5$, $b = 0.5$, $c = 2.5$ ohms; $A = 3.28$, $B = 29.50$, $C = 5.90$ ohms.

11. Three devices are connected in parallel to a generator which furnishes a total current of 117 amperes to them. The resistances of the devices are: No. 1, 24 ohms; No. 2, 36 ohms; No. 3, 48 ohms. What current does each receive? *Ans.* 54, 36, and 27 amperes respectively.

12. Three coils, *A, B,* and *C,* having resistances of 6, 8, and 12 ohms respectively, are connected in parallel and this group is joined in series with a coil *D* of 2 ohms. If the current in coil *B* is 9 amperes, how much current will there be in each of the other coils? *Ans.* 12 amperes in *A*, 6 amperes in *C*, 27 amperes in *D*.

13. What p.d. is maintained across the parallel group of the circuit in Problem 12, and what is the p.d. across the entire circuit? *Ans.* 72 volts; 126 volts.

14. Suppose that two resistors of 2 ohms and 4 ohms resistance are connected in parallel and this combination is joined in series with a 5-ohm resistor and a battery having an e.m.f. of 3 volts and an internal resistance of 0.8 ohm. Find the current in the 4-ohm resistor. *Ans.* 0.140 ampere.

15. A bell circuit is operated by three dry cells in series. Each cell has an e.m.f. of 1.5 volts, and an internal resistance of 0.4 ohm. What current will the bell receive if its resistance, including the line, is 12 ohms? *Ans.* 0.341 ampere.

16. Seven resistors, of 200 ohms each, are arranged in two groups, the first group comprising 4 resistors in parallel and the second group comprising 3 resistors in parallel. If the groups are connected in series across a 220-volt line, find the potential drop across each group. *Ans.* 94.3 volts across the group of four and 125.7 volts across the group of three resistors.

17. Sketch six combinations of four resistors connected to a pair of supply lines. Each resistor has a resistance of 200 ohms and the potential difference across the mains is 100 volts. What current will each combination receive? *Ans.* 0.125, 0.2, 0.3, 0.376, 0.5, 0.667, and 2.0 amperes.

18. Ten Daniell cells are joined in parallel and to an external resistance of 0.5 ohm. The e.m.f. of each cell is 1 volt and the internal resistance of each is 0.7 ohm. Find the current in the external circuit. *Ans.* 1.75 amperes.

19. Suppose the ten cells in Problem 18 were connected in series. What would be the current in the circuit? *Ans.* 1.33 amperes.

20. Two batteries, each composed of six cells in series, are connected in parallel and jointly supply current to an external circuit of 8 ohms resistance. Each cell has an e.m.f. of 2.0 volts and an internal resistance of 0.16 ohm. Compute the current in the external circuit and the potential difference across the terminals of each cell. *Ans.* 1.415 amperes; 1.887 volts.

21. Six voltaic cells, each having an e.m.f. of 1.5 volts and an internal resistance of 0.3 ohm, are connected in two groups, each composed of three cells in parallel. The two groups are joined in series and supply current to an external circuit of 0.8 ohm resistance. Find the current in each cell. *Ans.* 1.00 ampere.

22. Four Leclanché cells, each having an e.m.f. of 1.4 volts and an internal resistance of 0.4 ohm, are to supply the greatest possible current to a circuit of 5 ohms resistance. Would you connect the cells in series or in parallel? Determine the maximum current. *Ans.* Series; 0.848 ampere.

23. Two Edison storage cells are connected in parallel. One has an e.m.f. of 1.20 volts and a resistance of 0.06 ohm, and the other has an e.m.f. of 1.16 volts and a resistance of 0.08 ohm. What will be the current through the cells when the external circuit is open? *Ans.* 0.286 ampere.

24. A 32-volt storage battery is charged from 110-volt direct-current supply mains, a rheostat being connected in series with the battery to limit the charging current to 8 amperes. What should be the resistance of the rheostat? *Ans.* 9.75 ohms.

# Lesson IX

## WORK AND POWER

Effects of force—Torque—Work and energy—Rate of doing work—Electrical work and energy—Electrical power—Power calculations—Distinction between work and power—Cost of electric service—Heat units—Transformation of work into heat—Fuses—Questions and Problems.

**91. Effects of Force.**—A *force* is described technically as a push or a pull acting upon matter to change its condition with respect to *motion* or *distortion*. Thus, force must always be applied to a body to cause it to move, to increase or decrease its motion, or to stop the motion entirely; in short, any change in the speed of a body can be produced only by a force acting upon it. When a force is applied to a body and does not move it as a whole, then the action produces distortion in the body, that is, its particles move rather small amounts relatively to each other.

A man pushing a lawn mower exerts a force on the lawn mower, a locomotive pulling a train of cars exerts a force on the train, and a book resting on a table exerts a force on the table. In each of these cases it is necessary that the two bodies touch each other; for example, the man must be in contact with the lawn mower in order to exert a force on it. Moreover, as the lawn mower moves, the man must move along also and stay in contact with it if he is to exert a force on it. When a person throws a ball, he exerts a force on it only so long as it stays in contact with his hand. There are, however, some important exceptions to the principle that one body cannot exert a force on another unless the two are in contact. One exception is gravitation, by means of which a body, say the earth, exerts a force of attraction on other bodies, whether they are in contact with it or not. The other exceptions are the forces of electrostatics and magnetism, whereby two separated electric charges or two separated magnet poles act upon each other; these actions were described in the first two lessons.

If a body is undergoing a change in motion then a force must be acting upon it, but this does not mean necessarily that if a force is exerted on a body it will change its speed. For example, a man may exert a force on a heavy crate, while at the same time friction or some other agent exerts an equal force on it in the opposite direction, in which case the two forces balance each other, and the crate does not move. If, however, *all* of the forces acting on a body are taken into account, and if these do not balance, then the *unbalanced force* will always cause it to speed up, that is, *the unbalanced force produces acceleration.* Whenever a body is accelerating, there must be an unbalanced force acting upon it.

The force of gravitation causes bodies on the earth to accelerate downward when they are released and allowed to fall freely. If a body is constrained so that it cannot fall when released, the earth exerts the same force on it, but in this case the pull of the earth is balanced by some equal and opposite force exerted by the restraining agent. Thus, a box resting on a table is pulled downward by the earth, but is pushed upward by the table, and so it stays at rest. If the table were incapable of pushing upward on the box as much as the earth pulls downward on it, that is, if it were not strong enough to support the box, there would then be an unbalanced force acting upon the box which would make it accelerate downward, and the table, being in the way of its motion, would collapse; a result that might be expected in the case of a heavy box on a frail table. The force of attraction which the earth exerts on a body, that is, the pull of gravity on it, is called the *weight* of the body; it is a force directed toward the center of the earth.

Weight or force is often measured with a spring balance. The body to be weighed is suspended by a spring; as it settles downward the spring stretches and exerts an increasing upward force upon it, and a balance is reached when the restoring force due to the extension of the spring equals the downward pull of gravity. Such a device is calibrated by hanging bodies of known weight on it and marking the corresponding extensions of the spring on a scale. The scale may then be used to furnish a direct reading of any desired weight or force within its range. The units of force are the *gram* and the *pound* and they represent the forces exerted by the earth upon certain quantities of matter. One pound equals 453.6 grams; one kilogram = 2.2046 pounds.

**92. Torque.**—When a force is applied to a body to set it in rotation about some axis, the rotational effect which it produces depends upon the direction of the force as well as upon the place of its application with respect to the axis. The truth of this statement

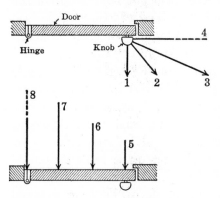

FIG. 94. Forces required to open a door

can be verified readily by opening a heavy door. If the hand exerts a force upon the door knob in the various directions shown from 1 to 4 in the upper part of Fig. 94, it will be observed that a smaller force is needed in direction 2 to open the door than in direction 3. A force along direction 4, parallel to the door, will produce no rotational effect, no matter how large the force may be. The most favorable direction is that along direction 1, perpendicular to the door, for the least force is required along this line.

Again, if the door is pushed at various places along its width in a direction at right angles to the door, as in the lower part of the figure, it will be observed that the least force is needed to open it at position 5, along the edge farthest from the hinges; that more and more force must be exerted in approaching the hinges, positions 6 and 7; and that a force applied at the hinges, position 8, will not produce rotation, no matter how great it may be.

Experience in turning a door, together with a variety of similar experiences, shows the need for a term to express the effectiveness of a force in setting a body into rotation. This rotational effect is known as *torque,* and involves the strength and direction of the force as well as its point of application. *Torque is measured by the product of the force and the perpendicular distance from the axis of rotation to the line of action of the force.* Or, calling this perpendicular distance the *lever arm,* torque is equal to the force times the lever arm. Let

$F$ = unbalanced force exerted to produce rotation,
$L$ = lever arm.

Then the torque $T$ is the product of these factors, **or**

$$T = F \times L \qquad\qquad \mathbf{40}$$

One of the usual units of torque is the *pound-foot;* it represents the turning effort produced by a force of 1 pound acting with a lever arm of 1 foot.

To clarify the terms torque and lever arm, consider the crank shown in Fig. 95 with its axis of rotation at $O$. The force $F$ tending to turn the crank clockwise about this axis produces a torque equal to $F \times OB$ for the position shown, where $OB$ is the lever arm. Note that the lever arm $L$ is not the length $l$ of the crank, but is the perpendicular distance from the axis at $O$ to the line of action of the force at point $B$. It will be appreciated that the lever arm will change as the crank turns, assuming the force to maintain its direction, and that the maximum value the torque could have with the steady force $F$ is the product $F \times l$.

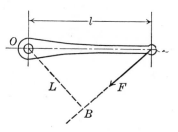

FIG. 95. A crank subjected to torque

**Problem 55.**—A force of 18 pounds is applied to the end of a crank 15 inches long in such a direction that the lever arm is 10 inches. Calculate the torque on the crank for this direction of the force.

(40)  $T = F \times L = 18 \times 10 = 180$ pound-inches $= 15$ pound-feet

**93. Work and Energy.**—In popular language, the term "work" is applied to any form of labor, physical or mental, for producing some kind of result, but in science and engineering the word has a definite technical meaning. To make the meaning clear, suppose that a man moves a piano from one place to another, meanwhile exerting a steady push on the instrument, or that he pulls an oar toward himself in rowing, or that he lifts a weight from the floor to the top of a table. In each of these instances, two things come into consideration: first, that the man exerts a *force*, and second, that he exerts it through a *distance* in the direction of that force. Under these conditions, the man is said to do *work*, the amount of work depending on the two factors: the force which he exerts, and the distance along the direction of the force through which he exerts it. Inanimate objects also can exert forces, for any agent which exerts a force through a distance does work; hence a general statement may be made as follows: *Any agent does work on a body when it exerts a force on the body and moves it along the direction of the force.*

The amount of work done is measured by the product of the force exerted and the distance moved through in the direction of the force.

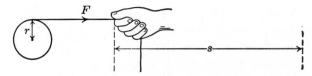

FIG. 96.  Work done to rotate a body

Let

$F$ = push or pull exerted on a body by some agency,
$s$ = distance the body moves in the direction of the force.

Then the amount of work $W$ which the agent does on the body is

$$W = F \times s \qquad\qquad \textbf{41}$$

A common unit of work is the *foot-pound;* it is the amount of work done on a body when a force of 1 pound acts steadily upon it while moving a distance of 1 foot in the direction of the force.

**Problem 56.**—A tugboat exerts a steady force of 600 pounds on a barge in towing it a distance of 1 mile. How much work does it do?

Since there are 5280 feet in 1 mile, $s = 5280$ feet, and the work done is

(41)     $W = F \times s = 600 \times 5280 = 3,168,000$ foot-pounds

Work must also be done in order to set a body into rotation. Suppose that a drum of radius $r$ has a cord fastened to the rim and that the cord is pulled with a force $F$, as illustrated in Fig. 96. If the cord is pulled a distance $s$, the work done in rotating the drum is $F \times s$. But the length of the cord withdrawn from the drum can be expressed in terms of its circumference and the number of turns it makes.

Let

$r$ = radius of the drum,
$N$ = number of revolutions of the drum.

Then the circumference of the drum is $2\pi \times r$, and the length of the cord withdrawn from it is $s = 2\pi \times r \times N$. The application of Formula (41) gives the work done as

$$W = F \times s = 2\pi \times r \times N \times F$$

In this expression the product of $F$ and $r$ is the torque exerted on the drum to rotate it, and, consequently, the work done can also be expressed as

$$W = 2\pi \times N \times T \qquad\qquad 42$$

**Problem 57.**—A rope is wrapped around the rim of a pulley 18 inches in diameter and a 10-pound weight is hung from the free end of the rope. The weight descends and the pulley turns through 8 revolutions. How much work is done on the pulley to rotate it?

The radius of the pulley is 9 inches, or $\frac{3}{4}$ foot, and the torque is $10 \times \frac{3}{4} = 7.5$ pound-feet. Hence the work done is

(42) $\qquad W = 2\pi \times N \times T = 2\pi \times 8 \times 7.5 = 377$ foot-pounds

Sometimes bodies move in opposition to the efforts exerted upon them, for instance: a heavy weight may slide down a steep incline in spite of a man's attempt to pull it upward, or a rotating wheel will continue to turn in a certain direction even after a brake is applied to exert a torque upon it in the opposite direction. In such cases *the body does work instead of having work done upon it;* Formula (41) may be used as before, but it will determine the amount of work done *by* the body rather than the amount of work done *on* it.

If an agent is able to do work, it is said to possess *energy*. For example, a man can do work and so he possesses energy; steam possesses energy since it is able to push the piston within the cylinder of a steam engine; the mainspring of a watch possesses energy when wound, since it is able to drive the hands of the instrument. *The amount of energy which an agent possesses is equal to the amount of work that it can do.*

There are many forms of energy; thus, coal has chemical energy, a hot substance has heat energy, a charged body has electrical energy, a stretched spring has mechanical energy, and a lamp emits light energy. Conversions from one form of energy to another are continually taking place. For example, chemical energy in gasoline is changed to energy of motion in the airplane engine, mechanical energy of motion is changed to electricity in the telephone magneto, electrical energy is changed into heat in the electric range and into light in the fluorescent lamp, light energy is changed to electricity in the photoelectric cell; many other conversions of energy will suggest themselves.

A body may possess mechanical energy of two kinds. First, when a body is in motion it will be able to exert a force and do work in coming to rest; such a body possesses energy because of its motion and is said to have *kinetic* energy. A moving hammer possesses kinetic energy, and this enables it to do work in driving a nail. Second, a body which has been lifted to a higher position is able to do work because of this fact; such a body possesses energy because of its position, and is said to have *potential* energy. A raised weight possesses potential energy, and it can do work in driving a clock while returning to its original level.

A body is not necessarily given potential energy by displacing it, but only when it is able to do more work in its new position than it could originally. A weight which has been raised or a spring which has been wound has gained potential energy, but a weight that is merely moved along a level floor from one position to another has not changed its potential energy. If a 10-pound weight is lifted 100 feet vertically from the ground, it acquires $10 \times 100 = 1000$ foot-pounds of potential energy. When it falls from that elevation it loses this amount of potential energy and gains kinetic energy; just before striking the ground it will have 1000 foot-pounds of kinetic energy. On striking, this energy is changed to heat energy, and becomes unavailable for further use. To restore the weight to its elevated position, some person or agent will have to do 1000 foot-pounds of work upon it. Energy cannot be destroyed, but it is sometimes wasted, as just pointed out. When a train is driven at constant speed along a level track neither its kinetic energy nor its potential energy is increasing, and thus all of the energy in the fuel burned is wasted in opposing friction to maintain this speed.

**Problem 58.**—A 2-ton weight in a pile driver is raised 12 feet above the top of a pile and then released. What average force does the weight exert upon the pile if it is driven 1 foot into the ground by the blow?

Since the weight comes to rest 13 feet below its initial position, its potential energy is reduced by

(41) $$W = F \times s = 2 \times 2000 \times 13 = 52{,}000 \text{ foot-pounds}$$

This energy is given to the pile in driving it down 1 foot, therefore the average force exerted on the pile is

(41) $$F = \frac{W}{s} = \frac{52{,}000}{1} = 52{,}000 \text{ pounds}$$

**94. Rate of Doing Work.**—Practically in all cases where work is done, the amount of work is not the only element of importance, but the time during which that work is done is also essential. Suppose, for example, that a motor-driven hoist is to be selected for raising a certain load. If the load has to be raised quickly, a more powerful hoist and a larger driving motor must be provided than if more time is allowed. Usually the size of machinery is determined, not by the total amount of work to be done, but by the rate at which it must be done; that is, the amount of work required per unit of time, and this rate is called *power*. More concisely, *power is the time rate of doing work*.

To FIND THE POWER OF ANY MACHINE:

*Divide the work done with the aid of the machine by the time needed to do this work.*

$$\text{Mechanical power} = \frac{\text{mechanical work done}}{\text{time of doing work}}$$

Let
$W$ = work done in foot-pounds,
$t$ = time in which the work was done in seconds,
$P$ = power of the machine doing the work in foot-pounds per second.

Then the rate at which the work was done is

$$P = \frac{W}{t}$$

43

If a machine operates steadily, performing the same amount of work every second, the power is said to be uniform. But if a machine works irregularly, doing more work during some intervals than in others, the power of the machine fluctuates from moment to moment, in which case Formula (43) gives the *average value* of the power throughout the time interval considered.

Power is estimated according to the amount of work done in a given period of time. As mechanical work is measured in foot-pounds, mechanical power would be stated as so many foot-pounds per minute, or per second. Another mechanical unit of power is the *horsepower;* it represents doing work at the rate of 33,000 foot-pounds per minute. If a body weighing 33,000 pounds be raised 1 foot every minute, or 16,500 pounds be raised 2 feet per minute, and so on, the rate of working is equal to 1 horsepower. *The horsepower is the power delivered by an agent while doing work at the rate of 33,000 foot-pounds per minute, or 550 foot-pounds per second.*

The horsepower of a steam engine may be calculated readily from certain dimensions of the piston and cylinder together with data obtained while the engine is operating. The area of the piston-head and the length of its stroke in the cylinder are the dimensions needed. The pressure of the steam upon the piston is found by attaching a recording indicator to the cylinder which shows graphically on an *indicator card* the varying steam pressures during a stroke of the piston. From this card the average or mean effective pressure throughout the stroke is obtained. The speed of the engine must be noted while the card is taken.

Let

$p$ = mean effective steam pressure in pounds per square inch,
$L$ = length of stroke in feet,
$A$ = area of piston-head in square inches,
$N$ = number of strokes per minute (twice the number of revolutions)

The total force acting on the piston is the product of the pressure (that is, force per unit area) and the area of one face of the piston, namely, $p \times A$. The distance that the piston moves in 1 minute is the length of one stroke times the number of strokes per minute, or $L \times N$. Hence, the work done per minute is the product of the force $(p \times A)$ and the distance covered in that time

$(L \times N)$; therefore the power is $p \times A \times L \times N$. Rearranging the letters to form the word "plan," and reducing to horsepower, the output of a steam engine becomes

$$P = \frac{p \times L \times A \times N}{33,000}$$

44

**Problem 59.**—The mean steam pressure of a steam engine is 45 pounds per square inch, the speed of the engine is 275 revolutions per minute, the length of stroke is 12 inches, and the area of the piston-head is ½ square foot. What horsepower is developed by the engine?

$L = 12$ inches $= 1$ foot,
$A = \frac{1}{2}$ square foot $= 72$ square inches,
$N = 275$ revolutions per minute $\times 2$ strokes per revolution $= 550$
       strokes per minute

(44)    $P = \dfrac{p \times L \times A \times N}{33,000} = \dfrac{45 \times 1 \times 72 \times 550}{33,000} = 54$ horsepower

**95. Electrical Work and Energy.**—In the study of electrostatics (Lesson I), consideration was given to the forces exerted between electric charges — namely, repulsion between like charges and attraction between unlike ones. It will now be appreciated that energy changes occur whenever such charges are separated or brought closer together, because in all such actions a force is exerted through a distance and work is done. The work is done *on* a charge when it is brought closer to a like charge against the repulsive force between them, and similarly work is done *by* a charge when it moves toward another of opposite sign. It is found that the force exerted between charges is inversely proportional to the square of the distance between them; because of this fact the determination of the work done on or by a charge when it moves relatively to the other is not a simple application of Formula (41), because the force is not constant nor can an average value be assigned to it readily. It is much easier to calculate the work done through analogy with the lifting of a weight against the force of gravitation.

When a weight is lifted from one place to another which is at a higher level, the mechanical work done on it is the product of the weight and the difference of level, §93. Just so, when an electric charge is shifted from one place to another which is at a higher potential, the electrical work done on it is the product of the charge and the difference of potential.

Let

$Q$ = charge in coulombs,
$E$ = difference of potential between two points in volts,
$W$ = work done in transferring the charge between these points in joules.

Then the work done *on* a + charge in moving it from one potential to a higher one, or *by* a + charge in moving to a lower potential, is

$$W = Q \times E \qquad\qquad 45$$

When 1 coulomb is transferred through a p.d. of 1 volt, the work done is 1 joule, §41. The joule is not as large a unit of work as the foot-pound; it develops that

$$1 \text{ joule} = 0.7375 \text{ foot-pound}$$
$$1 \text{ foot-pound} = 1.356 \text{ joules}$$

Work is also done when a charge circulates around an electric circuit. The *charge does work* in traversing the circuit, as evidenced by the evolution of heat and the operation of electro-mechanical devices; the *charge has an equal amount of work done upon it* as it moves through the battery or other source of electrical energy. The e.m.f. of a battery or other source is measured by the work done upon each unit of charge as it passes through the source. The foregoing equation can be expressed more usefully for application to electric circuits by replacing the charge $Q$ by its equivalent from Formula (1). Since the quantity $Q$ of charge transferred is equal to the average current $I$ in the circuit multiplied by the time of transfer $t$, the work done in any portion of a circuit, across which the potential drop is $E$, becomes the product of $E$, $I$ and $t$.

To FIND THE ELECTRICAL WORK PERFORMED IN ANY PART OF A CIRCUIT:

*Multiply the potential difference (in volts) by the current (in amperes) and by the time (in seconds).*

$$W = E \times I \times t \qquad\qquad 46$$
$$\text{joules} = \text{volts} \times \text{amperes} \times \text{seconds}$$

The electrical energy supplied to a circuit by a source of e.m.f. $E$ is expressed similarly.

**Problem 60.**—A current of 4 amperes is maintained through an electrical appliance for 1 hour by a p.d. of 110 volts across its terminals. How much electrical work has been performed?

The time is $60 \times 60 = 3600$ seconds, hence

(46) $\qquad W = E \times I \times t = 110 \times 4 \times 3600 = 1,584,000$ joules

By way of summary, the joule is the amount of electrical work done in a circuit, or of energy supplied to it, by a current of 1 ampere maintained in the circuit for 1 second under an e.m.f or p.d. of 1 volt.

Two other useful equations for work or energy can be obtained by employing Ohm's Law. This law is symbolized by Formula (18) as $I = \dfrac{E}{R}$, where $R$ is the resistance of the entire circuit or a definite part of it. The replacement of $E$ in Formula (46) by its equivalent $(I \times R)$ from the foregoing equation, yields Formula (47). The substitution of $I = \dfrac{E}{R}$ in Equation (46) yields Formula (48).

To FIND THE ELECTRICAL WORK PERFORMED IN ANY PART OF THE CIRCUIT:

*Square the current (in amperes) and multiply the result by the resistance (in ohms), and by the time (in seconds) that the current is maintained.*

$$W = I^2 \times R \times t \qquad\qquad 47$$
or $\qquad\qquad$ joules $= (\text{amperes})^2 \times \text{ohms} \times \text{seconds}$

**Problem 61.**—An electric iron of 40 ohms resistance takes a current of 2.87 amperes. How much energy is supplied to the iron in 15 minutes?

(47) $\quad W = I^2 \times R \times t = (2.87)^2 \times 40 \times 15 \times 60 = 296,500$ joules

To FIND THE ELECTRICAL ENERGY SUPPLIED TO A CIRCUIT:

*Square the e.m.f. (in volts) and multiply the result by the time (in seconds), and divide by the resistance (in ohms).*

$$W = \frac{E^2 \times t}{R} \qquad\qquad 48$$

$$\text{joules} = \frac{(\text{volts})^2 \times \text{seconds}}{\text{ohms}}$$

**Problem 62.**—A resistor of 26 ohms resistance is connected to a source of e.m.f. of 115 volts for 5 minutes. How much energy is supplied to it?

$$(48) \qquad W = \frac{E^2 \times t}{R} = \frac{(115)^2 \times 5 \times 60}{26} = 152,600 \text{ joules}$$

**96. Electrical Power.**—The idea of power as a rate of doing mechanical work was explained in §94. Numerically the power of a machine is the amount of work done by the machine divided by the time of doing it. In an electric circuit, the power is the rate of doing electrical work in it, and correspondingly,

$$\text{electrical power} = \frac{\text{electrical work}}{\text{time of doing work}}$$

A unit of electrical power is naturally the performance of a unit of electrical work in a unit of time; the basic unit is the *joule per second*. This unit is so widely used that a single word has been applied to it for convenience; it is called the *watt* after the Scottish engineer, James Watt (1736-1819). One watt is the power represented by the doing of 1 joule of work in 1 second; in short, *a watt equals 1 joule per second*.

The amount of work done in part of an electric circuit or in the entire circuit is given by Formula (46) and the rate of doing work is given by Formula (43). Hence the power in an electric circuit is obtained by combining the two equations to yield

$$P = \frac{W}{t} = \frac{E \times I \times t}{t}$$

The time *t* cancels out and the electrical power in a circuit develops to be the product of the e.m.f. *E* and the current *I*.

To FIND THE RATE OF EXPENDING ENERGY IN A CIRCUIT:

*Multiply the e.m.f. of the source (in volts) by the current (in amperes) that it supplies; the result is the power (in watts).*

$$P = E \times I \qquad\qquad \textbf{49}$$
$$\text{watts} = \text{volts} \times \text{amperes}$$

*One watt represents the power in a circuit when 1 ampere is supplied by 1 volt.* This formula may be transposed to determine *E* if the power and current are known, or to determine *I* if the power and e.m.f (or p.d.) are known.

**Problem 63.**—A 6-volt storage battery supplies the energy for starting an automobile. At what rate is energy being supplied to the circuit of the starting motor if it takes 200 amperes?

(49)             $P = E \times I = 6 \times 200 = 1200$ watts

**Problem 64.**—What current is taken by a 20-watt lamp on a 120-volt circuit?

(49)             $I = \dfrac{P}{E} = \dfrac{20}{120} = 0.167$ ampere

**Experiment 42.**—Connect a length of several feet of iron wire in series with a rheostat $R$ and an ammeter $A$ to the 110-volt service mains, and then connect a voltmeter $V$ across the ends of the iron wire, as shown in Fig. 97. First put all the resistance of the rheostat in the circuit so that the current is too small to heat the wire perceptibly. Read both meters and compute the power expended in the wire. Then increase the current to bring the wire to a red heat, and again read both meters and compute the power expended.

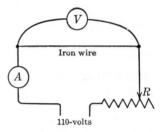

Fig. 97. Measuring the power expended in heating a wire

Also divide each potential reading by the corresponding current reading to show how the resistance of the iron wire has increased as a result of raising its temperature.

The watt is a rather small unit of electrical power and more convenient units are needed to express larger amounts. The *kilowatt* and the horsepower are two such units that are commonly used. One kilowatt equals 1000 watts, and 1 horsepower equals 746 watts. Therefore, if $E$ is in volts and $I$ is in amperes,

$$\text{kilowatts} = \frac{\text{watts}}{1000} = \frac{E \times I}{1000} \qquad 50$$

$$\text{horsepower} = \frac{\text{watts}}{746} = \frac{E \times I}{746} \qquad 51$$

It follows that the kilowatt is about 1⅓ times as large as the horsepower unit, or more accurately

1 kilowatt = 1.34 horsepower

1 horsepower = 0.746 kilowatt

The abbreviations of kilowatt and horsepower are kw. and hp. respectively.

**Problem 65.**—What is the power of a 115-volt generator which supplies its rated load with a current of 87 amperes?

(50)          $$P = \frac{E \times I}{1000} = \frac{115 \times 87}{1000} = 10 \text{ kilowatts}$$

**Problem 66.**—A 5-horsepower motor operates on 120-volt service mains. What current would the motor take if there were no losses?

(51)          $$I = \frac{746 \times \text{hp.}}{E} = \frac{746 \times 5}{120} = 31.1 \text{ amperes}$$

**97. Power Calculations.**—The combination of the power formulas of the preceding section with Ohm's Law gives two additional expressions which are useful in the calculation of electrical problems, whether applied to a whole circuit or to only part of it. The first is obtained by combining $P = E \times I$ with $I = \dfrac{E}{R}$ and eliminating $E$; the second formula is obtained by eliminating $I$ instead. The results are respectively

$$P = I^2 \times R \quad \text{and} \quad P = \frac{E^2}{R}$$

In these expressions, the symbols have the same significance as before—namely,

> $P$ = rate of expending energy in the circuit in watts,
> $E$ = e.m.f. supplied to the circuit in volts,
> $I$ = current through the circuit in amperes,
> $R$ = resistance of the circuit in ohms.

If $R$ represents the resistance of only part of a circuit, then the e.m.f. available in the circuit should be replaced by the p.d. across that part.

To FIND THE POWER EXPENDED IN A CIRCUIT OF KNOWN RESISTANCE:

*Square the current (in amperes) and multiply by the resistance (in ohms).*

$$P = I^2 \times R \qquad\qquad 52$$

**Problem 67.**—The resistance of the field magnets of a dynamo is 220 ohms and the magnetizing current is 2 amperes. What power is supplied to them?

(52)          $$P = I^2 \times R = 2 \times 2 \times 220 = 880 \text{ watts}$$

To FIND THE POWER EXPENDED IN A CIRCUIT OF KNOWN RESISTANCE:

*Square the available e.m.f. (in volts) and divide by the resistance (in ohms).*

$$P = \frac{E^2}{R}$$ 53

**Problem 68.**—The resistance of a telephone relay is 200 ohms. At what rate is energy expended in the relay when operated on 24 volts?

(53) $$P = \frac{E^2}{R} = \frac{24 \times 24}{200} = 2.88 \text{ watts}$$

Formula (52) is often used to determine the loss in transmitting electrical power through transmission and distribution lines. In such computations $R$ is the resistance of the lines only and $I$ is the current in them; the result is the so-called "$I$-square $R$ loss." If the loss is limited to a stipulated amount and the resistance of the lines for a given current is sought, transposition of the equation will yield the desired formula as $R = P \div I^2$.

**Problem 69.**—The two conductors which connect a motor to nearby service mains have a total resistance of 0.04 ohms. What will be the loss in these conductors when the current they supply to the motor is 90 amperes?

(52) $$P = I^2 \times R = 90 \times 90 \times 0.04 = 324 \text{ watts}$$

**Problem 70.**—An electric heater has a resistance of 44 ohms. How much current does it take when 1200 watts are being dissipated?

The result can be determined by solving Formula (52) for the current; then

$$I = \sqrt{\frac{P}{R}} = \sqrt{\frac{1200}{44}} = \sqrt{27.3} = 5.22 \text{ amperes}$$

**98. Distinction between Work and Power.**—If a certain weight is lifted a definite distance, the amount of *work* done is the same whether the action takes place in 1 minute, or 1 hour, or 1 month. In contrast, the *power* of any machine or other agent which performs this task is determined by how rapidly this amount of work is done. The power that can be exerted by a machine depends upon its design, and a large machine can do more work in a given period than a small one of the same type. The relation between work and power may be expressed by

$$W = P \times t$$

which is obtained by transposing Formula (43). In this form, the equation shows that if a machine exerts a power $P$ continuously for a period of time $t$, the machine does an amount of work $W$ which is equal to the product of $P$ and $t$.

This conception of work as the product of power and time values leads to some energy units which are widely used in engineering practice. Thus, the *watt-hour* is a unit of work, being the amount of work performed when a power supply of one watt is maintained over a period of one hour. Similarly, the *kilowatt-hour,* the unit upon which the cost of electrical energy is based, is the amount of work performed when a power supply of 1 kilowatt is maintained over a period of 1 hour. The basic combination of the watt and the second to form the *watt-second* will be recognized immediately as the joule, for the watt is defined as a joule per second. Since the watt-second is identical with the joule, the following relations exist between the units of work or energy:

$$1 \text{ watt-hour} = 3600 \text{ joules}$$
$$1 \text{ kilowatt-hour} = 1000 \text{ watt-hours} = 3,600,000 \text{ joules}$$

The *horsepower-hour* is also a unit of work, being the amount of work performed when power is supplied at the rate of one horsepower over a period of one hour. Since 1 horsepower is equal to 746 watts, it follows that

$$1 \text{ horsepower-hour} = 0.746 \text{ kilowatt-hour}$$
$$1 \text{ kilowatt-hour} = 1.34 \text{ horsepower-hour}$$

**99. Cost of Electric Service.**—The cost of electric service for power and light varies considerably from place to place throughout the country, and the rates depend upon the amount of service rendered. For residence purposes, the rate is based on the amount of energy used, and is often subject to a minimum monthly fee. For large consumers, the rate is based both on the amount of energy used and the maximum power demanded; in these cases distinction must be made between the *energy charge* and the *demand charge*. The following example will illustrate the use of sliding scales for these charges:

**Problem 71.**—A concern pays for electrical energy and for maximum power demand in accordance with the following monthly schedule:

| Energy Charge | Power Demand |
|---|---|
| First 1,000 kilowatt-hours at 5¢ each | First 50 kilowatts at $2.40 each |
| Next 4,000 kilowatt-hours at 3¢ each | Next 750 kilowatts at 2.00 each |
| Next 50,000 kilowatt-hours at 1.3¢ each | Above this total, 1.50 each |
| Above this total, at 1¢ each | |

What will the concern be charged for 75,000 kilowatt-hours of energy during a month when the maximum power demand was 300 kilowatts? The charges for energy and maximum demand are figured as follows:

$$1,000 \times \$0.05 = \$50.00$$
$$4,000 \times 0.03 = 120.00$$
$$50,000 \times 0.013 = 650.00 \qquad 50 \times \$2.40 = \$120.00$$
$$20,000 \times 0.01 = 200.00 \qquad 250 \times 2.00 = 500.00$$
$$\overline{\phantom{xxxx}} \qquad\qquad\qquad \overline{\phantom{xxxx}}$$
$$\$1,020.00 \qquad\qquad\qquad \$620.00$$

Therefore, the bill for the month in question will be 1020 + 620 = $1640.

**100. Heat Units.**—Everyone knows that more *heat* is needed to bring a kettleful of water to the boiling point than a cupful, starting in both cases with cold water at the same temperature. Inquiry shows that the quantity of heat required to produce a given rise of temperature is directly proportional to the amount of water heated. Again, more heat is needed to increase the temperature of any given quantity of water through, say 60 degrees, than the same quantity through 30 degrees; in fact, it takes twice as much. Thus, the heat required is proportional to the *quantity of water* and to the *rise of temperature*. In heat measurements, it is customary to use as a unit the amount of heat needed to raise the temperature of a unit quantity of water through 1 degree.

Two units of heat are in common use: the calorie and the British thermal unit. The *calorie* is the amount of heat required to raise the temperature of 1 gram of water through 1 centigrade degree. The *British thermal unit* is the amount of heat required to raise the temperature of 1 pound of water through 1 Fahrenheit degree. It is a simple matter to compute the amount of heat needed to produce a given temperature rise in any quantity of water. Thus, to raise 5000 grams of water from 10° C. to 70° C.

requires $5000 \times 60 = 300,000$ calories; again, to raise 50 pounds of water from 40° F. to 200° F. requires $50 \times 160 = 8000$ British thermal units.

Since 9 Fahrenheit degrees represent the same change of temperature as 5 centigrade degrees, and since there are 453.6 grams in a pound, it follows that there are $5/9 \times 453.6 = 252$ calories in 1 British thermal unit. Heat quantities are sometimes given in terms of the *kilogram-calorie;* this unit is equal to 1000 calories. Food values are stated in the larger unit for convenience; thus, the fuel value of the food consumed per capita in the United States is about 3500 kilogram-calories per day.

**101. Transformation of Work into Heat.**—Every observer is familiar with the production of heat from other forms of energy; for example, heat is produced from mechanical energy in an automobile brake, from electrical energy in an electric heater, and from chemical energy in the combustion of fuels. Heat is also produced as a by-product in most transformations of energy, and in many of these much of the heat is wasted. When one form of energy disappears, an exact equivalent of one or more other forms takes its place, so that the sum total of the energy is not changed. This constancy of energy is one of the important principles of science and is called the *conservation of energy.*

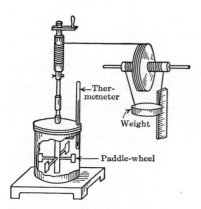

FIG. 98. Joule's experiment for measuring the mechanical equivalent of heat

The relationship between the amount of heat produced and the amount of mechanical energy expended was first determined experimentally by Joule about 1845. In one arrangement, a paddle wheel was mounted within a vessel containing a known amount of water, and turned by means of a falling weight, as indicated in Fig. 98. The work done in turning the paddle-wheel was converted to heat by friction in stirring the water, and caused a rise in temperature. By measuring the energy $W$ supplied to the paddle wheel and the amount of heat $H$ absorbed by the water, a constant relationship was found to exist between them in test after test. The constant ratio of the mechanical work done to the heat produced is called the *mechanical equivalent of heat.*

Let $J$ represent the mechanical equivalent of heat; then $J$ is numerically the ratio of $W$ to $H$, or

$$J = \frac{W}{H} \qquad\qquad 54$$

Joule's original results have been slightly modified in subsequent investigations; the accepted values in two sets of units follow:

RELATION OF HEAT TO WORK

*Metric Units*

1 calorie = 4.186 joules

0.239 calorie = 1 joule

*British Units*

1 British thermal unit = 778 foot-pounds

0.00129 British thermal unit = 1 foot-pound

Whenever a specified amount of work is transformed into heat, the quantity of heat produced can be determined at once from the values given above. Thus, the expenditure of 778 foot-pounds of mechanical energy would yield 1 British thermal unit of heat energy, and so the mechanical equivalent of heat is 778 foot-pounds per British thermal unit.

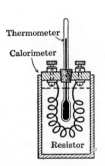

FIG. 99. Experiment for measuring the electrical equivalent of heat

The amount of heat liberated by an electric current may be determined by placing a resistor in some water and maintaining a known current through it for a definite time. Fig. 99 shows a convenient arrangement; the water is contained in a calorimeter and its temperature rise is measured by a thermometer. The amount of electrical work done by a current of $I$ amperes through a resistor of $R$ ohms resistance during a period of $t$ seconds is given by Formula (47) in joules as

$$W = I^2 \times R \times t$$

If all of this work is converted into heat in raising the temperature of $m$ grams of water through $t$ centigrade degrees, then the amount of heat produced thereby in calories is

$$H = m \times t$$

The ratio of the electrical work done to the heat produced is called the *electrical equivalent of heat;* its numerical value is

$$J = \frac{W}{H} = 4.186 \text{ joules per calorie}$$

and this is exactly the same as the mechanical equivalent of heat given ahead for these units. Thus, the expenditure of 4.186 joules of electrical or mechanical energy would yield 1 calorie of heat energy. Reciprocally 1 joule is equivalent to $\frac{1}{4.186} = 0.239$ calorie.

To FIND THE HEAT DEVELOPED IN A RESISTOR BY AN ELECTRIC CURRENT:

*Multiply 0.239 by the square of the current (in amperes), by the resistance (in ohms), and by the time (in seconds); the result will be in calories.*

$$H = 0.239 \times I^2 \times R \times t \qquad \textbf{55}$$

$$\text{calories} = 0.239 \times (\text{amperes})^2 \times \text{ohms} \times \text{seconds}$$

**Problem 72.**—How much heat is produced in a 5-ohm resistor when a current of 2 amperes is maintained in it for 15 minutes?

$$(55) \qquad H = 0.239 \times (2)^2 \times 5 \times 900 = 4300 \text{ calories}$$

**Problem 73.**—An electric immersion heater is rated at 500 watts. How long will it take to raise the temperature of 4 kilograms of water from 15° to 100° C., neglecting all losses?

Heat needed $= 4000 \times 85 = 340{,}000$ calories
Work to be done $= 4.186 \times 340{,}000 = 1{,}423{,}000$ joules or watt-seconds

$$= \frac{1{,}423{,}000}{3600} = 395 \text{ watt-hours}$$

Time required $= \dfrac{395}{500} = 0.79 \text{ hour} = 47.4 \text{ minutes}$

Formula (55) is often referred to as Joule's Law of electric heating. It shows that the amount of heat produced in a conductor is proportional to the square of the current in it, to the resistance of the conductor, and to the time that the current is maintained. A current of 1 ampere maintained for 1 second in a 1-ohm resistor produces 0.239 calories of heat; a current of 2 amperes in it for the same time produces four times as much heat. The formula may be arranged to yield the heat energy in British thermal units by using the constant 0.000948 instead of 0.239.

**Experiment 43.**—Place a 50-watt incandescent lamp in a jar of water so that the lamp base and the socket will just be above the water surface. Operate the lamp for a definite period and note the temperature rise of the water. Weigh the water and compute the amount of heat which it received. This will be in calories or British thermal units depending on the units used for measuring temperature and weight; convert to joules. Calculate the electrical energy supplied to the lamp in joules. Compare the two results and if there is any discrepancy between them, explain why this should exist.

**102. Fuses.**—When a piece of copper and a piece of lead wire of the same size are connected in series to an electric supply circuit through a rheostat, and the current is increased by gradually lowering the resistance of this rheostat, it will be observed that the wires get hotter and hotter and presently the lead will melt, thereby opening the circuit. Lead has a higher resistivity than copper and, consequently, more heat is produced in the lead wire than in the copper one for the same current, and furthermore, lead melts at a lower temperature than copper. It will also be found that lead containing a small percentage of tin melts at a still lower temperature. Tests such as these suggest the procedure, now so generally used, for the protection of copper wiring against excessive heating. Short pieces of lead-tin alloy of appropriate sizes are connected in series with electric circuits so that when the current in them becomes excessive the alloy will melt and automatically open the circuits. Such pieces of the alloy in the form of wire or strips, and provided with suitable terminals and housings, are called *fuses*. The function of a fuse, therefore, is to open the circuit before the temperature rise of the conductors, produced by an excessive current from any cause, becomes great enough to harm the insulation around them.

Fig. 100 illustrates a cartridge-type fuse at the left, a plug fuse at the center and a "littelfuse" at the right, part of each being shown in cross section to indicate the construction. Within the cartridge fuse is a porous insulating filling that resembles powdered chalk; often there is a small air chamber around the central part of the fuse wire, as indicated by the dotted line. When the fuse "blows" some of the fuse metal is melted and an arc tends to form across the gap; the powder cools and condenses the vapor to minimize ionization, and the arc is quickly extinguished. The plug fuse is provided with a screw shell of thin metal like that on incandescent lamps and it usually has a mica covering through which the condition of the fuse may be seen. The "littelfuse" is a narrow strip of pure zinc within a tiny glass tube, and this is mounted diagonally inside the glass housing.

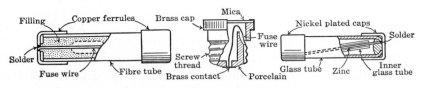

FIG. 100. Types of enclosed fuses

Fuses are connected in electric circuits at switchboards, panel boards or "cut-out blocks" that are located at places convenient to reach. They are rated in terms of the current which causes them to blow, although it is common practice to require each fuse to be able to carry 110 per cent of its rated current indefinitely. Cartridge fuses up to 60 amperes have metal ferrules, as illustrated, that engage spring clips which are connected to the circuit; those of greater rating have flat metal extensions that engage the circuit terminals like the blades of knife switches. Cartridge fuses are also available which permit the removal of the fusible strips; the cost of fuse renewals is lowered by their use. Plug fuses are made in sizes up to 30 amperes; "littelfuses" are available up to 8 amperes. The latter type fuses are also made for the protection of galvanometers and milliammeters down to 1/200 ampere.

**Experiment 44.**—Construct a lampboard by mounting four or more porcelain lamp sockets in a row on a wood base and join them in parallel, bringing the wires to a pair of terminals. Put a piece of 2-ampere fuse wire in series with the lampboard and gradually increase the current through it by screwing lamps into the sockets, until the fuse blows.

## QUESTIONS

1. What is meant by force? What are two of its basic units?
2. Distinguish between force and torque.
3. Explain how torque is measured and give an example.
4. Define work and energy.
5. Distinguish between the pound-foot as a unit of torque and the foot-pound as a unit of work.
6. Name three kinds of energy and give an example of each.
7. Explain the idea of power and cite a numerical illustration to bring out the distinction between the work done and the rate of working.
8. Define the units: joule, watt, horsepower.
9. Explain how to obtain the horsepower of a steam engine.
10. What factors must be known about an electric circuit in order to calculate the amount of electrical work performed in it?
11. What kind of units are the kilowatt and the kilowatt-hour? Define each.
12. Explain what is meant by the $I$-square $R$ loss.
13. Distinguish between temperature and heat.
14. State what is meant by a calorie and by a British thermal unit. Which is the larger of these units? What is the relation between them?
15. Describe an experiment for determining the mechanical equivalent of heat.
16. Give two numerical values for the mechanical equivalent of heat.
17. Equal lengths of No. 10 and No. 20 A.w.g. gage copper wire are connected in series and to a storage battery. Is there any difference in the current through the two wires? or in the amount of heat evolved from them?
18. Resistor $A$ has half the resistance of resistor $B$ and takes twice as much current. What are the relative amounts of heat produced in these resistors for the same duration of current?
19. Give a statement of Joule's Law of electric heating.
20. What is the purpose of fuses in electric wiring?

## PROBLEMS

1. A wheel 4 feet in diameter is mounted on a horizontal shaft and a rope is wound around the rim. What torque acts on the wheel when a 5-pound weight is affixed to the free end of the rope? *Ans.* 10 pound-feet.
2. What amount of work does a man, weighing 170 pounds, do when he walks upstairs to a floor that is 40 feet higher than his starting point? *Ans.* 6800 foot-pounds.

3. A punch-press does 5000 foot-pounds of work every 4 seconds. Calculate the power of the machine. *Ans.* 2.27 horsepower.

4. How heavy a load can a 15-horsepower hoist lift at a steady speed of 240 feet per minute without exceeding its rated output? *Ans.* 2063 pounds.

5. A test on a steam engine yields the following data: Mean effective steam pressure from an indicator card is 50 pounds per square inch, speed of the engine is 290 revolutions per minute, length of stroke is 10 inches, area of piston head is 0.75 square foot. What power is developed by the engine? *Ans.* 79.1 horsepower.

6. How much work is done in moving a charge of 2 coulombs along an electric circuit between two points which have a potential difference of 20 volts? *Ans.* 40 joules.

7. The current through a device is maintained constant at 4.0 amperes for 20 minutes. If the p.d. across its terminals is 80 volts, what energy is supplied to it during this period? *Ans.* 384,000 joules.

8. The output of a small electric power station is 900 amperes at 240 volts. What is the power of the station? *Ans.* 216 kilowatts.

9. How much current does a 300-watt, 120-volt lamp take? *Ans.* 2.5 amperes.

10. If 2.5 volts are impressed upon the filament of a certain vacuum tube and the current through the filament is 3.25 amperes, what power is expended in heating the filament? *Ans.* 8.13 watts.

11. What would be the rating of a 15-horsepower motor in electrical units? *Ans.* 11.2 kilowatts.

12. An electric iron has 28 ohms resistance and operates on 120 volts. At what rate does it use electrical energy? *Ans.* 514 watts.

13. A combined lighting and power load requires 140 amperes. If the wires which connect this load to the service mains have a total resistance of 0.05 ohm, how much power is lost in them? *Ans.* 980 watts.

14. An engine operates at 60 horsepower steadily for 5 hours; determine the amount of work done in this time. *Ans.* 300 horsepower-hours or $594 \times 10^6$ foot-pounds.

15. The power input to a motor delivering its rated load is 12 kilowatts. If it operates steadily at this load for one-half hour, how much electrical energy does it take? *Ans.* 6 kilowatt-hours or $21.6 \times 10^6$ joules.

16. A 12-inch electric fan takes 0.8 ampere on 120-volt service mains. How much does it cost to operate it for 8 hours if energy costs 6 cents per kilowatt-hour? *Ans.* 4.61 cents.

17. The current in a lamp of 300 ohms resistance is 0.4 ampere. At what rate is electrical energy converted into heat? *Ans.* 48 watts.

18. If 30 joules of mechanical energy are converted entirely into heat, how much heat will be produced? *Ans.* 7.17 calories.

19. A 120-volt electric heater consists of a coil of wire having a resistance of 27.8 ohms. Find the time required to produce 15,000 calories with this heater. *Ans.* 121 seconds.

20. How much heat is evolved in one-half hour by a' 115-volt incandescent lamp taking a currrent of 0.4 ampere? *Ans.* 78.5 British thermal units.

21. The hot resistance of an electrical laundry iron is 22 ohms and it is connected across 110-volt mains. Suppose the iron to be placed into a vessel containing 8 pounds of water, the temperature of which is 60° F., and the current to be turned on for 15 minutes. What will be the temperature of the water at the end of that time, not allowing for radiation and other losses? *Ans.* 118.6° F.

22. How much would it cost to heat electrically the water in a pool measuring 50 by 20 feet, the water having an average depth of 6 feet? One cubic foot of water weighs 62.4 pounds. The water is supplied at 45° F. and is to be heated to 68° F. The cost of electrical energy is 1.3 cents per kilowatt-hour. Assume that no heat is wasted. *Ans.* $32.80.

# Lesson X

---

# ELECTROMAGNETISM

---

Magnetic effect of current—Direction of magnetic field—Intensity of magnetic field—Field around a circular conducting loop—Solenoids—Magnetic flux—Permeability—Electromagnets—Circuit breakers—Polarized electromagnets—Force exerted on a conductor—Action between conductors carrying current—Questions and Problems.

**103. Magnetic Effect of Current.**—The discovery of electromagnetism was made in 1820 by the Danish physicist, Hans C. Oersted (1777-1851). He observed that magnetic needles placed near wires would deflect when currents were established in the wires, and would return to their normal north-south positions when the currents were discontinued. Further investigation showed that a magnetic field exists around every conductor that carries current, and that the field has a definite direction at each point in the vicinity of the conductor.

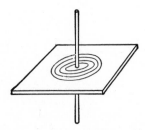 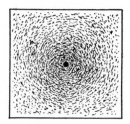

FIG. 101. Magnetic field pictured around a wire carrying current

**Experiment 45.**—Put a heavy copper wire perpendicularly through a piece of cardboard, and fasten the cardboard in a horizontal position, as shown in perspective at the left of Fig. 101. Establish a current in the wire and sift iron filings on the cardboard. Upon tapping the card, the

194

filings arrange themselves like rings centered on the wire and have a greater density near it, as shown in the plan view at the right of the figure. The resulting picture of the magnetic field could be made permanent by starting with cardboard that has been soaked in paraffin and later applying heat to cause the filings to adhere.

Tests with iron filings sprinkled around a wire in which there is a current show that the magnetic field is concentric about the wire and that the field is stronger near the wire than it is further away.

**104. Direction of Magnetic Field.**—The direction of the field around a wire can be studied by bringing the wire near a poised magnetic needle. If the needle is in its normal north-south position and the wire is placed horizontally over it parallel to the needle, then the needle will deflect as soon as current is established in the wire. The needle will tend to assume a po-

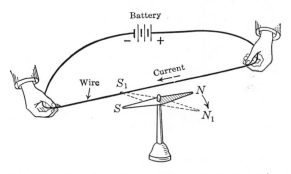

Fig. 102. Deflection of magnetic needle near a wire carrying current

sition at right angles to the wire, thereby accommodating through itself the greatest number of lines of force of the field about the wire.

In Fig. 102 the compass needle NS is aligned in the earth's magnetic field, and the wire is shown above the needle and parallel to it. Upon closing the circuit there is a current in the wire directed from right to left, and the needle swings toward a position at right angles to the wire and comes to rest at $N_1S_1$. When the circuit is opened the needle resumes its initial position along the magnetic meridian. If the current is directed from left to right, the needle will point in the opposite direction to that shown in the figure.

Simple forms of apparatus for studying the relation between the direction of current in a wire and the field around it are shown in Fig. 103. The Oersted stand at the left consists of a rectangular brass frame provided with binding posts and supported on a wooden base, together with a magnetic needle pivoted on an adjustable support so that the magnetic field can be explored at various places around the wire. A modification of this apparatus is shown at the right; it is merely an L-shaped wire mounted in a block of wood and equipped with a connector at each end. A pocket compass can be placed above and below the horizontal portion of the wire, and all around its vertical portion. Iron filings may also be spread on the platform around the vertical

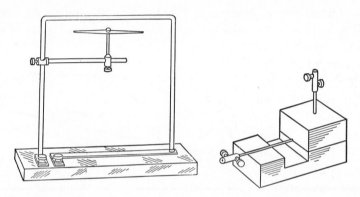

FIG. 103. Devices for showing directions of magnetic fields about wires

portion to visualize the magnetic field about a current-carrying conductor.

**Experiment 46.**—Connect a dry cell to an Oersted stand and place the needle below the upper conductor (as shown in Fig. 103) and then above it; note that the needle will point one way for one position and in the opposite direction for the other. Next reverse the terminals of the cell and observe that the needle will point oppositely to the earlier directions. Finally, lower the needle support and turn it to various positions and explore the magnetic field around the left vertical conductor. Note that the needle points in a counterclockwise direction (looking down) when the current in this conductor is upward, and clockwise when the current is downward.

Fig. 104 shows three views of the magnetic field around a wire. In the perspective view at the center, the current is represented in direction by the arrow along the axis of the wire, and the field by the two loops around the wire. In the other views the wire is shown end-on by the innermost circles and the lines of force are shown around them. When the current is directed toward the observer, as represented by a dot within the wire, the magnetic lines will be counterclockwise, as shown at the left. When the current is away from the observer, as represented by a cross within the wire, the magnetic lines will be clockwise, as shown at the right. These directions indicate how an isolated N magnet pole would move about the wires if free to do so.

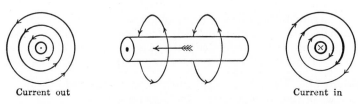

Current out                                      Current in

Fig. 104. Diagrams of field around a current-carrying wire

If the direction of the current in a straight wire is known, then the direction of the circular magnetic field around that wire can be determined by the following rule which is pictured in Fig. 105:

*Grasp the wire with the right hand and extend the thumb to point in the direction of the current, then the fingers will indicate the direction of the lines of force around the wire.*

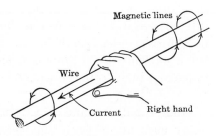

Fig. 105. Right-hand rule for finding direction of current or of magnetic field

**105. Intensity of Magnetic Field.**—The strength of the magnetic field around a wire is greatest right at the wire and diminishes in receding from it. The intensity may be expressed numerically in terms of a unit called the *oersted*, named after the discoverer of electromagnetism. This unit is defined in such a way that *at a distance of 1 centimeter from the axis of a single straight conductor the field intensity is 1 oersted when the current in the wire is 5 amperes.* As the current is increased or decreased, the field intensity will vary proportionately.

To FIND THE INTENSITY OF THE MAGNETIC FIELD AT A POINT NEAR A STRAIGHT WIRE CARRYING CURRENT:

*Divide the current in the wire (in amperes) by 5 and by the distance (in centimeters) of the point in question from the wire; the result will be in oersteds.*

$$\mathfrak{IC} = \frac{I}{5 \times r} \qquad\qquad 56$$

where

> $I$ = current through the wire in amperes,
> $\mathfrak{IC}$ = field intensity at a point near the wire in oersteds,
> $r$ = distance of this point from the axis of the wire in centimeters
>> (1 inch = 2.54 centimeters, or 1 centimeter = 0.394 inch).

**Problem 74.**—What is the field intensity 3 inches away from a straight conductor when the current in it is 90 amperes?

Since 1 inch = 2.54 centimeters, $r = 3 \times 2.54 = 7.62$ centimeters.

$$(56) \qquad \mathfrak{IC} = \frac{I}{5 \times r} = \frac{90}{5 \times 7.62} = 2.36 \text{ oersteds}$$

Formula (56) shows that the magnetic field intensity around a straight conductor varies directly with the strength of current in it and inversely as the distance away from it. If the field intensity at a distance of 3 inches from a wire carrying 90 amperes is 2.36 oersteds, it will be one-third this value at the same place for a current of 30 amperes, and three times this value at a distance of 1 inch from the wire for the original current of 90 amperes.

**106. Field Around a Circular Conducting Loop.**—There are many uses in electrical devices for wires bent in the form of circular loops and particularly for windings with many turns; therefore, it is desirable to know the direction and strength of the field which such loops produce when carrying an electric current.

**Experiment 47.**—Mount a circular turn of wire vertically in a piece of cardboard, so that one-half of the loop will be above the horizontal plane, as indicated at the left in Fig. 106. Connect the loop to a dry cell and tap the cardboard while sifting iron filings over it. The filings will be found to arrange themselves in circular fashion around each side of the loop, but near its center the filings form lines that are nearly parallel with the axis of the loop.

If a compass needle is used to explore the magnetic field around a loop, the N-pole of the needle will always point in the direction of the field. The arrows in both views of Fig. 106 indicate the direction of the lines of force around a circular loop, and indicate how a compass needle will point when placed anywhere on the cardboard or at points above and below it. Apply the right-hand rule, §104, to confirm the fact that the arrows correctly portray the directions of the field. All the lines enter the loop at one face and leave at the other and, specifically for the direction of current shown, all the lines of force are directed toward the left within the loop of wire. In this respect, the behavior of the

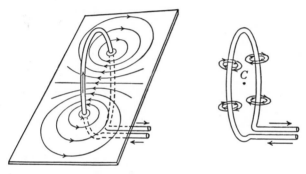

Fig. 106. Magnetic field around a conducting loop
Lines of force make complete rings around a circular loop of wire carrying current.

loop with current in it is just like that of a magnet. It was pointed out in Lesson II that magnetic lines issue from a N-pole and enter the S-pole of a magnet; similarly, the left face of the loop illustrated possesses north polarity and the right face south polarity. When such a loop is mounted in a vertical plane so that it can turn freely, it will rotate in the earth's field until its N-face points toward the north.

The intensity of the magnetic field at the center of a circular conducting loop can be computed when the radius of the loop and the current in it are known. For two loops placed side by side and connected so that the same current will be directed in the same way around their common axis, the intensity of the field will be twice as great. For a flat coil of $N$ loops or turns similarly connected, the intensity will be $N$-times as great. The field is also directly proportional to the current in the coil. Finally, the strength of the field at the center of the coil is inversely proportional to its radius.

TO FIND THE FIELD INTENSITY AT THE CENTER OF A FLAT CIRCULAR COIL CARRYING CURRENT:

*Multiply π by the number of turns of wire in the coil and by the current (in amperes); then divide this product by 5 and by the radius of the coil (in centimeters).*

$$\mathcal{3C} = \frac{\pi \times N \times I}{5 \times r} \qquad\qquad 57$$

where

$\mathcal{3C}$ = magnetic field intensity at the center of a flat coil in oersteds,
$N$ = number of turns of wire in the coil,
$I$ = current in the coil in amperes,
$r$ = radius of each turn in centimeters,
$\pi$ = ratio of the circumference of the coil to its diameter = 3.1416.

**Problem 75.**—A flat coil has a radius of 12 centimeters and is composed of 20 turns. Determine the field intensity at the center of the coil (point $C$ in Fig. 106) when the current in it is 10 amperes.

$$(57) \qquad \mathcal{3C} = \frac{\pi \times N \times I}{5 \times r} = \frac{\pi \times 20 \times 10}{5 \times 12} = 10.5 \text{ oersteds}$$

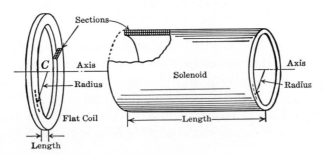

FIG. 107. Comparison of two types of windings

Flat coil at left has a length much shorter than its radius, while solenoid at right has relatively great length measured along its axis.

Formula (57) applies only to a flat circular coil, such as is shown at the left in Fig. 107, for which the length measured along the coil axis is very short in comparison with its radius. There is another form of winding in general use in which the turns are spread over a considerable length along the axis, as shown at the right in the figure. It is called a *solenoid,* and the preceding for-mula for field intensity does not apply to this type of winding.

**107. Solenoids.**—The turns of a solenoid are generally wound uniformly close together on a straight insulating tube or spool and the winding is always in the same direction, layer upon layer, like a spool of thread. When there is current through the sole-noid, each turn of wire acts magnetically like the loop described in the last section with lines of force surrounding it, and most of the lines cluster and link all the turns as shown in Fig. 108.

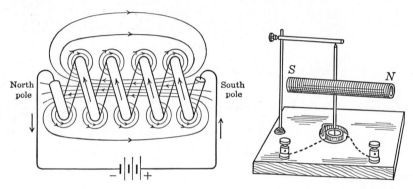

FIG. 108. Magnetic field in and around a        FIG. 109.  Poised solenoid
                solenoid

The lines of force are in the same direction throughout the cen-ter of the solenoid, and are parallel to its axis and fairly uniform to within a short distance of its ends. With the current in the direction shown, the lines through the solenoid are directed toward the left; consequently, the left end acts like the N-pole and the right end like the S-pole of a magnet. This polarity can be reversed by establishing current in the opposite direction. If a solenoid is mounted so that it may rotate freely on a transverse axis while connected with a source of current, it may be used to test polarity just like a compass needle.

**Experiment 48.**—Wind some insulated copper wire on a short mailing tube and mount the solenoid so formed on a transverse axis and pivots as shown in Fig. 109. Arrange the terminals of the winding to dip into two concentric circular grooves containing mercury, each groove being con-nected to a binding post. When a current is maintained through the solenoid, it takes up a north-south position NS, just as in the case of a poised needle. Bring a magnet or another solenoid near one end of the poised solenoid and observe the repulsion or attraction between them.

A convenient rule for determining the direction of the magnetic field through a solenoid follows:

*Grasp the solenoid in the right hand so that the fingers point around it in the direction of the current; the outstretched thumb will point to the N-pole of the solenoid.* Fig. 110 illustrates this rule pictorially. Obviously, if the polarity is known, the rule permits the determination of current direction.

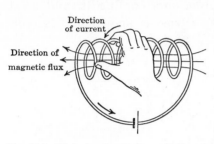

FIG. 110. Right-hand rule for polarity of a solenoid

The field intensity at the center of a solenoid depends upon the number of turns of wire per unit axial length of the solenoid and upon the current in its winding; the intensity is directly proportional to these two factors.

TO FIND THE INTENSITY OF THE MAGNETIC FIELD WITHIN A SOLENOID:

*Multiply the current by the number of turns of the winding per unit of length of solenoid and multiply this product by an appropriate constant.*

$$\mathcal{H} = K \times I \times n \qquad \textbf{58}$$

where

$\mathcal{H}$ = field intensity along the axis of a solenoid in oersteds,
$I$ = current in the solenoid in amperes,
$n$ = number of turns of the winding in one unit axial length of the solenoid,
$K$ = constant; its value is 1.257 for the centimeter and 0.495 for the inch as the length unit.

The formula shows that the field intensity within a solenoid does not depend upon the radius of its winding.

**Problem 76.**—A solenoid has 900 turns of wire distributed over a length of 15 inches and the average radius of a turn is 1.3 inches. What is the intensity of the field through the center of the winding when the current in it is 3.5 amperes?

The number of turns per inch of axial length is $900 \div 15 = 60$, and this is the value of $n$. Since the inch is taken as the unit of length, it is necessary to choose 0.495 as the value of the constant $K$. Therefore, the field intensity within the solenoid becomes

(58)     $\mathfrak{K} = 0.495 \times I \times n = 0.495 \times 3.5 \times 60 = 104$ oersteds

Had the length of the solenoid been expressed in the equivalent number of centimeters, in this case $15 \times 2.54$ or 38.1 centimeters, then the number of turns per centimeter length of winding would have been $n = 900 \div 38.1 = 23.6$. By using $K = 1.257$, the result is

(58)     $\mathfrak{K} = 1.257 \times I \times n = 1.257 \times 3.5 \times 23.6 = 104$ oersteds

as before. In either calculation, there was no need for the radius, except to appreciate that the winding is long in comparison with its radius as implied by the definition of a solenoid.

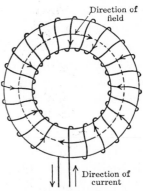

FIG. 111.  Ring-shaped solenoid

There is another type of solenoid that is used quite often; it is a *ring solenoid* or *toroid*. The winding of this type of solenoid encircles a ring-shaped core, like the paper wrapping around an automobile tire. Fig. 111 shows a ring solenoid and the directions of the current in the winding and of the magnetic field through the core. All the magnetic lines of force are within the winding, except for some leakage, and consequently, the solenoid does not show external polarity. The formula ahead also applies to the toroid and gives the field intensity at any point along the center line of the core, that is, along the dotted line in the figure.

**108. Magnetic Flux.**—The reader has become familiar with the use of lines to represent magnetic fields and with their designation as magnetic lines of force. When a straight solenoid has a current through it, a magnetic field surrounds the winding and lines of force are directed out at one end and in at the other. The larger the current in the winding the greater will be the field intensity and the more lines are imagined to surround it. Inserting an iron core and leaving the current unchanged does not alter the intensity of the field in the solenoid, but it does change very materially the attracting power of the solenoid for magnetic substances. For this reason, the combination of a solenoid and an iron core, called an electromagnet (§17), is widely used in electrical apparatus.

The greater attractive power of the electromagnet over the air-core solenoid is ascribed to a large increase of magnetic lines within it brought about by the magnetization of the iron core. Suppose that the field intensity along the air core of a solenoid is $\mathcal{H}$ oersteds, where the value of $\mathcal{H}$ is determined by the current in the winding and the number of turns per unit length, as explained in the preceding section. It would be appropriate to represent this intensity of field by imagining $\mathcal{H}$ *lines of force* to be drawn through 1 square centimeter of area placed at right angles to the core axis. Upon inserting the iron core, additional lines are produced, and these lines, together with the lines of force which represent $\mathcal{H}$, are called *lines of induction*. The number of lines of induction passing perpendicularly through an area of 1 square centimeter is represented by the symbol $\mathcal{B}$. In a vacuum and in air, the lines of force represented by $\mathcal{H}$ and the lines of induction represented by $\mathcal{B}$ are identical, but inside of a magnetic substance, $\mathcal{B}$ is larger than $\mathcal{H}$, often hundreds or thousands of times as large.

The term *magnetic flux* refers to the total number of lines of induction extending through any specified region. The symbol for this quantity is the Greek letter $\Phi$ (phi). The unit of magnetic flux is the *maxwell;* this unit is named after the English physicist, J. Clerk Maxwell (1831-1879). *One maxwell is one line of magnetic flux.* If, for example, there are 5000 lines of induction through the cross-section of an iron bar, then the magnetic flux in it is 5000 maxwells.

Now assume that the bar has a sectional area of 10 square centimeters and that the lines of induction are uniformly distributed throughout this section, then the number of lines per square centimeter of area, that is $\mathcal{B}$, will be $5000 \div 10$ or 500 maxwells per square centimeter. This idea of closeness or density of lines of induction gives rise to the designation of $\mathcal{B}$ as *flux density*. The unit of flux density is called the *gauss,* after Karl F. Gauss (1777-1855), German mathematician and physicist. *A gauss is one maxwell per square centimeter.* One gauss is represented by a single line of magnetic flux extending perpendicularly through an area of 1 square centimeter.

To FIND THE TOTAL LINES OF INDUCTION THROUGH A REGION:

*Multiply the flux density (in gausses) by the area of the region (in square centimeters).*

Let

$A$ = area of region in square centimeters.
$\mathcal{B}$ = flux density, assumed uniform throughout this region, in gausses,
$\Phi$ = magnetic flux in maxwells.

Then, if the lines of induction extend perpendicularly through the area under consideration, the total number of lines of induction through the region is

$$\Phi = \mathcal{B} \times A \qquad 59$$

**Problem 77.**—An iron bar having a square cross section 1 inch on a side is magnetized to have a flux density of 2800 gausses. What is the magnetic flux through the bar?

The sectional area = $2.54 \times 2.54 = 6.45$ square centimeters

(59) $\qquad \Phi = \mathcal{B} \times A = 2800 \times 6.45 = 18{,}060$ maxwells

**109. Permeability.**—The capability of a substance for accommodating magnetic flux is termed its *permeability*. This means that the permeability of a magnetic material is the ratio of the number of lines of induction through it to the number through an equal volume of air of like shape, assuming that both are subject to the same field intensity. Stated another way, permeability expresses the ratio between the flux density produced in a magnetic substance to the field intensity that occasions it. The symbol for permeability is the Greek letter $\mu$ (mu).

To FIND THE PERMEABILITY OF A MAGNETIC SUBSTANCE UNDER GIVEN MAGNETIZATION:

*Divide the flux density (in gausses) by the field intensity (in oersteds).*

$$\mu = \frac{\mathcal{B}}{\mathcal{H}} \qquad 60$$

where $\qquad \mu$ = permeability of the substance,
$\mathcal{B}$ = flux density in the substances in gausses,
$\mathcal{H}$ = field intensity in oersteds.

The permeability of a magnetic material does not have a fixed value for a particular specimen, but varies with the field intensity to which it is subjected and with its previous magnetic history.

**Problem 78.**—A specimen of silicon steel at a field intensity of 5 oersteds has a flux density of 12,500 gausses, and at a field intensity of 20 oersteds has a flux density of 14,500 gausses. What are the corresponding permeabilities of this material?

At the lower flux density

(60) $$\mu = \frac{\mathcal{B}}{\mathcal{K}} = \frac{12,500}{5} = 2500$$

and at the higher density

(60) $$\mu = \frac{14,500}{20} = 725$$

Substances are classed into three groups according to their permeabilities. For *diamagnetic* substances the permeability $\mu$ is less than unity, for *paramagnetic* substances it is somewhat greater than unity, and for *ferromagnetic* substances it is very much larger. The values of $\mu$ for all known diamagnetic substances are but slightly less than unity; the most diamagnetic substance, bismuth, has a permeability of 0.99998. The values of $\mu$ for paramagnetic substances are but slightly greater than unity; for example, platinum has a permeability of 1.00002. Iron, nickel and cobalt are the ferromagnetic elements, and certain alloys are also ferromagnetic. Naturally, magnets are made of ferromagnetic substances. As already pointed out, the permeability of any ferromagnetic substance is not a constant quantity but depends greatly upon the strength of the magnetic field in which it is located.

To determine whether a substance is diamagnetic or paramagnetic, it is but necessary to suspend a rod of it horizontally between the poles of a powerful magnet. If the rod aligns itself so that its longer dimension lies in the direction of the field the substance is paramagnetic (or ferromagnetic); if its assumes a position crosswise to the direction of the field the substance is diamagnetic.

The table on the next page lists a number of ferromagnetic materials with their maximum permeability values and the corresponding flux densities. The values are only approximate inasmuch as definite figures depend on the purity of the substance, the method of preparation, and the thermal treatment.

PERMEABILITIES OF MAGNETIC MATERIALS

| | $\mu$ Maximum | $\mathcal{B}$ Gausses |
|---|---|---|
| Cobalt ................................. | 170 | 3000 |
| Iron-cobalt alloy (Co 34%) ................ | 13,000 | 8000 |
| Heusler alloy (Cu 60%, Mn 24%, Al 16%).... | 200 | 2000 |
| Iron, purest commercial annealed............ | 6000 to 8000 | 6000 |
| Nickel ................................... | 400 to 1000 | 1000 to 3000 |
| Permalloy (Ni 78.5%, Fe 21.5%)........... | over 80,000 | 5000 |
| Perminvar (Ni 45%, Fe 30%, Co 25%)....... | 2000 | 4 |
| Silicon steel (Si 4%) ..................... | 5000 to 10,000 | 6000 to 8000 |
| Steel, cast .............................. | 1500 | 7000 |
| Steel, open-hearth ....................... | 3000 to 7000 | 6000 |

The Huesler alloys (only one of which is tabulated) were discovered by F. Heusler, a German physicist, and are interesting in that the ingredients are nonmagnetic substances. In contrast, there are steels which by proper thermal treatment are rendered practically nonmagnetic. Iron ceases to be ferromagnetic at 770° C.

**110. Electromagnets.**—The electromagnet, formed of a solenoid surrounding an iron core, finds many applications in electrical equipments. The magnetic field set up by the current in the solenoid acts inductively upon the iron and rearranges its molecular magnets to exhibit external magnetism. When the current is stopped, much of the magnetism is lost because most of the molecular magnets return to their random positions. The softer the iron the greater the number of molecular magnets that can return and the smaller will be the residual magnetism in the core.

**Experiment 49.**—Wind two iron rods in opposite directions as illustrated at I in Fig. 112, and connect the windings separately to a couple of dry cells so that the currents will be directed as shown. Test the polarities of the electromagnets so formed with a compass needle and verify the correctness of the right-hand rule and the markings in the figure. Reverse the current as shown at II and check on the polarities indicated. Finally, place an iron yoke across the two rods as shown at III to form a horseshoe magnet and join the two windings in series so that the polarity of one free pole will be north and the other south. Make a sketch to show how two bar electromagnets wound in the same direction can be connected to form a horseshoe magnet.

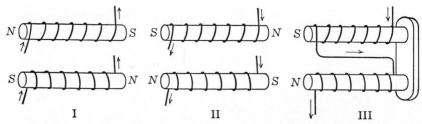

FIG. 112. Magnetization of iron rods with electric current

The strength of a horseshoe may be tested by applying an iron armature of adequate sectional area to the poles and exerting a pull at its midpoint sufficient to detach the armature.

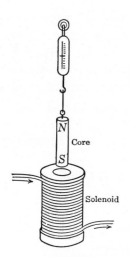

FIG. 113. Measuring pull of a solenoid on iron core

Experiment 50.—Mount a solenoid with its axis vertical and suspend an iron rod above it from a spring balance, as shown in Fig. 113. Connect the winding to a suitable battery and magnetic poles N and S will be induced in the rod as indicated for the current direction noted. As a result, the rod will be drawn toward the solenoid and accommodate through itself more and more lines of induction. The pull will increase when part of the rod is within the solenoid. Measure the force exerted when the rod is at different elevations above and within the winding.

Horseshoe electromagnets are used in telegraph sets, telephone receivers, lifting magnets, relays and controllers, electric bells and chimes, circuit breakers, and a variety of other devices. They are designed in shape and size to perform the required service with appropriate values of current. Perhaps the most important application of electromagnets is in generators and motors where they are used to create the intense magnetic fields necessary for the development of large quantities of electrical and mechanical power.

The telegraph *sounder,* illustrated in Fig. 114, consists of an electromagnet fastened to a metal base, and a soft-iron armature mounted upon a lever that is pivoted to move between two stops. When current is established through the coils, the armature is attracted to the cores, and when the current is discontinued the armature is released and pulled away from them by a spring. The clicks produced by the lever upon attraction and release of the armature are interpreted in accordance with a telegraph code.

On long telegraph lines having high resistance, the current would be too small to operate the sounders, and instead, more sensitive instruments with light armatures are used to open and close local circuits containing the sounders; such instruments are called *relays*.

FIG. 114. Telegraph sounder
Central Scientific Company

A telegraph relay comprises an electromagnet, a pivoted lever carrying an armature and a contacting tongue, and one or more fixed contacts. These parts are illustrated in Fig. 115. When the magnet $M$ is energized by the establishment of current in it, the armature $A$ is attracted to it against the action of spring $S$. This action causes the tongue to leave the fixed contact at $D$ and move over to the other fixed contact at $C$, thereby completing the circuit that may be connected to terminals 1 and 2. When the electromagnet is deprived of current, the spring pulls the lever back again to the idle contact at $D$. In this way the current in one circuit controls the operation of another.

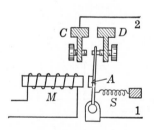

FIG. 115. Operation of a relay

Relays are extensively used in telephone central offices for signaling purposes and are mounted in racks for easy access. They are designed for compactness and for operation with small currents. Fig. 116 shows a relay with springs for making and breaking a circuit. Relays of larger construction are used as *contactors* for operating electric motors at distant or inaccessible places, such as in elevator or motorcar operation.

The familiar *electric bell* is really an adaptation of the relay, in which the contacts are included in the circuit of the electromagnet. Fig. 117 shows the parts of a bell and the scheme of connections. The armature $A$ is supported by a flat spring $S$ which keeps the armature contact $C$ against the fixed stop. When the magnet $M$ is energized by current from a battery, the armature is attracted and the hammer $H$ carried by the armature strikes

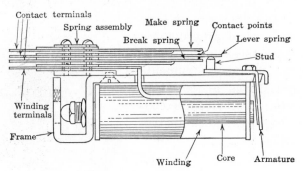

FIG. 116. Telephone relay

the gong $G$. In the meantime the contact at $C$ is opened, which action stops the current and causes the magnet to release the armature. The spring carries the armature back, and the contact at $C$ is again made; this action re-establishes current in the magnet and

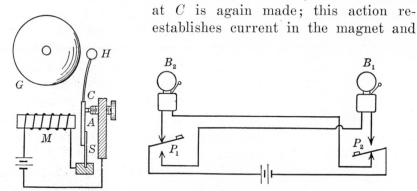

FIG. 117. Circuit of        FIG. 118. Connection of two bells controlled
electric bell                   from opposite points

causes the hammer to strike the gong again. This process is continued, the number of times the gong is struck per minute depending entirely upon the natural rate of vibration of the moving system extending from $S$ to $H$. The ringing of an electric bell is usually controlled by a strap key or push button, placed at a convenient point in the circuit.

Experiment 51.—Make up a bell circuit as shown in Fig. 118 to enable two persons to call each other over a reasonable distance. Each push button should have an upper and a lower contact, so that when either push button is depressed its lower contact will be made while the upper one is broken. Demonstrate that pressing push button $P_1$ will ring bell $B_1$, and pressing $P_2$ (as illustrated) will ring bell $B_2$.

A form of electromagnet that can produce powerful forces at short distances is designed to have a stubby cylindrical iron core, a coil of heavy wire upon it, and an iron shell around the winding. A cut-away view of such a magnet is depicted in Fig. 119. The central core is one pole of the magnet and the entire rim of the shell is the other. Such ironclad magnets are well adapted for lifting magnetic substances and many are in use in large industrial plants for handling iron and steel parts of all descriptions. The lifting power of an electromagnet is proportional to the square of the flux density and to the area of the contacting surface.

FIG. 119. Ironclad magnet for lifting purposes
Electric Controller & Manufacturing Company

**111. Circuit Breakers.**—It is often necessary to open an electric circuit automatically when the current in it exceeds a predetermined value; the device for doing this is called a *circuit breaker*. The operating principle of the circuit breaker is the attraction between an electromagnet and its armature, or between a solenoid and its iron core, when the current becomes excessive, and the ensuing motion releases a spring through trigger action which causes the circuit to be opened rapidly. Circuit breakers are designed to interrupt the large currents that are developed under accidental short-circuit.

The most usual form of circuit breaker is the plain *overload* type which, as its name suggests, opens the circuit in the event of overload or excessive current. This type is available for all classes of service from the small breaker installed in outlet boxes for protecting branch circuits to the huge breakers installed on switchboards or in compartments at central stations. Fig. 120 shows a three-pole breaker of medium capacity; when the armature is attracted, the mechanism releases a spring to open the contacts.

Circuit breakers may be made for instantaneous response or for time-limiting action; in the latter case opening of the circuit is delayed for a brief period, the amount of delay becoming automatically less as the overload becomes greater.

Other features may be introduced in circuit breakers, such as a "no-voltage" coil for opening the circuit when the e.m.f.

FIG. 120. Circuit breaker
Roller-Smith Company.

falls to a predetermined point, or a "shunt-trip" device for opening the circuit from push buttons placed at conveniently located points, or a "reverse-current" arrangement opening the breaker upon reversal of the direction of the current. In addition to such protective features, circuit breakers may be equipped for closing as well as for opening the circuit from a remote point; this is accomplished by closing mechanisms operated by motors or by solenoids.

**112. Polarized Electromagnets.**—A combination of a permanent magnet and an electromagnet is called a *polarized* electromagnet.

In this type the whole flux path is normally under the influence of the permanent magnet alone, but when there is a current through the electromagnet coils the polarity of the cores due to the permanent magnet may be strengthened, partly or wholly neutralized, or even reversed.

Polarized electromagnets are extensively used in telephone ringers, Fig. 121. The coils $M$ are formed of many turns of fine wire wound upon soft iron cores, the cores being attached to the iron yoke $Y$. The soft iron armature $N$, pivoted at $F$, has the clapper rod $C$ attached to its center so that every movement of the armature will cause the ball at the upper end of the clapper to strike one gong or the other. The permanent magnet $N'$ extends from the yoke, back of the coils, to a point somewhat below the armature; it gives the lower ends of the magnet cores $S$ polarity.

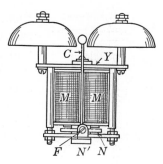

FIG. 121. Telephone ringer using polarized electromagnet

The armature is magnetized inductively by the permanent magnet, and a S-pole is induced at its middle point and a N-pole at each end. With no current in the coils, either end of the armature will be attracted to its adjacent magnet core. When current is directed through the electromagnet winding so as to cause the left core to become a N-pole and the right one a S-pole, the right-hand end of the armature will be attracted and the other will be repelled, causing the clapper to be tilted to the left. On reversing the current, the polarity of the magnet cores will be reversed, causing the clapper to be tilted to the right. When alternating current is used in ringing, the polarity of the magnet cores is reversed just as often as the direction of current in the coils is reversed, causing the clapper to be shifted from one side to the other every time the current reverses, and the ball to strike one of the gongs each time.

A polarized relay commonly used in telegraph circuits is illustrated diagrammatically in Fig. 122. The permanent magnet $N'S'$ is of horseshoe form, and is also bent in the arc of a circle as viewed from above. The two electromagnets are mounted vertically and carry pole pieces which face each other. Two armatures, mounted on a common shaft, are arranged so that each swings between a pair of pole pieces of the electromagnet. Each armature, being pivoted near a pole of the permanent magnet, is magnetized inductively; the free end of the upper one has S-polarity and the corresponding end of the lower one has N-polarity. The cores of the electromagnet are also magnetized inductively by the permanent magnet with N-poles at their upper ends and S-poles at the lower ends. The moving element has no directive springs, and when the arma-

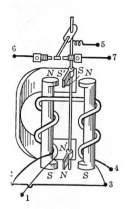

FIG. 122. Construction of polarized relay

tures are placed midway between the electromagnet poles they will be attracted equally by them and the forces will balance. There are two windings on the electromagnet, namely 1-3 and 2-4, which may be connected in series or in parallel as preferred; they are connected in series in the figure.

When the electromagnet is energized by a current entering at terminal 1, the magnetism produced strengthens the poles of the left-hand core and weakens those of the right-hand one, causing both armatures to be attracted to the left and contact to be made between tongue contact 5 and the contact screw 6. When the current is reversed, the armatures will move and close contact 7. In a polarized relay used for unidirectional current, the armature is held by means of a spring toward one pole of the electromagnet instead of being balanced, and a current of proper polarity will move the armature to the opposite pole and operate the relay.

**113. Force Exerted on a Conductor.**—One of the important laws of physics states that for every action there is an equal and opposite reaction. The term *action* means the force which one body exerts upon a second one, and *reaction* means the force which the second body exerts on the first. For example, if a man pulls on a rope with a force of 50 pounds, the rope pulls in the opposite direction on the man with a force of 50 pounds. In the same way, when a conductor carrying a current exerts a certain force on a magnetic substance, that substance will exert an equal and opposite force on the conductor. Thus, the solenoid illustrated in Fig. 113 pulls on the iron rod with a certain force depending on its position; at that position the rod pulls on the solenoid with the same force in the opposite direction.

The direction of the force exerted on a conductor can be visualized by the tendency for magnetic lines to become as short as possible, and at the same time to exert a sidewise thrust upon one another when directed in the same way, §21. Fig. 123 illustrates a straight wire in cross-section located in a magnetic field between the poles N and S. The current is shown by the dot within the conductor to be directed toward the reader and, consequently, the magnetic flux which it sets up will be counterclockwise. Below the conductor the lines between the poles and those produced by the current in the wire are both to the right, and this means that the magnetic field there will be strong; above the conductor these two agencies are in opposition and the resulting field there will be

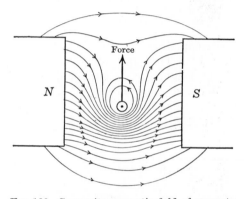

FIG. 123. Composite magnetic field of magnets and a current-carrying conductor

weak. The distribution of the lines of the composite magnetic field is pictured in the figure. The fact that the wire will be pushed upward in this field can be visualized by the tension along the lines of force and by the repulsive action between them where they have the same direction below the conductor.

The following rule employing the LEFT HAND may be used in determining the direction of the force which acts on a wire that carries an electric current when located in a magnetic field:

*Place the thumb and the first and second fingers of the left hand at right angles to each other, and hold the hand so that the thumb points in the direction of the magnet flux and the first finger points in the direction of the current; then the second finger will indicate the direction of force on the wire and its resulting motion.*

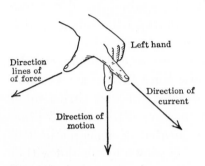

FIG. 124. Left-hand rule for determining direction of force on a conductor in a magnetic field

These directions are illustrated in Fig. 124. Applying this rule to Fig. 123, turn the left hand so that the thumb will point to the right and the first finger forward, then the second finger, pointing upward, will show that the force on the wire is upward, as indicated.

**Experiment 52.**—Using a baseboard as in Experiment 48, pivot a rectangular coil having a single turn so that its ends will dip into the mercury troughs for completing the circuit with a source of electricity, as indicated in Fig. 125. Turn the coil so that its vertical plane will be at right angles to the magnetic meridian, and then bring a permanent magnet near one of the coil sides, as shown. The coil will deflect in accordance with the

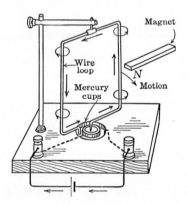

FIG. 125. Current-carrying coil deflected by a magnet

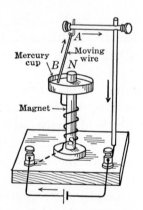

FIG. 126. Rotation of a current-carrying wire around a magnet pole

left-hand rule. Reverse the magnet so that the S-pole will be near the wire and observe the force action. Repeat, holding the magnet near the other coil side.

**Experiment 53.**—To the top of an electromagnet, fasten a disk of wood in which a groove has been turned for the reception of mercury. Hook one end of a copper wire *AB* to a support, as shown in Fig. 126, so that it will be centrally over the core of the electromagnet. Arrange the other end of the wire to dip into the mercury trough, thereby completing the series circuit comprising the electromagnet, the wire *AB,* and battery. The magnetic field of the electromagnet is nearly at right angles to the wire and the wire will rotate steadily about the pole. Apply the left-hand rule and show that it agrees with the observed motion of the wire, which is counterclockwise looking from above. Interchange the battery terminals and explain why the direction of rotation of the wire does not change.

The amount of force exerted on a conductor with current through it and located in a magnetic field depends upon the flux density of the field, the current in the wire, and the length of the wire. Let

$\mathcal{B}$ = flux density of the region in gausses,
$I$ = current in the wire in amperes,
$L$ = length of the straight wire in centimeters,
$F$ = sidewise force on the wire in pounds.

Then the force acting at right angles to the flux and at right angles to the conductor is

$$F = \frac{\mathcal{B} \times I \times L}{4,445,000} \qquad 61$$

**Problem 79.**—A conductor 2 feet long is located in a magnetic field where the flux density is 2000 gausses and is directed perpendicularly to the flux. What force acts on the wire when it carries a current of 25 amperes?

The length of the conductor is $L = 2 \times 12 \times 2.54 = 61$ centimeters, and the force on it at right angles to both conductor and flux is

$$(61) \qquad F = \frac{\mathcal{B} \times I \times L}{4,445,000} = \frac{2000 \times 25 \times 61}{4,445,000} = 0.69 \text{ pound}$$

## 114. Action Between Conductors Carrying Current.—There is still another action which results from the fact that every wire is surrounded by a magnetic field when there is current in it, and this action is the force exerted by one wire carrying current upon another, when the two wires are sufficiently close to each other. The action may take place between two neighboring wires in the same circuit or between wires of separate circuits. When the wires are straight and parallel, the force action between them is a transverse one of repulsion or attraction depending on the relative directions of current.

Fig. 127 shows in cross section two parallel wires carrying current and surrounded by magnetic fields. The directions of current in them is indicated as before, a cross denoting that the

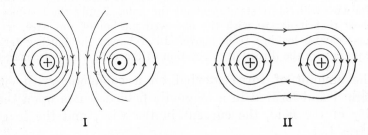

FIG. 127. Magnetic fields around parallel conductors
I—Currents in opposite directions—repulsion.
II—Currents in same direction—attraction.

current is directed into the paper and a dot that the current is forward. At I, the currents are in opposite directions in the two wires and repulsion takes place between them; this action is in agreement with the statements made before that the lines of force seem to push sidewise upon each other and thereby push the wires apart. At II, the currents are in the same direction and attraction takes place between the wires; this action indicates that the lines of force enveloping both wires tend to shorten themselves and thereby bring the wires together.

**Experiment 54.**—Hang two long pieces of tinsel wire close to each other from a suitable support, as shown in Fig. 128. When connected to a battery in the

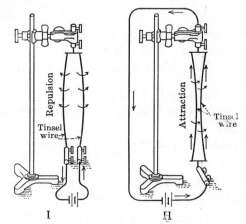

FIG. 128. Action between tinsel wires carrying currents

manner illustrated at I, the currents will be directed oppositely in the two wires and, consequently, they repel each other and spread apart as depicted. When the wires are connected in parallel as shown at II, the currents are in the same direction and the wires attract each other. A similar experiment can be carried out with two coils of copper wire, by using the two leads from each coil to provide for its bifilar suspension.

An arrangement known as Roget's helix serves very nicely to demonstrate the attraction between wires in which the current is directed the same way; the device is illustrated in Fig. 129. A spring with many turns of brass or phosphor bronze wire is hung from a support and the lower end dips into a cup of mercury. When supplied with current, the mutual attraction of the individual turns contracts the spring to such an extent that the lower end breaks contact with the mercury. This action interrupts the current and the spring assumes its normal length, again closing the mercury contact. The alternate contractions and extensions of the spring keep it in vibration as long as the current is continued.

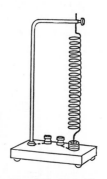

Fig. 129. Roget's jumping spiral

In any solenoid or electromagnet, the magnetic field tends to bind the wires closer together, since the current is in the same direction through all the turns as in Roget's helix. Consequently, the windings of electrical machines and power apparatus must be designed to withstand the forces due to the currents in such coils, even under short-circuit conditions.

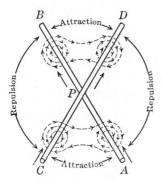

Fig. 130. Action between wires placed at an angle to each other

When conductors are oriented at an angle to each other and current is established in them, they tend to become parallel and the currents will be directed the same way. This behavior is indicated by conductors AB and CD in Fig. 130 which cross at point P. The dotted lines show the paths of magnetic flux around the wires; contraction of these lines of force and their sidewise thrust upon each other will help the reader to understand the action, as noted in the figure.

The combination of conductors that are parallel to each other and conductors that make an angle with each other are provided by two rectangular loops of wire, one within the other, connected to the same circuit or separate circuits. With one of the loops movable, and with current in both of them, the force action between the loops will cause the movable one to align itself with the fixed one. The motion will stop when the planes of the loops are parallel and when their magnetic fields are directed in the same way.

**Experiment 55.**—Clamp a coil within the pivoted conducting loop of Experiment 52, as shown in Fig. 131, and connect the two in series to a battery. Turn the loop $AB$ so that its plane makes an angle with that of the fixed coil $CD$ and release it; the loop will move to bring itself parallel to the coil. This motion results from the flux action around the horizontal conductors of the loop and coil as well as around their vertical conductors. Finally, reverse the direction of current in the loop *or* in the coil, and observe that the loop will turn through a half revolution from its former position and again come to rest. If a stationary coil is not available, the wires to the battery may be lengthened and merely one of them held near the parts of the loop to observe the mutual action between current-carrying conductors.

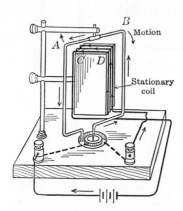

FIG. 131. Movable loop aligns itself with fixed coil to have same current direction

To summarize, parallel wires carrying currents in the same direction attract each other; when the currents are oppositely directed in two wires they repel each other. Wires placed at an angle to each other tend to become parallel, making the current direction the same through them. Coils of wire carrying current will tend to align their planes and cause the directions of their magnetic fields to coincide. These statements apply to wires that form parts of the same circuit or parts of independent circuits. These principles are utilized in many types of electrical instruments and machines.

## QUESTIONS

1. There is a current through a wire held east and west over a compass needle. How will the needle be affected? Explain.
2. An electric feeder extends up a vertical wooden pole from an underground duct. When you approach the pole from the south, the N-end of a compass needle held in your hand is deflected east. Is the current in the feeder directed up or down the pole?

3. Two parallel lines, with one conductor above the other, are stretched horizontally in a north-south direction, and equal currents are maintained through them in the same direction. A compass is held midway between the wires. How will its needle be affected?

4. Imagine that you are looking at a circular coil with the current in it directed clockwise. Would the magnetic flux through it be directed toward or away from you?

5. One end of a solenoid attracts the N-pole of a compass needle. What is the direction of the current around the coil when viewed from this end?

6. State the two uses of the right-hand rule that relate the directions of current in, and the magnetic flux around, a part of a circuit.

7. A current is directed through a coil of wire wrapped around a tumbler in the same direction that the fingers of the right hand point when clasping it to drink. What is the polarity of the end of the coil that you observe while drinking?

8. What factors influence the intensity of the magnetic field at the center of a flat circular loop of wire? and along the axis of a solenoid?

9. A number of turns of wire are wound in a clockwise direction around a lead pencil, and then alongside are wound an equal number of turns in the opposite direction. Sketch the appearance of the magnetic field you would expect to see revealed by iron filings around the winding with current in it. Indicate the polarity and the direction of current.

10. What is meant by magnetic flux?

11. Distinguish between field intensity and magnetic flux density.

12. Define the oersted, the maxwell, and the gauss.

13. The pole of an electromagnet having a soft steel core deflects a compass needle 44 degrees when held at a distance of one foot. A soft iron core is substituted for the steel and the deflection is found to be 58 degrees. How do you account for this increase, for neither the distance nor the current strength was altered?

14. Define magnetic permeability.

15. Distinguish between diamagnetic, paramagnetic, and ferromagnetic substances.

16. Wind a steel key ring with insulated wire so that when a current is maintained through the winding the ring will possess two poles diametrically opposite each other. Illustrate by a sketch the direction of winding, direction of current, and direction of the magnetic lines of force.

17. Explain the operation of an electric bell.

18. Make a sketch of a call circuit which includes one bell and three push buttons, and which permits any push button to ring the bell.

19. Make a sketch of an ironclad magnet with its winding, and mark upon it the polarity for any chosen current direction.

20. What is the purpose of a relay? of a circuit breaker?
21. Explain the operation of a polarized ringer or a polarized relay.
22. Explain, through the action of lines of force, what takes place when a wire is located in a magnetic field and a current is established in the wire.
23. State the left-hand rule which relates the directions of current and magnetic flux to the direction that a current-carrying wire moves in a magnetic field.
24. How can the direction of the moving wire in Experiment 53 be reversed? Could a permanent magnet be used in this test instead of the electromagnet?
25. A vertical wire carrying a current rotates around the S-pole of a magnet in a direction against the hands of a clock as viewed from above. Is the current directed up or down the wire?
26. A copper disk is mounted between the poles of a horseshoe magnet and current is directed through the disk from its center to the circumference. Make a sketch indicating the direction in which the disk will rotate. How can the direction of rotation be changed?
27. Two wires are fastened to the ceiling and hang vertically down 2 inches apart. With current in the wires, the distance between them reduces to 1½ inches. How do you explain this? If the current were reversed in both wires, how would they be affected?
28. Two wires are placed across each other at an angle of 60°. Show how currents should be directed in both wires so that they will cause this angle to decrease.

## PROBLEMS

1. At what distance from a straight wire in which the current is 10 amperes will the field intensity be just 1 oersted? *Ans.* 2 centimeters.
2. A pair of long parallel wires 1 foot apart carry 20 amperes in opposite directions. Find the intensity of the magnetic field at a point halfway between them. *Ans.* 0.525 oersted.
3. Calculate the intensity of the magnetic field at the center of a flat circular coil of 40 turns of wire which has a radius of 9 centimeters, assuming the current in the winding to be 0.5 ampere. *Ans.* 1.40 oersteds.
4. A mailing tube has one layer of wire closely wound around it which extends over a length of 20 centimeters axially. The winding consists of 240 turns and the current through it is 0.6 ampere. Calculate the field intensity along the axis of the tube. *Ans.* 9.05 oersteds.
5. A solenoid 50 centimeters long and 4 centimeters in diameter is completely wound with wire to have 10 turns per centimeter of length. Determine the field intensity at the center of this solenoid when 2 amperes are maintained in the winding. *Ans.* 25.1 oersteds.

6. An iron ring is wound by repeatedly weaving the wire through the hole and wrapping it around the ring in a manner similar to winding tape around a bicycle tire. The ring has an average length measured around the circumference of 20 inches, and there are 600 turns of wire on it. A current of 0.4 ampere is in the winding and the flux is confined to the circular path through the iron. If the permeability of the iron under the conditions stated is 950, what is the flux density in the ring? *Ans.* 5640 gausses.

7. The pole pieces of a generator are square in section and measure 7.5 inches on each edge. What will be the flux density in a pole piece if there are 2.5 million lines of induction through it? *Ans.* 6,920 gausses.

8. The flux density produced in a bar of nickel by a field intensity of 2.5 oersteds is 2000 gausses. What is the permeability of nickel under the conditions stated? *Ans.* 800.

9. A wire 15 centimeters long is placed between the field poles of a generator and carries a current of 5 amperes. It experiences a force of 1 ounce in a direction at right angles to itself and to the magnetic field. What is the flux density at the wire? *Ans.* 3700 gausses.

10. Two parallel wires are 5 centimeters apart and the currents in them are 250 amperes each. Compute the force which one wire exerts upon the other per meter of length. *Ans.* 0.0563 pound.

# Lesson XI

## ELECTRICAL INSTRUMENTS

Galvanometers—Moving-needle galvanometer—D'Arsonval galvanometer—Ballistic galvanometer—Reading devices for mirror-type galvanometers — Sensitivity of a galvanometer — Shunts — Ammeters — Ammeter shunts—Movable-iron instruments—Dynamometer ammeter—Hot-wire ammeter—Voltmeters and multipliers—Connecting ammeters and voltmeters in circuit—Wattmeters—Thomson watthour meter—Sangamo watthour meter—Reading the watthour meter register—Questions and Problems.

**115. Galvanometers.**—An instrument which is used for detecting the presence of an electric current in a circuit, and for determining its direction and relative strength, is called a *galvanometer*. Practically all galvanometers depend for their operation on the magnetic effect of the current and their action is based upon the principles: (1) that a magnetic needle placed near a circuit is deflected when a current is established through the circuit, or (2) that a coil suitably pivoted between the poles of a permanent magnet will be deflected when there is a current in that coil. According to these principles of action, galvanometers may be divided into two classes: first, those in which the coil is stationary and the magnetic body is arranged to move, and second, those in which the magnet is stationary and the coil is arranged to move. Each class is constructed in a variety of forms.

In galvanometers having the moving element supported on pivots, the deflections are shown by a pointer moving over a graduated scale. In instruments having the moving element suspended, the deflections are observed by the motion of a small mirror attached to the element. This is done either by directing a ray of light upon the mirror and permitting the reflected ray to fall upon a scale, or by observing the image of a scale in the mirror by means of a small telescope.

**116. Moving-Needle Galvanometer.**—A simple galvanometer of the moving-magnet class consists of a coil of wire mounted in the vertical plane, a horizontal magnetic needle poised on a needle-point at the center of the coil, and a pointer and scale for indicating the deflection of the needle. Fig. 132 shows the construction of such an instrument for student use; essentially it is an elaboration of the current detector described in §25.

The galvanometer coil is wound in two sections on a rectangular wooden bobbin, the moving system consists of a short magnetic

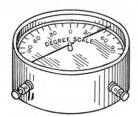
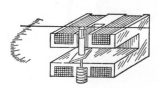

FIG. 132. Detector galvanometer and its construction

needle and a long aluminum pointer fixed at right angles to each other, and the scale is aligned so that one end of the pointer will lie over the zero mark when the magnetic needle is parallel with the coil. These parts are housed in a glass-covered box and the coil terminals are brought out to binding posts. The galvanometer coil may be composed of a few turns of heavy wire for use with large currents, or may be wound with many turns of fine wire for detection of rather small currents. A galvanometer of this type wound with No. 30 A.w.g. copper wire has a resistance of about 30 ohms and gives a deflection of 1 degree from its position of rest with a current of approximately 10 microamperes.

In use, the galvanometer is first placed with its coil parallel to the needle, which means in line with the earth's magnetic field; in this position, the pointer will read zero. Then, with current through the coils, the pointer will swing to the right or left of zero depending on the direction of the current. The value of the deflection depends upon the strength of current through the coil.

but is not proportional to the current; thus, if a certain current produces twice the deflection of another current the strength of one is not double the other. With the needle parallel to the coil, or at the zero scale position, a small current deflects it considerably, but as the angle between needle and coil increases, a relatively greater current is required to produce the same change in deflection. Consequently, the scale readings provide only a general idea of current strength. Actually, the current is proportional to the tangent of the angle of deflection (§170), and galvanometers of the type described are called *tangent* galvanometers.

Fig. 133 depicts another form of tangent galvanometer for student use. The particular instrument shown has two coils wound on the same circular frame, one has 5 and the other 10 turns of No. 20 A.w.g. copper wire, and these may be connected in series. The deflection of a tangent galvanometer depends upon the relative intensities of the magnetic field due to the current in the coil and of the field due to the earth; the needle will point in the direction of the resultant of these magnetic fields. The greatest possible deflection of the needle will be 90 degrees. The earth's magnetism may be considered as approximately constant at any particular place.

FIG. 133. Tangent galvanometer

Central Scientific Company

117. **D'Arsonval Galvanometer.**—The kinds of galvanometers now generally used are of the class in which the movable element consists of a small coil of wire instead of a magnetic needle. The coil is located in the magnetic field between the poles of a permanent magnet. With current in the coil, forces act to deflect it from its rest position, and the amount of deflection serves as a measure of the current. This type of galvanometer is named after the French physicist, Arsène d'Arsonval (1851-1940), and the principles involved are also employed in most ammeters and voltmeters used in electrical testing.

Fig. 134 shows a rectangular coil of a d'Arsonval galvanometer in the uniform field between the magnet poles NS, together with a mirror $M$ so that the deflections of the coil can be read with a lamp and scale, or with a telescope and scale. The current is conducted to and from the coil by means of a flat metal ribbon at the top which serves as the suspension, and by a helix of similar material below the coil. With current established, the coil sets up its own magnetic field and tends to turn so that its lines of force are in the same direction as those of the permanent magnet. The coil will turn one way or the other, depending upon the direction of current through it. This tendency to rotate is op-posed by the torsion of the suspension wire, and the motion continues until the turning effort due to the current is bal-anced by that of the suspension. With pole pieces of proper design on the magnet, *the deflection of the coil may be made directly proportional to the current.*

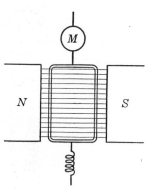

FIG. 134. Moving element of a d'Arsonval galvanometer

A top view of one turn of the galvan-ometer coil is shown in Fig. 135 together with the lines of force of the composite field produced by coil and magnet. As ex-plained in the preceding lesson, the left-hand conductor with cur-

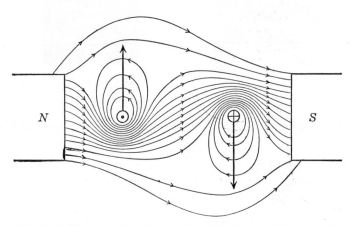

FIG. 135. Flux around galvanometer coil when carrying current

rent directed out of the page will be pushed upward, and the right-hand conductor with current directed into the page will be pushed downward; the two actions combine to produce clockwise rotation of the coil as seen from above.

**Experiment 56.**—Make a coil of many turns of fine wire and suspend it by its lead-in wires between the poles of a permanent horseshoe magnet so that it will come to rest in the position shown in Fig. 134. Connect it through a rheostat of high resistance to a dry cell, and observe that the coil moves because of the current in the coil. Increase the current more and more and the deflection will increase until it reaches a limiting value of 90 degrees.

Fig. 136 illustrates two designs of moving-coil galvanometers. Both have laminated horseshoe permanent magnets equipped with pole pieces, and the coils are available in a variety of windings with resistances ranging from about 30 to 2000 ohms. The designs

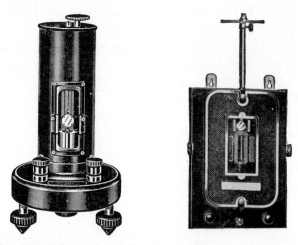

Fig. 136. Table and wall designs of d'Arsonval galvanometer
Leeds & Northrup Company.

permit easy substitution of another coil or replacement of the suspension wire.

Portable forms of d'Arsonval galvanometers that are quite sensitive, and particularly well adapted for commercial testing and for student use in the laboratory, are shown in Fig. 137. The coils of these instruments are pivoted in jeweled bearings; each coil has two spiral springs to conduct the current to and from the coil, and these springs act against each other to control the deflection.

The coil windings of portable galvanometers usually have resistances between about 10 and 700 ohms. External devices are provided for adjusting the moving elements so that the indicators will read zero before current measurements are begun.

The advantage of the moving-coil type of galvanometer over the moving-magnet type lies primarily in its independence of the earth's magnetic field and of other external fields. The magnets

FIG. 137. Portable d'Arsonval galvanometers
Left—Leeds & Northrup Company
Right—Weston Electrical Instrument Corporation

of d'Arsonval galvanometers are very strong and produce such high field intensities that the extraneous fields have no appreciable effect; therefore, these instruments can be used even in reasonable proximity to dynamos or large magnets.

**118. Ballistic Galvanometer.**—The d'Arsonval galvanometers considered so far may be classified as current galvanometers, that is, they produce steady deflections when there is a uniform current through the coils. Another form of d'Arsonval galvanometer which is used for measuring the effect of momentary currents, such as those produced by induction or condenser discharges, §§157 and 167, is called a *ballistic galvanometer*. It is constructed just like the other moving-coil galvanometers but it frequently has a wider coil and a heavier movable element to give it a longer period of swing. Its purpose is to measure electric *charge* rather than current.

With a momentary current through a ballistic galvanometer, the impulse given to the coil does not move it appreciably before the current ceases, due to the inertia of the relatively heavy movable element. As a result, the element swings slowly to one side and reaches a maximum deflection, the so-called *throw* of the instrument, and then returns slowly to zero. Thus, there is no steady deflection and the reading taken is the throw. It is the throw of a ballistic galvanometer which measures the quantity of electricity that traverses its coil. A current galvanometer is calibrated so that its steady deflection can be expressed in microamperes, while a ballistic galvanometer is calibrated so that its throw, or maximum momentary deflection, can be expressed in microcoulombs.

**119. Reading Devices for Mirror-Type Galvanometers.**—The devices used for reading the deflections of galvanometers having

mirrors on their movable elements are of two general types: the lamp and scale, and the telescope and scale. Fig. 138 illustrates a lamp and scale device equipped with a 6-volt lamp that may be operated from a storage battery or through a transformer from 110-volt alternating-current service mains. The scale is one-half meter long and etched on a plate glass; there are actually two scales with 500 millimeter divisions each, one marked 0 to 50 centimeters and the other 25 to 0 to 25 centimeters. A ray of light is projected from the lamp to the galvanometer mirror and the reflected beam is directed upon the scale as shown in Fig. 139. The reading is indicated by a circular patch of light which is split by an index line. This device may be used in daylight if the scale is so placed that it does not face a window. The lamp and scale device can also be arranged for vertical mounting by using a reflecting prism close to the galvanometer.

FIG. 138. Lamp and scale reading device

Leeds & Northrup Company

Fig. 140 illustrates a telescope and scale device for reading galvanometer deflections. The telescope has a magnification of

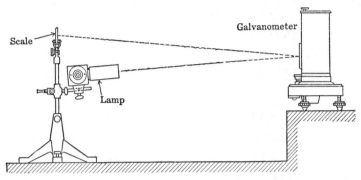

FIG. 139. Usual method of arranging reading device with mirror-type of galvanometer

4 to 12 diameters, and the scale of 500 millimeter divisions and reversed numerals is printed on cardboard and mounted on wood.

Telescope and scale devices are also made with a bracket instead of a tripod for attachment to the wall or directly on the galvanometer.

In setting up either reading device, it is placed at a convenient distance in front of the galvanometer, and the adjusting screw on the instrument is turned to bring the galvanometer coil and its mirror to the zero position. With current through the coil, the ray of light reflected from the

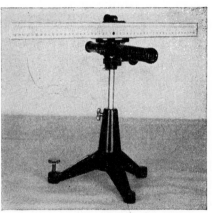

FIG. 140. Telescope and scale device on tripod
Leeds & Northrup Company

mirror will turn through twice the angle that the mirror turns, and the deflection of the instrument may be read.

**120. Sensitivity of a Galvanometer.**—The sensitivity of a current galvanometer may be expressed by the amount of current required to produce a given deflection. The sensitivity may also be indicated by the resistance which is placed in the galvanometer circuit so that 1 volt shall produce a certain deflection. For a ballistic galvanometer the sensitivity is expressed by the quantity of electricity that must be discharged through it in a very short time to produce a given throw. It is standard practice in measuring sensitivity to take the deflection or throw as one division of whatever size when the scale is attached to the galvanometer, although these divisions are usually 1 millimeter. When the scale is detached from the galvanometer, the deflection or throw is taken as 1 millimeter at a distance of 1 meter from the mirror. Portable galvanometers of the types shown in Fig. 137 have current sensitivities of from 5 to 20 microamperes per division (millimeters).

The *megohm sensitivity* of a galvanometer is defined as the external resistance in megohms through which the current due to a potential difference of 1 volt will produce a 1-millimeter deflection at 1 meter. For example, a certain galvanometer has a current sensitivity of 0.014 microampere per millimeter division at 1 meter distance; the megohm sensitivity of this instrument is 1 volt divided by the current in microamperes, that is, the reciprocal of 0.014 or 71.4 megohms. The *ballistic sensitivity* of a galvanometer is expressed as so many microcoulombs per millimeter division at 1 meter.

It can be shown from the principles of electromagnetism (specifically Formula 61) that the torque produced on a coil of a d'Arsonval galvanometer is directly proportional to the current in it, to the area enclosed by each turn of the coil, to the number of turns, and to the flux density in the air gap where the coil is located. These facts show that the larger the coil, the greater the number of turns, and the stronger the magnetic field of a galvanometer, the more sensitive it will be. In selecting a current galvanometer for a particular service, its sensitivity should be such that the deflections will be large enough to yield precise results and the time of swing be sufficiently short to avoid delay in coming to rest.

External resistors are generally connected across the terminals of d'Arsonval galvanometers in order to damp their deflections; this is brought about by electromagnetic induction, §144. The lower the resistance of the resistor the greater will be the damping. If a galvanometer is much underdamped the coil oscillates considerably about its position of rest after a deflection, and if much overdamped it returns to its rest position so slowly that there is uncertainty when it has come to rest. The resistance which will give a galvanometer the minimum amount of damping without over-shooting its rest position is called its *critical damping resistance*. The presence of this resistance as a shunt on the galvanometer, of course, lowers its sensitivity, but renders the instrument much more serviceable.

There is still another way of expressing the sensitivity of a current galvanometer; it is called the *voltage sensitivity*. This is the potential difference that must be impressed on the circuit, including the galvanometer coil and the external critical damping resistance, to produce the 1-millimeter deflection at 1 meter. The voltage sensitivity is equal to the product of the current sensitivity and the total resistance for critical damping.

**Problem 80.**—A certain galvanometer has a coil of 35 ohms resistance and a critical damping resistance of 165 ohms. The current sensitivity of this instrument is 0.007 microampere per millimeter division at 1 meter's distance from the mirror. Compute its megohm and voltage sensitivities.

The megohm sensitivity is $\dfrac{1}{0.007} = 143$ megohms, and the voltage sensitivity is $0.007 \times (35 + 165) = 1.4$ microvolts, both per millimeter deflection at 1 meter.

**121. Shunts.**—If a current that is to be measured by a galvanometer is too great for that instrument, a definite part of the current may be by-passed around the galvanometer through a resistor called a *shunt,* and the rest will be measured by the instrument. If, for example, the resistance of the galvanometer is 2 ohms and that of the shunt is 1 ohm, there will be twice as much current through the shunt as through the galvanometer; in this case the galvanometer reading must be multiplied by 3 to obtain the total current in the circuit. Thus, the purpose of a shunt is to increase the range of the galvanometer. In the case mentioned the shunt is said to have a *multiplying power* of 3.

**Experiment 57.**—Set up a d'Arsonval galvanometer and connect it to a dry cell and a resistor of such resistance as to yield a large deflection of the instrument. Connect across the terminals of the galvanometer a rheostat, preferably of the slide-wire type, to serve as a shunt, and note that the deflection is reduced. If the deflection is reduced to one-third its original value, the multiplying power of the shunt is 3.

To determine the effectiveness of a shunt, consider the circuit shown in Fig. 141 to consist of a galvanometer $G$ and shunt $S$ connected in parallel, and joined to a battery and a resistor in series. Let

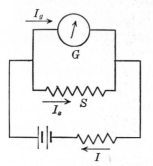

$G$ = resistance of the galvanometer,
$S$ = resistance of the shunt,
$I$ = total current to be measured,
$I_g$ = current in the galvanometer circuit,
$I_s$ = current in the shunt.

The p.d. across the galvanometer is the product of its resistance and the current through it, that is $G \times I_g$; and similarly the p.d. across the shunt is $S \times I_s$. Since these potential differences are equal for the parallel connection, §81, it follows that

FIG. 141. Shunted galvanometer

$$G \times I_g = S \times I_s$$

Since the total current $I$ from the battery is the sum of $I_s$ and $I_g$, and the value of $I_s$ may be obtained from the expression above, it follows that

$$I = I_s + I_g = \frac{G}{S} \times I_g + I_g$$

The multiplying power of the shunt is the ratio of the total current, $I$, under measurement to that part of it, $I_g$, which traverses the galvanometer. This ratio is given by the preceding equation as

$$\frac{I}{I_g} = \frac{G}{S} + 1$$

To FIND THE MULTIPLYING POWER OF A SHUNT FOR A PARTICULAR GALVANOMETER:

*Divide the resistance of the galvanometer by the resistance of the shunt and add one to the quotient.*

If $n$ is the multiplying power of the shunt, then

$$n = \frac{G}{S} + 1 \qquad \textbf{62}$$

**Problem 81.**—Find the multiplying power of a shunt for a galvanometer when the resistance of the instrument is 2000 ohms, and the resistance of a shunt placed across its terminals is 500 ohms.

$$(62) \qquad n = \frac{G}{S} + 1 = \frac{2000}{500} + 1 = 4 + 1 = 5$$

The readings of the instrument are to be multiplied by 5 to obtain the value of the total current.

**Problem 82.**—What must be the resistance of a shunt to give it a multiplying power of 50 when used with a galvanometer of 200 ohms resistance? Solve Formula (62) to obtain the shunt resistance; then

$$S = \frac{G}{n-1} = \frac{200}{50-1} = \frac{200}{49} = 4.08 \text{ ohms}$$

A universal type of shunt which is extensively used with galvanometers to reduce their current sensitivities is called an Ayrton shunt; a shunt of this type may be used with different galvanometers having a wide range of resistances. The arrangement of the circuit for a shunt of four ratios is shown in Fig. 142; it will be observed that the galvanometer is bridged by the entire resistance of the shunt composed of four resistors $a$, $b$, $c$ and $d$ in series. Let the current through the galvanometer for position 1 of the switch arm be $I$. The resistances of the shunt are so calculated that when the arm is on contact marked 0.1 the galvanometer

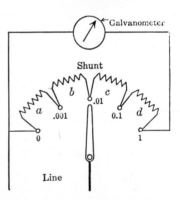

FIG. 142.  Diagram of Ayrton shunt

current will be $0.1 \times I$, when on contact marked 0.01 the galvanometer current will be $0.01 \times I$, and when on contact 0.001 the galvanometer current will be $0.001 \times I$. Note that when the contact arm is moved from right to left, resistance is cut out of the shunt and added to the galvanometer circuit. Consideration will show that if $R$ be the entire resistance of the shunt, assumed large with respect to that of the galvanometer, then

$$d = \frac{9}{10}R, \qquad c = \frac{99}{100}R - d, \qquad \text{and} \qquad b = \frac{999}{1000}R - d - c$$

The appearance of an Ayrton shunt is shown in Fig. 143.

Problem 83.—An Ayrton shunt, with four ranges as indicated in Fig. 142, has an aggregate resistance of 25,000 ohms; calculate the component resistances.

Since $R$ = 25,000 ohms, the individual resistances are as follows:

$$d = \frac{9}{10} \times 25,000 = 22,500 \text{ ohms}; c = \frac{99}{100} \times 25,000 - 22,500 = 2250 \text{ ohms};$$

$$b = \frac{999}{1000} \times 25,000 - 22,500 - 2250 = 225 \text{ ohms};$$

$$\text{and } a = 25,000 - 22,500 - 2250 - 225 = 25 \text{ ohms}.$$

FIG. 143. Shunt box
Leeds & Northrup Company

**122. Ammeters.**—A great variety of measuring instruments have been developed based upon the principles of electromagnetism explained in the previous lesson. They carry names which indicate their use, such as ammeter for measuring current, voltmeter for measuring e.m.f. or p.d., and the wattmeter for measuring electric power. They are calibrated to read directly in the units of these quantities; in this respect they differ from galvanometers.

Ammeters that are based on electromagnetism for their operation are classified according to their construction into two types:

FIG. 144. Meters for measuring current and e.m.f.
Weston Electrical Instrument Corporation

(1) those having a fixed permanent magnet and a movable coil, and (2) those having a fixed coil and a moving piece of iron.

There is also a type of ammeter based on the heating effect of the electric current; it is called a hot-wire ammeter, §126.

The moving-coil type of ammeter is in reality a portable d'Arsonval galvanometer equipped with a shunt of such resistance that the current in the coil will be only a small but definite part of the current through the instrument. The appearance of two models is shown in Fig. 144 and a cut-away view of another is shown in Fig. 145.

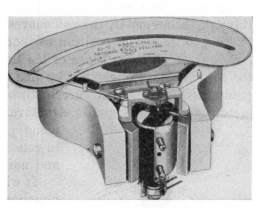

FIG. 145. Interior view of ammeter
General Electric Company

The magnetic structure of these instruments is illustrated in Fig. 146. The permanent magnet $M$ is fitted with two soft-iron pole pieces $P$ and $P$, and between them a somewhat smaller cylindrical iron core $C$ is supported rigidly by a brass plate fastened to the pole pieces. In a newer design of ammeter, illustrated in Fig. 147, the magnetic structure is formed of two sector-shaped alnico magnets NS, placed within a soft-iron ring $R$ to complete the magnetic flux path, and a soft-iron core $C$. In both types of construction the magnetic flux passes radially across the gap from the pole pieces to the core, and this is the region wherein the coil swings.

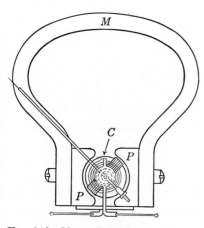

FIG. 146. Magnetic structure of most ammeters

The movable coil consists essentially of a light rectangular coil of copper wire, usually wound upon an aluminum frame, and mounted to rotate in the annular space between the core and pole pieces. A light tubular pointer is attached rigidly to the coil and the free end moves over a graduated scale. The terminals of the coil are connected to the upper and lower spiral springs, which serve as the two lead-in wires for the current. With a current through the ammeter, the coil moves through the magnetic field, tending to take up a position so that its lines of force will be in the same direction as those of the field. The coil will move until the torque on it is balanced by that of the springs, and then the pointer will indicate the current through the meter. By appropriate design of the magnetic structure, the deflection of the coil is made proportional to the current; in consequence, the scale is uniform and not cramped at either end.

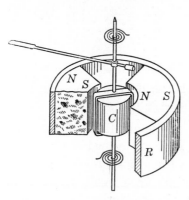

FIG. 147.   Concentric magnet construction in ammeters

General Electric Company

It will be explained later that the aluminum frame on which the coil is wound has electromotive forces induced in it when the coil rotates in the magnetic field; these cause eddy currents (§151) around the frame in the opposite direction to the current in the coil. In consequence, the eddy currents tend to stop the motion of the coil and bring the moving element to rest quickly at the proper position. This action prevents the needle from oscillating and renders the instrument *dead-beat*.

The pointer, while very close to the scale throughout its range of motion, necessarily lies a short distance above it; consequently, in reading the position of the pointer, care should be taken to view it perpendicularly to the scale. If a reading is taken by viewing the pointer from one side or the other, its value will vary accordingly and the error is said to be due to *parallax*. To avoid this error a mirror is usually placed below the scale and the reading is taken when the eye sees the reflection of the pointer and the pointer itself brought together.

The movable coil is quite light in weight and is mounted in jewel bearings so that friction will be a minimum; as a result, the instrument is rendered sensitive and can respond to minute variations of current. Naturally, it should be handled carefully to avoid jarring. Every ammeter has a low resistance so that the potential drop across it will be small; care must be taken to have enough resistance in the circuit associated with the meter to limit the current to a value within its range. Caution should also be exercised to connect the meter terminal marked + toward the positive side of the current source. Above all, *never connect an ammeter across service mains* for it would draw so much current as to burn out the coil and otherwise damage the instrument.

**123. Ammeter Shunts.**—Shunts that are used with movable-coil ammeters to increase their range are made of special alloy strips that do not change their resistance appreciably with changes

FIG. 148. Forms of shunts for movable-coil meters
Weston Electrical Instrument Corporation

of temperature. The shunt may be placed in the instrument, or mounted separately, or inserted in the busbars on the back of a switchboard. Fig. 148 shows three styles: I is a typical switchboard shunt, II is a portable testing shunt, and III is a portable precision shunt permitting selection of seven ranges by means of a rotary switch.

Special leads are provided to connect the shunt to the instrument and these should never be shortened; if they were their resistance would be decreased, the current in the coil circuit would be increased, and the indicated readings would be higher than the correct current values. One advantage of using external shunts with switchboard instruments in power stations is the saving in copper and cost of construction, for instead of running heavy copper cables to a distant ammeter, a shunt may be inserted in the main circuit and the two small-sized shunt leads wired to the instrument. The resistance of the instrument and its shunt is very low, and little energy will be lost when they remain continually in circuit.

For the sake of standardization, ammeters over a wide range, and the shunts to be used with them, are adjusted to have a potential drop of 50 millivolts. This means that with rated current through the shunt there is a p.d. of 50 millivolts across it, and the associated instrument will give a deflection across the entire scale. Thus, the instrument used with a shunt is virtually a milli-voltmeter, §127. Suppose, for example, that the coil of such an instrument has a resistance of 5 ohms. If full-scale deflection is produced on 50 millivolts, then the limiting current through the meter is given by Formula (18) as 0.05 volt ÷ 5 ohms = 0.01 ampere. A 2-ampere shunt used with this meter would have to carry 2.00 − 0.01 = 1.99 amperes, and its resistance would have to be 0.05 volt ÷ 1.99 amperes = 0.0251 ohm. Since the meter by itself gives a full-scale deflection on 0.01 ampere, and with this particular shunt the current through the combination is 2.00 amperes, it follows that the multiplying power of the shunt is 2.00 ÷ 0.01 or 200.

Problem 84.—Regard the 5-ohm instrument mentioned above as a gal-vanometer and compute the resistance of a shunt that will give it a multiply-ing power of 200.

The multiplying power of a shunt is given by Formula (62) and this can be solved for the resistance $S$ of the shunt. Take the galvanometer resistance $G$ as 5 ohms and the multiplying power $n$ of the shunt as 200; then the resistance of the shunt is

$$S = \frac{G}{n-1} = \frac{5}{200-1} = \frac{5}{199} = 0.0251 \text{ ohm}$$

This result agrees with the previous value.

124. Movable-Iron Instruments.—A very satisfactory type of instrument for measuring current and potentials, less expensive than the movable-coil type, makes use of the repulsion between pieces of iron of like polarity. The principle can be explained by means of Fig. 149. At I, two pieces of iron are supported by strings within a coil of wire; with current through the coil in the direction indicated, each piece of iron acquires S-polarity at its upper and N-polarity at its lower end, causing one piece to repel the other, as shown. The same result will be obtained when the current is directed the other way, except that the polarities in-

duced in the pieces of iron will be reversed. At II, the coil is turned
to have its axis horizontal and one piece of iron is fixed near one
side; the repulsion causes the other piece to move to the right

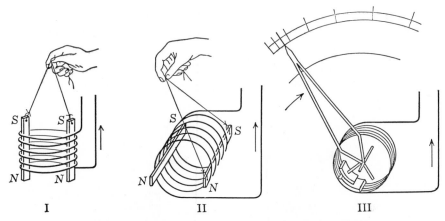

FIG. 149. Operating principle of moving-iron type ammeters

when there is current in the coil. At III, the movable iron is
mounted on a pivot so that the motion is restricted to rotation;
a pointer attached to the iron indicates the strength of current
in the coil on a suitably calibrated
scale. If the direction of current
changes at short intervals, the polarity of the fixed and movable
pieces of iron reverses periodically
but the repulsion continues until
the current ceases. Therefore, this
type of ammeter is particularly
adapted to the measurement of alternating currents.

Fig. 150 shows the interior construction of a moving-iron ammeter. The coil of copper wire
is fixed and has a curved tongue

FIG. 150. Construction of moving-vane
ammeter

of iron fastened to its inner cylindrical surface. The moving
element consists of a small iron vane fastened to a light pivoted
shaft, and a pointer made of thin aluminum tubing which carries

a small damper. With current through the coil, there will be repulsion between the pieces of iron, and this causes the moving element to deflect. The damper on the pivoted system moves within a fan-shaped enclosure, compressing the air in front of it and lessening the pressure on the back, and this action brings the element to rest with a few slight over-swings. This mechanical method of damping is utilized, instead of that based on electromagnetic induction, because the instrument lacks the permanent magnet and the moving metal coil frame of the d'Arsonval type ammeter.

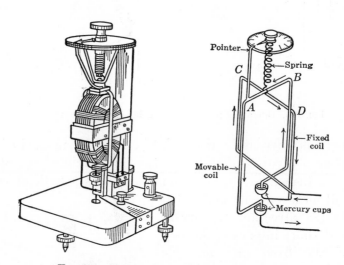

FIG. 151.  Siemens dynamometer and its circuit

**125. Dynamometer Ammeter.**—The dynamometer type of ammeter is an instrument for measuring current by the reaction between two coils, one of which is fixed and the other movable. The general appearance and connections of a Siemens *dynamometer* are illustrated in Fig. 151. The fixed coil *CD*, actually containing a number of turns of wire, is fastened to a vertical support. The movable coil *AB*, having only a few turns and large enough to embrace the fixed coil when their planes are at right angles to each other, is suspended by a strong piece of thread below the dial. The ends of this coil dip into two cups of mercury, located one above the other along the coil axis. Connections are made to these cups as indicated, so that the two coils are in series when connected to an external circuit.

One end of a spring is rigidly fastened to the movable coil, and the other end terminates in a mill-headed screw on the face of the dial, which screw can be turned so as to apply torsion to the spring. The planes of the coils are adjusted to be at right angles to each other. With current through both coils, the movable one tends to turn, and this tendency is counteracted by turning the torsion screw. The movable coil carries an upwardly-extending pointer which swings between two stop pins on the dial and points directly to a fixed zero line when the coils are at right angles. To the torsion screw is attached a pointer which sweeps over a degree scale. When current through the movable coil deflects it against a stop pin, the torsion screw is rotated in a direction to oppose this action; the number of degrees through which the torsion pointer is turned to bring the coil back to its original position gives the reading desired.

It is found that the current is directly proportional to the square root of the angle of torsion. For example, if with one current the deflection was 36 degrees and with another current 144 degrees, then the currents used in the test are to each other as the square roots of 36 and 144, or as 6 is to 12; that is, one current is half as strong as the other. To determine the current in amperes, the square root of the angle turned through by the torsion screw is multiplied by a constant found by calibration and furnished by the makers.

The fixed coil is usually divided into two parts having different numbers of turns, and the terminals are brought out to separate posts. This arrangement gives the instrument a double range whereby both small and large currents can be measured with accuracy. The dynamometer is connected in circuit like an ammeter and has the advantage of being adapted for use with either direct or alternating currents. When used on a direct-current circuit, it is desirable to take two readings made with the same current, one in the opposite direction from the other, and to consider the average of these readings as the true value.

**126. Hot-Wire Ammeter.**—The hot-wire type of ammeter utilizes the heating effect of the electric current for measuring current; its operating principle is the expansion of a thin wire when heated by the current through it. Instruments of this type are not affected by extraneous magnetic fields and may be used to measure either direct or alternating currents, but there are certain objections to their use, namely: they are slow in action, require frequent resetting to zero, and take more energy than other types. However, the hot-wire ammeter is particularly well adapted for measuring alternating currents of high frequency, such as are used in radio communication, because of the fact that the self-induction (§157) of the wire is practically zero.

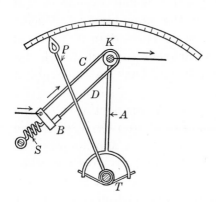

Fig. 152 shows the usual mechanism of a hot-wire ammeter. The wire CD passes around the pulley K and is held taut by a spring S acting on the insulating plate B. In use, there is current only through one branch of the wire, and consequently that branch lengthens as a result of the heat produced by the current. The slack is taken up by a slight rotation of the pulley, and this causes arm A (pivoted at K) to turn. The arm has two

Fig. 152. Hot-wire ammeter

prongs at its lower end and between them a thread is stretched after looping itself around a pulley at T. This pulley is on the shaft of the pointer P. A slight expansion of branch C of the wire causes pulley K and arm A to turn clockwise, and this motion advances pointer P to the right over the scale. The purpose of the mechanism described is to produce large scale deflections with very small changes in length of the hot wire.

The expansion of metals as the result of heating is also utilized in the *thermostat,* a device for closing and opening circuits. It consists of two strips of dissimilar metals, welded or riveted together, with one end fixed as shown in Fig. 153. When the composite strip is heated, the two metals expand to different extents and the strip bends. If an adjustable contact is provided at one side, then electrical connection can be made between posts *A* and *B* when a certain temperature is reached. When the strip cools it straightens out and opens the contact. There are many applications for thermostats in temperature control and circuit protection, and a bi-metallic material has been developed in sheet form, one face having a higher expansion rate than the other.

**Experiment 58.**—Cut a strip of sheet brass and another of sheet iron about 6 inches long and a half-inch wide. Rivet the strips together and mount the parts of the thermostat as shown in Fig. 153. Connect the terminals *A* and *B* to a bell circuit and apply a lighted match to the strip until the bell begins to ring. Note that the brass expands more than the iron. Then observe how the strip strengthens itself when the match is removed.

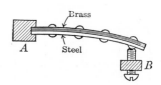

FIG. 153. A thermostat

**127. Voltmeters and Multipliers.**—Voltmeters for measuring electromotive force and potential difference are constructed in the same manner as ammeters of the moving-coil or moving-vane types. The only difference between ammeters and voltmeters is in the amount of resistance; ammeters have very low resistance, and voltmeters have very high resistance. Both instruments deflect in proportion to the current through them, but the voltmeter is calibrated in terms of the potential difference which produces the current through its coil. The coil on the moving element of the voltmeter has a resistor of high resistance connected in series with it so that the instrument may be connected directly across a generator or service mains and yet take only a small current. Because of this the voltmeter protects itself against injury, but care must be exercised not to apply potential differences exceeding the range of the instrument. When a voltmeter is placed in parallel with any part of a circuit, the total resistance of the circuit is practically the same as before because the voltmeter resistance is so very high, the current in the circuit is not materially changed, and the small current taken by the voltmeter produces a deflection which indicates directly the p.d. between its terminals.

The range of any voltmeter may be increased by adding a resistor to the voltmeter circuit; such a series resistor is called a *multiplier*. A multiplier may be mounted within the voltmeter itself or placed in an external case. Each is adjusted in resistance to suit the voltmeter with which it is to be used, so that the potential values will be simple multiples of the instrument readings.

The connections of a double-range voltmeter are shown in Fig. 154. The outer terminals are used for the 3-volt range, and the center and right-hand terminals are used for the 150-volt range, the circuit in either case being closed by the push button in the lower right corner. Naturally, the resistance between the 150-volt terminals is much higher than that between the 3-volt terminals. In using a double-range or multiple-range instrument, care should be taken to make connection with the proper terminals. If in doubt about the value of the e.m.f. to be measured, always use the high-reading scale first and then, if necessary, change to an appropriately lower one.

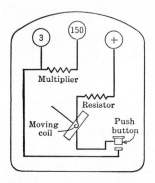

Fig. 154. Connections of a double-range voltmeter

Voltmeters, like ammeters, are made in a variety of styles. Millivoltmeters are moving-coil instruments calibrated to read in thousandths of a volt; they are used with shunts to read the values of current in the circuits wherein the shunts are inserted.

Problem 85.—A 3-volt voltmeter has a resistance of 300 ohms. What should be the resistance of a multiplier for this instrument so that potentials up to 150 volts can be measured?

A full-scale deflection of the instrument is produced by a current of $\frac{3 \text{ volts}}{300 \text{ ohms}} = 0.01$ ampere. If current of the same strength is to be established when the instrument and its multiplier are connected in series across 150-volt mains, then the combined resistance should be 150 volts ÷ 0.01 ampere = 15,000 ohms. Therefore, the multiplier alone should have a resistance of 15,000 − 300 = 14,700 ohms. Then, whichever scale is used, the current will be the same for full-scale deflection.

A voltammeter is a combination instrument in which the coil may be connected to read either current or e.m.f. depending on the position of a switch. Fig. 155 shows such an instrument with three current and three potential ranges; it is equipped with fuses to protect the coil against damage.

Fig. 156 gives the connections of a Weston voltammeter having three current and three potential ranges, as indicated. When the 3- or 15-ampere ranges are used, a part of the shunt is joined in series with the coil, but since the shunt resistances are so very low there will be hardly any change in resistance of the coil circuit. The key normally presses against its upper contact, which means that the instrument will read current values; to read potential differences it is necessary to depress the key so that one of the multipliers will be included in the coil circuit.

FIG. 155. Multi-range voltammeter
The Winslow Company

## 128. Connecting Ammeters and Voltmeters in Circuit.

—The connections diagrams of ammeters, voltmeters, and voltammeters are collected in Fig. 157. An ammeter is used to measure the current in a circuit and is connected in series with it as shown in diagram I. Ammeter $A$ will indicate the current supplied by generator $G$ to all the lamps $L$ connected in parallel. When the total current is too large for the ammeter at hand, the current is measured by connecting a millivoltmeter $MV$ across a shunt $S$ with special leads, and placing the shunt in series with the lamp circuit, as shown in diagram II. If a particular shunt has a rating of 5 amperes, then the instrument will give a full-scale reading of, say 50 millivolts, when the current supplied to lamps $L$ is 5 amperes; thus, each division of the milli-

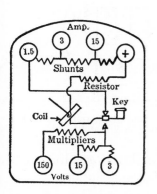

FIG. 156. Internal connections of a multi-range voltammeter

voltmeter scale corresponds to a definite current value, and the total current in the circuit can be determined easily from the reading taken.

Diagram III shows the connection of voltmeter $V$ to the lamp circuit; the voltmeter is connected directly across the line and indicates on its scale the p.d. across the generator or across the lamps. When the range of the voltmeter is too small for the p.d. across the circuit, a multiplier $M$ is connected in series with the

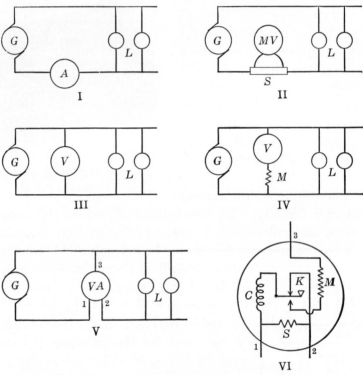

FIG. 157. Connections of ammeter at I, millivoltmeter and shunt at II, voltmeter at III, voltmeter and multiplier at IV, and voltammeter at V and VI

instrument as indicated in diagram IV, and the readings are multiplied by the figure appropriate for that multiplier.

The connection of a voltammeter $VA$, to read the p.d. and current in the lamp circuit, is depicted in diagram V and the internal connections of this instrument are shown at VI. The current terminals 1, 2 include the shunt $S$ bridged by coil $C$, and the potential terminals 1, 3 include the coil $C$ and multiplier $M$ upon depression of key $K$.

Be sure never to connect an ammeter across the line wires or to use the wrong terminals of a multi-range instrument. It has become a general habit to test dry batteries by connecting an ammeter of about 30-ampere range *momentarily* across its terminals; if this is done make certain that the ammeter is one of the cheaper varieties which does not have quite the low resistance of the better grades. Don't connect an ammeter across a storage battery, for its internal resistance is very much less than that of a dry cell, and the current will certainly burn out the instrument. The proper connection of an ammeter is in series with the load.

**Experiment 59.**—To gain experience with multi-range instruments, test the e.m.f. of a dry cell and of a 6- or 12-volt storage battery, as well as the p.d. of direct-current lighting service mains, with a voltammeter of the ranges shown in Fig. 156. Then connect the instrument to read the currents taken by a variety of 110-volt lamps and of a group of lamps connected in parallel.

**129. Wattmeters.**—The electric power expended in a direct-current circuit is equal to the product of the potential difference $E$ across the circuit and the current $I$ in it. These quantities may be determined by a voltmeter and an ammeter; when the readings of the two instruments are multiplied together the result will give the power expended in the circuit. The result can also be read directly by using a single instrument called a *wattmeter;* it indicates the instantaneous values of the power expended in a circuit to which the instrument is connected.

The principle of the wattmeter is based on the interaction between two coils, one stationary and the other movable, as in the Siemens dynamometer, §125. The stationary coil develops a magnetic field through the region where the movable coil is located, and the latter is deflected when current is supplied to it. The stationary or *current coil* is wound with a few turns of heavy copper wire having a low resistance; it is connected in series with the line like an ammeter. The movable or *potential coil* is wound with many turns of fine wire, and is connected in series with a high resistance across the line like a voltmeter. The construction and connections of the wattmeter are shown in Fig. 158. The stationary coil is divided into two parts, *AA,* and takes the entire current of the circuit. The movable coil *B*, constructed and mounted like the coils of ammeters and voltmeters, is connected

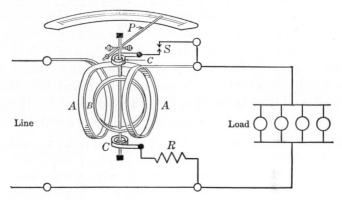

FIG. 158. Construction of a wattmeter and its connection to a circuit

in series with a high resistance *R* and a push-button switch *S*. The movable coil turns against the torsion of the springs *CC*, and its pointer *P* swings over a scale graduated in watts.

FIG. 159. Portable wattmeter
Weston Electrical Instrument Corporation

When the wattmeter is connected to a load circuit as shown, the *current* in the potential coil *B* will be proportional to the potential difference across the load, and that in the current coil *A* will be proportional to the current in the load circuit. On closing the switch, an electromagnetic force acts upon the movable coil which depends on the current through both coils, and the deflection of the pointer is, therefore, directly proportional to the power expended in the circuit.

Fig. 159 shows the external view of a portable wattmeter. This instrument can be used on direct- and alternating-current circuits and is rated according to the carrying capacity of the current coil and the limiting potential to be applied across the other coil. Most wattmeters have double current ranges, made possible by connecting the two parts of the current coil in series or in parallel, and they generally have triple potential ranges, by using additional internal multipliers.

**130. Thomson Watthour Meter.**—Meters for the measurement of electrical energy are called *watthour meters,* and these devices take care not only of the power supplied to a load but also of the duration of that load. Charge for electric service is made by public utility companies on the basis of energy supplied by them and the amounts are determined from monthly readings of watthour meters located on customers' premises.

The wattmeter described in the previous section gives the instantaneous values of power in watts expended in a circuit, just as a voltmeter indicates the momentary values of the potential in volts. In order to determine the watthour consumption of electrical energy with such a wattmeter, it would be necessary to take a number of readings during the period of test, then calculate the average of these power values, and multiply this average number of watts by the test interval expressed in hours. A watthour meter, on the other hand, gives directly the total consumption of energy in watthours, for it automatically multiplies the instantaneous indications of power by the corresponding time intervals, sums up these products, and indicates the total on a register.

The principle of the watthour meter is substantially that of the wattmeter, but the design is modified so that the movable coil can make one revolution after another. To appreciate how this rotation is produced, consider the galvanometer coil in Fig. 135 to move clockwise in the magnetic field between the poles N and S, and that its motion is not opposed by the torsion of any suspension wire or springs. When the coil has turned through 90 degrees it will come to a stop, because the forces indicated have pulled the conductors as far upward and downward as they can go. If the current through the coil is now reversed, the forces will be reversed and the coil can turn through 180 degrees farther before stopping. Another current reversal at that place will permit the coil to turn another 180 degrees, and so on. There will be two such current reversals and two 180-degree twists given to the movable coil each revolution, and continuous rotation will result.

In the watthour meter, the torque producing the rotation will depend upon the currents in both the current and potential coils. Since it is desirable to have the rotation as uniform as possible, the movable coil is divided into a number of parts and arranged about a vertical axis, with their planes at equal angles to each other, so that as one part moves away from the axis of the current coil another part takes its place. The reversals of current would have to be timed correctly in each part of the moving coil. Such an arrangement would constitute a *motor*, §227, the moving coil forming the *armature*, the stationary coil the *field winding*, and the current-reversing mechanism the *commutator*. The number of revolutions of the watthour meter is recorded by placing a worm gear on the armature shaft which meshes with a train of wheels associated with a register. Since the number of revolutions in an hour depends on the currents in the coils, the dial could be calibrated in watthours, provided the speed is made proportional to the power consumed.

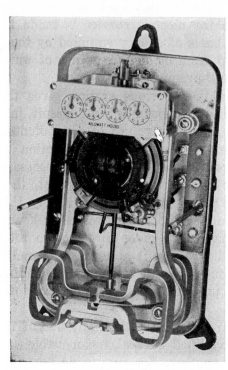

FIG. 160. Thomson watthour meter rated at 75 amperes and 220 volts
General Electric Company

The Thomson watthour meter incorporates these features of construction; a general view is shown in Fig. 160. Neither the current nor potential coil has any iron associated with it. The armature is spherical in form, and revolves on a vertical shaft between the two parts of the stationary field coil. Current is led to and from the armature by silver-tipped brushes that press against a commutator mounted on the armature shaft. The rotat-ing element is very light and delicately poised between jewel centers, so that the friction is reduced to a minimum. The con-nections of the watthour meter are the same as those given in Fig. 158 for a wattmeter.

The force acting on a current-carrying conductor located in a magnetic field is given by Formula (61) as $F = \dfrac{B \times I \times L}{4,445,000}$. Ap-plying this equation to the watthour meter, $F$ is the force on each armature conductor in pounds, $L$ is its length in centimeters, $I$ is the current in it in amperes, and $B$ is the flux density of the field in gausses. But the flux density produced by the field coil is proportional to the load current, and the current in the armature is proportional to the p.d. across the line. Consequently, the force acting on each armature conductor of definite length is proportional to the product of the load current and the p.d. across the line, and this means that the torque (force times lever arm) acting on the armature will be proportional to the power ex-pended in the load.

In order to compensate for the slight friction in the rotating armature a compensating coil is included in the armature circuit and placed so as to strengthen the field set up by the current coils; it is adjusted so that the armature will just be on the verge of rotation when there is no current in the field coils. If the meter should rotate when no electrical energy is being used, the meter is said to "creep"; this will occur if the compensating coil is too close to the field coils.

It has been mentioned that the speed of the armature should be proportional to the power; this is done by introducing a drag on the rotating element that is proportional to the driving torque. Such a controlling drag is obtained by attaching an aluminum or copper disk to the armature shaft and arranging it to rotate between the poles of stationary permanent horseshoe magnets so as to cut their magnetic lines of force. Eddy currents, §151, are induced in the disk, and the reaction of their magnetic fields tends to retard the rotation. As a result, the number of revolutions of the armature in a given period of time will be proportional to the energy supplied during that period.

Fig. 161 shows the appearance of a watthour meter for operation on alternating current. The principle utilized is that of a rotating field, explained in §250.

### 131. Sangamo Watthour Meter.

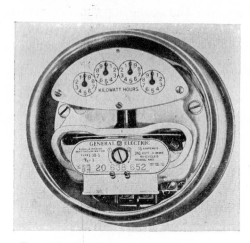

FIG. 161. Single-phase 60-cycle watthour meter
General Electric Company

The Sangamo direct-current watthour meter consists of a copper disk which revolves within a chamber filled with mercury. The principle of operation may be understood by referring to Fig. 162, which shows the relations of the various parts, and also the potential and current circuits of the meter.

An electromagnet $NS$ is energized by a potential winding $B$ connected across the line wires. The mercury chamber $C$ is made of insulating material and has molded in it the contact ears $E_1$ and $E_2$ diametrically opposite each other, and also has molded in it above the armature space a spirally-laminated soft steel ring $R$, which acts as a return for the magnetic lines of force from the electromagnet. The shaft $T$ carries the copper disk $A$ within the mercury chamber, the worm $W$ to drive the recording mechanism, and the aluminum disk $D$ for regulating the armature speed by revolving between the poles of the permanent magnets $MM$. The shaft is supported at the upper end by a jewel bearing. A series winding $G$ serves to strengthen the field of the electromagnet as the load increases, and compensates for a drop in speed due to increased mercury friction.

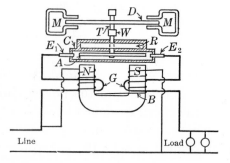

FIG. 162. Arrangement of parts and circuits of Sangamo direct-current watthour meter

The magnetic flux produced by the potential coil $B$ passes through the copper disk $A$, and completes its path through the steel ring $R$. Due to the position of the contact ears in the mercury, there is a current diametrically through the disk and this current path is directed at right angles across the magnetic field. This path may be viewed as a strip of the disk, and since the disk as a whole is free to move, the strip moves out of the field because of the electromagnetic force on it. The disk rotates from its initial position, and then the current enters at a new point on its periphery. This means that a new current strip is established in the disk like the one mentioned ahead, and it, too, will be impelled to move; this constant change in path of current through the disk produces a continuous rotation. The torque is proportional to the current in the disk and to the magnetic field, the latter being proportional to the p.d. of the circuit; therefore, the torque is proportional to the power in watts. The speed is rendered proportional to the torque by means of disk $D$, as explained at the end of the previous section.

Compensation for friction on light loads is provided for in this meter, but not shown in the figure, by an adjustable shunt circuit connected across terminals $E_1$ and $E_2$ that includes a thermocouple. This device is operated by a heating coil connected in series with coil $B$. The e.m.f. produced by the thermocouple sets up a current through the disk, and this current, reaching with the magnetic flux, produces sufficient torque to overcome friction under light loads.

**132. Reading the Watthour Meter Register.**—The dials of a watthour meter are graduated in watthours or kilowatt-hours and read like the dials on a gas meter. The usual register contains four dials each with 10 divisions, and the figure marked above each dial indicates the amount of energy recorded by a complete revolution of its pointer. Therefore the movement of a pointer over one division denotes one-tenth the amount of energy marked above its dial. One revolution of the pointer on a dial moves the pointer on the next dial to the left of it just one division. To illustrate, a complete revolution of the pointer on the "10-dial" moves the pointer on the "100-dial" one division and registers 10 kilowatt-hours.

Care must be exercised in reading the registers because the pointers of two dials turn clockwise, while the pointers of the others turn counterclockwise. Fig. 163 shows the dial-hands for a meter reading of 9121 kilowatt-hours. To read the register of a watthour meter, begin with the dial on the right-hand side, that is, the dial of lowest capacity, then note the reading of the second dial, and so on, putting the numbers down in their proper order from right to left.

Watthour meter readings are cumulative, and to ascertain the amount of electrical energy consumed during any interval of time, it is necessary to subtract the reading at the beginning of the period from that taken at its close. To avoid high speeds of rotation, meters of large capacity are subject to a multiplying constant, such as 10, 100 or 1000, and this value appears on the dial face; the registration of such meters must be multiplied by the constant to determine the actual consumption of electrical energy.

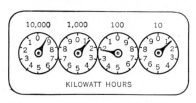

KILOWATT HOURS

Fig. 163. Reading a watthour meter

## QUESTIONS

1. Give a general classification of galvanometers according to the principles employed in their design.
2. State how you would proceed to construct a detector galvanometer.
3. Explain the principle of the d'Arsonval galvanometer.
4. What is a ballistic galvanometer and how is it used?
5. How is the deflection of a galvanometer measured with a lamp and scale device?
6. What does the term sensitivity mean as applied to a galvanometer?
7. The sensitivity of a certain galvanometer is four megohms. What is meant by this statement? Express the sensitivity of this instrument in terms of current.
8. Upon what factors does the sensitivity of a d'Arsonval galvanometer depend?
9. Why are damping resistances used with galvanometers?
10. What advantage does a dead-beat galvanometer possess over one that does not have this feature?
11. Explain the purpose of a shunt and derive the formula for the multiplying power of a shunt.
12. Classify ammeters by their different types of construction.

13. What are the relative advantages of moving-coil, moving-iron, and dynamometer-type ammeters?
14. Explain the operation of the iron-vane type of ammeter.
15. How would you arrange a low-resistance galvanometer so that it could be used for measuring potential difference?
16. Since the mechanical construction and the resistance of the movable coil of a voltmeter and an ammeter may both be the same, what then is the essential difference in the instruments?
17. Explain how to use ammeter shunts and voltmeter multipliers.
18. Give a numerical example to illustrate the use of a multiplier in extending the range of a voltmeter.
19. Make a diagram to show how an ammeter may be provided with two ranges. Do likewise for a voltmeter.
20. What precautions should be observed in using ammeters and voltmeters?
21. Describe the principle of a wattmeter.
22. Make a sketch of a wattmeter connected to a motor circuit so that it can indicate the power being taken by the machine.
23. Explain the difference between a wattmeter and a watthour meter.
24. What is the principle of operation of a Thomson watthour meter?
25. How does the Sangamo watthour meter differ from the Thomson meter, and upon what principle does it operate?
26. Indicate the positions of the pointers on the register of a watthour meter for a reading of 253,400 watthours.

## PROBLEMS

1. The resistance of a galvanometer coil is 120 ohms and a critical damping resistance of 20,000 ohms is used with it. It takes 2 microamperes to give the instrument a deflection of 10 centimeters on a scale 1 meter away from its mirror. Compute its current, megohm, and voltage sensitivities. *Ans.* 0.02 microampere, 50 megohms, and 400 microvolts, all per millimeter deflection at 1 meter.
2. The resistance of a galvanometer shunt is 0.2 ohm and that of the instrument with its leads is 1.0 ohm. (a) What p.d. is required to send 1.2 amperes jointly through the galvanometer and shunt in parallel? (b) How much of the current does the galvanometer take? *Ans.* (a) 0.2 volt; (b) 0.2 ampere.
3. What is the multiplying power of the shunt in Problem 2? *Ans.* 6.
4. A four-coil Ayrton shunt, having ratios of 1, 0.1, 0.01 and 0.001, has a total resistance of 10,000 ohms. Calculate the resistance of each coil. *Ans.* 9000, 900, 90, and 10 ohms.
5. What will be the resistance of a shunt required to increase the range of an ammeter from 150 to 750 amperes? The resistance of the instrument is 0.008 ohm. What will be the multiplying power of the shunt? *Ans.* 0.002 ohm; 5.

6. The moving coil of a certain ammeter has a resistance of 4.0 ohms and deflects full scale when the current in it is 0.0125 ampere. Compute the resistance of the shunt needed to make this instrument a 3-ampere ammeter. *Ans.* 0.01674 ohm.

7. An ammeter coil with its leads has a resistance of 20 ohms, and the shunt has a resistance of 0.01 ohm. If the current through the circuit to which the shunted ammeter is connected is 10 amperes, what current does the ammeter coil receive? *Ans.* 0.005 ampere.

8. A Siemens dynamometer is connected in series with some incandescent lamps and the torsion screw must be turned through 121° to bring the movable coil back to the zero position. Some lamps are then turned off and the angle indicated by the torsion pointer is 81°. What is the strength of current in each case if the constant of the instrument is 2? *Ans.* First 22 and then 18 amperes.

9. A millivoltmeter of 2 ohms resistance yields full-scale deflection when 50 millivolts are impressed across it. What must be the resistance of an external 20-ampere shunt for use with this millivoltmeter? *Ans.* 0.002503 ohm.

10. The moving coil of an instrument has a resistance of 10 ohms and produces a full-scale deflection when the current in it is 0.005 ampere. (a) Find the shunt resistance necessary to make this coil serve for a 5-ampere ammeter. (b) Find the series resistance necessary to make this coil serve for a 3-volt voltmeter. *Ans.* (a) 0.01001 ohm; (b) 590 ohms.

# Lesson XII

## ELECTRICAL MEASUREMENTS

Methods of measuring resistance—Resistance standards—Wheatstone bridge—Slide-wire bridge—Commercial bridges and portable testing sets—Ohmmeters—The megger and the megohmer—The potentiometer—Direct-reading potentiometer—Measurement of temperature by resistance change—Thermoelectric pyrometer—Questions and Problems.

**133. Methods of Measuring Resistance.** In the previous lesson are described the indicating instruments used in the measurement of current, quantity of electricity, potential difference, electric power, and electrical energy, all of them basic electrical quantities. Further measurements commonly made in direct-current circuits are considered in the present lesson; these include measurements of resistance, of e.m.f. or p.d., and of temperature.

Measurements of resistance in electrical work are made for many purposes and they extend over a wide range of values. A number of methods are available, and attention will be given to the more common ones. The most fundamental of them is the method which applies Ohm's Law and involves observations of current and of potential difference; this is called the ammeter-voltmeter method of measuring resistance.

*Ammeter-voltmeter Method.*—The resistor under measurement is connected to a source of electricity with an ammeter in series with it, and a voltmeter is connected across its terminals, as shown in Fig. 164. Simultaneous readings are made of the ammeter $A$ and voltmeter $V$, and from these readings the resistance of the resistor $X$ is found by dividing the voltmeter reading by the ammeter reading, in accordance with Formula (21).

The ammeter-voltmeter method of resistance measurement is well adapted to general work in the electrical repair shop, the laboratory, the power station, or the manufacturing plant. It is particularly useful in measuring the resistance of generator and motor windings, of lamps, and of all sorts of electrical appliances while in normal operation. Care must be taken not to use excessive current, otherwise there will be unnecessary heating and the measurement will give too high a value for the resistance. The ammeter-voltmeter method is used in Experiments 35, 39, 40 and 42.

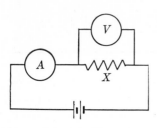

FIG. 164. Ammeter-voltmeter method of measuring resistance

A millivoltmeter will be useful for observing the p.d. when the resistance is quite low, as, for example, in measuring the armature winding of a large dynamo. On the other hand, when the method is applied to high resistances, the current will usually be small and a milliammeter can be used to advantage.

**Problem 86.**—When the current through a resistor is 2.5 amperes, the reading of a voltmeter connected across its terminals is found to be 40 volts. What is the resistance of the resistor?

$$(22) \qquad R = \frac{E}{I} = \frac{40}{2.5} = 16 \text{ ohms}$$

**Problem 87.**—In measuring the resistance of a bonded rail joint of a trolley track, the potential drop across the joint is found to be 25 millivolts when the current through the rail and its copper bond is 500 amperes. What is the resistance across the joint?

$$(22) \qquad R = \frac{E}{I} = \frac{0.025}{500} = 0.00005 \text{ ohm} = 50 \text{ microhms}$$

*Substitution Method.*—The resistor under measurement is connected in series with a galvanometer or ammeter to an appropriate source of e.m.f. and the galvanometer deflection is noted. Then a resistance box, like that shown in Fig. 73, is substituted for the resistor, and the resistance of the box is varied until the galvanometer yields a deflection identical with the previous value. Since the current through the galvanometer and the e.m.f. in the circuit are the same in the two connections, it follows that the resistance of the resistor under test is equal to the readings of the dials on the resistance box.

The connection diagram shown in Fig. 165 makes the substitution of resistors a simple matter. A movement of switch $S$ throws either resistor $X$ or the adjustable resistance box $R$ into the circuit of the galvanometer $G$.

*Comparative Drop Method.*—The resistor under measurement is connected in series with a known resistance to a source of electricity, and the p.d. across each is measured with a voltmeter. The connection diagram is shown in Fig. 166. The potential drop across the known resistance $R$ is measured by connecting the

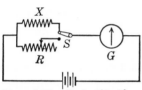

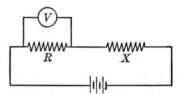

Fig. 165. Substitution method of measuring resistance

Fig. 166. Comparative drop method of measuring resistance

voltmeter $V$ directly across its terminals as indicated, and then both voltmeter leads are disconnected from $R$ and connected across the resistor $X$ under test. Since the current is the same through both $R$ and $X$, the observed potential drops will be directly proportional to their resistances. Consequently, the resistance of the resistor can be determined from the comparative meter readings and a knowledge of the known resistance.

Let $E_R$ be the potential drop across the known resistance $R$, and $E_X$ be the potential drop across resistor $X$; then the currents in $R$ and $X$ are respectively

$$I = \frac{E_R}{R} \quad \text{and} \quad I = \frac{E_X}{X}$$

by Ohm's Law. Since these currents must be equal for the series connection,

$$\frac{E_R}{R} = \frac{E_X}{X}$$

from which the resistance under test is

$$X = R \times \frac{E_X}{E_R}$$

63

The comparative method is adapted to the measurement of either high or low resistances, but for accurate results the known resistance should be chosen as close as possible to the supposed resistance of the resistor under test.

**Problem 88.**—A resistor of 5 ohms resistance is used in measuring the resistance of a heating coil by connecting the two in series to a storage battery. The drop across the known resistance is found to be 2 volts and that across the coil 10 volts; what is the resistance of the coil?

$$(63) \qquad X = R \times \frac{E_X}{E_R} = 5 \times \frac{10}{2} = 25 \text{ ohms}$$

*Voltmeter Method.*—The resistor under measurement is connected in series with a voltmeter across a suitable source of e.m.f.

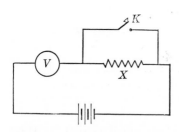

FIG. 167. Voltmeter method of measuring resistance

and a switch or key is connected across the resistor so that it may be short-circuited. Fig. 167 shows the connection plan. A reading of voltmeter $V$ is taken with key $K$ closed, and again when the key is opened so that resistor $X$ is included in the circuit. From these readings and a knowledge of the voltmeter resistance it is possible to determine the resistance of $X$.

To calculate this resistance, let $R$ be the resistance of the voltmeter, $E$ be the voltmeter reading with key $K$ closed, and $E_1$ be the voltmeter reading with the key open. With the key closed, the voltmeter reads the potential difference $E$ across the battery. With the key open, the current through the circuit is given by Ohm's Law as

$$I = \frac{E}{R + X}$$

since the voltmeter of resistance $R$ and the resistor $X$ are in series. The potential drop across the voltmeter is $E_1$ and this, by the same law, must be the product of the resistance of the voltmeter and the current through it, namely

$$E_1 = R \times I = R \times \frac{E}{R + X}$$

Solving for the resistance of the resistor under test,

$$X = R \times \left( \frac{E}{E_1} - 1 \right) \qquad \qquad \textbf{64}$$

**Problem 89.**—When a voltmeter of 150,000 ohms resistance is connected directly across a generator it indicates 110 volts. When it is connected in series with a winding of high resistance it indicates 4.4 volts. What is the resistance of the winding?

$$(64) \quad X = R \times \left(\frac{E}{E_1} - 1\right) = 150,000 \times \left(\frac{110}{4.4} - 1\right) = 3,600,000 \text{ ohms}$$

A modification of this method, suitable for the measurement of very high resistances, is the so-called *direct-deflection method,* which employs a galvanometer of known sensitivity instead of the voltmeter of Fig. 167, and omits the short-circuiting key. For example, suppose that a galvanometer having a current sensitivity (§120) of 0.125 microampere is used in measuring the insulation of a cable. This sensitivity means that the instrument would give a deflection of 8 divisions with 1 microampere, or 8 divisions with a potential difference of 1 volt applied to a resistance of 1 megohm. If now, 240 volts are used in the test on the cable, applied between conductor and sheath, and the deflection of the galvanometer is 150 divisions, then the insulation resistance of the cable is $240 \times \frac{8}{150} = 12.8$ megohms.

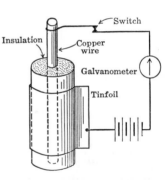

FIG. 168. Measuring resistance of insulation around wire

**Experiment 60.**—Wrap some tinfoil around a piece of insulated wire such as is used in house wiring and make connections as indicated in Fig. 168. Use a sensitive galvanometer and a radio B battery. Be certain that the insulation is in good condition, otherwise the galvanometer may be ruined. Take several readings of the galvanometer and compute the insulation resistance of the wire from the average of these readings and the known sensitivity of the instrument.

**134. Resistance Standards.**—For accurate measurement of resistance by comparison methods, use is made of *standard resistors* which are constructed with great care to achieve constancy of resistance. They are made with wire of exceptionally low temperature coefficient, are wound and treated to eliminate strain, and are aged to insure permanent resistance values. Such resistors may be calibrated by the National Bureau of Standards and certificates may be obtained which specify the resistances to an accuracy of one part in a million.

Fig. 169 shows the appearance of a 1-ohm standard resistor of high stability and also gives the connection diagram. Terminals $A$ and $B$ are the "current" terminals of resistor $R$ and these make connection with the calibration circuit through mercury cups. Terminals $C$ and $D$ are the "potential" terminals for enabling the p.d. to be measured across the resistor itself without including the potential drop in the lead-in rods. Some standards are arranged for suspension in oil and others are sealed in oil to avoid changes in resistance due to fluctuations of atmos-

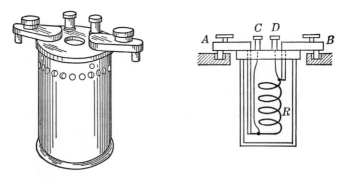

Fig. 169. Standard resistor and its connections
Leeds and Northrup Company

pheric humidity. Standard resistors are expensive and are used mainly for the calibration of other resistors which serve as secondary standards, or for the accurate measurement of large currents with the aid of potentiometers, §140.

**135. Wheatstone Bridge.**—A method of measuring resistance by comparison with a known standard was devised in 1833 by S. H. Christie and was brought to public attention by the English physicist, Sir Charles Wheatstone (1802-1875). The method involves a *bridge circuit* of four resistors with galvanometer and battery connections; the arrangement is called a Wheatstone bridge. The simplest diagram of such a bridge, and one in which the circuits can be traced easily, is the lozenge illustrated in Fig.

170. It is composed of resistance arms *A, B, R* and *X,* together with the galvanometer *G* joined across opposite corners of the lozenge, and the battery joined across the other corners. Two of the resistances, *A* and *B,* are the *ratio arms* which usually have definite values such as 1, 10, 100 or 1000 ohms each, the third is the *rheostat arm R* which has a known resistance that can be varied in small steps over a wide range, and the fourth is the *unknown arm X,* which comprises the resistor under measurement. In using the bridge, resistances *A* and *B* are given suitable values, and then resistance *R* is manipulated until the galvanometer ceases to deflect. When this adjustment has been made, the bridge is said to be *balanced,* and the resistance of *X* can be found from a knowledge of the values of *A, B* and *R.*

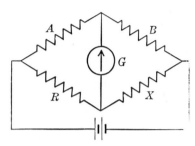

FIG. 170. Diagram of Wheatstone bridge

Fig. 171 illustrates the construction of a Wheatstone bridge

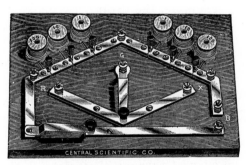

FIG. 171. Lozenge form of Wheatstone bridge for student use

Central Scientific Company

which follows the lozenge pattern very closely. It is made up of metal straps with plugs and binding posts mounted on a wooden base, six coils to enable a selection of resistance values for the bridge arms, and two keys for controlling the battery and galvanometer circuits. Gaps in the straps allow for the insertion of the rheostat arm at *R,* the unknown arm at *X,* the battery at *B,* and the galvanometer at *G.*

The theory of the Wheatstone bridge will be considered in connection with Fig. 172, wherein the resistance arms *A, B, R* and *X* meet at points marked *Y, C, Z* and *D,* and keys $K_1$ and $K_2$ are in the battery and galvanometer circuits respectively. When key $K_1$ is closed, current from the battery enters the bridge at $Y$, at which point it divides into two parts, one part through arms $A$ and $B$, and the other through $R$ and $X$; the two parts unite at $Z$ and continue to the battery. The galvanometer $G$, connected across points $C$ and $D$, is still out of circuit because key $K_2$ is open.

The current through the two upper arms $A$ and $B$ is the same, and will be designated as $I_C$; also the current through the lower arms $R$ and $X$ is the same, and this will be called $I_D$. Because of these currents, there will be drops of potential over all four arms

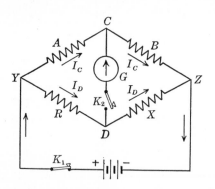

of the bridge. The potential drop from $Y$ to $C$ is the product of the resistance $A$ ohms and the current $I_C$ amperes, or $A \times I_C$ volts, by Ohm's Law. Likewise the drop from $C$ to $Z$ is $B \times I_C$ volts, that from $Y$ to $D$ is $R \times I_D$ volts, and that from $D$ to $Z$ is $X \times I_D$ volts. These four drops of potential will usually have different values; for example, the drop between $Y$ and $C$ will be different from that between $Y$ and $D$, and consequently

FIG. 172. Currents in a Wheatstone bridge

there will be a difference of potential between $C$ and $D$. On depressing the galvanometer key $K_2$, there will be a current through the galvanometer as a result of that p.d. and the instrument will show a deflection. If, however, the resistances are so proportioned with respect to each other that the drop from $Y$ to $C$ (namely $A \times I_C$) will equal the drop from $Y$ to $D$ (namely $R \times I_D$), then on closing key $K_2$, there will be no current through the galvanometer because no p.d. exists between its terminals $C$ and $D$. When this condition prevails,

$$A \times I_C = R \times I_D$$

and this necessarily means that

$$B \times I_C = X \times I_D$$

Dividing the first equation by the second member by member, it follows that

$$\frac{A}{B} = \frac{R}{X}$$

since $I_C$ cancels out on one side and $I_D$ on the other. This is the equation for the balanced Wheatstone bridge, and it shows the relationship that must prevail between the four resistances in order that the galvanometer shall not show a deflection. If the values of the bridge arms $A$ and $B$ and of the rheostat arm $R$ are known, the value of the resistance $X$ under test is found to be

$$X = \frac{B}{A} \times R \qquad\qquad 65$$

**Problem 90.**—The resistance of a coil of wire is being measured on a Wheatstone bridge and the rheostat arm is found to read 0540 when the galvanometer ceases to deflect. The bridge arms used are $A = 100$ ohms and $B = 10$ ohms. What is the measured resistance of the coil?

$$(65) \qquad X = \frac{B}{A} \times R = \frac{10}{100} \times 540 = 54 \text{ ohms}$$

It is to be noted that the current in a Wheatstone bridge does not divide equally between the bridge arms and the other pair of arms even when the bridge is balanced. For example, in Problem 90 the total resistance of the bridge arms is $A + B = 100 + 10 = 110$ ohms, and that of the other arms is $R + X = 540 + 54 = 594$ ohms; consequently, the current through the bridge arms is over five times that through the others. Suppose that arm $B$ had been increased to 100 ohms, changing the bridge ratio $B/A$ to unity. The rheostat arm would then have shown a reading of 0054 at balance for the coil under test. Under these conditions $A + B$ would have been 200 ohms and $R + X$ 108 ohms; consequently, the current through the latter would have been almost twice as great as that through the bridge arms.

**Experiment 61.**—Set up a Wheatstone bridge and a portable galvanometer and measure the resistance of some electrical device. Suppose this to be a solenoid having a resistance in the neighborhood of 20 ohms. Use bridge arms of 100 ohms each. If the bridge does not have its own rheostat arm, then use a decade resistance box such as is shown in Fig. 73. Set the resistance of the rheostat arm at 10 ohms as an initial trial. Depress first the battery key and then the galvanometer key in order to allow the current to become steady before introducing the galvanometer. The galvanometer will deflect, say to the *left*. Release the keys and add resistance to the rheostat arm. If on depressing the keys again, the deflection is still to the left but less than before, release the keys and add more resistance. If on the next trial, the galvanometer deflects to the *right*, then too much resistance has been added and some must be removed from the rheostat arm.

Proceed in this manner until a balance is obtained, and calculate the resistance of the device under test.

In the experiment, the connections of the bridge, battery and galvanometer are such that when the galvanometer needle swings to the left it indicates that resistance should be added to the rheostat arm, and when it swings to the right it indicates that resistance should be removed. In using a bridge it is desirable at the outset to establish the significance of left and right deflections of the galvanometer.

When a Wheatstone bridge is used with bridge arms of equal resistance, then at balance the resistance of the device under measurement is equal to the resistance in the rheostat arm. In this case $A = B$ in Formula (65) and, therefore, $X = R$. This means that the desired resistance value can be read directly from the setting of the rheostat arm without reference to the formula. In measuring a high resistance, $B$ should be made larger than $A$, and in measuring a low resistance $A$ should be made larger than $B$. In this way the range of measurement extends considerably beyond the resistance values available in the rheostat arm. Suppose that in a particular Wheatstone bridge, either bridge arm can be made 10, 100 or 1000 ohms, and that the rheostat arm can be varied from 1 to 9999 ohms; then the range of the bridge is from 0.01 ohm to 999,900 ohms. For greatest precision of measurement the bridge arms should be chosen which are closest to the resistance under measurement and which give the result to four places.

**136. Slide-Wire Bridge.**—There is a modification of the Wheatstone bridge which makes use of a single wire instead of the two bridge coils; it is called a *slide-wire* bridge, because the galvanometer lead is arranged to slide along the wire and divide it into two parts which then serve as the bridge arms. Fig. 173 shows a simple form of slide-wire bridge for student use. The wire is stretched between posts $Y$ and $Z$ directly over a scale, which is usually a meter long and divided into millimeters. The parts of the bridge are marked with the same letters as are the corresponding parts of the lozenge-form bridge shown in Fig. 172. Both forms operate upon the same principle, but in the slide-wire form the potentials are balanced, not by adjusting the rheostat arm $R$, but by moving the slider $S$ along the wire, thereby increasing the resistance of one part and decreasing that of the other part of the wire.

The resistance under measurement is connected to the posts at $X$, and a fixed or standard resistance of appropriate value is connected at $R$. The battery and key $K_1$ are connected between posts $Y$ and $Z$, and the galvanometer is connected between post $D$ and some point $C$ on the slide wire with the slider $S$ serving as the key. The slide wire must be of uniform cross section so that

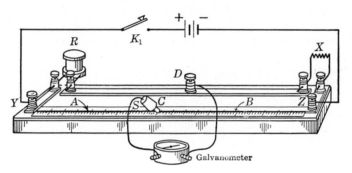

FIG. 173. Student's slide-wire bridge

the resistance per unit length is the same from end to end; it is usually made of manganin or some other metal of high resistivity.

In making a measurement, the key is closed and the slider is touched to the wire. If a deflection of the galvanometer is observed, the slider is touched to another place along the wire, and so on until a point is found where no deflection is obtained. The bridge is then balanced and the lengths of parts $A$ and $B$ of the wire are read from the scale. Since the resistances of these parts are directly proportional to their lengths, it follows from Formula (65) that the resistance under test is

$$X = \frac{\text{length of } B}{\text{length of } A} \times R \qquad 66$$

where $R$ is the resistance of the fixed resistor. Several different fixed resistors are furnished with the slide-wire bridge; they usually have resistances of 1, 10, 100 and 1000 ohms. The resistor to be selected for any measurement is the one that has the closest value to the anticipated resistance of $X$, for the error in measurement is then the least. The slide-wire form of Wheatstone bridge is also adapted to measuring low resistances, and several special designs of such bridges are available for this purpose.

In moving the slider, care should be exercised not to scrape the wire, since the accuracy of measurement depends upon the uniformity of cross section of the bridge wire. Instead of running the slider along the wire, it is best to make several trial contacts at different points and to note the direction and amount of the galvanometer deflection. About the same pressure of the hand should be applied in making contact at the different locations.

Problem 91.—A spool of wire, estimated to have a resistance between 10 and 30 ohms, is connected to a slide-wire bridge for measurement. A 10-ohm resistor is chosen for the rheostat arm and the following data are recorded when balance is obtained: $A = 350$ scale divisions, $B = 650$ divisions. What is the resistance of the spool?

$$(66) \qquad X = \frac{B}{A} \times R = \frac{650}{350} \times 10 = 18.57 \text{ ohms}$$

### 137. Commercial Bridges and Portable Testing Sets.—The lozenge form of Wheatstone bridge illustrated in Fig. 171 is used

merely in teaching the principles involved. The commercial forms of the instrument consist of bridge and rheostat arms mounted in a box with the coils inside and the switching facilities above. Wheatstone bridges with self-contained galvanometers and batteries are called *portable testing sets*. Such bridges and testing sets are designed to measure resistances ranging from a small fraction of one ohm to several million ohms.

FIG. 174. "Post Office" pattern of Wheatstone bridge

Leeds & Northrup Company

*Post-Office Bridge.*—One of the older forms of Wheatstone bridge is the so-called Post-Office pattern shown in Fig. 174. It consists of an arrangement of resistance coils, brass blocks, and tapered plugs that form three arms of the bridge, the coils being inserted in the circuit by removing plugs from tapered holes between adjacent blocks.

The plan of the bridge and its connections are shown in Fig. 175, in which the letters correspond to similar parts in the diagram of the lozenge form. The posts marked $BA$ and $GA$ are the terminals to which the battery and galvanometer are connected respectively. Both $A$ and $B$ arms are provided with four resistors each so that an appropriate selection may be made. The rheostat arm has sixteen resistors having resistance values on the "1-to-4" plan as indicated; the setting is read by adding the numbers of the unplugged holes. For measuring low and medium resistances one or two cells in series suffice to operate the bridge, while for very high resistances, such as insulation resistance, many more are necessary.

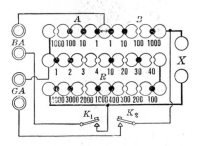

Fig. 175. Connections of "Post-office" bridge

The value of $X$ for the setting shown is 256.7 ohms.

*Decade Bridge.*—Most bridges manufactured today are of the decade pattern in which the resistance coils that constitute the rheostat arm are arranged in several groups of nine or ten coils per group, each group being designated a decade. Figs. 176 and 177 show Wheatstone bridges with five and four decades respectively; the former has a 0.1-ohm decade of ten coils and both bridges have decades of 1, 10, 100 and 1000 ohms with nine coils each. The bridge arms in Fig. 176 are controlled by two plugs set between metal blocks, while in Fig. 177 they are controlled by a single dial which indicates directly the number by which the setting of the rheostat arm is to be multiplied. The usual multiplying values of the bridge dial are 0.001, 0.01, 0.1, 1, 10, 100 and 1000.

The connections of two of the decades are shown in Fig. 178. The contact arms can be moved over the individual studs to change the resistance between terminals $M$ and $N$. The dial control of the rheostat arm is much quicker and involves less contact resistance than in the Post-Office type of bridge. The coils are wound on metal spools which are soldered to rods extending from the contact studs; this arrangement facilitates the dissipation of heat from the windings.

FIG. 176. Decade pattern of Wheatstone bridge with switches exposed

Leeds & Northrup Company

A portable testing set is illustrated in Fig. 179, together with its connection diagram. The four decade dials of the rheostat arm are shown at the right, the bridge dial at the upper left, the galvanometer at the lower left, and the battery indicated is located in the case. In using the testing set, the device to be measured is connected to posts $X_1$ and $X_2$, the bridge dial is set to the desired ratio, and then the rheostat arm is varied until the balanced condition is indicated by a zero reading of the galvanometer. If an outside battery is to be used, the internal one is disconnected and the other is joined to posts $Ba$; if an outside galvanometer is to be used, the one belonging to the set is disconnected and the other is joined to posts $Ga$. The set may be used as a four-decade resistance box by connecting with terminals $X_1$ and $R$, but the key $GB$ should be kept open.

FIG. 177. Decade pattern of Wheatstone bridge with switch parts concealed

Leeds & Northrup Company

**138. Ohmmeters.**—Instruments for the direct measurement of resistance, called ohmmeters, are more used at present than formerly. The earlier instruments are of the bridge type and the later ones are of the meter type. Ohmmeters for measuring very high resistances are called meggers and megohmers.

Bridge-type ohmmeters operate on the principle of the slide-wire bridge. The wire is broken into two or more lengths to make the instrument portable, and the scale is laid off in ohms, or in percent of a fixed resistance value, so that the reading may be made directly in ohms. Fig. 180 shows an in-

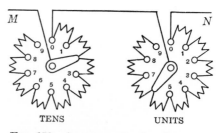

Fig. 178. Arrangement of resistors in decade

strument of this type which is suitable for measuring all sorts of resistances, as well as for locating breaks, crosses and grounds in line circuits. The balanced condition may be determined with a galvanometer using an internal battery, or with a telephone receiver using a small induction coil as the source of alternating e.m.f. The two switches at the center of the instrument make the shift from one test method to the other very convenient.

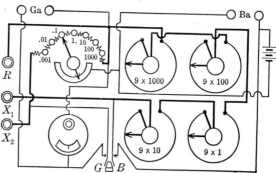

Fig. 179. Portable testing set and its connections
Rubicon Company

The meter type of ohmmeter is an indicating instrument having a scale calibrated in ohms on which the pointer indicates the resistance directly, just as a voltmeter indicates volts. Two connection schemes for this type of ohmmeter are given in Fig. 181. Herein, $A$ represents a milliammeter with its scale calibrated in

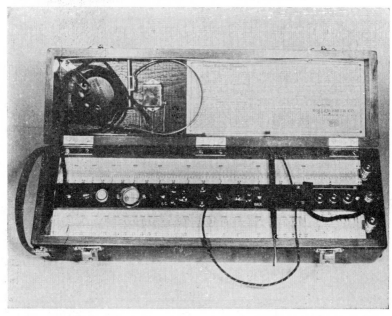

FIG. 180. Direct-reading ohmmeter
Roller-Smith Company

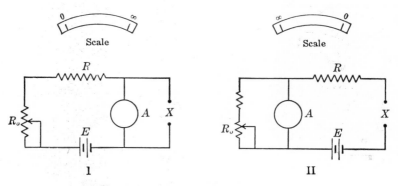

FIG. 181. Meter-type ohmmeter circuits

ohms, $E$ is a battery of several cells, $R$ is a resistor to limit the current, $R_0$ is a variable resistor which serves as a zero-set adjustment for bringing the pointer to its zero position, and $X$

denotes the terminals to which the resistance under measurement is connected. Over each connection scheme is a sketch of the milli-ammeter scale showing the resistance markings of zero and infinity at its ends; the pointer is assumed to swing to the right as the current through the instrument increases.

In the ohmmeter shown at I the resistance under measurement is connected as a shunt on the instrument. When the terminals $X$ are open-circuited, the current through the instrument is lim-ited by its own resistance and by that of resistors $R_0$ and $R$. The latter is designed to permit the pointer of the meter with normal e.m.f. to show full-scale deflection, and this point on the scale is marked $\infty$ to indicate that the resistance at $X$ is infinite. When a resistor is connected across the terminals it diverts a portion of the current from the meter and the deflection will be less. The lower the resistance at $X$ the smaller will be the deflec-tion. When the terminals are short-circuited the scale reading will be 0, showing zero resistance at $X$. Before making meas-urements with this ohmmeter, the variable resistor $R_0$ is adjusted to make the meter read $\infty$ when the terminals $X$ are open. Should the battery e.m.f. be low, it would be necessary to lessen the resistance of $R_0$ so that the current through the meter would be sufficient to permit the pointer to deflect full scale.

In the ohmmeter shown at II the resistance under measure-ment is connected in series with the instrument. When the ter-minals $X$ are short-circuited the current through the meter is deter-mined chiefly by resistor $R$. Its resistance with normal e.m.f. is such as to give the instrument a full-scale deflection, and this point on the scale is marked 0 to show that the resistance at $X$ is zero. When a resistor is joined to the terminals, the current becomes less and the deflection decreases; the value of the re-sistance would be indicated by the pointer at some position to the left of 0. When the terminals $X$ are left open, there will be no current through the instrument and the pointer will indicate infinite resistance. Before using this ohmmeter, the variable resistor $R_0$ is adjusted so that the meter will read 0 when the terminals are short-circuited. Should the battery e.m.f. be low, the resistance of $R_0$ must be increased so that it would shunt less current from the meter and permit the pointer to deflect across the full scale.

Ohmmeters of the two types described are made in a variety of forms for use in servicing radio receivers. Frequently they are provided with multipliers and shunts so that the instrument can be used as a voltmeter or milliammeter of several ranges; such combinations are known by a variety of names, including Multitester and Multimeter.

**139. The Megger and Megohmer.**—Two instruments that are particularly designed for measuring high resistances are sold

FIG. 182.   Megger insulation
tester

James G. Biddle Company

under the trade names of "Megger" and "Megohmer." They are used chiefly in testing the insulation of dynamo-electric machines, power and communication lines, signaling and train control equipment, high-tension insulators, and wiring in buildings and moving craft.

The megger consists of a direct-reading ohmmeter and a hand-driven direct-current generator assembled in a moulded case, as illustrated in Fig.

182. The resistance to be measured is connected to the two terminals of the instrument and, upon turning the small crank of the generator armature, a pointer indicates the resistance value on a scale.

The ohmmeter of the megger has two coils that move together in the field between the poles of a permanent magnet. These coils are shown at $A$ and $B$ in Fig. 183 rigidly fastened to the moving system; $A$ is called the current coil and $B$ is called the potential coil. They move around the stationary $C$-shaped iron core $C$ that is located between the polepieces of the permanent magnet $M$. Current is conducted to the coils through ligaments $L$ that are hung loosely around insulating spools, so as to offer the least possible restraining torque. There are no controlling springs as in a voltmeter or ammeter and, hence, the pointer $P$ may come to rest at any place on scale $OS$ when the generator is not

being operated. When the generator is operated, both coils receive current from it and the torques developed tend to turn
the system in opposite di-
rections. The system
comes to rest when the
opposing torques are bal-
anced, and the position of
the pointer then indicates
t h e resistance under
measurement. The entire
system is pivoted between
spring - supported jewel
bearings.

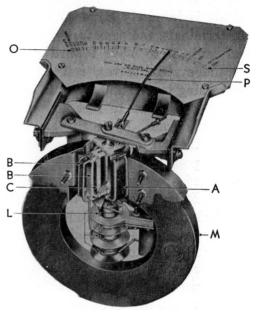

FIG. 183. Ohmmeter of the megger

The operation of the
megger can be understood
by means of Fig. 184,
which shows the electrical
connections. Current coil
$A$ is connected in series
with resistor $R'$ and the
armature of the hand gen-
erator to the instrument
terminals marked "Line" and "Earth." Potential coil $B$ is connected in series with resistor $R$ directly across the generator
armature.

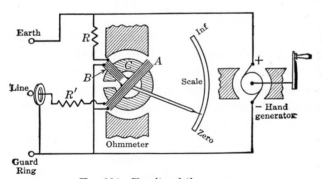

FIG. 184. Circuits of the megger

If nothing is connected across the terminals of the megger
there will be a current only in the potential coil $B$. This action

causes this coil to take up a position opposite the gap in the
C-shaped core and makes the indicator point to *Inf* at the upper
end of the scale, showing that the resistance between the terminals is infinitely large. When a resistor is connected across
the terminals, the armature will supply a current also to coil *A*
and cause it to move toward the position shown in the figure.
As the system moves, coil *B* offers an increasingly stronger
restraining torque and, when it balances the torque due to coil *A,*
the system comes to rest and the pointer will stop somewhere
along the scale. By introducing resistors of known resistances
across the terminals and marking the corresponding position
of the pointer in each case, a scale can be prepared that is
calibrated directly in ohms or megohms of resistance. Resistors
*R* and *R'* are placed in the coil circuits to protect them from
unduly large currents. No harm is done when the terminals of the
instrument are short-circuited, for coil *A* merely overpowers the
other and the pointer moves to zero at the lower end of the scale.
A compensating coil *B'* (Fig. 183) is connected in series with coil
*B* and prevents interference from stray magnetic fields and to
realize a more proportional scale.

The megger instruments in most common use are equipped
with 500-, 1000- or 2500-volt generators. In order that these
e.m.f.'s be kept steady for testing purposes, a slip-clutch device
is built into the driving mechanism which causes the armature
to rotate at constant speed so long as the generator is turned at
or above its rated speed.

The megohmer has a self-contained 6-volt storage battery,
instead of the direct-current generator in the megger instruments,
and uni-directional test potentials of 500 or 600 volts are produced by a special vibrator-transformer circuit which yields a
steady potential difference. Fig. 185 shows the appearance of
this instrument. Any of the four ranges can be selected by turning the switch at the right, and the adjustment of the pointer to
the zero position is effected by the switch at the left. The center
button permits the state of charge of the battery to be determined;
when the button is depressed, the pointer will deflect to the CHG
position if the battery is fully charged. The battery may be charged
from service mains, either direct or alternating current, by plug-

ging in the connecting cord to the appropriate socket at the upper left part of the case.

**140. The Potentiometer.**—The potentiometer is an instrument for measuring potential differences or electromotive forces by comparing them with the e.m.f. of a standard cell, a galvanometer being used to indicate the condition of balance. The potenti-

FIG. 185.  Direct-reading megohmer
Herman H. Sticht Company, Inc.

ometers made by different manufacturers differ in electrical and mechanical details, but the basic principles are the same.

Fig. 186 shows the elementary circuit of a potentiometer. The line $AB$ represents a wire of uniform resistance stretched alongside a scale (not shown) with equal subdivisions. Current is established through this wire by battery $W$, a variable resistance $R$ being included in the circuit to adjust the current to an appropriate value; this current is directed from $A$ to $B$ and is spoken of as the "working current." A voltaic cell $E$, in series with a galvanometer $G$ and key $K$, is connected across a part $MO$ of the wire $AB$, and the part included can be altered by sliding the contacts $M$ and $O$ along the wire.

With the working current through the wire, the potential is higher at $A$ than at $B$, and the potential difference between these points is directly proportional to the resistance of the wire. Since the wire is uniform in cross section, its resistance is directly proportional to its length. Consequently, the difference of potential between any two points along the wire, say between $M$ and $O$, bears the same relation to the total p.d. between $A$ and $B$, as the scale distance $MO$ bears to the scale length $AB$. It is obvious that point $M$ has a higher potential than point $O$ along the wire, so $M$ is positive with respect to $O$. Next suppose that the galvanometer key $K$ is closed, introducing

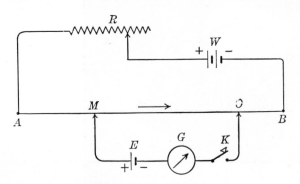

FIG. 186. Diagram of potentiometer circuit

into the circuit cell $E$, with its positive terminal connected to $M$ and its negative terminal joined to $O$. If the p.d. between these points $M$ and $O$ is greater or less than the e.m.f. of the cell $E$, there will be a current through the galvanometer, and the instrument will deflect in one direction or the other. By moving the contacts $M$ and $O$ along the wire, their positions can be adjusted so that the p.d. between them will be exactly equal to the e.m.f. of cell $E$; this balanced condition will be indicated by the galvanometer showing no deflection when the key is closed.

The principle of counterbalancing one p.d. with another permits the measurement of an unknown e.m.f. when a standard of e.m.f. is at hand. A standard cell of $E_s$ volts is first connected in the galvanometer circuit and the distance $MO$ is read from the scale when balance is attained. The cell of unknown e.m.f. $E_x$ is then substituted for the standard cell and with the same working current a new scale distance, say $M'O'$, is read at balance. It follows from the foregoing explanation that

$$\frac{E_s}{E_X} = \frac{\text{distance } MO}{\text{distance } M'O'}$$

and consequently the unknown e.m.f. is

$$E_X = \frac{M'O'}{MO} \times E_s \qquad\qquad 67$$

**Problem 92.**—In a potentiometer test a cell of 1.02 volts was used as the standard source of e.m.f., and balance was obtained when 12.4 inches of the potentiometer wire were included by the galvanometer circuit. A cell of unknown e.m.f. was connected similarly to the same wire and the balanced condition showed that 23.9 inches separated the sliding contacts. What is the unknown e.m.f.?

$$(67) \qquad E_X = \frac{M'O'}{MO} \times E_s = \frac{23.9}{12.4} \times 1.02 = 1.966 \text{ volts}$$

**Experiment 62.**—Stretch a piece of manganin wire along a meter stick and use this as the slide wire of a potentiometer. Use a lead storage battery to supply the working current, and a new dry cell to serve as the standard e.m.f. Knowing the value of this e.m.f., measure the e.m.f.'s of several other cells.

**141. Direct-Reading Potentiometer.**—The potentiometer may be designed to indicate the value of an unknown e.m.f. directly in volts, making it unnecessary to calculate the result by using Formula (67). It has been pointed out that the p.d. between two points along the wire $AB$ in Fig. 186 is directly proportional to the resistance between these points. To make a potentiometer direct reading it is necessary only to select some convenient value for the working current and to adjust the series resistance $R$ until this value is obtained; the p.d. between any two points on the wire will be the product of the working current and the resistance between these points. For example, with a working current of 0.02 ampere each ohm along the wire will correspond to 0.02 volt, and the scale along the wire may be so marked.

The circuit of the Leeds & Northrup direct-reading potentiometer is shown in Fig. 187, and the general appearance of the instrument is illustrated in Fig. 188. The circuit is based on the elementary diagram of Fig. 186 and bears corresponding letters.

It includes also a double-throw switch $S$ to enable either the standard cell $E_S$, or the e.m.f. $E_X$ under measurement, to be connected to the circuit conveniently.

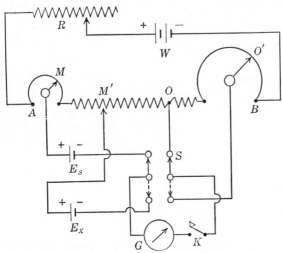

The points $M$ and $O$ on the potentiometer wire lead to the standard cell, $O$ being a fixed connection and $M$ being adjustable to allow for the small variations in the e.m.f. of the standard cell. The working current is standardized at 0.02 ampere, and consequently the resistance of the wire between $M$ and $O$ will be the e.m.f. of the standard cell (1.0183 volts) divided by 0.02 ampere, or 50.915 ohms.

FIG. 187. Circuit of direct-reading potentiometer

FIG. 188. Appearance of precision potentiometer
Leeds & Northrup Company

To use the potentiometer, switch $S$ is first thrown to the upper position and the resistance $R$ is regulated until the galvanometer does not deflect when the key $K$ is closed, thus showing that the working current has the right value to make the potentiometer direct reading. Next, switch $S$ is thrown downward and contacts $M'$ and $O'$ are moved so the galvanometer again shows no deflection; the e.m.f. $E_x$ can then be read directly in volts from the positions of these contacts. Finally, a check reading with the standard cell is made to be certain that the working current has not changed during the measurement.

The potentiometer can be used to measure currents as well as e.m.f.'s by utilizing a standard resistor, §134. The current to be measured sets up a p.d. between the terminals of the resistor and this p.d. is measured by the potentiometer as previously described. Since the resistance of the standard resistor is known accurately, the current in it can be found directly by Ohm's Law.

**142. Measurement of Temperature by Resistance Change.**—It was pointed out in §67 that the resistance of a metallic conductor depends upon its temperature, increasing as the temperature increases. The change of resistance is proportional to change in temperature, and is given by Formula (17) as $R_2 - R_1 = R_1 \times a \times t$ where $R_1$ is the resistance at the initial temperature, $R_2$ is the resistance at a temperature $t$ degrees higher, and $a$ is the temperature coefficient of resistance for the metal. If $R_1$ and $R_2$ be measured for a particular metal of known temperature coefficient $a$, it is possible to obtain the only unknown factor in the equation, namely the temperature rise $t$. Thus, by transposing, the temperature rise is

$$t = \frac{R_2 - R_1}{a \times R_1} \tag{17}$$

Consequently, a difference between two temperatures may be determined by measuring the resistances of a coil of wire at those temperatures. This method of temperature measurement is accurate and may be employed over the range from the lowest temperatures to over 1200° C. by utilizing an appropriate metal (usually platinum) for the resistance coil. The measurement of high temperatures is spoken of as *pyrometry*.

Problem 93.—The resistance of a certain platinum wire is 5.2 ohms at 20° C. When this wire is heated red hot its resistance is 22.5 ohms. Find the temperature of the hot wire, assuming the resistance of platinum changes 0.0038 per ohm per centigrade degree.

The change of resistance is $22.5 - 5.2 = 17.3$ ohms, and the temperature coefficient of resistance is 0.0038. Therefore, the temperature rise is

$$(17) \qquad t = \frac{R_2 - R_1}{a \times R_1} = \frac{17.3}{0.0038 \times 5.2} = 875° \text{ C.}$$

and the temperature of the wire is $20 + 875 = 895°$ C.

In measuring the resistance of the coil in temperature tests, allowance must be made for resistance change in the leads to the coil. This effect may be eliminated in the Wheatstone bridge method by introducing a third lead as shown in Fig. 189. Herein $A$ and $B$ are the ratio arms, $C$ is the rheostat arm, and the resistance coil $P$ forms the fourth arm of the bridge. The connecting cord between the coil $P$ and the bridge may be of any convenient length and is formed of the three numbered wires. It will be noted that wire 1-2 is in the $C$ arm and wire 4-5 is in the $P$ arm; consequently, by making the wires exactly of the same size and using a $1:1$ ratio for $A:B$, the resistance of the leads is eliminated. Then the resistance of coil $P$ is equal to $C$.

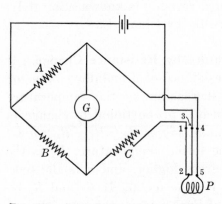

FIG. 189.   Three-lead resistance thermometer

For convenience, an ohmmeter of the meter type, §138, may be used as the resistance measuring device, the scale being graduated directly in degrees centigrade or Fahrenheit. A resistance thermometer is particularly adapted for measuring the temperatures of windings in electrical machinery.

143. Thermoelectric Pyrometer.—Another electrical method of measuring temperature is widely used; it utilizes a *thermocouple*.

If an electric circuit is formed of two dissimilar metals and one junction of those metals is subjected to a higher temperature than the other, a current is produced in that circuit because of the contact potentials existing at the junctions, §270. Over certain ranges of temperature, the current produced by such a thermocouple is found to be proportional to the difference of the temperatures. Consequently, by keeping one junction at constant temperature and subjecting the other to the temperature under measurement, the latter temperature may be determined by observing the current produced.

Many metals are used to form thermocouples, and the combinations are broadly classed as rare-metal and base-metal couples. Of the former about the most satisfactory couple is that of Le Chatelier, which has one element of platinum and the other of an alloy of 90 per cent platinum and 10 per cent rhodium; of the latter the copper-constantan couple is frequently used for the range from 500° C. to the lowest temperatures. The following table shows the electromotive forces available with these junctions at various standard temperatures, the cold junction being kept at 0° C.

TEMPERATURE-MILLIVOLT RELATIONS IN THERMOCOUPLES

| Melting or Boiling Point | Degrees Centigrade | Degrees Fahrenheit | E. M. F. in Millivolts | |
|---|---|---|---|---|
| | | | Le Chatelier Couple | Copper-Constantan Couple |
| Water, b.p. .............. | 100 | 212 | 0.643 | 4.276 |
| Naphthalene b.p. .......... | 217.9 | 427.8 | 1.585 | 10.248 |
| Tin m.p. ................. | 231.9 | 449.0 | 1.706 | 11.009 |
| Benzophenone b.p. ........ | 305.9 | 582.6 | 2.365 | 15.203 |
| Cadmium m.p. ............ | 320.9 | 609.6 | 2.503 | 16.083 |
| Zinc m.p. ................ | 419.4 | 786.9 | 3.430 | |
| Sulphur b.p. ............. | 444.5 | 920.1 | 3.672 | |
| Antimony m.p. ........... | 630.0 | 1166 | 5.530 | |
| Aluminum m.p. .......... | 658.7 | 1217.6 | 5.827 | |
| Silver m.p. .............. | 960.2 | 1760.3 | 9.111 | |
| Copper m.p. ............. | 1082.8 | 1981.0 | 10.534 | |
| L₂SiO₃ m.p. .............. | 1201 | 2193.8 | 11.941 | |
| Nickel m.p. ............. | 1452.6 | 2646.6 | 14.973 | |
| Palladium m.p. .......... | 1549.5 | 2821.1 | 16.144 | |
| Platinum m.p. ........... | 1755 | 3191 | 18.608 | |

The construction of two forms of base-metal thermocouples is shown in Fig. 190. At the top are shown two dissimilar wires twisted together at one end and welded; the wires themselves are insulated from each other by porcelain beads. The lower illustra-

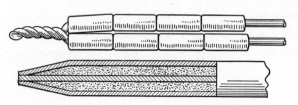

tion shows the inner metal rod welded to the outer tube and also the insulation between them. The thermal junction may be placed in a fur-nace or in molten

FIG. 190.  Construction of thermocouple

metals for ascertaining their temperatures, but they must be pro-tected from furnace gases or from direct contact with those liquids.

**Experiment 63.**—Construct a thermocouple by twisting together one end of a copper wire and one end of an iron wire, making the junction about a half inch long. Connect the free ends of these wires to a gal-vanometer. On heating the junction with a match an e.m.f. will be developed and the galvanometer will deflect.

## QUESTIONS

1. Name four methods of measuring resistance and give the details of each.
2. Which method of measuring resistance would you recommend for testing the insulation between the winding and core of an electro-magnet?
3. Which method would you use for measuring the resistance of an incandescent lamp when illuminated?
4. Why are standards of resistance equipped with four terminals?
5. What is the fundamental principle of the bridge method of measuring resistance?
6. Describe the procedure in measuring resistance with a Wheatstone bridge.
7. Derive the equation for use in connection with a balanced Wheatstone bridge.
8. The highest and lowest resistances available in the rheostat arm of a Wheatstone bridge are 10,000 ohms and 0.1 ohm respectively. The $A$ and $B$ arms have each 1-, 10-, and 100-ohm coils. What are the highest and lowest resistances that the bridge is capable of measuring?

9. What is the difference between a plug-type and a decade-type resistance box? What are the advantages of one type over the other?
10. How is the adjustment for balance made in a Wheatstone bridge? in a slide-wire bridge?
11. Using a 10-ohm standard resistor with a slide-wire bridge having a wire 10 inches long, specify the calibration of the wire so as to indicate directly by the position of the slider the resistance of an unknown.
12. Give the circuit of a meter-type ohmmeter and state the purpose of each resistor.
13. Describe the basic operating principle of the megger.
14. What is a potentiometer and for what purposes is it used?
15. Make a simplified wiring diagram of a potentiometer and explain how the instrument operates.
16. What are the two electrical methods for measuring high temperatures? Explain each.

## PROBLEMS

1. The drop in potential across the series field coils of a generator is 0.75 volt when the current through the winding is 350 amperes. What is the resistance of these coils? *Ans.* 0.00214 ohm.
2. A rheostat, battery, galvanometer, and an unknown resistance are joined in series. With 40 ohms in the rheostat the galvanometer deflection is 33 divisions. The unknown resistance is cut out of circuit and 65 ohms are added in the rheostat to yield the same deflection as before. What is the value of the unknown resistance? *Ans.* 65 ohms.
3. You are called upon to measure the insulation resistance of a motor using a galvanometer which has a sensitivity of 0.000012 ampere per division. With a 250-volt source, the galvanometer is found to give a deflection of 4 divisions. What is the insulation resistance of the motor? *Ans.* 5.2 megohms.
4. Two electric heaters, one of 30 ohms and the other of unknown resistance are connected in series to a source of electricity. The p.d. across the 30-ohm heater is 47 volts and that across the other one is 33 volts. What is the resistance of the latter heater. *Ans.* 21.1 ohms.
5. Balance is obtained in a resistance measurement on a Wheatstone bridge when $A = 10$ ohms, $B = 100$ ohms, and $R = 14.5$ ohms. What is the resistance of the device under test? *Ans.* 145 ohms.
6. In Fig. 173, the slider $S$ on the slide wire is one-fifth of the distance $YZ$ from $Y$ when the bridge is balanced. If the standard resistor used in the test has a resistance of 1 ohm, what is the resistance of the unknown? *Ans.* 4.0 ohms.
7. In a potentiometer test, balance of the galvanometer is attained at 210 divisions with a standard cell of 1.05 volts. For another cell the balance is attained at 430 divisions. What is the e.m.f. of this cell? Give a complete sketch. *Ans.* 2.15 volts.

8. A nickel coil of a resistance thermometer has 5 ohms resistance at 20° C. At some other temperature its resistance is 7.48 ohms. What is that temperature if nickel has an average temperature coefficient of 0.0062 per centigrade degree? *Ans.* 100° C.

9. A copper-constantan couple is placed in an oven and the instrument used with it indicates 11 millivolts. What is the temperature of the oven? *Ans.* 449° F.

# Lesson XIII

---

# ELECTROMAGNETIC INDUCTION

---

Electromagnetic induction—E.m.f. induced in a wire by a magnet—Direction of induced e.m.f.; Lenz's Law—Interaction between two circuits—Value of the induced e.m.f.—Effect of changing the flux linked with a coil—Disk-type generator—Eddy currents—Principle of the induction coil—Construction of induction coils—Electrolytic interrupter—Coils for automobile ignition systems—Questions and Problems.

**144. Electromagnetic Induction.**—A current of electricity through a wire was shown in earlier lessons to set up a magnetic field directed around the wire. A counterpart of this effect in circuits is to be studied in this lesson. If a wire is arranged to form a closed circuit and is then moved across a magnetic field so that it will cut the magnetic flux, a current of electricity will be produced in the wire. This effect was discovered by Faraday in 1831; he observed that electric currents could be produced in circuits when they are moved in a magnetic field or when a magnet is moved near them. In order to have an electric current in a circuit there must be an e.m.f. acting in it, and so it is apparent that whenever a magnetic field and an electric circuit move with respect to each other an *e.m.f. is induced* in the circuit.

The effect of inducing an e.m.f. in a wire by the action of a magnetic field is termed *electromagnetic induction*. This is a most interesting and important branch of the study of electricity, for it is the operating principle of many kinds of electrical apparatus, such as dynamos, induction coils and transformers.

**145. E.m.f. Induced in a Wire by a Magnet.**—To investigate electromagnetic induction, consider a wire to be connected to a sensitive galvanometer and so located that a portion of the wire is within the influence of a permanent magnet. The arrangement is illustrated in Fig. 191. Suppose the wire *AB* to be *moved down* (into page) past the N-pole of the magnet. There will be a momentary current in the circuit due to the induced e.m.f. in *AB,* causing the needle of the galvanometer *G* to be deflected, say to the right of zero. If the wire is then *moved up* past the same pole there will be another momentary current in the circuit, but in the opposite direction to the former current, as indicated by

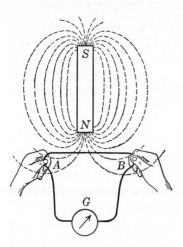

a deflection of the galvanometer needle to the left of zero. In either case the current will exist only while the wire is *moving* through the field of the magnet.

If the wire be moved rapidly up and down past the magnet, the current will alternate in direction with each change in direction of motion, setting up an *alternating current,* §169, in the circuit. When the oscillating motion of the wire is very rapid, the needle will not have sufficient time to make a full swing for each current pulse traversing the instrument first one way and then the other. As a result the needle of the galvanometer will remain

FIG. 191. Current established in wire by moving it near magnet

close to the zero mark of the scale, but vibrate noticably about that position.

Further experimentation with the galvanometer circuit near a magnet shows: that the results are the same whether the magnetic field is produced by a permanent magnet or by an electromagnet, that if the wire is moved past the S-pole of the magnet the direction of the induced e.m.f. and of the current produced thereby in each instance is opposite to the previous direction, and that if the wire is held stationary and the magnet is moved similar results will be observed. The development of current in the circuit by induction does not weaken the magnet, for it is produced by the expenditure of muscular energy. Thus, energy of motion is converted into electrical energy in a complete circuit, just as chemical energy of a voltaic cell is converted into electrical energy when it produces current in the circuit.

**Experiment 64.**—Connect a wire across the terminals of a student's galvanometer and move the wire close to a bar magnet to verify the statements of this section.

**Experiment 65.**—Connect the two ends of a wire about 30 feet long to a galvanometer, and swing slowly as large a portion of the wire as possible around a horizontal east-west axis. Observe the deflections of the instrument and deduce the nature of the induced e.m.f. which results from cutting the earth's magnetic field first in one direction and then in the other.

**146. Direction of Induced E.m.f.; Lenz's Law.**—Experiments on induced electromotive force conducted by the Russian physicist,

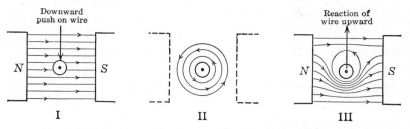

FIG. 192. Action and reaction on a wire moved in a magnetic field
Dot in wire indicates that current is forward.

H. F. Emil Lenz (1804-1865), led to the generalization called Lenz's Law. This law states, in effect, that whenever a current is established by an induced e.m.f. in a circuit, its direction is such that the magnetic field set up by this current tends to stop the motion which produced it. To illustrate, Fig. 192 shows a wire in cross section located in the air space between the poles NS of a magnet, the magnetic lines of force being directed to the right. When the wire is pushed down through the field as indicated at I, the induced current will be directed toward the reader; this condition is pictured by a dot in the wire to represent the point of an arrow. The induced current would of itself set up a magnetic field around the wire in a counterclockwise direction as indicated at II. Since this wire with its own field lies in the field produced by magnet NS, the lines will combine as shown at III and produce a stronger field below the wire than above it, as a result the wire will be pushed upward, as explained in §113. To summarize, a downward push on the wire sets up a current in it so directed as to make its magnetic field produce a reacting force upward, and vice versa. This is what is meant by Lenz's Law.

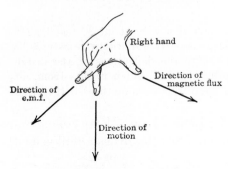

There are a number of rules which are used to determine which way the induced e.m.f. is directed, but the most common one employs the thumb and the first two fingers of the *right* hand. These fingers are outstretched and they represent the three factors involved, namely, magnetic flux, e.m.f. or current, and direction of motion. It doesn't matter

FIG. 193.  Right-hand rule for direction of induced e.m.f.

with which finger the sequence of these factors begins so long as the order remains unchanged, but to avoid confusion only one rule will be given for determining with the RIGHT HAND the direction of the induced e.m.f. in a conductor:

Place the thumb and the first and second fingers of the right hand at right angles to each other, as in Fig. 193, and *hold the hand so that the thumb points in the direction of the magnetic flux and the second finger points in the direction of motion of the wire; then the first finger will indicate the direction of the induced e.m.f. in that wire.*

To illustrate, Fig. 194 shows a wire in cross section, directed perpendicularly to the page, and located in an upwardly-directed magnetic field as represented by the vertical arrows. If the wire is moved to the left, experiment shows that the e.m.f. will be directed into the page;

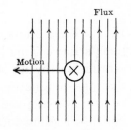

FIG. 194.  I n d u c e d e.m.f. is directed into page when motion and flux are in plane of page as shown

this direction is pictured by a cross inside the wire to designate the tail of an arrow headed into the page. Hold the *right hand* as given by the foregoing rule and verify the result stated. If either the flux *or* the direction of motion be reversed, the induced current will be reversed. If both the flux and motion are reversed, the current will be in the same direction as in the figure.

Again, when one pole of a magnet is thrust toward a coil of wire, the direction of the current caused by the induced e.m.f. will be such as to make the side of the coil facing the magnet of the *same polarity* as that pole. In Fig. 195, the S-pole of a magnet is plunged into a coil and the current is induced in it by this action directed as shown by arrows on the wire; this current produces S-polarity on the right-hand face of the coil. Hence, there is *magnetic repulsion* between magnet and coil when one *approaches* the other. When the magnet is withdrawn, the direction of the induced current is reversed, and the side of the coil facing the magnet will now have *opposite polarity* to the pole of the magnet. Consequently, there is *magnetic attraction* between magnet and coil when one *recedes* from the other. In each instance the repulsion or attraction tends to

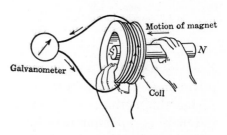

FIG. 195. Attraction and repulsion between coil and magnet

oppose the motion which initiated the current. The above statements are expressed concisely in Lenz's Law, as follows:

*In all cases of electromagnetic induction the direction of the induced e.m.f. is such that the magnetic field set up by the resulting current tends to stop the motion producing that e.m.f.*

To produce current in the coil, energy must be expended in bringing the magnet to the coil and in taking it away, muscular energy if the magnet is moved by hand, or mechanical energy if moved by a machine. Very little energy will be required if the terminals of the coil are left open, for the induced e.m.f. cannot then set up a current, and with no current in the circuit there will be neither attraction nor repulsion to overcome. The additional energy required to move the magnet with the coil circuit closed is expended in producing the current, and the greater the amount of work done the larger will be the current. It is in this way that mechanical energy is converted into electrical energy in the electric generator.

**Experiment 66.**—Connect a voltaic cell momentarily to a detector galvanometer and note whether the needle is deflected to the right or left of zero when the current enters at one of the instrument terminals. Having determined the direction of deflection for a particular direction of current through the instrument, substitute a coil of wire for the cell and repeat the tests mentioned. Find the direction of the current in the coil by tracing the direction of the winding, noting the direction of deflection of the galvanometer needle and applying the right-hand rule.

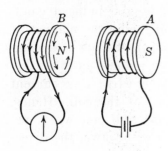

FIG. 196. Induction in one coil produced by current in another when the coils are brought together

Electromagnetic induction may also be illustrated by using two coils of wire, one for producing the magnetic field and the other to be acted upon by the resulting flux. In Fig. 196, coil $A$ is energized by a battery and is moved *toward* coil $B$ connected with a galvanometer, the arrows on the wires indicating the currents during this action. The near face of coil $B$ assumes $N$-polarity, and there is *repulsion* between the two coils. When coil $A$ is moved away from coil $B$, the polarity of the latter is reversed and *attraction* results; this opposes their separation. Such repulsion and attraction between the coils takes place only while they approach or recede from each other.

**Experiment 67.**—Use a pair of coils such as shown in Fig. 197 to verify the force actions mentioned above, and ascertain the direction of the induced current in each case.

**147. Interaction between Two Circuits.**— When two circuits are close to each other, a current in one of them will induce an e.m.f. in the other whenever that current changes. This is another example of electromagnetic induction, although it does not involve any motion of the circuits themselves. It is the changing magnetic flux around one circuit which affects the other one and develops the e.m.f. in it.

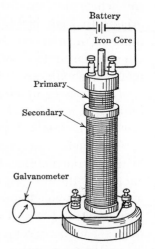

FIG. 197. Induction coil with removable primary

To study this action, consider the two circuits shown in Fig. 198, one including a battery and a switch or key, and the other a galvanometer. They are distinguished by calling one the *primary circuit* and the other the *secondary circuit,* or simply primary and secondary as noted in the figure. The parts of these circuits which are in close proximity to each other are the wires $AB$ of the primary and $CD$ of the secondary. When the primary circuit is closed, current will be directed through it as shown and magnetic flux will encircle all of it. Some of the magnetic flux which surrounds wire $AB$ is visualized by loops centered on this wire and extending past wire $CD$ of the secondary circuit.

When there is no current in the primary there will be no flux around it, but when there is a definite current in the circuit the flux loops are pictured as being in fixed positions around that circuit. The change from one condition to the other takes place by assuming the flux lines to originate in the wire at the moment of closing the switch and to grow outward by expanding into larger and larger loops, the extent of this growth depending upon the amount of current in the wire. Thus, *while current is being established* in primary wire $AB$ the flux loops expand and pass wire $CD$ of the secondary circuit. This is equivalent to saying that wire $CD$ cuts the flux of the primary circuit and has an e.m.f. induced in it by this action; this e.m.f. sets up a current in the secondary circuit and causes the galvanometer to deflect.

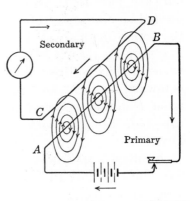

FIG. 198. Changing current in one circuit sets up e.m.f. in another nearby

When the primary current is maintained at a steady value, whether for long or short periods of time, the flux will be steady also, and no e.m.f. will be developed in the secondary. Then, when the switch is opened, the flux loops will shrink and converge upon the primary wire and vanish, causing the collapsing flux to pass wire $CD$ of the secondary. This corresponds to saying that this wire cuts the flux of the primary circuit, an action which again induces an e.m.f. in the secondary circuit and causes the galvanometer to deflect. It is to be noted that these e.m.f.'s are momentary and result only when the flux changes.

To find the direction of the e.m.f. induced in the secondary while the current in the primary is being established and being discontinued, refer again to the two circuits shown in Fig. 198. Upon closing the switch, current will be directed from $A$ to $B$ in the primary, the flux loops will grow outward and be cut by wire $CD$ of the secondary. Instead of considering the loops to move outward past the stationary wire $CD$, the flux loops may be regarded as stationary and the wire moved toward $AB$. By viewing the action in this way it is possible to apply the right-hand rule in obtaining the direction of the induced e.m.f. Between the two wires the flux is directed upward, the supposed motion of wire $CD$ is toward the right, and, consequently, the induced e.m.f. is directed from $D$ toward $C$, and the current it produces will also be so directed. Note that the currents in $AB$ and $CD$ are in opposite directions.

Similarly, while the current in $AB$ is reduced to zero and the flux loops shrink, the action may be viewed as moving wire $CD$ away from $AB$ through a stationary flux; the right-hand rule now shows that the induced e.m.f. is directed from $C$ to $D$, and the current will be likewise. Thus, the currents in the two parallel wires will be in the same direction. Summing up, when current is being established in one circuit, the e.m.f. induced thereby in another circuit is directed the opposite way; when the current in one circuit wanes the e.m.f. in the other is directed in the same way. This result is in agreement with Lenz's Law, §146. The development of an e.m.f. in one circuit by a change of current in another one is called *mutual induction*.

**Experiment 68.**—Using a pair of coils like those of Fig. 197, connect the primary coil to a source of direct current and the secondary coil to a galvanometer or milliammeter. With the coils fixed in position, note that the needle of the instrument will give a momentary deflection whenever the primary circuit is completed or is interrupted, and that the direction of deflection on "making" the circuit is opposite to that on "breaking" the circuit. Then repeatedly close and open the primary circuit rapidly, and observe that the momentary induced currents become regular and change their direction with each make and break of the primary, thus setting up an alternating current in the secondary circuit.

When an electromagnet is supplied with an alternating current, its magnetic field will continually expand and contract. A secondary coil brought near this electromagnet would be continually cut by the varying flux, and a continuing alternating current would be induced, the character of which is like that in the primary circuit. The alternating-current transformer depends on this principle (§260).

**148. Value of the Induced E.m.f.**—The magnitude of the induced e.m.f. generated in a conductor when it moves through a magnetic field is proportional to the rate at which the magnetic flux is cut. *When a conductor cuts lines of induction at the rate of* 100,000,000 *per second, an e.m.f. of* 1 *volt is induced in it.* If the rate of cutting the flux is known, the induced e.m.f. can be computed as follows:

Let

$\Phi$ = magnetic flux in maxwells cut by the conductor,
$t$ = time of cutting the magnetic flux in seconds,
$E$ = average value of induced e.m.f. in volts.

Then, the average induced e.m.f. in the conductor during the time interval is

$$E = \frac{\Phi}{t \times 10^8}$$ 68

To FIND THE AVERAGE E.M.F. INDUCED IN A CONDUCTOR:

*Divide the magnetic flux that the conductor cuts by the time taken for the conductor to cut this flux, and divide by* 100 *million.*

**Problem 94.**—The magnetic flux between the poles of a particular horseshoe magnet is 30,000 maxwells, and a conductor is moved to cut all these lines of induction in 1/40 second. What e.m.f. is induced in the conductor during this period of time?

The time interval is 0.025 second. Then

(68) $E = \dfrac{\Phi}{t \times 10^8} = \dfrac{30,000}{0.025 \times 10^8} = 1{,}200{,}000 \times 10^{-8} = 0.012$ volt

Just as a number of voltaic cells can be connected in series to build up a larger e.m.f. than is available from one cell, so a number of conductors can be connected in series and arranged to move together through a magnetic field to yield a proportionately higher induced e.m.f. If 100 such conductors were connected in series and each arranged to cut the entire flux of the magnet mentioned in Problem 94 in the time noted, the induced e.m.f. would be $100 \times 0.012$ or 1.2 volts.

**Problem 95.**—A coil composed of 120 turns of wire is placed on a table top and one pole of a magnet is brought downward toward it. If the magnetic flux through the coil changes as a result of this action from 5,000 to 80,000 lines of induction in a period of 0.03 second, what will be the magnitude of the e.m.f. induced in it during this interval of time?

The e.m.f. induced in a single turn of the coil by a flux change of $80,000 - 5000$ or 75,000 maxwells is

$$(68) \qquad E = \frac{\Phi}{t \times 10^8} = \frac{75,000}{0.03 \times 10^8} = 0.025 \text{ volt}$$

Consequently, the entire coil composed of 120 turns (assumed to be wound in the same direction and close together) would develop an e.m.f. of $120 \times 0.025 = 3$ volts.

Another way of expressing the magnitude of the induced e.m.f. requires a knowledge of the length of the conductor and its speed in moving through a region where the magnetic flux has a uniform density.

Let

$\mathcal{B}$ = flux density of the region in gausses,
$L$ = length of a straight conductor in centimeters,
$v$ = velocity of the conductor in centimeters per second moving at right angles to itself and to the magnetic flux,
$E$ = induced e.m.f. in the conductor in volts.

Then

$$E = \mathcal{B} \times L \times v \times 10^{-8} \qquad\qquad \textbf{69}$$

This formula shows that the induced e.m.f. depends *directly* upon the flux density of the region, the length of the conductor being moved through it, and the speed with which the conductor cuts the flux perpendicularly.

**Problem 96.**—A wire 5 meters long is moved horizontally in a direction perpendicular to itself through a region where the magnetic flux is directed vertically and has a uniform density of 200 gausses. Find the e.m.f. induced in this conductor when its speed is 3.6 meters per second.

The length of the conductor is $5 \times 100 = 500$ centimeters, and its speed is $3.6 \times 100 = 360$ centimeters per second; then

$(69) \qquad E = \mathcal{B} \times L \times v \times 10^{-8} = 200 \times 500 \times 360 \times 10^{-8} = 0.36 \text{ volt}$

**Experiment 69.**—With two bar magnets of different strengths and with two coils of different numbers of turns connected successively to a galvanometer, show that the induced e.m.f. depends upon the amount of flux cut by the coils, upon the length of wire (i.e., the number of turns) in the coils, and upon the speed with which the coil is moved near the magnets.

**149. Effect of Changing the Flux Linked with a Coil.**—It has been pointed out that the e.m.f. induced in a coil of wire is proportional to the change of magnetic lines of force that thread through it. If there is *no change in the flux* linked with the coil there will be *no e.m.f.* induced in it. In Fig. 199 a loop of wire is shown in various positions within a uniform magnetic field that is directed from the N-pole to the S-pole of a magnet; the

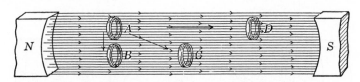

Fig. 199. Moving a coil through a uniform magnetic field without inducing an e.m.f.

plane of the coil is kept at right angles to the lines of force. When the coil is moved vertically downward across the field from position *A* to position *B,* magnetic lines of force are cut, but no induction results since the number of lines of force threading through the coil have not been altered. To explain this result, it will be noted that the upper half of the coil cuts the flux in the *same direction* as the lower half, consequently the direction of the induced e.m.f. in one-half is the same as in the other; the two e.m.f.'s in the loop are opposed to each other, and, being of the same value, no current will be established. If the coil is held in a vertical position and moved from position *A* across the field to either position *C* or *D,* no induction will take place for the same reason.

If the coil be now turned from its vertical position, *A* in Fig. 200, through say 45° to position *B, the number of lines of force threading through it will be decreased,* and during this angular motion an induced e.m.f. will establish a current around the coil in the direction of the arrow. In this case the upper and lower halves of the coil cut the lines of force in opposite directions, consequently the induced e.m.f.'s are also opposite in direction and, therefore, add to each other in setting up a current around the coil. When the coil is moved through the next 45°, or from $B$ to $C$, the number of magnetic lines through the coil changes further, and the change is greater than when it is moved from $A$ to $B$. This difference can be appreciated by noting the relative number of lines through the coil in the three positions. At the 90° position, all the lines of force have, so to speak, been emptied out of the coil. It can be inferred that the *rate of change* of flux becomes progressively greater as the coil turns from position $A$ to position $C$. At the latter position the rate of change of flux is a maximum. In consequence, the induced e.m.f. varies from zero at position $A$ to its maximum value at position $C$.

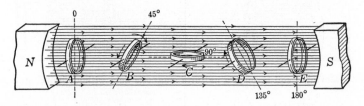

Fig. 200.  Induction in a closed coil when rotated in a magnetic field

If the motion of the loop be continued another 45° from $C$ to $D$, lines of force will again thread through the coil and electromagnetic induction will continue. The direction of the induced current, as found by the right-hand rule, is indicated in the figure. The induced e.m.f. gradually decreases during the motion of the coil from $C$ to $D$, because the rate of change in the number of lines of force decreases in the manner in which it increased during motion from $B$ to $C$. Motion from $D$ to $E$ corresponds to that from $A$ to $B$, and at $E$ the full number of lines are again through the loop; at this position there is no induction since there is no change of magnetic flux. Thus, during the revolution of the coil through a half-turn, from positions $A$ to $E$, the e.m.f. gradually increases from zero to a maximum at the 90° position, and gradually decreases again to zero at the 180° position. The same will be true of the second half of the revolution in turning the coil from 180° to 360°, except that the direction of current is reversed. If such a coil is mounted on a shaft and rotated continually through the magnetic field in the manner described, it becomes a simple *alternating-current* generator, §202.

The law of electromagnetic induction for any conducting circuit placed in a magnetic field may be summarized as follows:

IF BY A CHANGE IN POSITION OR A CHANGE IN THE STRENGTH OF FIELD THE AMOUNT OF MAGNETIC FLUX PASSING THROUGH OR INTERLINKED WITH THE CIRCUIT IS ALTERED, AN E.M.F. WILL BE INDUCED IN THE CIRCUIT PROPORTIONAL TO THE RATE AT WHICH THE NUMBER OF LINES IS ALTERED.

**150. Disk-Type Generator.**—The development of e.m.f. in a conductor by induction can be demonstrated effectively by rotating a metal disk between the poles of a permanent magnet; the arrangement is called a Faraday disk dynamo and is illustrated in Fig. 201. The disk is pivoted to rotate freely between cone bearings, and the bearing support is pivoted so that it can be tilted upward to remove the disk from the magnetic field. The e.m.f. is induced

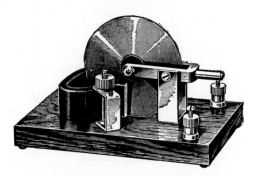

FIG. 201. Faraday's disk dynamo

in that portion of the disk, between the central shaft and the rim, which is moving between the magnet poles. Contact is made with the shaft through its bearings and with the disk by having it dip in a trough of mercury. The amount of e.m.f. generated depends upon the strength of the magnet, the closeness of its poles to each other, and the speed of the disk.

**Experiment 70.**—Set up a Faraday disk dynamo and connect it to a galvanometer. Spin the disk by hand and note the direction of deflection of the galvanometer. Reverse the direction of rotation and observe that the deflection is also reversed. Knowing the direction of current through the galvanometer, check the correctness of the current directions in Fig. 202 and verify the right-hand rule for the direction of the induced e.m.f.

**Experiment 71.**—Replace the galvanometer of Experiment 70 by a source of current, such as a 6-volt storage battery, and the disk will revolve as a motor. The speed can be varied by inserting a rheostat in the circuit. When used in this way, the disk dynamo is known as Barlow's wheel.

**151. Eddy Currents.**—Currents are also established by induction in metal parts of electrical apparatus when they move through magnetic fields. Such currents do not circulate through external circuits, but are confined to the parts wherein the e.m.f.'s are induced; they are called *eddy currents*. Suppose, for example, that the circuit of the Faraday disk dynamo were left open or that its disk were lifted sufficiently to break contact with the mercury pool. On spinning the disk, e.m.f.'s would be induced in it as before, but with the external circuit open, the currents

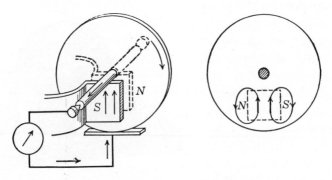

FIG. 202. Induction in metal disk with and without external circuit
Arrows indicate currents induced in disk when rotated between the magnet poles.

would be limited to internal paths. These eddy currents would set up magnetic fields which tend to stop the rotation of the disk.

The right-hand part of Fig. 202 shows a metal disk rotating clockwise in a magnetic field and not connected to an outside circuit. Imagine the magnetic field to extend through the dotted rectangle and be directed toward the reader. The eddy current paths are represented by two closed loops; the left-hand one sets up flux directed out of the page and is marked N, and the other one sets up flux directed into the page and is marked S. Thus, the field is strengthened at the left and weakened at the right, and as a result that portion of the disk within the rectangle is pushed to the right, as indicated by the left-hand rule, §113. This action tends to stop the disk, as predicted by Lenz's Law.

A compass needle in a metal case will come to rest very quickly because eddy currents are induced in the case by the oscillating magnetic needle, and these tend to stop it. Eddy currents circulate in the metallic bobbin of a d'Arsonval galvanometer coil when it moves in the magnetic field of the instrument, and these currents damp the motion. It is for this reason also that moving-coil voltmeters and ammeters are so dead-beat. Similar damping action takes place in the copper or aluminum disk of the watt-hour meter as it rotates between the pole pieces of its permanent magnets, §130.

The energy of eddy currents circulating locally in metal parts is converted directly into heat; such losses of energy take place in generators, motors, transformers and other electrical equipment. To reduce the loss as much as possible, any massive conductor, such as the iron core of a transformer or dynamo armature, is made up of laminations so placed in the magnetic field that their planes are parallel to the lines of force. The thinner the laminations the lower will be the loss due to eddy currents.

**Experiment 72.**—Close the circuit of an electromagnet and strike one pole flatwise with a piece of sheet copper; a cushioning effect will be observed. Eddy currents are induced in the copper and the reaction of the magnetic field produced by them tends to oppose the motion. When the current is turned off the sheet will strike the pole with greater force.

**Experiment 73.**—Fasten a copper penny to a thread and suspend the coin between the poles of a horseshoe electromagnet. Twist the thread and then allow it to unwind. Establish current through the magnet and observe that the motion of the penny will cease, due to the reaction of the eddy currents. When the circuit is broken the thread carrying the coin will continue to untwist.

**Experiment 74.**—Suspend a permanent bar magnet horizontally and centrally over a copper disk and then rotate the disk about a vertical axis. If the magnet is free to move, it will be dragged around in the same direction as the disk. Explain the action with a diagram.

**152. Principle of the Induction Coil.**—An induction coil consists of a straight core made up of a cylindrical bundle of soft iron wires, a primary coil composed of two or more layers of coarse wire, and a secondary coil composed of thousands of turns of fine wire, both coils being wound around the core as shown in Fig. 203.

The primary is connected to a battery through an automatic interrupter for making and breaking the circuit. At the "make" and at the "break" of the primary circuit an e.m.f. is induced in the secondary circuit due to changing the magnetic flux that threads through it, and this induced e.m.f. may be sufficiently high to produce a series of sparks through the air from one secondary terminal to the other. The appearance of an inexpensive type of induction coil is illustrated in Fig. 204; it gives sparks an inch long when operated on 3 to 5 dry cells connected in series.

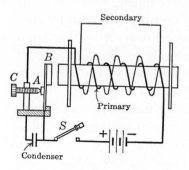

FIG. 203. Connections of induction coil

The interrupter operates like the vibrator of an electric bell, §110. In Fig. 203 a strip of spring brass or steel, fixed at its lower end, is fitted with a soft iron armature $B$ at the other. On its opposite side it carries a piece of platinum $A$, which is aligned with a platinum-tipped adjustable thumbscrew $C$. When the battery circuit is closed at switch $S$, a current is set up from $A$ to $C$ and through the primary winding. This current magnetizes the iron core and causes the armature to be attracted. Contact $A$ is drawn away from screw $C$ by this action, breaking the primary circuit; as a result the magnetism of the core ceases and the spring goes back again, "making" the circuit. These events are repeated over and over again. The strip of metal vibrates continually and the circuit is made and broken a few hundred or perhaps a thousand times per minute.

FIG. 204. Box-type induction coil

On every "make" the induced current in the secondary is in one direction and on every "break" the induced current is in the opposite direction. Interrupted currents in the primary, therefore, produce alternating currents in the secondary.

The rapidity of magnetization and demagnetization of the iron core determines the rate of change of the magnetic flux that threads through the secondary coil, and hence, the amount of e.m.f. induced. A condenser (§165) is connected across the vibrator contacts to reduce the sparking there and to make the primary current fall abruptly to zero. It is found that the flux collapses more rapidly than it rises, and hence the e.m.f. developed on the break is much higher than that on the make; as a result the secondary e.m.f. is practically unidirectional except for relatively short spark lengths. In operating a coil it is possible to tell the polarity of the secondary winding by observing the spark; the spark appears thicker and more brilliant near the negative terminal.

**Experiment 75.**—Operate a small induction coil on a dry battery and measure the length of spark produced between the secondary terminals as the number of cells included in the primary circuit is varied. Note that the spark appears thicker near one terminal than near the other.

**153. Construction of Induction Coils.**—Induction coils are usually rated according to the number of inches that the spark will jump between the secondary terminals through the air. Generally the primary is wound with two or more layers of insulated copper wire, ranging from No. 10 to No. 16 A.w.g., thoroughly insulated from the core and from the secondary. The secondary is wound over the primary and consists of many turns of copper wire which may range in size from No. 30 to No. 40. Induction coils are usually operated on

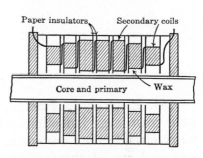

Fig. 205. Sectional view of multi-coil secondary winding of large induction coil

from about 4 to 25 volts, according to the size. The application of excessive potentials causes sparking and perhaps destruction of the platinum contacts.

When an induction coil is designed to produce sparks of 2 inches or more in length, the secondary is usually wound in a number of sections and separated from each other by appropriate insulation in order to reduce the potential difference between the terminals of each section. This type of construction is shown in Fig. 205; naturally the sections are connected so that the current in all of them will circulate in the same direction.

A certain 12-inch induction coil has 64 sections ⅛ inch wide in its secondary winding which aggregates 77,400 turns of No. 33 A.w.g. single silk-insulated wire, the average diameter inside being 5 inches and outside 6¾ inches. The primary of this coil has 2 layers of No. 11 A.w.g. cotton-covered wire wound to an axial length of 20½ inches over an iron core 2⅜ inches in diameter. A hard-rubber tube 3¾ inches in outside diameter and having a wall ⅜ inch thick is part of the insulation between the two windings.

The following table gives the sparking distances and approximate corresponding e.m.f.'s between opposed sharp needle points under ordinary atmospheric conditions:

SPARKING DISTANCES IN AIR

| Volts (Effective) | Distance (Inches) | Volts (Effective) | Distance (Inches) |
|---|---|---|---|
| 5,000 | 0.22 | 60,000 | 4.65 |
| 10,000 | 0.47 | 70,000 | 5.9 |
| 20,000 | 1.00 | 80,000 | 7.2 |
| 30,000 | 1.62 | 100,000 | 9.6 |
| 40,000 | 2.44 | 125,000 | 12.4 |
| 50,000 | 3.55 | 150,000 | 15.0 |

**154. Electrolytic Interrupter.**—Independent interrupters are used with large induction coils for making and breaking the primary circuit; they are connected directly to an electric light circuit and are of the following types: *magnetic, mechanical,* and *electrolytic.* The magnetic interrupter is practically a relay for closing and opening the primary circuit and its own winding is supplied with current from the lighting circuit and regulated by a rheostat. This type of interrupter is called a vibrator. A mechanical interrupter is any device that will open and close two contact points by means of a purely mechanical contrivance, such as the contact wheel or "timer" used with the ignition systems on automobiles (§155), or the mercury jet interrupter in which mercury intermittently impinges on a pair of electrodes.

The electrolytic or Wehnelt interrupter, a simple form of which is shown in Fig. 206, consists of a glass or porcelain jar containing a dilute solution of sulfuric acid, $H_2SO_4$, in which is immersed a large lead electrode, Pb, and a small platinum electrode, Pt. The platinum wire is introduced into the electrolyte through a glass tube and presents a very small but adjustable surface to the electrolyte. If these two electrodes are connected in series with the primary of an induction coil in such a manner that the platinum is connected to the positive terminal of the source of supply, the current in the circuit will be subjected to regular and very rapid interruptions.

When current is established through the electrolyte from the platinum to the lead plate, it sets up electrochemical action and liberates gases; one of them, oxygen, envelopes the platinum tip and insulates it from the solution, thereby opening the primary circuit. When the current stops, there is nothing to sustain the oxygen bubbles and they collapse, allowing the current to be reestablished through the primary. This action is very rapid and continues indefinitely; the interruptions of the primary current are sharp. The speed of the interrupter depends upon the area of the platinum exposed, the characteristics of the coil, and the applied potential difference. This type of interrupter will not function well on continuous potentials of less than 80 volts.

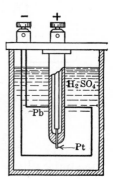

FIG. 206. Wehnelt electrolytic interrupter

**155. Coils for Automobile Ignition Systems.**—Induction coils are used to produce the sparks in automobile engine cylinders for igniting the gasoline vapors. The primary winding has comparatively few turns of heavy wire and the secondary winding has thousands of turns of fine wire, and usually one end of the secondary winding is connected to one end of the primary winding to form a common terminal. Laminated silicon iron forms the core and a shell of like material is placed around the windings to increase the magnetic flux. The potentials built up by the coil range roughly from 5000 to 15,000 volts.

Fig. 207 shows the connections of a typical ignition system. The low-tension circuit at the left includes the storage battery, the primary of the induction coil, the circuit breaker mechanism, and the condenser; the high-tension circuit at the right includes the secondary of the induction coil, the distributor cap and rotor, and

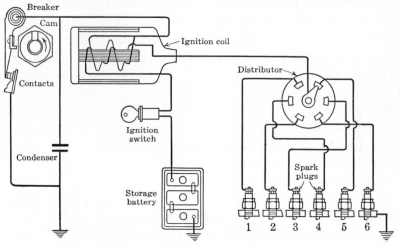

FIG. 207. Automobile ignition system
The grounded terminals connect to engine and frame.

the spark plugs on the engine. The rotation of the cam causes the breaker lever to close and open the contacts, thereby making and breaking the circuit of the primary winding. As a result of this action, e.m.f.'s are induced in the secondary winding and these are conveyed to the spark plugs in the order of firing by means of the distributor rotor and contact cap.

The condenser serves the usual purpose of reducing the spark at the breaker contacts when the circuit is opened and thereby making the break more rapid; this results in a quick collapse of the magnetic field in the coil and the generation of a high e.m.f. The contact points of the breaker are timed to break the circuit just at the instant when the spark is needed in each cylinder; at

FIG. 208. Distributor for automobile ignition
General Motors Corporation

the same time the distributor rotor makes connection with the contact in the distributor cap that leads to the spark plug in the appropriate cylinder. The appearance of a distributor is indicated in Fig. 208.

In every automobile ignition system means are provided for advancing and retarding the spark for more effective car operation. One such arrangement is a centrifugal control mechanism which rotates the cam to give the desired spark advance for the particular engine speed. Another is a vacuum control which is designed for greater gasoline economy. A combination of both centrifugal and vacuum advance is often used.

## QUESTIONS

1. What is meant by electromagnetic induction?
2. If a permanent magnet is placed inside a coil of wire, and if then the terminals of the coil are connected to a galvanometer, will the needle of the instrument be deflected? Give a reason for your answer.
3. In Question 2, after having connected the galvanometer to the coil, suppose the magnet were withdrawn from the coil. Would the needle be deflected? If so, how would the current be directed around the coil as viewed from the end from which the magnet was withdrawn?
4. Indicate in general terms how long an induced current lasts.
5. How would you determine the direction of the induced e.m.f. in a wire that is moved past one of the poles of a magnet?
6. Give the right-hand rule for the direction of an induced e.m.f.
7. State Lenz's Law and illustrate it by an example.
8. Why is more force required to thrust a magnet inside a coil when the coil terminals are connected together than when the terminals are not connected so as to form a closed circuit?
9. What determines the magnitude of an induced e.m.f.?
10. What factors determine the amount of e.m.f. that may be induced in a conductor?
11. How many lines of force must be cut by one conductor per second to generate one volt?
12. Is it possible to move a conducting circuit in a magnetic field and not have a current induced in it? Illustrate your answer.
13. Explain the character of the e.m.f. induced in a loop of wire that is turned about a diametral axis within a magnetic field.
14. Explain the action that takes place in a metal disk when it is rotated in a magnetic field.
15. The core of an electromagnet protrudes upward through its winding and a thin metal cylinder is placed around the upper part of the core. Upon closing the circuit of the magnet the cylinder jumps up. Why?
16. What are eddy currents and of what use are they?

17. Make a complete sketch of an induction coil and indicate the directions of current in the primary and secondary circuits at "make" and at "break."
18. What is the difference between the current from a battery and that from the secondary of an induction coil?
19. Explain fully why one secondary terminal of an induction coil can appropriately be called a cathode and the other an anode.
20. What is the advantage of using a condenser with an induction coil?
21. Explain the operation of an electrolytic interrupter.
22. Describe and explain the operation of an automobile ignition system.

## PROBLEMS

1. A wire is moved through a magnetic field having a total flux of one million maxwells in a time interval of one-fiftieth of a second. What is the average e.m.f. induced in this wire during the stated interval? *Ans.* 0.5 volt.
2. At what rate must a coil of 10 turns cut magnetic lines of force to develop 1 volt? *Ans.* $10^7$ maxwells per second.
3. A coil of 400 turns is located in a magnetic field and a flux of 20,000 maxwells passes through it. The coil is then turned to a new position, so that the flux through it is reduced to zero. If the time of turning the coil from one position to the other is 0.1 second, what average e.m.f. will be induced in the coil during the interval? *Ans.* 0.8 volt.
4. Find the e.m.f. induced in a wire 50 centimeters long that is moved at a speed of 6 meters per second transversely through a magnetic field having a flux density of 10,000 gausses. *Ans.* 3 volts.
5. A conductor 1 foot long moves through a magnetic field in air perpendicularly to the flux at a speed of 90 feet per second. What must be the intensity of the field if the conductor is to develop 2 volts? *Ans.* 2390 oersteds.

# Lesson XIV

## INDUCTANCE AND CAPACITANCE

Mutual induction—Self-induction—Inductance of a solenoid—Magnetic circuits—Magnetomotive force—Reluctance—Law of the magnetic circuit—Calculation of magnetic circuits—Electric fields—Condensers—Electrolytic condensers—Capacitance—Capacitors in parallel and in series—Questions and Problems.

**156. Mutual Induction.**—In considering the action of one circuit upon another in the preceding lesson, it was pointed out that a change of current in any circuit produces an alteration in the magnetic field around it, and the accompanying change in flux sets up an e.m.f. in any other circuit that may be located nearby. The current in a direct-current circuit will change when the circuit is closed or opened, or when the load is varied. The same is true in an alternating-current circuit, but in this case even the maintenance of current without any switching of the circuit or alteration of load involves changes of current value continually.

All changes of current induce e.m.f.'s in neighboring circuits. The more rapidly the current changes in one circuit the greater will be the e.m.f. induced in the other; in fact, the value of this e.m.f. depends directly upon the *rate of change of current*. The value also depends upon the closeness of the circuits to each other, more particularly, how closely the two are interlinked with magnetic flux; the extent of interlinkage or coupling is called the *coefficient of mutual induction*. Specifically, the coefficient of mutual induction of two coils is the factor by which the rate of change of current in one coil must be multiplied to obtain the e.m.f. induced in the other.

The coefficient of mutual induction, more briefly spoken of as *mutual inductance,* is expressed in terms of a unit called the *henry*:

it is named after the American physicist, Joseph Henry (1797-1878). Two coils are said to have a mutual inductance of 1 henry when a *change of current* of 1 ampere per second in one coil causes an e.m.f. of 1 volt to be induced in the other. Should the current change twice as fast in the first coil, that is at the rate of 2 amperes per second, the induced e.m.f. in the other would be 2 volts, and so on. From these facts it will be evident that the mutual inductance of any two coils is equal to the e.m.f. induced in one of them divided by the rate of change of current in the other.

If the two coils are brought closer together, they will be linked by more lines of magnetic flux than before and, consequently, for the same rate of current change in one coil the induced e.m.f. in the other will be greater. Thus, the mutual inductance of any pair of coils depends upon their proximity. Further, the mutual inductance of the coils would be greatly increased by placing them on an iron rod, because the magnetic flux linking the coils would then be much greater than before. When so placed, however, the two coils would not have a constant mutual inductance because a change in current would not in general cause a proportional change of magnetic flux through the iron.

**Problem 97.**—Two coils, $A$ of 300 turns and $B$ of 600 turns, are placed a few inches apart. Coil $A$ is connected in series with a battery and a rheostat $R$, while coil $B$ is connected to a galvanometer $G$, as shown in

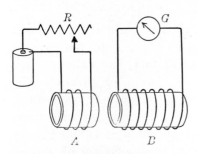

FIG. 209. Induction of e.m.f. in coil $B$ while current changes in coil $A$

Fig. 209. The current in $A$ is made to change uniformly from 2 to 32 amperes in 0.03 second, and as a result 2 volts are induced in $B$ and maintained for this short interval. What is the mutual inductance of the coils?

The change of current is 30 amperes in 0.03 second, which is at the rate of $30/0.03 = 1000$ amperes per second. This is the rate of change of current and does not imply that the current is ever 1000 amperes in coil $A$; in fact, the problem states that the current rose only to 32 amperes. Since the mutual inductance is the e.m.f. induced in one coil divided by the rate of current change in the other, the mutual inductance of coils $A$ and $B$ becomes 2 volts divided by 1000 amperes per second which is 0.002 henry, or 2.0 millihenries.

The direction of the induced e.m.f. can be found by Lenz's Law, §146. Increasing the current in coil $A$ is equivalent to moving this coil mechanically nearer to coil $B$; an action that causes the e.m.f. induced in $B$ to be opposite in direction to the current in $A$. Also, decreasing the current in coil $A$ causes the e.m.f. induced in coil $B$ to have the same direction as the current in $A$.

Usually the e.m.f. induced in a circuit by current changes in another is a desired effect; in a case of this kind the two circuits are designed to develop a particular e.m.f. for the purpose intended. The induction coil and the transformer are well-known examples. There are also many cases where the e.m.f. induced in a circuit disturbs its normal operation and provisions must be made to minimize the induction. An example of the latter is the mutual induction between a telephone circuit and nearby electric lighting, street railway or power lines, which carry relatively large currents that fluc-

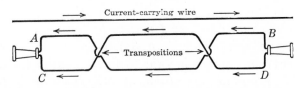

Fig. 210. Transposition of the wires of a telephone line

tuate in value. These lines set up induced currents in the telephone circuit and make it "noisy." Such disturbances can be reduced by transposing the telephone wires as shown in Fig. 210. Here the current-carrying wire represents an electric power line located near and parallel to the telephone line.

The effect of transposing the wires is to make the average distance between the inducing wire and each wire of the telephone circuit the same so that the total e.m.f. developed by electromagnetic induction in wire $AB$ will equal the total e.m.f. induced in wire $CD$. Hence, these e.m.f.'s will neutralize each other. The induction between two or more parallel telephone circuits may be noticed by the faint sound of voices at the receivers, causing what is termed "cross-talk." Most of this disturbance is avoided by the use of twisted-pair conductors because the wires are repeatedly transposed.

**157. Self-Induction.**—When two circuits are close together, a change of current in one of them produces an e.m.f. in the second because of the change in flux linking the second coil, as already explained. A change of current in one of the coils will cause a change of flux not only through the other coil but also through the very coil in which the current is changing. Hence a change of current *in any coil* will cause an e.m.f. to be induced in that same coil, an effect called *self-induction*. The direction of this e.m.f. is always such as to oppose the change of current which caused it; for this reason the e.m.f. is called the *counter e.m.f. of self-induction*.

The factor by which the rate of change of current in a circuit must be multiplied in order to obtain the amount of counter e.m.f. induced in itself is called the *coefficient of self-induction*. It also bears the simpler name of *inductance*. The unit of inductance, like that of mutual inductance, is the henry. *A circuit has an inductance of 1 henry if a current change of 1 ampere per second causes an e.m.f. of 1 volt to be induced in it.* A circuit in which a large counter e.m.f. of self-induction is set up for a given rate of current change is said to have a large inductance.

A coil of many turns of wire has more inductance than the same wire has when unwound and forming only a single loop, because a change of flux about each turn affects all turns nearby. A coil wound upon an iron core has more inductance than a like coil without iron. Thus, the inductance of a coil depends upon the coil itself as well as its magnetic environment. Specifically, the inductance of a coil is measured by the amount of energy associated with the magnetic field around it. The coil possesses inductance whether there is current through it or not, but the effects of inductance depend upon the presence of current.

When a current is established in a wire by impressing a potential difference across its ends, magnetic loops originate at the center of the wire and grow outward. In so doing they "cut" through the entire sectional area of the wire. This cutting of the wire by its own lines of force induces in it the e.m.f. of self-induction, and this *opposes* the applied p.d. which established the current. With a steady impressed p.d. the induction in a circuit is only momentary, and only a brief interval of time is required for the current in the circuit to reach its ultimate value. When the current through the wire is stopped, the magnetic field collapses, and in so doing the flux again cuts the wire, but in the opposite direction. A momentary induced e.m.f. is set up in the *same direction* as the applied p.d. and tends to maintain the current. Thus, these momentary e.m.f.'s due to self-induction oppose the growth and decay of current in a circuit.

**Experiment 76.**—To illustrate the effect of inductance, set up a circuit as depicted in Fig. 211, which shows an electromagnet connected in parallel with a lamp and joined to a direct-current generator through a resistor and a switch. The resistance should be adjusted so that with the switch closed the lamp filament will be just perceptably red.

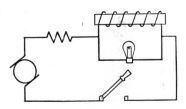

FIG. 211. Experiment to illustrate effect of inductance

Upon closing the switch, the lamp will flash brightly for a moment and then become dim. This action is explained by the fact that the magnetic field around the coil had first to be established and that during its formation the e.m.f. of self-induction hindered the current growth in the coil, consequently it did not serve effectively as a shunt across the lamp. Upon opening the switch quickly, the lamp will flash even more brightly, because the large e.m.f. induced in the coil by the rapidly decaying flux then establishes a strong pulse of current through the lamp.

Circuits having large inductance, like the field coils of dynamos, may develop such large e.m.f.'s when they are opened rapidly that the insulation may be endangered. Sometimes multi-blade switches are used in field circuits so that they may be opened simultaneously at a number of places, thus reducing the danger of breakdown of the insulation.

With direct current in a circuit containing inductance, there is no inductive action after a steady current has been established, and this usually requires only a fraction of a second. With alternating current, however, since the current is continually varying in value, the effect of self-induction continues as long as the current is maintained, causing a reduction in the strength of the current in the circuit (§179).

Perhaps the most frequently observed effect of inductance is the bright spark which appears at the place where a circuit is broken, due to the momentary e.m.f. induced in the circuit when the flux around it collapses. When this occurs the energy of the magnetic field is converted into heat energy at the spark.

For some purposes it is necessary to have coils of wire with hardly any inductance, and this means, of course, that there must be very little magnetic flux around them. Such so-called *non-inductive coils* are wound by arranging the wire in a long "hair-pin" loop and winding the two conductors so formed side by side until the coil has the desired resistance. The current in such coils circulates clockwise through one half the loop and counterclockwise through the other, consequently, the magnetic flux around each half is neutralized by that around the other. Another way to minimize the inductance of a winding is to wrap the wire around a flat sheet of insulating material. The resistance coils used in apparatus for electrical measurements are wound non-inductively.

**158. Inductance of a Solenoid.**—It can be shown that the inductance of a solenoid without an air-core depends upon three factors: the number of turns of wire, the average radius of these turns, and the length of the solenoid itself. The inductance is directly proportional to the square of the number of turns and to the square of the radius; it is inversely proportional to the length of the solenoid.

Let

> $n$ = number of turns on the solenoid,
> $r$ = average radius of a turn in inches,
> $l$ = length of solenoid in inches,
> $L$ = inductance of solenoid in henries.

Then the approximate inductance of the solenoid is given by

$$L = \frac{(n \times r)^2}{l \times 10^7}$$

**70**

TO ESTIMATE THE INDUCTANCE OF A SOLENOID IN HENRIES:

*Multiply the number of turns by their average radius in inches, square the result, then divide by the length of the solenoid in inches, and by 10 million.*

**Problem 98.**—An air-core solenoid is 2 feet long and wound with 600 turns of wire. Calculate its inductance on the supposition that the average radius of a turn is 1.25 inches.

(70)  $L = \dfrac{(n \times r)^2}{l \times 10^7} = \dfrac{(600 \times 1.25)^2}{24 \times 10^7} = \dfrac{5625}{24 \times 10^5} = 2.34 \times 10^{-3}$ henry

or 2.34 millihenries.

**159. Magnetic Circuits.**—Since the inductance of an electric circuit depends so much upon the magnetic field around that circuit, further attention will be directed to the region in which the magnetic flux is set up. Magnetic flux always forms closed loops and this fact accounts for the application of the term *magnetic circuit* to the path that the flux loops follow. Just as electric current follows a closed path in an electric circuit, so does magnetic flux follow a definite path in a magnetic circuit.

A simple magnetic circuit of uniform cross section is a solid iron ring as represented at I in Fig. 212. The magnetic flux is set up by current in a winding of insulated wire which usually surrounds the entire ring. The loops of flux lie entirely within the

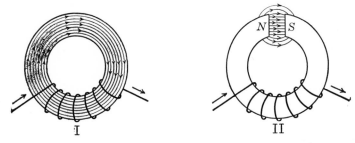

FIG. 212. Simple forms of magnetic circuits

ring (except for a slight amount of leakage) and are directed as shown for the current direction indicated. The ring does not exhibit polarity since the flux does not leave or enter the iron.

When an air-gap is made by sawing out a small section of the ring, as shown at II, the lines of flux pass through the gap to complete their paths, and strong poles are developed where the cut was made. Since air has a much lower permeability than iron, the same current through the winding will produce less flux than in the complete ring at I. This is equivalent to saying that the presence of the air gap adds opposition to the establishment of magnetic flux. The opposition to the formation of flux in a magnetic circuit is called *reluctance*. It is analogous to resistance in an electric circuit.

There is a good deal of similarity between electric circuits carrying current and magnetic circuits carrying flux. To produce current in an electric circuit requires a source of electromotive force, such as a battery or generator. Similarly, to produce flux in a magnetic circuit requires a magnetizing agency called *magnetomotive force;* this agency is provided by a winding around the magnetic circuit with current in it. The analogy between electric and magnetic circuits will be discussed again after further consideration of magnetomotive force and reluctance.

**160. Magnetomotive Force.**—The effectiveness of a winding in establishing flux through a magnetic circuit depends upon two factors, namely the number of turns of wire and the current through them. Increasing the number of turns on a winding and using the same current, increases the magnetization proportionately; so does increasing the current in the same winding. These facts can be stated more tersely by saying that the magnetomotive force of a winding is directly proportional to the number of turns and to the current through them.

Let

$N$ = number of turns on the winding,
$I$ = current through the winding in amperes.

Then the magnetomotive force is given by

$$\text{m.m.f.} = N \times I \qquad\qquad 71$$

and is expressed in ampere-turns. The size of wire used for the winding has no direct bearing on the magnetization, but it does affect the number of turns that can be placed in a limited winding space as well as the current that can be accommodated without excessive heating.

To FIND THE MAGNETOMOTIVE FORCE OF A WINDING IN AMPERE-TURNS:

*Multiply the number of turns on the winding by the current through it.*

**Experiment 77.**—Use a pair of electromagnets of the same size but wound with widely different numbers of turns, or a corresponding pair of telegraph sounders. Connect the devices to a source of direct current and note the pull required to detach the keeper from the electromagnet poles or to detach the armature from the sounder poles. Then adjust the current so that the product of the current strength and number of turns is the same for two like devices, and observe that the pulls are then equal.

Magnets for a given purpose may be wound with fine wire or with coarse wire; each type has its advantage depending upon the use. The magnets of telephone receivers or telegraph relays are wound with many turns of fine wire, because these instruments are usually connected to long lines of small size and the current is necessarily small; the required magnetomotive force is produced by a small current through a large number of turns. In contrast, the coils forming the series field winding of a generator or motor are wound with relatively few turns of coarse wire; the necessary magnetomotive force is produced by a large current through a small number of turns.

In calculations of magnetic circuits, it is necessary to express the m.m.f. in terms of a different unit, one which is based upon the experimental evidence that 1 ampere-turn will produce 1.257 lines of force through an air path 1 centimeter in length and 1 square centimeter in cross-sectional area. This unit of m.m.f., expressed as 1.257 magnetic lines through a centimeter cube of air, is called the *gilbert,* after the English physicist, William Gilbert (1540-1603).

Let

$N$ = number of turns on the winding,
$I$ = current in amperes,
$M$ = magnetomotive force in gilberts.

Then the m.m.f. of the winding is

$$M = 1.257 \times N \times I \qquad\qquad 72$$

To find the magnetomotive force of a winding in gilberts:

*Multiply the number of ampere-turns by 1.257.*

**Problem 99.**—A solenoid is wound with a total of 500 turns of wire. What m.m.f. is produced by this solenoid with a current of 2.4 amperes? The number of ampere-turns is $500 \times 2.4 = 1200$. Hence, the m.m.f. is $1200 \times 1.257 = 1508$ gilberts.

It is often of importance in computations of magnetic flux to know the amount of m.m.f. per unit length of the magnetic circuit. This quantity, called the *intensity of the magnetic field* (§105), is found by dividing the magnetomotive force acting on the magnetic circuit by the length of that circuit.

Let

$M$ = m.m.f. of the winding in gilberts,
$l$ = length of the flux path in centimeters,
$\mathcal{K}$ = field intensity in oersteds.

Then the magnetic field intensity is

$$\mathcal{K} = \frac{M}{l} \qquad\qquad \textbf{73}$$

This equation also shows that, if the length of the flux path is known, the m.m.f. required to produce a desired field intensity is obtained by multiplying $\mathcal{K}$ by $l$.

**Problem 100.**—A wooden ring, having an average diameter of 2 inches, is wound as shown in Fig. 212 with 250 turns of insulated wire over the entire surface of the wood. What field intensity will be produced through the ring by a current of 1.5 amperes through the winding?

The length of the flux path is $2\pi$ inches or $2\pi \times 2.54$ centimeters. Combining equations (72) and (73), the magnetic field intensity is

$$(73) \qquad \mathcal{K} = \frac{M}{l} = \frac{1.257\ N \times I}{l} = \frac{1.257 \times 250 \times 1.5}{2\pi \times 2.54} = 29.5 \text{ oersteds}$$

**161. Reluctance.**—It was pointed out in §159 that every magnetic circuit presents some opposition to the establishment of flux in it, and that this opposition or reluctance in a magnetic circuit is the counterpart of resistance in an electric circuit. The reluctance of a flux path depends upon the dimensions and material of the magnetic circuit just as does resistance in an electric circuit.

The reluctance of a magnetic circuit can be calculated when three factors of the circuit are known: its length, its cross-sectional area, and the permeability of the material of which it is formed. The reluctance *increases* as the length of the circuit increases; it *decreases* as the sectional area increases or as the permeability increases. That is, the reluctance is directly proportional to the length of the magnetic circuit, and is inversely proportional to the sectional area and permeability of the circuit.

Let

$l$ = length of the magnetic circuit in centimeters,
$A$ = cross-sectional area of the circuit in square centimeters,
$\mu$ = permeability of the material constituting the circuit,
$\mathcal{R}$ = reluctance of the circuit.

Then,

$$\mathcal{R} = \frac{l}{A \times \mu}$$ **74**

The unit of reluctance, to which no name is assigned, is the reluctance offered by a portion of a magnetic circuit 1 centimeter long, 1 square centimeter in cross section, and of unit permeability.

TO FIND THE RELUCTANCE OF A MAGNETIC CIRCUIT:

*Divide the length of the circuit in centimeters by the cross-sectional area of the circuit in square centimeters and divide by the permeability of the material.*

The permeability of a magnetic substance, §109, is the ratio of the number of lines of induction per unit area set up in the substance to the number that would be set up in air under the same conditions, that is, the ratio between the flux density $\mathcal{B}$ in the substance to the intensity of the magnetic field $\mathcal{H}$ acting upon it. Thus, the permeability is given by Formula (60) as

$$\mu = \frac{\mathcal{B}}{\mathcal{H}}$$

where

$\mathcal{B}$ = flux density in lines of induction per square centimeter,
$\mathcal{H}$ = field intensity in oersteds.

PERMEABILITY OF IRON AND STEEL

| FLUX DENSITY | | PERMEABILITY | | |
|---|---|---|---|---|
| Lines per Square Inch | Lines per Square Centimeter | Soft Iron or Annealed Steel Sheet | Soft Cast Steel | Cast Iron |
| 20,000 | 3,100 | 6260 | 955 | 370 |
| 30,000 | 4,650 | 6260 | 975 | 290 |
| 40,000 | 6,200 | 6260 | 975 | 200 |
| 50,000 | 7,750 | 6130 | 970 | 125 |
| 60,000 | 9,300 | 5640 | 920 | 90 |
| 70,000 | 10,850 | 4470 | 830 | |
| 80,000 | 12,400 | 3130 | 715 | |
| 90,000 | 14,000 | 1840 | 532 | |
| 100,000 | 15,500 | 810 | 330 | |
| 110,000 | 17,100 | 270 | 190 | |

The permeability of air and other non-magnetic substances is unity, since in such substances the flux density $\mathcal{B}$ is numerically the

same as the field intensity ℋ. Thus, 1 oersted of field intensity
sets up 1 gauss of flux density in non-magnetic substances, but sets
up a flux density $\mu$ times as great in a magnetic substance of permeability $\mu$.

In magnetic materials the value of the permeability is not the
same for all flux densities, therefore in calculating the reluctance
of a specimen it is necessary to know the flux density intended. The
accompanying table gives the permeability of three materials at
different flux densities.

**Problem 101.**—Compute the reluctance of a bar of soft iron 1 inch
square and 1 foot long when the flux density through the bar is to be
90,000 lines per square inch.

The permeability of the iron for the stated flux density is given in the
table as 1840; the length of the bar is $12 \times 2.54 = 30.5$ centimeters; and
the cross-sectional area of the bar is $(2.54)^2 = 6.45$ square centimeters.
Hence the reluctance of the bar from end to end is

$$(74) \qquad \mathcal{R} = \frac{l}{A \times \mu} = \frac{30.5}{6.45 \times 1840} = .00257 \text{ reluctance unit}$$

**162. Law of the Magnetic Circuit.**—Just as electromotive force
(e.m.f.) is the agency which establishes current in an electric circuit, so magnetomotive force (m.m.f.) is the agency which sets up
flux in a magnetic circuit. The two circuits are analogous, and resistance in the one corresponds to reluctance in the other.

In a metallic circuit the strength of the current can be obtained
by dividing the e.m.f. available in the electric circuit by its resistance. Similarly, in a magnetic circuit the amount of flux can
be obtained by dividing the m.m.f. available in the circuit by its
reluctance. Thus,

$$\text{magnetic flux} = \frac{\text{magnetomotive force}}{\text{reluctance}}$$

Let

$\Phi$ = magnetic flux in maxwells,
$M$ = m.m.f. acting on the circuit in gilberts,
$\mathcal{R}$ = reluctance of the circuit in reluctance units.

Then

$$\Phi = \frac{M}{\mathcal{R}}$$

**75**

This equation is analogous to the expression for Ohm's Law and on this account is frequently styled the "Ohm's Law of the magnetic circuit."

To FIND THE FLUX IN A MAGNETIC CIRCUIT:

*Divide the magnetomotive force in gilberts by the reluctance in reluctance units.*

Fig 213 illustrates the parallelism between electric and magnetic circuits. At the left is shown an electric circuit, with most of its resistance at $R$, and a battery of e.m.f. $E$ which sets up a current $I$. At the right is shown a magnetic circuit with most of its reluctance at $\mathcal{R}$, and surrounded by a coil of wire carrying a current; this magnetizing agency sets up a magnetomotive force $M$ to establish a flux $\Phi$ through the circuit.

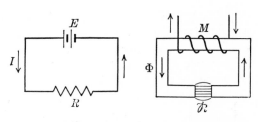

FIG. 213. Electric and magnet circuits compared

The equations and units for the two circuits are given below in parallel columns:

| *Electric* | *Magnetic* |
|---|---|
| current $= \dfrac{\text{e.m.f.}}{\text{resistance}}$ | flux $= \dfrac{\text{m.m.f.}}{\text{reluctance}}$ |
| $I = \dfrac{E}{R}$ | $\Phi = \dfrac{M}{\mathcal{R}}$ |
| amperes $= \dfrac{\text{volts}}{\text{ohms}}$ | maxwells $= \dfrac{\text{gilberts}}{\text{reluctance units}}$ |

If the total flux $\Phi$ through the circuit is known, and the sectional area $A$ through which it is uniformly distributed is given, then the flux density in the magnetic circuit can be calculated by Formula (59), namely

$$\mathcal{B} = \Phi \div A$$

While the parallelism between the two kinds of circuits is seemingly exact, there are important differences which make the calculation of magnetic circuits less certain. In the electric circuit, the resistance does not depend upon the strength of the current, except insofar as it is influenced by heating. In the magnetic circuit, on the other hand, the reluctance depends upon the density of the magnetic flux, because the permeability is not constant. Also, in the electric circuit, the current is practically confined to the conductors, whereas in the magnetic circuit there is usually more or less magnetic leakage through the surrounding medium, because there are no materials which serve as insulators of magnetic flux.

**163. Calculation of Magnetic Circuits.**—Most magnetic circuits are composed of two or more parts, and usually one of them is an

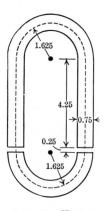

FIG. 214. Horseshoe magnet and keeper

air gap. This makes it necessary in magnetic calculations to compute the reluctance of each part separately, and to add the results to obtain the total reluctance of the circuit. Before the reluctance of any part can be computed, it is necessary to know its permeability, and this depends not only upon the material but also upon the flux density in that part of the circuit.

Suppose that the dimensions of a magnet have been decided upon and that it is desired to have a definite flux density in the air gap. First, determine the permeability for each part of the magnetic circuit from suitable tables or curves, and compute the reluctance of each part. Second, add these values to get the total reluctance $\mathcal{R}$. Third, determine the total magnetic flux by multiplying the flux density $\mathcal{B}$ by the cross-sectional area $A$ of the air gap, that is $\Phi = \mathcal{B} \times A$ as given by Formula (59). Having ascertained the total reluctance of the circuit and its total flux, the last step is to calculate the m.m.f. from the law of the magnetic circuit, that is $M = \Phi \times \mathcal{R}$ as given by Formula (75).

**Problem 102.**—Fig. 214 gives the dimensions in inches of a cast steel horseshoe core and keeper, separated by an air gap of one-quarter of an inch; the dotted line represents the total length of the magnetic circuit. Find the reluctance of each part of the magnetic circuit and the ampere-turns required to produce a flux of 40,000 maxwells through the circuit.

Lengths of both limbs of the core up to the curved portion $= 4.25 \times 2 =$ 8.5 inches. Since the circumference of a circle is twice the radius times 3.1416, the length of the curved portion of the core is one-half the circumference $=$ radius $\times 3.1416 = 1.625 \times 3.1416 = 5.10$ inches. Then, the total length of the core is $8.5 + 5.10 = 13.60$ inches; the length of the keeper is 5.10 inches.

Area of the core of diameter $d = 0.75$ inch is $d^2 \times 3.1416/4 = 0.75 \times 0.75 \times 0.7854 = 0.441$ square inch $= 0.441 \times 2.54 \times 2.54 = 2.85$ square centimeters. This is also substantially the sectional area of the air gap.

$$(59) \qquad \mathcal{B} = \frac{\Phi}{A} = \frac{40{,}000}{2.85} = 14{,}000 \text{ lines per square centimeter}$$

The permeability $\mu$ for cast steel at a flux density of 14,000 gausses is 532. The reluctance of core and keeper combined is

$$(74) \quad \mathcal{R} = \frac{l}{A \times \mu} = \frac{(13.60 + 5.10)\, 2.54}{2.85 \times 532} = 0.031 \text{ reluctance unit}$$

and the reluctance of both gaps, each of 0.25 inch length, is

$$\mathcal{R} = \frac{l}{A \times \mu} = \frac{0.5 \times 2.54}{2.85 \times 1} = 0.446 \text{ reluctance unit}$$

Total reluctance $= 0.031 + 0.446 = 0.477$ reluctance unit

Consequently, the magnetomotive force is

$$(75) \qquad M = \Phi \times \mathcal{R} = 40{,}000 \times 0.477 = 19{,}080 \text{ gilberts}$$

and the ampere-turns are $19{,}080 \div 1.257 = 15{,}180$.

**164. Electric Fields.**—The region around electric charges is under strain in a manner similar to that of the region around magnet poles. Since the latter region is called a magnetic field, it is natural that the region around electric charges should be called an *electric field*; it is also called an electrostatic field. The substance in which the field exists is designated as the *dielectric*; it may be a solid, liquid, or gaseous insulator.

Throughout an electric field forces will act upon charges placed in it. The force upon any given charge will generally vary in direction and amount from point to point in the field, and this indicates that the electric field has a certain direction and a definite intensity at every point in it. Electric fields may, therefore, be represented by lines in the same manner as magnetic fields.

In Fig. 215, I shows the electric field about a pair of unlike charges, and II and III show the electric fields about like charges, both positive and both negative. The lines show the directions of force action at all points, and by their closeness to each other indicate the relative strengths of the electric field. The well-known force action between electric charges, that unlike charges attract and like ones repel, can be visualized by the behavior of the lines of

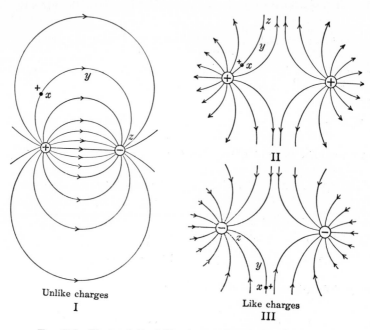

FIG. 215. Electrostatic fields about pairs of electric charges

electric force around the charges in tending to shorten themselves and in exerting sidewise thrusts upon each other, just like magnetic lines of force.

The lines indicate the path that would be followed by a minute positive exploring charge placed at any point in the electric field, if that charge were free to move through the dielectric. This could be demonstrated by submerging charges in an insulating liquid or in a gas, and observing the motion of a small positive charge introduced into the field. Thus, a minute positive charge introduced at point $x$ will move along the line $x,y,z$. In a solid dielectric, the lines indicate imaginary paths along which a positive exploring charge might move if it could do so.

The force of attraction or repulsion between two electric charges is directly proportional to the amounts of the charges and inversely proportional to the square of the distance between them. Thus, if the distance between two charges is halved, the force between them would be quadrupled. It will be remembered that a force accelerates any body upon which it acts if the body is free to move. Therefore in gases, where there is great freedom of movement, charged particles are accelerated considerably and acquire high velocities, although they are impeded by the presence of neutral gas molecules.

**165. Condensers.**—Two conductors separated from each other by some insulating material or dielectric form a *condenser,* and the conductors are termed the *plates* of the condenser. Condensers are used to reduce sparking at contact points, to neutralize the effects of inductance, to obtain pulses of current for various purposes, and

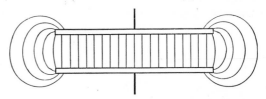

Fig. 216. Electric field of a condenser

to accomplish many objectives in alternating-current circuits.

When a condenser is connected to the terminals of an electrostatic generator or other direct-current source, the plates become charged, one positively and the other negatively. If the plates are parallel the electric field between them and just beyond take the appearance depicted in Fig. 216. The vertical lines within the plates are drawn equidistant to indicate that the electric field there is uniform. The charges remain on the plates after disconnecting the condenser from the machine until it is decided to remove them; this is done by bridging a wire from plate to plate, causing the condenser to discharge through the wire and become neutral again. In this way a condenser has the ability to store energy in the form of an electric field.

Fig. 217 shows the construction of two types of condensers illustrated in cross section. At the left is shown a pile of parallel dielectric plates with tinfoil sheets between them; alternate sheets lead to terminal 1 and the intermediate sheets lead to terminal 2.

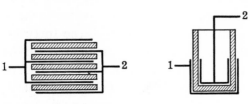

At the right is shown a glass jar with metal coatings on the lower parts of the inner and outer surfaces; it is styled a *Leyden jar*; two of these jars are pictured on the electrostatic generator shown in Fig. 7. The flat type of

FIG. 217. Types of condensers
The shaded parts represent the dielectric.

condenser is much more compact than the jar form, and the construction is simpler.

**Experiment 78.**—Charge a Leyden jar by touching its center terminal to a terminal of an electrostatic generator or to the plate of an electrophorus, §8. Then relieve the charge by holding one end of a "discharger" against the outer coating of the jar and bringing its other end nearer and nearer to the center terminal until a spark is produced. A heavily insulated wire may be used instead of a discharger.

For use in telephony, condensers are commonly made with two tinfoil strips many feet long and several inches wide together with four paper strips slightly exceeding these dimensions. The strips are placed together, alternately two of paper and one of tinfoil, and then wound by machine on a form of cylindrical shape. The condenser so assembled is immersed in a closed tank of molten paraffin and the air is exhausted from the tank; upon the subsequent admission of air the paraffin is forced into all the recesses

FIG. 218. Variable condenser
General Radio Company

of the condenser; afterward it is removed from the tank and allowed to cool.

In radio work, condensers generally have air as the dielectric and this makes it possible to move the plates connected to one terminal with respect to those connected to the other so as to vary the effective area of the dielectric. Fig. 218 illustrates such a variable condenser for station selecting or tuning purposes.

Experiment 79.—Make up a condenser of a number of sheets of tinfoil and paper, cut to any convenient size, and assemble them as indicated in Fig. 219. The overhanging tinfoil lugs are then clamped together to form the two terminals of the condenser. It would be desirable to coat the paper with paraffin or a mixture of beeswax and rosin.

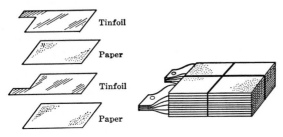

Tinfoil

Paper

Tinfoil

Paper

FIG. 219. Details of condenser construction

Experiment 80.—Connect the condenser constructed in Experiment 79, or else a telephone condenser, in series with a galvanometer and double-contact key to a source of direct current, and provide a discharge wire in the manner shown in Fig. 220. Depress the key to its lower contact and observe that the galvanometer deflects only momentarily when the condenser is connected to the source. Then release the key so that it will touch its upper contact, and note that the galvanometer again deflects momentarily but in the opposite direction when the condenser discharges.

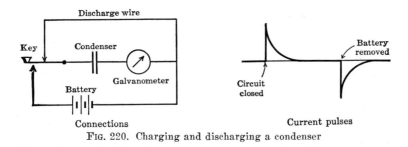

FIG. 220. Charging and discharging a condenser

This experiment shows that if a battery is connected to a condenser there is a pulse of current through the circuit for just a moment, and there will be no current thereafter as long as the circuit remains intact. When the battery is removed from the circuit and replaced by a connecting wire, there will be another pulse of current which shows itself by a spark at the contacts where this wire is introduced. Disregarding these momentary pulses, the presence of a condenser in a circuit means that a direct current cannot be maintained through it; this result is to be expected since the plates of a condenser are separated by a dielectric and, therefore, one side of the condenser is insulated from the other.

In further explanation, when the battery is placed in circuit by depressing the key, its e.m.f. causes electrons to accumulate on the right-hand condenser plate. This plate becomes negatively charged, and the other plate, having given up electrons, becomes positively charged. This motion of electrons continues until the difference of potential between the two plates builds up to a value equal to the e.m.f. of the battery; thereafter there is no electron flow. Not until the key is raised to its upper contact will there be any further motion of electrons, and then they will travel in the opposite direction until the neutral condition of the circuit is re-established. The inital charge and subsequent discharge of the condenser take place very quckly, but nevertheless the electron motion is revealed by the deflections of the galvanometer. Indeed, the character of the current pulses can be observed if an oscilloscope, §348, is used instead of the galvanometer. These pulses will appear as shown at the right of the figure, with current strength plotted vertically against time plotted horizontally.

**166. Electrolytic Condensers.**—Within recent years a different type of condenser has come into use; it employs an electrolyte and is called an *electrolytic condenser*. The plates of this type of condenser are termed anode and cathode in keeping with the designation of the electrodes in electrolytic cells. The anode is of aluminum foil and has a large surface, while the cathode is the container, usually also of aluminum but not necessarily so.

There are two varieties of electrolytic condensers—the wet and the dry types. Probably the electrolyte most commonly used in the wet type is a solution of borax and boric acid in water; another used extensively is a solution of ammonium citrate in water. The dry type of condenser employs an electrolyte in the form of a paste, generally a solution of boric acid, glycerine and ammonia. Paper or gauze packed between the anode and cathode is impregnated with this solution.

When a unidirectional p.d. is applied to an electrolytic condenser so that the positive terminal of the source is connected to the anode or center electrode of the condenser, and the negative terminal to the cathode or outside electrode of the condenser, a slight current is established through the electrolyte. This current produces on the surface of the anode a very thin polarizing film, which serves as the dielectric of the condenser.

If the p.d. on the condenser is reversed, there will be a considerably larger current through the electrolyte and the polarizing film will tend to break down. For this reason electrolytic condensers are generally used in circuits where a polarizing potential is available, as in filters for rectifiers, §195, §272. In all such applications care must be taken to connect the positive side of the system to the anode of the condenser. More recently, electrolytic condensers have been developed which will operate satisfactorily for short periods without a direct polarizing potential; they are employed in starting capacitor motors, §256.

Electrolytic condensers have the advantages of taking little space for a given rating, and of being self-healing when broken down by potential differences exceeding their operating range.

**167. Capacitance.**—The ability of a condenser to store energy because of charges on its plates, and to establish an electric field between them, is expressed as *capacitance;* formerly this was called capacity. A condenser is said to have more capacitance than another if it receives more charge than the other from the same source of e.m.f.

In charging a condenser from a source of e.m.f., electrons are transferred from one plate to the other until a state of equilibrium is reached in which the plates have a potential difference equal to the e.m.f. of the source. Each plate will acquire a definite charge, one positive and the other negative. If a battery of higher e.m.f. were used, the charges would be found proportionately larger. This means that for a given condenser the ratio of the charge on the plates to the potential difference between them would remain the same. It is this ratio of condenser charge to potential difference which is defined as the capacitance of the condenser. The unit of capacitance is the *farad,* named after Faraday.

Let

Q = charge on the condenser in coulombs,
E = applied potential difference in volts,
C = capacitance of the condenser in farads.

Then

$$\text{capacitance} = \frac{\text{charge}}{\text{p.d.}}$$

$$C = \frac{Q}{E} \qquad\qquad \textbf{76}$$

TO FIND THE CAPACITANCE OF A CONDENSER IN FARADS:

*Divide the charge on the plates in coulombs by the p.d. across the plates in volts.*

*A condenser has a capacitance of 1 farad when a potential difference of 1 volt charges it with 1 coulomb of electricity.* The farad is an enormously large unit of capacitance, and for convenience a smaller unit, the microfarad, is generally used. A farad $= 10^6$ microfarads.

The capacitance of a condenser is determined entirely by the material and dimensions of the dielectric between the plates, and is not affected by the kind of metal used for the plates. The capacitance is directly proportional to the effective area of the dielectric and inversely proportional to its thickness; it is also proportional to the *dielectric constant* of the material between the plates.

Let

A = total area of dielectric between the plates in square inches,
s = thickness of the dielectric in inches,
K = dielectric constant,
C = capacitance of the condenser in microfarads.

Then the capacitance of the condenser in microfarads can be calculated from the equation

$$C = \frac{2.24 \times K \times A}{s \times 10^7} \qquad\qquad \textbf{77}$$

Since the capacitance of a condenser is directly proportional to the dielectric constant, it is possible to define the dielectric constant of a material as the ratio of the capacitance of a condenser with that material as dielectric to its capacitance when the dielectric is a vacuum or air. Some typical values of dielectric constant are given in the following table:

DIELECTRIC CONSTANTS

Glass, crown  ........................ 5   to  7
Glass, flint  ......................... 7   to 10
India rubber  ........................ 2.1 to  2.3
Mica  ............................... 5.7 to  7
Paper, dry  ......................... 2   to  2.5
Paraffin wax  ........................ 2   to  2.3
Water (pure)  .......................     81

**Problem 103.**—Calculate the capacitance of a condenser formed of 41 tinfoil sheets measuring 6.5 inches by 4 inches, separated by larger sheets of mica 5 mils thick and having a dielectric constant of 6.

Between 41 metal plates there are 40 dielectric sheets. The effective area of each dielectric sheet is $6.5 \times 4 = 26$ square inches and the thickness is 0.005 inch. Therefore, the capacitance of the condenser is

$$(77) \quad C = \frac{2.24 \times K \times A}{s \times 10^7} = \frac{2.24 \times 6 \times 40 \times 26}{0.005 \times 10^7} = 0.28 \text{ microfarad}$$

Oceanic cables act as condensers of very large capacitance. The conductor at the center serves as one plate of the condenser, and the sheathing together with sea water forms the other plate, the gutta percha and other insulating layers between them being the dielectric. Such a cable 2000 miles long has a capacitance of approximately 0.001 farad; when this amount is written as 1000 microfarads it gives a better picture of the large value of this capacitance.

The capacitance of a condenser may be measured experimentally by comparison with a standard condenser, using a ballistic galvanometer, §118. The condensers are charged separately from the same battery and each is discharged in turn through the instrument, the maximum throw being noted in each case. The deflections being proportional to the charges, and these in turn being proportional to the capacitances, it follows that the capacitances are in the same proportion as the deflections.

Because a condenser has capacitance, it is logical to call the device a *capacitor,* and this term is coming into wide use. It parallels the use of the term resistor for a device which has resistance.

**168. Capacitors in Parallel and in Series.**—Condensers are often connected in parallel in order to increase the capacitance of a circuit. Let $C_1$, $C_2$, and $C_3$ be the capacitances of three capacitors that are connected in parallel as in Fig. 221. They are equivalent to a single capacitor of which the capacitance $C$ is to be determined. The potential differences across the three capacitors will be represented by $E_1$, $E_2$, and $E_3$, and the charges on them by $Q_1$, $Q_2$, and $Q_3$, respectively. The corresponding potential difference and charge for the equivalent capacitor will be taken respectively as $E$ and $Q$.

For the parallel connection, each capacitor has the same potential difference as the source, or

$$E = E_1 = E_2 = E_3 = \ldots$$

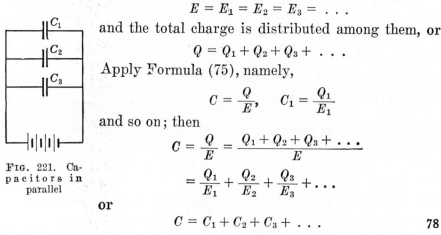

and the total charge is distributed among them, or

$$Q = Q_1 + Q_2 + Q_3 + \ldots$$

Apply Formula (75), namely,

$$C = \frac{Q}{E}, \qquad C_1 = \frac{Q_1}{E_1}$$

and so on; then

$$C = \frac{Q}{E} = \frac{Q_1 + Q_2 + Q_3 + \ldots}{E}$$

$$= \frac{Q_1}{E_1} + \frac{Q_2}{E_2} + \frac{Q_3}{E_3} + \ldots$$

Fig. 221. Capacitors in parallel

or

$$C = C_1 + C_2 + C_3 + \ldots \qquad \textbf{78}$$

showing that the combined capacitance of several capacitors connected in parallel is equal to the sum of the individual capacitances.

To find the capacitance of a number of capacitors connected in parallel:

*Add the capacitances of all the capacitors so connected.*

Condensers are sometimes connected in series in order to lessen the potential differences across them; the total capacitance will be reduced by this arrangement. In the series connection of Fig. 222, the same momentary flow of electrons occurs in all of the capacitors. Thus, the electrons which gather on the right plate of capacitor $C_3$ will hold bound an equal positive charge on its left plate, and this means the transfer of an equal number of electrons to the right side of capacitor $C_2$, and so on. In consequence, all capacitors will acquire the same charge, or

$$Q = Q_1 = Q_2 = Q_3 = \ldots$$

The applied potential difference is divided among the individual capacitors, or

$$E = E_1 + E_2 + E_3 + \ldots$$

Then

$$\frac{1}{C} = \frac{E}{Q} = \frac{E_1 + E_2 + E_3 + \ldots}{Q} = \frac{E_1}{Q_1} + \frac{E_2}{Q_2} + \frac{E_3}{Q_3} + \ldots$$

or

$$\frac{1}{C} = \frac{1}{C_1} + \frac{1}{C_2} + \frac{1}{C_3} + \ldots \qquad 79$$

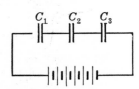

FIG. 222. Capacitors in series

an expression which shows the relation between the capacitances $C_1$, $C_2$, $C_3$, ... of the individual capacitors and the equivalent capacitance $C$ when these are connected in series.

To FIND THE CAPACITANCE OF A NUMBER OF CAPACITORS CONNECTED IN SERIES:

*Find the reciprocal of the capacitance of each capacitor, add these values, and take the reciprocal of this result.*

**Problem 104.**—Fig. 223 shows the connection of three condensers of 2, 3 and 4 microfarads in a series-parallel combination joined to a 300-volt battery. Find the total capacitance of the circuit, the charge on each capacitor, and the p.d. across each.

The parallel connection of the 2- and 4-microfarad capacitors gives an equivalent capacitance of

$$(78) \quad C = C_1 + C_2 = 2 + 4 = 6 \text{ microfarads}$$

The circuit now reduces to a series connection of 3- and 6-microfarad capacitors; their equivalent capacitance is given by

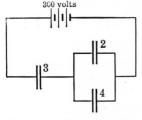

FIG. 223. Series - parallel connection of capacitors

$$(79) \quad \frac{1}{C} = \frac{1}{C_1} + \frac{1}{C_2} = \frac{1}{3} + \frac{1}{6} = \frac{3}{6}$$

whence $C = 2$ microfarads. Three hundred volts impressed on an "equivalent capacitor" of 2 microfarads results in a charge of

(76)                    $Q = C \times E = 2 \times 300 = 600$ microcoulombs

With this charge on the 3-microfarad capacitor, the p.d. across it will be

$$E = \frac{Q}{C} = \frac{600}{3} = 200 \text{ volts}$$

and the p.d. across the other pair of capacitors with the same aggregate charge will be

$$E = \frac{Q}{C} = \frac{600}{6} = 100 \text{ volts}$$

The charge on the 2-microfarad capacitor will be

$$Q = C \times E = 2 \times 100 = 200 \text{ microcoulombs}$$

and similarly that on the 4-microfarad capacitor will be 400 microcoulombs.

**Experiment 81.**—Connect a ballistic galvanometer to a 2-microfarad condenser in the manner shown in Fig. 220 and measure the throw of the instrument. Do the same for a 4-microfarad condenser and note that the throw is twice the previous one. Then connect the two in parallel and observe the throw; repeat for the two in series. The results will verify Formulas (78) and (79) experimentally.

In verifying experimentally the potential distribution in circuits containing capacitors in series, it is necessary to use voltmeters that do not require current for their operation; a useful instrument for this purpose is the so-called *electrostatic voltmeter* in which the deflection depends upon the force action between charged plates.

## QUESTIONS

1. Explain how a changing current in one circuit can produce an e.m.f. in an adjacent circuit.
2. Define coefficient of mutual induction.
3. Suppose the coils mentioned in Problem 97 are interchanged so that $A$ is connected to the galvanometer and $B$ is the coil in which the current changes at the rate stated. The orientation of the coils stays unchanged. Is the mutual inductance of the coils now less than before, the same, or greater?
4. Give an illustration where mutual induction is of great importance, and also give one where this effect is objectionable.
5. Explain in detail how the e.m.f. of self-induction is developed in an electric circuit.

6. What is meant by the inductance of a circuit?
7. Define the henry of mutual inductance, of self-inductance.
8. How can a resistance coil be wound to have a minimum of inductance?
9. Which has more inductance, an incandescent lamp or an electromagnet? Why?
10. In what ways does a magnetic circuit resemble an electric circuit?
11. What are magnetomotive force and reluctance? and what are their units?
12. How does the reluctance of an iron bar compare with that of a brass bar of the same dimensions?
13. Which is the larger unit, the ampere-turn or the gilbert?
14. A solenoid of length $l$, wound with $N$ turns, carries a current $I$. Give the m.m.f. of its winding and the field intensity at its core, in terms of these symbols.
15. State the factors which determine the amount of reluctance in a magnetic circuit.
16. Is the reluctance of a certain piece of iron always the same? Explain.
17. Give the law of the magnetic circuit and mention how it parallels that for an electric circuit.
18. Sketch the electric field between two charged spheres, one being positive and the other negative.
19. Name the parts of a condenser and state the purpose of each.
20. How would you construct a condenser of the flat or rolled type?
21. What is an electrolytic condenser?
22. Explain the action of a condenser that is used with an induction coil.
23. What is meant by capacitance?
24. A condenser has a capacitance of 1 microfarad. How much charge will it receive when 1 volt is impressed upon its terminals?
25. What relation exists between the capacitance of a condenser, the p.d. across the terminals, and the charge received?
26. Define the farad.
27. Explain how the capacitance of a condenser can be calculated from the dimensions of the dielectric and the dielectric constant.
28. Compare the result of connecting condensers in series or parallel with that of connecting resistances in series or parallel.
29. Show how the three condensers of Fig. 223 can be reconnected to produce the most capacitance; again to produce the least.

## PROBLEMS

1. Five volts are induced in a circuit when the current in a nearby circuit changes at the rate of 800 amperes per second. What is the mutual inductance of the circuits? *Ans.* 6.25 millihenries.
2. An electromagnet has a resistance of 5 ohms and an inductance of 0.25 henry. If the current is reduced uniformly from 10 amperes to zero

in 0.08 second, what counter e.m.f. of self-induction will be induced?
*Ans.* 31.3 volts.

3. A spool with a wooden core wound full of wire has an inductance of 100 millihenries. This wire is removed and the spool is rewound with wire having half the diameter of the first, the new winding again filling the spool. How much inductance will the new winding have? *Ans.* 1.6 henries.

4. Calculate the inductance of an air-core solenoid having 2000 turns, a length of 20 inches and a mean radius of 1 inch. *Ans.* 0.02 henry.

5. A winding of 360 turns on a mailing tube has a length of 10 inches and an average diameter of 1½ inch. Calculate the inductance of this winding. *Ans.* 0.73 millihenry.

6. What m.m.f. would be developed by the winding of Problem 5 when the current is 2 amperes? *Ans.* 720 ampere-turns or 905 gilberts.

7. Three relays are adjusted to operate on 250 ampere-turns, and have the following constants: Relay A—2400 turns, 20 ohms resistance; Relay B—4500 turns, 75 ohms resistance; Relay C—7500 turns, 150 ohms resistance. (a) Which relays would operate if all three were connected in series across a 20-volt battery? (b) What applied p.d. would cause all three relays to operate? *Ans.* (b) 25.5 volts.

8. A transformer core forms a hollow rectangle with a space measuring 15 by 10 centimeters for the winding to go through, and the cross section of the iron for the flux to go through is a square measuring 3 centimeters on a side. What is the reluctance of the core when the permeability is 1000? *Ans.* 0.0069 reluctance unit.

9. What is the reluctance of an iron rod 25 inches long and ½ inch in diameter when the permeability is 500? *Ans.* 0.10 reluctance unit.

10. A square iron rod 2 centimeters on a side and 40 centimeters long is bent and welded to form a closed ring. Upon this core is wound a coil of 2500 turns. What current is needed in the winding to establish a flux density of 15,000 lines per square centimeter within the core, if the permeability of the iron with this density is 600? *Ans.* 0.318 ampere.

11. The ring of Problem 10 is cut in two and the halves are separated to form air gaps of 2 millimeters at each side. Neglecting the change that this makes in the permeability of the iron, compute the magnetic flux in the core produced by the same current. *Ans.* 8,580 maxwells.

12. A radio transmitting condenser of 0.05 microfarad capacitance has 10,000 volts impressed upon it. What will be the charge on the condenser? *Ans.* 500 microcoulombs.

13. A condenser is made up of 54 sheets of tinfoil, each 10 inches long and 6 inches wide, which are separated by sheets of waxed paper of dielectric constant 2.25 and having a thickness of 0.008 inch. Alternate sheets of tinfoil are connected to one terminal of the condenser, and the remaining sheets of tinfoil are connected to the other terminal. Find the capacitance of the condenser. *Ans.* 0.200 microfarad.

14. A condenser consists of two brass plates each 10 inches long and 8 inches wide, separated by a layer of air 0.2 inch thick. The condenser is connected across a 2000-volt battery. Find (a) the charge on the condenser. Then a large sheet of glass 0.2 inch thick and having a dielectric constant of 8 is inserted between the plates, completely filling the space between them. (b) How much additional charge will the condenser take from the battery? *Ans.* (a) 0.179 microcoulombs; (b) 1.253 microcoulombs.

15. Two condensers of 5 and 10 microfarads capacitance are connected in series across 120-volt direct-current supply mains. Find the total capacitance, the charge on each condenser, and the potential difference across each. *Ans.* 3.33 microfarads; 400 microcoulombs on each; 80 volts on the 5- and 40 volts on the 10-microfarad condenser.

16. Two condensers having capacitances of 2 and 4 microfarads are connected in parallel, and this combination is joined in series with a condenser of 6 microfarads capacitance across a 50-volt battery. Compute the charge on the 4-microfarad condenser. *Ans.* 100 microcoulombs.

# Lesson XV

## ALTERNATING CURRENTS

Alternating currents of electricity—Generation of alternating electromotive force—Graphic representation of an alternating potential—Frequency—Expressing values of alternating currents and e.m.f.'s—Effective and average values—Phase—Polyphase systems—Addition of alternating e.m.f.'s—Harmonics—Questions and Problems.

**169. Alternating Currents of Electricity.**—Most of the subject matter so far presented deals with continuous or so-called direct currents. A current of this kind is always directed one way around an electric circuit and quite often has a constant strength for long periods of time. An *alternating current* of electricity is a current which changes its direction around a circuit at regular intervals of time, and these intervals are much shorter than one second. During such an interval the strength of the current may vary in any way, but usually its value rises and falls in a regular manner.

The electron picture of an alternating current is the transfer of electrons first one way through the circuit and then the other, changing direction regularly at short intervals. Any one electron may travel only a short distance along the circuit before it is urged to travel the other way. The number of electrons that pass any one cross section of the circuit will vary from moment to moment. This means that the electrons are speeded up and then slowed down, then speeded up in the reverse direction and slowed down, again reversed, and so on. The agency which produces this motion of the electrons is the *alternating electromotive force* acting in the circuit.

Nearly all of the electricity generated today is in the form of alternating current. Such currents can be readily stepped up or down in potential without the use of rotating machinery, and electrical energy can be transmitted and distributed over long lines at high potentials, with resulting economy of material and operating expense.

The influence of operating potential on the cost of transmission lines can be appreciated through a numerical example: Suppose 5000 kilowatts of power are to be transmitted over a copper line with a potential drop of 3 per cent, and assume the weight of copper required when the energy is delivered at 1000 volts to be 10,000 pounds. Then the power loss in the line, the resistance of the line wires, and the amount of copper necessary for transmission at other potentials are as follows:

| Line Potential E Volts | Line Current I Amperes | Line Drop e Volts | Power Loss I×e Watts | Line Resistance $R = \frac{e}{I}$ Ohms | Line Material Pounds |
|---|---|---|---|---|---|
| 1000 | 5000 | 30 | 150,000 | 0.006 | 10000 |
| 2000 | 2500 | 60 | 150,000 | 0.024 | 2500 |
| 5000 | 1000 | 150 | 150,000 | 0.15 | 400 |
| 10000 | 500 | 300 | 150,000 | 0.60 | 100 |

The figures in the last column show that for transmitting a certain amount of power with the same percentage line loss *the weight of copper wire required is inversely proportional to the square of the transmitting potential.*

The attainment of the high potentials necessary to realize the economy in transmission above mentioned is much easier and cheaper with alternating than with direct currents. To change the potential of a direct-current supply requires two machines coupled together to form a motor-generator, §249. The maximum potential which can be obtained satisfactorily from a single direct-current generator is in the neighborhood of 5000 volts, the limitation being imposed by insulation and commutation. Higher continuous potentials are obtained by connecting the generators in series. On the other hand, alternators can be designed for more than 20,000 volts because the armature is stationary and may be more readily insulated. Further, transformers may be used to change the alternating potential over a wide range. The original cost and upkeep of a transformer is much less than of a motor-generator, and its efficiency is considerably higher. It is primarily the transformer, §260, which has made possible the transmission of large amounts of electrical energy over long distances; line potentials of 60,000 to 200,000 volts are common.

**170. Generation of Alternating Electromotive Force.**—The production of alternating current is based on the cutting of magnetic

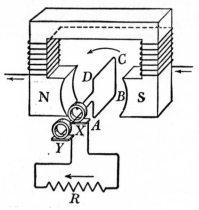

flux by conductors first in one direction and then in the other. Most electric generators are of the alternating type, and these set up currents which traverse the circuit first in one direction and then the other, reversing their directions many times a second.

The simplest way to develop an alternating current is to place a coil of wire in a magnetic field between two poles of an electromagnet, and rotate the coil about an axis in the plane of the coil and at right angles to the flux. Fig. 224

FIG. 224. Elementary alternating current generator with one armature turn

shows the arrangement and it illustrates an elementary alternating-current generator or *alternator*. The electromagnet is called a *bipolar field structure* and the rotating coil, together with its iron core and steel shaft (not shown), is called the *armature*. The coil *ABCD* connects with two *slip rings* which are mounted concentrically with the shaft and insulated from each other and from the shaft. Connection with the external circuit *R* is made through *brushes* X and Y which press against the slip rings; this collecting device keeps the revolving coil in steady contact with the stationary external circuit. With proper design, the wiping contacts between brushes and slip rings will have low resistance. The conductors of an armature winding in which e.m.f.'s are induced are often called *inductors*. The single turn armature shown in the figure has two inductors, *AB* and *CD*.

At an instant during rotation when the coil is in the position shown, no e.m.f. will be generated, since at this instant neither inductor is moving in a direction to cut the magnetic flux between the poles N and S. As the coil begins to rotate in a counterclockwise direction from this position, inductor $AB$ moves upward and inductor $CD$ moves downward through the field, setting up small e.m.f.'s directed from $A$ to $B$ and from $C$ to $D$, as determined by the right-hand rule. These induced e.m.f.'s add together and make brush $X$ positive and brush $Y$ negative, and a current is produced in circuit $R$ having the direction shown by the arrow. The current keeps increasing in magnitude until the coil is horizontal, and at this instant the inductors cut the flux at right angles. Since the rate of cutting flux at this position is the greatest, the e.m.f. induced will be a maximum. As the coil turns farther, the e.m.f. becomes smaller, finally reaching zero again when inductors $AB$ and $CD$ have interchanged the places they have in the figure. During the second half-revolution of the coil the same effect is produced, but the e.m.f. is in the opposite direction because $AB$ is then mov-

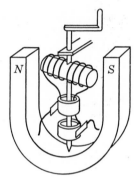

FIG. 225. Model of alternating-current generator

ing downward and $CD$ upward through the magnetic field; as a result the current in the external circuit $R$ is reversed. This process continues and the current is reversed twice in every revolution of the coil within the bipolar field.

**Experiment 82.**—Construct a simple alternating-current generator of the type suggested in Fig. 225. Connect a direct-current voltmeter to the slip rings and rotate the armature slowly by hand. Note that the pointer of the voltmeter will deflect first one way and then the other. If the speed of rotation is increased, the needle of the meter will move less and less and eventually it will merely vibrate about the zero position. Then replace this meter by an alternating-current voltmeter and observe that the deflection is unidirectional but not steady, and that the deflection is increased when the speed is raised.

To investigate how the e.m.f. or current varies from moment to moment, consider the coil $ABCD$ of Fig. 224 to be viewed in cross section as shown in Fig. 226, with the ends $A$ and $D$ of its two inductors facing the reader, and suppose it to revolve at constant speed in a uniform magnetic field. As already stated, the e.m.f. induced will be zero as the coil passes position $AD$, and will have a maximum value, say $E$, as its passes position $A'D'$

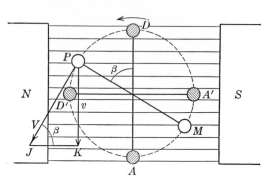

along the axis of the poles NS, for there the inductors move at right angles to the flux. At some intermediate coil position such as $MP$, the induced e.m.f. will have a value between these extremes of zero and $E$, and it can be found by determining the rate of cutting flux at that position.

FIG. 226. Coil rotating in a uniform magnetic field

Such a determination requires the resolution of inductor velocity into components directed both along and at right angles to the flux.

Certain quantities can be expressed with definiteness only when their directions are known; these quantities are called *vectors*. Examples of a vector quantity are: the displacement of a box along a chute, the force used in stretching a spring, and the velocity of a moving conductor. A vector quantity can be represented by a line with an arrow head; the length of the line represents, to some convenient scale, the numerical value of the quantity, and the arrow head indicates the direction of that quantity.

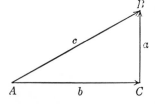

FIG. 227. Relations between sides and angles of a triangle

Fig. 227 shows a triangle with a right angle at $C$ and acute angles at $A$ and $B$; the sides of the triangle are designated $a$, $b$, and $c$, with side $a$ opposite angle $A$, and so on. If sides $a$ and $b$ represent vectors that can be added, then the hypotenuse of the right-angled triangle represents their sum or *resultant*. Thus, if $a$ and $b$ are forces acting on the same body, their resultant force $c$, acting alone on that body, will produce the same effect as the forces $a$ and $b$ jointly.

A vector quantity can be *resolved* into *components*, that is, broken up into parts which together have the same effect as the original quantity. Thus, in the figure, vector $c$ can be resolved into components $a$ and $b$ which are at right angles to each other.

The ratios between the sides of a right triangle are called *trigonometric functions* of the angles of the triangle. The functions most commonly used are the *sine, cosine* and *tangent* of an angle; these are abbreviated respectively as sin, cos and tan. These functions are defined as follows: The sine of either acute angle is the ratio of the length of the side opposite that angle to the length of the hypotenuse. The cosine of either acute angle is the ratio of the side adjacent to that angle to the hypotenuse. The tangent of either acute angle is the ratio of the side opposite that angle to the side adjacent to that angle. These statements are symbolized as follows:

| *Function* | *For Angle A* | *For Angle B* |
|---|---|---|
| $\sin = \dfrac{\text{opposite side}}{\text{hypotenuse}}$ | $\sin A = \dfrac{a}{c}$ | $\sin B = \dfrac{b}{c}$ |
| $\cos = \dfrac{\text{adjacent side}}{\text{hypotenuse}}$ | $\cos A = \dfrac{b}{c}$ | $\cos B = \dfrac{a}{c}$ |
| $\tan = \dfrac{\text{opposite side}}{\text{adjacent side}}$ | $\tan A = \dfrac{a}{b}$ | $\tan B = \dfrac{b}{a}$ |

It will be observed that $\sin A = \dfrac{a}{c} = \cos B$; that is, the sine of an angle is equal to the cosine of its complementary angle. Values of these functions for angles between $0°$ and $90°$ are tabulated in the Appendix. The values for larger angles are obtained by applying the rules at the end of the table.

The speed of the inductors in Fig. 226 is the same at all points along the circular path but the velocity is different from point to point because of the change in the direction of motion. The velocity of the inductor at position $P$ is represented in direction and amount by the vector marked $V$, a line drawn from $P$ tangent to the dotted circle that indicates the path of the inductor.

Vector $V$ is shown as the hypotenuse of the right-angled triangle $JPK$, and so the velocity of the inductor at $P$ can be resolved into components $JK$ along the horizontal direction and $PK$ along the vertical. Consequently, the line $PK$ represents the component of the velocity $V$ that is perpendicular to the flux between the poles NS; this component of the inductor velocity is marked $v$, and it determines the rate at which magnetic flux is cut by inductor $P$. At position $D$ the velocity vector would be horizontal and its vertical component would be zero; at position $D'$ the velocity vector and its vertical component would be coincident. The vertical component for an intermediate position of inductor $P$ depends on the angle that coil $MP$ makes with its initial position $AD$ perpendicular to the flux; this angle is denoted by the Greek letter $\beta$ (beta). The value of component $v$ relative to that of vector $V$ is proportional to the *sine* of angle $\beta$.

The angle $\beta$ between $MP$ and $AD$ is about 60° and the angle at $J$ in the triangle $JPK$ has the same value. The sine of an angle of 60° has a value of 0.866. Therefore, the length of side $v$ is 0.866 that of hypotenuse $V$. In general, then, the vertical component $v$ of the conductor velocity $V$ depends upon $\sin \beta$, that is $v = V \times \sin \beta$. Since the momentary e.m.f. induced in a conductor is proportional to its velocity at right angles to the magnetic flux, it follows that at coil position $MP$, the momentary e.m.f. is

$$e = E \times \sin \beta \qquad\qquad 80$$

This equation shows that the e.m.f. generated in a coil rotating at constant speed within a uniform field is equal to the maximum e.m.f. $E$ multiplied by the sine of the angle of the coil position.

When such an alternating e.m.f. is generated in a circuit, the current established will undergo similar variations, and the instantaneous current $i$ will be related to the maximum value $I$ in the same way, that is

$$i = I \times \sin \beta \qquad\qquad 81$$

**Problem 105.**—A search coil rotating in a bipolar magnetic field generates an e.m.f. of 2 millivolts at the instant when its plane is parallel to the flux. What are the instantaneous e.m.f.'s generated as the coil passes positions 15, 30, 45, 60 and 75 degrees beyond position $AD$ in Fig. 226?

Since the e.m.f. is 2 millivolts when the coil passes the position aligned with the magnetic flux, this is the maximum value generated in it. At position $AD$ the induced e.m.f. is zero. At other positions the instantaneous value is given by Formula (80); thus, at 15 degrees,

$$e = E \times \sin \beta = 2 \times \sin 15 = 2 \times 0.259 = 0.518 \, \text{millivolt}$$

The sines of 15, 30, 45, 60 and 75 degrees are respectively 0.259, 0.500, 0.707, 0.866, 0.966; therefore, the e.m.f.'s generated at these instants are respectively 0.518, 1.000, 1.414, 1.732 and 1.932 millivolts.

**171. Graphic Representation of an Alternating Potential.**—The successive instantaneous values of an alternating e.m.f. or current may be represented by a wave-like curve such as shown in Fig. 228. This curve is called a *sine curve,* and is the typical form of waves supplied by alternating-current generators. Specifically, the figure illustrates a sinusoidal wave of potential having a maximum value of 100 volts in accordance with the scale at the left.

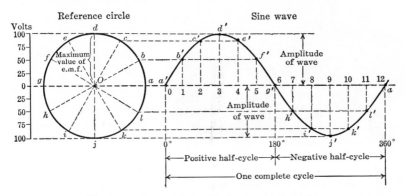

Fig. 228. Construction of a sine wave of e.m.f.

The construction of the sine wave is begun by drawing the circle centered at $O$ with a radius of 100 volts. Any suitable scale may be used; in this case 1.4 centimeters represents 100 volts. This circle is then divided into a convenient number of equal parts *ab, bc,* etc.; in the illustration there are 12 parts each forming a sector measuring $360 \div 12$ or 30 degrees at the center.

On the horizontal datum line through the center of the circle, lay off 12 equal intervals to correspond with the 12 parts of the circle, as indicated by 0-1, 1-2, . . . 11-12. The intervals may be drawn to any suitable scale; they are here shown of 0.5-centimeter length and each represents a 30-degree displacement. Dotted construction lines are drawn horizontally through points *d, ec,* . . . *ik, j* on the circle; others are drawn vertically along the datum through points 0, 1, 2, . . . 12. The points of the sine wave are located at the intersections of corresponding construction lines.

Thus, point $c'$ of the sine curve, which corresponds to $c$ on the reference circle, is two 30-degree sectors or 60 degrees from $a$; therefore, it is located by the intersection of the dotted lines through $c$ and 2.

The curve through points $a'$, $b'$, . . . $l'$, $a$ represents a complete cycle of the e.m.f. wave. The part of the cycle from 0 to 6 is positive, and the potential during this interval rises from zero, reaches a positive maximum of 100 volts, and falls to zero again. At point 6 the e.m.f. reverses its direction and is negative over the interval from 6 to 12. During this interval the potential rises to a negative maximum of 100 volts and then falls once more to zero.

FIG. 229.  Generator for analysis of wave form
Central Scientific Company

Either the sine wave or the circle of reference may be used to determine the value of the e.m.f. at any part of the cycle. Thus, the value ⅛ cycle beyond $a$ is found by drawing a line directed $360 \div 8 = 45$ degrees to the horizontal through the center of the circle; this line intersects the circle at a height which measures 70.7 volts on the vertical scale at the left. This point can be located on the sine wave by erecting a vertical line 45 degrees from point 0, that is, midway between points 1 and 2, and scaling off its intersection on the wave; its value is 70.7 volts as before.

The wave in Fig. 228 may also be read in terms of percentages, taking the maximum value to represent 100 per cent. For example, if a sinusoidal current has a peak value of 5 amperes, its instantaneous value at the 45-degree point would be $70.7 \times 5 \div 100$ or 3.535 amperes. Similarly, at 240 degrees, the instantaneous current is found to be $-86.6 \times 5 \div 100$ or $-4.33$ amperes.

Fig. 229 shows a generator specially designed to make possible the measurement of its e.m.f. wave form. Two sets of permanent magnets are mounted with like poles adjacent in order to produce a uniform and strong magnetic field between the pole pieces attached to the poles. A flat coil is mounted to turn in this field about an axis perpendicular to the flux, and an escapement wheel is provided to limit the motion of the coil to 10-degree twists. The coil is connected through brushes to a ballistic galvanometer and a reading of the throw is taken for every 10-degree twist during a whole revolution. Since the throws of the galvanometer are proportional to the number of lines of force cut in these short time intervals, a plot of the readings will show the approximately sine wave form that would be produced by the generator if the coil were rotated uniformly.

**Experiment 83.**—With a generator such as that pictured in Fig. 229, carry out a wave analysis test by noting the throws of a ballistic galvanometer connected to the generator terminals. A typical set of readings for 10-degree rotations of the generator coil over a half revolution follows:

| Angle ...0 | 10 | 20 | 30 | 40 | 50 | 60 | 70 | 80 | 90 | degrees |
|---|---|---|---|---|---|---|---|---|---|---|
| Throw...0.4 | 1.1 | 2.0 | 2.8 | 3.5 | 4.1 | 4.7 | 5.1 | 5.4 | 5.3 | divisions |

| Angle .......100 | 110 | 120 | 130 | 140 | 150 | 160 | 170 | 180 | degrees |
|---|---|---|---|---|---|---|---|---|---|
| Throw....... 5.1 | 4.6 | 4.1 | 3.5 | 2.8 | 2.0 | 1.3 | 0.5 | −0.4 | divisions |

Plot the results for a complete revolution of the coil, using cross-section paper and laying off the deflections vertically.

**172. Frequency.**—When, as described in the two foregoing sections, the alternating e.m.f. or current has passed from zero to its maximum value in one direction, to zero, then to its maximum value in the other direction, and back to zero, the complete set of values passed through during that time is called a *cycle*. This cycle of values, which is represented by the sine curve depicted in Fig. 228, is completed during an interval of time called a *period*. A period is represented by the time elapsing from one positive maximum to the next positive maximum, or from one negative maximum to the next negative maximum, or from the point where the curve crosses the horizontal datum line to its next crossing in the same direction. Thus, a cycle comprises the succession of values which occur from any one point on the curve to the next point where the curve indicates the same value and character of e.m.f. or current. The time elapsing from 0° to 360°

constitutes a period, since it represents the time of one complete cycle of events.

The term *frequency* is applied to the number of cycles completed in a unit of time—one second. It is expressed in *cycles per second,* although it is quite customary to speak of the frequency merely in *cycles.* If the current from an alternating-current generator performs the cycle of events shown in Fig. 228 from $a'$ to $a$ sixty times per second, it is said to have a frequency of 60 cycles. The frequency of an alternating current is always that of the e.m.f. producing it. For electric power and lighting, frequencies of 25 and 60 cycles are standard in this country, but the latter is the more usual. In radio practice, the frequencies are in the millions of cycles per second, and even extend to several billion.

The number of poles and the speed jointly determine the frequency of an alternating-current generator. A cycle of current values is developed by the movement of a conductor completely past one N-pole and one S-pole. This is accomplished in a bipolar alternator in one entire revolution. If this machine makes 20 revolutions in one second then its frequency will be 20 cycles per second. In a 6-pole alternator 3 cycles of current values will be developed per revolution; hence if such a machine makes 20 revolutions per second then the frequency will be $3 \times 20 = 60$ cycles. In general, let

$$P = \text{number of } pairs \text{ of poles,}$$
$$N = \text{speed in revolutions per minute,}$$
$$f = \text{frequency in cycles per second.}$$

Then the frequency is

$$f = P \times \frac{N}{60} \qquad\qquad \textbf{82}$$

To FIND THE FREQUENCY OF THE E.M.F. OR CURRENT FROM ANY ALTERNATING-CURRENT GENERATOR:

*Multiply the number of pairs of poles by the speed of the armature in revolutions per second.*

**Problem 106.**—What would be the frequency of the current furnished by an alternator having 10 poles and revolving at 720 revolutions per minute?

The machine has 5 pairs of poles; consequently the frequency is

$$(82) \qquad f = P \times \frac{N}{60} = 5 \times \frac{720}{60} = 5 \times 12 = 60 \text{ cycles}$$

**173. Expressing Values of Alternating Currents and E.m.f.'s.—** It has been shown that an alternating current is one which is continually changing in value and periodically reversing its direction. The heavy curve in Fig. 230, for example, illustrates an alternating current that has a maximum value of 5 amperes. Starting at *A,* the current increases from zero to its maximum value at *B,* then decreases to zero again at *C;* it then passes through a similar set of values in the opposite direction through *D* to *E.* When the current is at its highest value in either direction it amounts to 5 amperes, but at all other instants it is smaller than this. The question naturally arises: What value should be assigned to this current? The answer is dictated by the *effect* which the current is capable of producing in a circuit.

It has become the universal custom to express alternating currents in terms of the value of the direct current which would produce the same heating effect. Thus, *1 ampere of alternating current in any circuit produces the same amount of heat as 1 ampere of direct current in that circuit.* Obviously, the heating effect of an alternating current will increase and decrease as the current increases and decreases during the cycle, but the average heating can be compared with that produced by direct current.

An alternating current varies so rapidly that the heating effect appears to be uniform, but if the frequency is low enough, the variation under favorable conditions may be noticed. For example, if an incandescent lamp having a thin filament is connected to an alternator, and the machine is slowed down to yield a current at about 20 cycles, the light will flicker perceptibly; if the frequency is raised to 40 or more cycles, the light appears quite steady to the eye.

The variation in the heating effect of an alternating current over a cycle is determined by Formula (52) and the result is indicated in Fig. 230. Suppose a current, represented by the full-line curve *ABCDE,* to reach a maximum value of 5 amperes during each half cycle, and that this current is established in a circuit of 2 ohms resistance. When the current has its highest value of 5 amperes at *B,* the rate at which heat is expended is $P = I^2 \times R = 5^2 \times 2 = 50$ joules per second, or 50 watts. This power value is laid off to a convenient scale as *FG* along a line through *B.* At another instant during the cycle, say $X$, the current is $XY$ and its value is measured to scale, this value is squared and multiplied by the resistance (2 ohms); the result represents the watts expended in heating at instant $X$ and is shown by line $XZ$. This process is continued for a number of instants along the cycle and a curve is drawn through the resulting points; this dotted curve shows the heating effect of the particular current in the 2-ohm circuit.

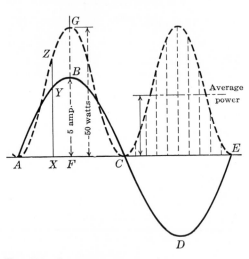

Fig. 230. Obtaining effective value of an alternating current

Average power is 25 watts.

This heating curve rises rather slowly from point $A$, but as the current increases, the heating effect rises rapidly, because it increases with the square of the current. After reaching its highest value at $FG$, the curve falls to zero at the end of the first half cycle and then forms a similar lobe during the second. It should be observed that the heating curve is drawn altogether *above* the horizontal axis $AE$; this is correct for squaring the negative values of current yields products which are positive. To find the average power, divide one lobe of the heating curve, say that between $C$ and $E$, into strips of equal width by drawing the vertical lines shown. The average height of these lines is obtained by adding their lengths and dividing by the number of lines. The sum of these 10 lines represents 250 watts to the same scale as before, giving the average power as 25 watts.

The value so obtained gives the average power $P$ expended in the circuit to produce heat; it is the average of all the values $I^2 \times R$. Since the resistance $R$ of the circuit is the same for all of these products, it follows that the average power divided by the resistance will be the *average of the squares of all the values of the current* at the different instants. The *square root of the average of these squares* must give the value of the alternating current that will produce the same power or heating effect as a corresponding direct current. This value of an alternating current is sometimes called the *square root of mean square value* (r.m.s.), but it is usually called the *effective value.*

In the numerical illustration the average power is 25 watts and the resistance is 2 ohms, therefore the average of the squares of the current values is $25/2 = 12.5$, and its square root is 3.54 amperes. This is the effective value of the current. In other words, although this alternating current is continually rising and falling between the limits +5 amperes and −5 amperes, it only produces as much heat in the circuit as 3.54 amperes of direct current.

The relation between the maximum value of 5 amperes and the effective value of 3.54 amperes is as $\sqrt{2}$ is to 1. This ratio of 1.414 to 1 is the same for all sine waves of current (or e.m.f.). Therefore, the effective value of a sinusoidal alternating current is equal to the maximum value divided by 1.414 *or* multiplied by 0.707; it follows that the maximum value of the current is equal to the effective value multiplied by 1.414. In equation form these relations for sine waves of current or e.m.f. are

$$\left. \begin{array}{l} \text{effective value} \ \ = 0.707 \times \text{maximum value} \\ \text{maximum value} = 1.414 \times \text{effective value} \end{array} \right\} \qquad \textbf{83}$$

*Whenever values of alternating quantities are expressed it is understood that effective values are meant;* thus, an alternating current of 10 amperes means an effective current of 10 amperes (its maximum or peak value is 14.1 amperes, if sinusoidal). Alternating-current ammeters and voltmeters are calibrated to indicate effective values.

**Problem 107.**—An alternating-current voltmeter reads 120 volts when inserted in a particular circuit. Between what maximum values do all the instantaneous values of the sine-wave e.m.f. lie?

Since the meter reads the effective e.m.f. value, the maximum value is $1.414 \times 120 = 170$; therefore, all e.m.f. values fall between −170 and +170 volts.

**174. Effective and Average Values.**—In stating the amount of an alternating e.m.f. or current, reference is always made to the effective value as defined in the foregoing section. Commercial instruments used to measure these quantities are calibrated so that their scales read effective values in volts and amperes. In such an instrument the fluctuations of current in the coil are too rapid for the pointer to follow, and the indication is necessarily a mean of the instantaneous current values.

Care should be taken not to confuse the *effective value* of an alternating current with the *average value*. By the *effective* value is meant that current value which produces the same heating effect in a circuit as the same number of amperes of direct current. By the *average* value is meant simply the average of all the instantaneous values of the current during an alternation.

In Fig. 231, the curve *ABC* represents a half cycle of current having a maximum value of 5 amperes. If a number of equi-distant vertical lines are drawn, as shown, and their lengths added, and if this total is divided by the number of lines, the result will be the average height of the curve and represent the average current. Doing this for the sine curve gives $31.8 \div 10 = 3.18$ amperes as the average current, and the graph of the average current

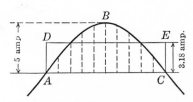

Fig. 231. Obtaining average value of an alternating current

is shown by the horizontal line *DE*. The average current *AD* multiplied by the length *AC* gives the area of the rectangle *ADEC*, and this equals the area bounded by the curve *ABC* and the axis *AC*. The ratio of this average value of 3.18 amperes to the maximum value of 5 amperes is as 2 is to $\pi$, or 0.636 is to 1. Consequently the maximum value of a sine curve is $1 \div 0.636 = 1.57$ times the average value.

The *average value* of an alternating current is simply the *average of the values* during an alternation, but the *effective value* is the *square root of the average square* of all the values during the alternation. For convenience the relations between average and maximum values and between effective and maximum values are given together:

average value    $= 0.636 \times$ maximum value;
maximum value $= 1.57 \times$ average value;
effective value    $= 0.707 \times$ maximum value;
maximum value $= 1.41 \times$ effective value.

The effective value, as shown by the above relations, is somewhat greater than the average value. These ratios apply to sine
curves of e.m.f. and current only; for other shapes of waves the
relations might be quite different. For example, a wave with a
sharp peak would have a higher maximum value compared with
the effective value than that given above.

**175. Phase.**—The term *phase* is used to express the displacement between two alternating quantities which have the same

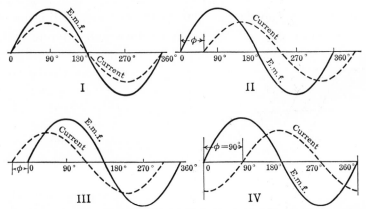

Fig. 232.  Current and potential relations in alternating-current circuits

frequency but which do not rise and fall in unison. It is applied
to the large number of circuits where the current is not in step
with the alternating e.m.f. which is impressed upon the circuit.

The curves of impressed e.m.f. and current in a circuit are frequently plotted together in the same diagram, as illustrated in
Fig. 232. They have the same horizontal scale representing angles
in degrees (or time in seconds) but have their individual vertical
scales of volts and amperes. In some circuits the zero and maximum values of the current curve will occur at the same positions
as do the corresponding values of the potential curve. In such a
case, as depicted at I, the current is said to be *in phase* with the
e.m.f.

In other circuits the current will reach a maximum or a zero
value at a time later than the corresponding values of the impressed e.m.f.; this condition is represented at II. In such a case

the current is said to be *out of phase with,* and to *lag* the impressed
e.m.f. In still other circuits the curves are placed as shown at
III and the current and potential are again *out of phase,* but the
current is said to *lead* the e.m.f. The distance between the zero
ordinate of one sine curve and the corresponding zero ordinate of
the other is measured in degrees and is called the *angular dis-*
*placement* or *phase difference.* This *angle of lag* or of *lead* is
usually represented by the Greek lower-case letter $\phi$ (phi).

When one curve has its zero ordinate coincident with the maximum ordinate of the other, as in Fig. 232 IV, there is a displacement of a quarter cycle ($\phi = 90°$). If the zero ordinates of the
two curves coincide, but the positive maximum of one coincides
with the negative maxi-
mum of the other, then
$\phi = 180°$, and the curves
are in *opposite phase.*

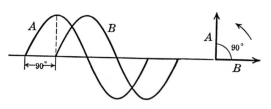

FIG. 233. Two alternating quantities represented by
vectors

Alternating    e.m.f.'s
and currents are often
represented by vectors
rather    than    by    sine
curves, particularly when
two or more of these quantities are involved. To appreciate this
representation, reference will again be made to the sine wave of
Fig. 228. This curve was constructed from points on the reference
circle at the left where certain of its radii terminated. Thus, the
point $b'$ on the wave was determined by the height of the radius
$Ob$ in the circle. Consequently, if the line $Oa$ were regarded as a
vector and it were revolved around the center $O$, the end of the
vector would sweep out the reference circle $a$, $b$, $c$, etc., and the
heights of this vector above the horizontal line through the center
$O$ would be represented by the successive points of the sine wave
$a'$, $b'$, $c'$, etc. In this way a rotating vector may be used to represent an alternating e.m.f. or alternating current.

In Fig. 233 are shown two like sine waves, wave $B$ being drawn
90 degrees to the right of wave $A$. The base line also represents
time, for the length of either wave is the period, or the time
required to complete one cycle of values. Since wave $B$ begins

when wave $A$ has its maximum positive value, wave $B$ lags $A$ by one-quarter of a cycle. The waves can be represented much more easily by drawing two vectors 90 degrees apart as shown at the right and representing their rotation by an arrow. As the vectors $A$ and $B$ rotate together uniformly in the direction shown, maintaining the same angle of 90 degrees between them, their arrow heads would rise and fall in the manner shown by the corresponding sine curves.

The alternating current established in a circuit by an impressed e.m.f. is shown vectorially in Fig. 234, and the parts I to IV correspond with similarly labelled parts of Fig. 232. The vertical direction has been chosen for the e.m.f. vector $E$ and the current vector $I$ is shown in various positions. The lengths of lines $E$ and $I$ represent the maximum values of the alternating potential and current respectively, although they

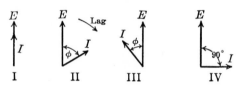

FIG. 234. Vector diagrams of alternating quantities

are more frequently drawn to represent effective values. At I the current is in phase with the impressed e.m.f., at II the current lags $\phi$ degrees, at III the current leads $\phi$ degrees, and at IV the current lags 90 degrees.

### 176. Polyphase Systems.

The term *phase* is used also when referring to the angular displacement between two or more like quantities, either alternating e.m.f.'s or alternating currents. It is likewise used in distinguishing the different types of alternating-current generators. For example, a machine designed to generate a single e.m.f. wave is called a *single-phase* alternator, and one designed to generate two or more e.m.f. waves is called a *polyphase* alternator.

A machine which generates two separate e.m.f.'s for maintaining currents through two distinct circuits, so that the e.m.f. in one circuit is a maximum when the e.m.f. in the other one is zero, is called a *two-phase* generator, §240. The arrangement of the two circuits (four wires) for carrying these currents is termed a *two-phase* (sometimes also quarter-phase) system. The simultaneous e.m.f. curves of the two circuits differ in phase by 90 degrees as shown in Fig. 235.

A machine which generates three e.m.f.'s that are 120 degrees apart in phase is called a *three-phase* alternator; the e.m.f. wave forms are depicted in Fig. 236. A system of conductors carrying the currents of such an alternator is called a *three-phase* system, and requires in practice three wires, although theoretically, the system consists of three circuits of two wires each. Since the algebraic sum of the currents in the three circuits (if balanced) is at every instant equal to zero, the three return wires, one on each circuit, may be dispensed with, leaving but three wires.

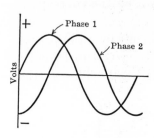

FIG. 235. Sine e.m.f. curves of a two-phase alternator

Any arrangement of conductors for two or more alternating currents that are definitely related to one another in time constitutes a polyphase system, §240.

**177. Addition of Alternating E.m.f.'s.**—If several e.m.f.'s are impressed upon a circuit at the same time, the effect is the same as that produced by a single e.m.f. which has at each instant a potential equal to the sum of the various components at that instant. For two sinusoidal e.m.f.'s $E_1$ and $E_2$ having the same frequency and the same phase, the resultant is evidently a sine wave equal to their sum; that is, the maximum value of the resultant $E$ is equal to the sum of the maximum values of $E_1$ and $E_2$. Since with a sine wave the effective value is 0.707 times the maximum value, it follows that the effective value of the resultant e.m.f. is equal to the sum of the effective values of $E_1$ and $E_2$.

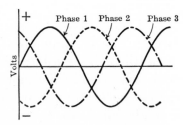

FIG. 236. Sine e.m.f. curves of a three-phase alternator

The more general case of the addition of two alternating potentials involves e.m.f.'s of the same frequency, but of different magnitude and phase. In Fig. 237 are shown two sine waves representing potentials $E_1$ and $E_2$, the angle between them being $\phi$.

Adding the ordinates of these curves for each point along the horizontal time (or degree) axis results in the sinusoidal wave $E$. It is quite clear from the figure that the maximum value of the resultant wave $E$ is *not* equal to the sum of the maximum values of waves $E_1$ and $E_2$, but is less than this sum.

The vector diagram at the left of the figure shows how the maximum value of the resultant of the two e.m.f.'s may be ascertained more readily. Vectors $E_1$ and $E_2$ represent to a common scale the maximum values of two e.m.f.'s and they are drawn with an angle $\phi$ between them from a common point. A parallelogram is constructed upon these lines as sides, and the diagonal

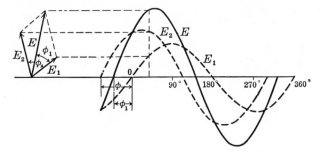

FIG. 237. Addition of e.m.f.'s having the same frequency

is then drawn as shown. The length of this diagonal represents to the same scale the maximum value of the resultant e.m.f. The position of the diagonal is $\phi_1$ degrees ahead of $E_1$; therefore the resultant $E$ leads potential $E_1$ by an angle of $\phi_1$ degrees.

**Problem 108.**—Find the resultant e.m.f. produced by two alternators of the same frequency connected in series. One generates an e.m.f. of 110 volts and the other an e.m.f. of 40 volts, the smaller e.m.f. lagging the other by 90 degrees.

The resultant is obtained by adding a vector representing 40 volts at right angles to another vector representing 110 volts; its magnitude is

$$\sqrt{(40)^2 + (110)^2} = \sqrt{1600 + 12,100} = \sqrt{13,700} = 117 \text{ volts.}$$  The ratio 40/110 is the tangent of the angle by which the resultant lags the 110-volt e.m.f.; this angle is found to be 20 degrees.

**178. Harmonics.**—Alternating e.m.f.'s of different frequencies applied to the same circuit will give, in general, an irregular wave form. In practice, the frequencies of some e.m.f.'s are multiples of the frequency of another, called the *fundamental,* or *first harmonic.* The potential curve having twice this frequency is termed the *second harmonic;* another having three times this frequency, the *third harmonic,* and so on. The resultant instantaneous e.m.f. is obtained by adding the potential values of all the components at that instant.

When both odd and even harmonics are present, the resulting curve will have unlike lobes, but when only odd harmonics occur, as is usual in electrical machinery, the lobe above the horizontal axis

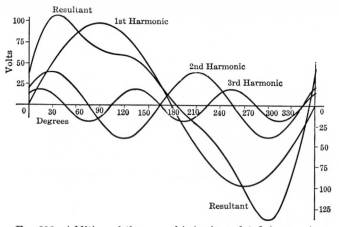

Fig. 238. Addition of three e.m.f.'s having related frequencies

and the other below it will be similar. Fig. 238 shows the resultant e.m.f. of three sinusoidal components having the following maximum values: 1st harmonic 100 volts, 2nd harmonic 40 volts, and the 3rd harmonic 20 volts; the latter two lead the first by 15 degrees on the scale of the first harmonic.

It is possible by graphical and analytical methods to determine the harmonics which are present in any complicated wave shape that may have an experimental or a theoretical origin.

## QUESTIONS

1. How does an alternating current differ from a continuous or direct current?
2. What advantage has alternating current over direct current?
3. Sketch a rectangular coil of wire in a bipolar field in four positions 90 degrees apart. Assuming the terminals of the coil to be provided

with collector rings, indicate polarities and direction of the current in the internal and external circuits in each sketch.

4. What is a vector quantity?
5. The names of four physical quantities follow: velocity, mass, force, and time. State which are vectors and why.
6. Draw accurately a sine wave having a length of 4 inches and a maximum ordinate of 1.5 inches.
7. What do you understand by the terms frequency and period?
8. How would you determine the frequency of any alternator?
9. What is meant by the effective value of an alternating current? How is this value determined?
10. How does one ampere of alternating current compare with one ampere of direct current?
11. What are the relations between the average, effective, and maximum values of a sinusoidal alternating current?
12. What is meant by phase angle? by opposite phase? by two-phase? by polyphase?
13. Construct a vector diagram to indicate the phase relations of a three-phase system.
14. Explain how to obtain the resultant of two alternating e.m.f.'s of the same frequency that are impressed simultaneously upon a circuit (a) when they are in phase, and (b) when they are out of phase.
15. What is meant by a third harmonic wave?
16. Sketch the shape of the resultant wave of a fundamental sine curve with a symmetrically-located third harmonic.

## PROBLEMS

1. A sine wave of potential has a maximum value of 250 volts. Assuming the positive half cycle to begin at the 0-degree point, calculate the value of this wave at the 120-degree point. *Ans.* 216.5 volts.
2. If 3000 pounds of copper are needed to transmit a given amount of electric power at a certain p.d., how much copper would be needed to transmit the same amount of power over the same distance at twice the p.d., assuming the same percentage drop in potential. *Ans.* 750 pounds.
3. A 60-cycle alternator generates an e.m.f. represented by a sine curve having a maximum value of 155 volts. (a) What is the value of the e.m.f. at an instant 1/720 second after passing through zero in a positive direction? (b) What would an alternating-current voltmeter read if connected across the alternator? *Ans.* (a) 77.5 volts; (b) 109.6 volts.
4. An alternator has 10 poles and its armature rotates at a speed of 300 revolutions per minute. (a) What will be the frequency of its e.m.f.? (b) How many times would the current change its direction in 1 minute? *Ans.* (a) 25 cycles; (b) 3000.

5. What must be the speed of a 12-pole alternator to yield 60-cycle current? *Ans.* 600 revolutions per minute.

6. A turbo-alternator has a stationary armature and its bipolar field structure revolves at 3600 revolutions per minute. What is the frequency of the e.m.f. generated. *Ans.* 60 cycles.

7. An ammeter in a certain circuit indicates 15 amperes. What would be the maximum value of this alternating current? *Ans.* 21.2 amperes.

8. A particular sine wave of e.m.f. has a maximum value of 30 volts. What are its average and effective values? *Ans.* 19.1 and 21.2 volts respectively.

9. Two 60-cycle alternators coupled to the same shaft generate 80 volts and 60 volts with a constant phase difference of 90 degrees. What single alternating e.m.f. would produce the same effect in a circuit as the two from the alternators when simultaneously impressed upon that circuit? *Ans.* 100 volts.

10. Two e.m.f.'s, each of 145 volts and 60 cycles, are 120 degrees apart in phase. If both act on the same circuit, what is the value of their resultant, and what is its phase relative to the components? *Ans.* 145 volts; midway between them.

# Lesson XVI

## ALTERNATING-CURRENT CIRCUITS

Properties of an electric circuit—Inductive reactance—Reactors—
Capacitive reactance—Current and potential relations in capacitive circuits—Components of impressed potential difference—Impedance—Graphical representation of resistance, reactance and impedance—Angle of lag or
lead—Circuits having resistance, inductance and capacitance—Ohm's Law
for alternating-current circuits—Questions and Problems.

**179. Properties of an Electric Circuit.**—The amount of direct
current produced in a metallic circuit by a given e.m.f. is entirely
determined by the total resistance of the circuit. The amount of
alternating current produced in a circuit depends not only upon
the resistance, but also upon any *inductance* (self or mutual) and
*capacitance* that may be included in the circuit. These two circuit
properties are described in Lesson XIV. Inductance and capacitance have no effect upon a direct current after a steady condition
has been established, and this condition is usually reached in a
fraction of a second. In an alternating-current circuit either property may be far more important than the resistance, and in some
cases may control the current almost completely.

The difference in the effects of inductance and capacitance in
direct- and alternating-current circuits is due to the fact that the
alternating current is constantly changing its value and periodically altering its direction. In consequence, the magnetic field
(associated with inductance) or electric field (associated with
capacitance) must be established first in one direction, then in the
opposite direction, many times per second. The result of such
rapidly changing magnetic and electric fields will be considered
in this lesson.

Resistance in an alternating-current circuit has exactly the same effect as it has in a direct-current circuit; it always occasions a loss which appears as heat. If an alternating current of $I$ amperes (effective value) is maintained in a circuit having a resistance of $R$ ohms, the loss will be $I^2 \times R$ watts, just as in a direct-current circuit, §97. Should the alternating-current circuit contain only resistance, then the strength of current will be the e.m.f. of the source divided by the resistance, as dictated by Ohm's Law; if the effective value of the e.m.f. is used, then the current will also be the effective value. In such a circuit the current wave will be in phase with the e.m.f. wave, as shown in Fig. 232 I.

When an alternating current is maintained in a circuit that includes a coil of wire, the magnetic field around the coil changes

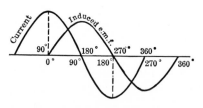

FIG. 239. E.m.f. of self-induction lags the current by 90 degrees

continuously, thereby developing in the circuit an e.m.f. which changes in value from moment to moment. For example, when the current rises in the positive direction, the lines of force of the field are directed one way through the coil and increase in number; after the current reaches its maximum value and begins to decrease, the lines of force diminish and reach zero value when the current becomes zero; then when the current rises in the negative direction the magnetic lines through the coil are reversed and increase in number, and so on. The e.m.f. induced in such a circuit, instead of being momentary, as it is when a direct current is established or interrupted, acts continuously and varies in value like the alternating current in the circuit.

The amount of e.m.f. induced in the coil depends upon the rapidity of cutting the magnetic field by its own turns. Since the magnetic flux associated with the coil varies most rapidly when the current passes through its zero point (changing from + to − or vice versa), the induced e.m.f. is a maximum at that moment. When the current has the maximum value in either direction, the flux does not vary and, consequently, the induced e.m.f. is momentarily zero. Therefore, the e.m.f. developed in the circuit does not rise and fall in unison with the current in it, but *lags* the current by exactly a quarter of a cycle, as shown in Fig. 239.

The e.m.f. induced in the circuit containing the coil of wire, or in any circuit containing inductance, acts in oppostion to the e.m.f. that was impressed upon the circuit to produce the current. Because of this fact the induced e.m.f. is called a counter e.m.f. The effect of this counter e.m.f. of self-induction in the circuit is to reduce the strength of the current in it.

**180. Inductive Reactance.**—The effect of inductance in an alternating-current circuit is to choke the current through the development of a counter e.m.f. The choking effect is called *inductive reactance* and, like resistance, is expressed in ohms. Unlike resistance, reactance does not entail any loss of energy, because it is due to a counter e.m.f. and not to something resembling friction. The value of the inductive reactance depends upon both the inductance of the circuit and the frequency of the source of alternating current.

Let

$L$ = inductance of the circuit in henries,
$f$ = frequency of the power supply in cycles per second,
$\pi$ = 3.1416, a numerical constant which is the ratio of the circumference of a circle to its diameter,
$X_l$ = inductive reactance in ohms.

Then the inductive reactance of the circuit is

$$X_l = 2\pi \times f \times L \qquad \textbf{84}$$

To FIND THE INDUCTIVE REACTANCE OF A CIRCUIT:

*Multiply the inductance of the circuit in henries by the frequency of the alternating e.m.f., and by 2 π.*

**Problem 109.**—What would be the inductive reactance of a coil of wire having an inductance of 0.02 henry when connected to a source of e.m.f. having a frequency of 60 cycles per second?

(84) $\qquad X_l = 2\pi \times f \times L = 6.28 \times 60 \times 0.02 = 7.54$ ohms

**Problem 110.**—Determine the inductance of an electromagnet which has an inductive reactance of 18 ohms when traversed by a 25-cycle current. Transpose Formula (84) and solve for $L$; whence the inductance is

$$L = \frac{X_l}{2\pi \times f} = \frac{18}{6.28 \times 25} = 0.115 \text{ henry}$$

**Problem 111.**—The inductive reactance of a particular winding at 60 cycles is 5 ohms. What will be its reactance at 6000 cycles per second?

Since inductive reactance $X_l$ is directly proportional to the frequency $f$, the reactance of the winding at 6000 cycles will be

$$X_l = \frac{6000}{60} \times 5 = 500 \text{ ohms}$$

To derive Formula (84), consider a sine current wave of frequency $f$ to have a maximum value of $I$ amperes. The current strength will then vary from $+I$ to $-I$ amperes in a half period, that is, in a time interval of $\frac{1}{2}$ of $1/f$ second. The *average* rate of change over this current range of $2I$ amperes is, therefore, $2I \div \dfrac{1}{2 \times f} = 4 \times f \times I$ amperes per second. Remembering that a circuit having an inductance of 1 henry will set up an e.m.f. of self-induction of 1 volt when the current therein changes at the rate of 1 ampere per second, it follows that the induced e.m.f. in a circuit of $L$ henries, in which the current changes by an average of $4 \times f \times I$ amperes in 1 second, will have the *average* value of $4 \times f \times L \times I$ volts. The corresponding maximum e.m.f. value is obtained by multiplying the foregoing expression by $\pi/2$ or 1.57, as explained in §174; thus both e.m.f. and current will be expressed in terms of maximum values. The induced e.m.f. is, therefore,

$$E_l = 2\pi \times f \times L \times I \qquad\qquad 85$$

In order to change to effective values, divide $E_l$ and $I$ by $\sqrt{2}$ in view of the fact that both e.m.f. and current are sinusoidal waves. Since this means dividing both sides of the equation by the same quantity, the result is the same, and Equation (85) applies also to effective values. If this equation is then divided by the current, the inductive reactance sought for becomes

$$X_l = \frac{E_l}{I} = 2\pi \times f \times L$$

**Experiment 84.**—Connect a solenoid of several ohms resistance to the blades of a double-throw switch so that it can be supplied either with direct current (D.C.) or with alternating current (A.C.), both at 110 volts, as shown at I in Fig. 240. A lamp $L$ is joined in series with solenoid $S$, and a key $K$ is connected across it. Upon throwing the switch to the lower position, the circuit receives direct current. It will be found that the lamp is practically as brilliant with the solenoid in circuit as it is when the solenoid is short-circuited by depressing key $K$. Neither is there any change in the brilliancy of the lamp when an iron core is inserted in the coil. The switch is then thrown to the upper position and the circuit receives alternating current. The lamp will now be illuminated as brilliantly as before with the solenoid out of circuit, but will be dimmed when the solenoid is put into the circuit by opening key $K$. The current through the lamp has been decreased because the inductance of the solenoid has occasioned a counter e.m.f. If an iron core is inserted in the coil, the current will be reduced further, and the lamp may cease to be illuminated.

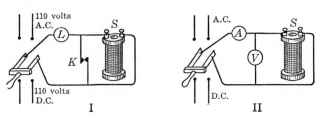

Fig. 240.  Effect of inductance

**Experiment 85.**—Replace the lamp in Experiment 84 by an ammeter $A$ and the key by a voltmeter $V$, both instruments being suitable for measuring direct and alternating current. The connections are shown at II in Fig. 240. Measure the current in the solenoid and the p.d. across it first with the circuit joined to direct current service mains and then to alternating current mains having the same p.d. Then reduce the p.d. of the direct-current source in order that the direct-current reading of the ammeter may be the same as that for alternating current. In a particular test, a p.d. of 30 volts on D.C. produced the same current as a p.d. of 110 volts on A.C.

**181. Reactors.**—A coil or winding which utilizes the counter e.m.f. of self-induction for the operation, control, or protection of electric circuits is called a *reactor,* or a *reactance coil,* or a *choke coil.* Such a coil possesses much inductance and relatively little resistance. Reactors having iron cores are often used with alternating-current circuits in such places as resistors or rheostats are used with direct-current circuits, that is, for reducing the line potential to an amount appropriate for the device being operated. The potential drop in a reactor of negligible resistance which carries an alternating current of $I$ amperes is $X_l \times I$, where $X_l$ is the inductive reactance in ohms. This drop is effected without loss of power, neglecting losses in hysteresis and resistance, for energy is alternately stored in the magnetic field of the reactor and returned to the supply circuit; the device is, therefore, more economical in operation than a resistor which would perform the same function.

It is often desirable to vary the inductance of reactors, and for this purpose several simple arrangements may be utilized. The coil may have a sliding iron core, or its winding may have several taps. Reactors having U-shaped magnetic circuits are sometimes provided with movable pole-pieces, which serve to change the length of the air gap, and thereby to alter the inductance. The variable reactor used in radio has one part of the winding stationary and the other movable; the two are joined in series and the inductance depends on the angle between the two parts of the winding.

Reactors without iron cores are used with lightning arrester equipments and for limiting the current in circuits and machines under short-circuit conditions. Since a lightning discharge is oscillatory in character and of enormous frequency, a coil which would offer a negligible reactance to an alternating current of commercial frequencies will offer a high reactance to a lightning discharge. A choke coil of but few turns will offer so much opposition to a lightning discharge that this high-frequency current will find a path of less opposition to ground through an air gap suitably provided in the circuit. In this way reactors can protect electrical machinery against all sorts of current surges.

Reactors for limiting current under short circuits are subjected to high transient potentials and currents, and must be designed carefully so that they will not be deformed by forces set up by the mutual attraction and repulsion between turns when traversed by abnormally large currents. These reactors are formed of circular and helical coils supported in porcelain cleats or cast in concrete. Where several reactors of the same polyphase circuit are located close together, they must be installed rigidly to prevent any movement during the short-circuit conditions.

**182. Capacitive Reactance.**—When a condenser is connected to a source of alternating current with an alternating-current ammeter joined in the circuit, it will be found that the meter indicates the presence of current as long as the condenser remains connected in circuit. Apparently the capacitor acts as though it were a complete current path, although, the reader will remember, there is no connection between adjacent plates of a condenser. What actually occurs is this: the condenser is charged during the first quarter of a cycle, is discharged during the second quarter, is charged again, but in the opposite direction, during the third quarter of the cycle, and is discharged during the fourth quarter, this process continuing as long as an alternating p.d. is applied to the capacitor. During the charging and discharging operations electrons surge to and fro through the connecting wires and through the ammeter, and this means that there is current through them. For this reason, it is usual to say that alternating current "flows through" a condenser even though its adjacent plates are insulated from each other.

Charging a capacitor by applying a difference of potential between its adjacent plates causes an electric field to be established between the plates. When the p.d. changes in value or in direction, the field changes accordingly. The ability of a condenser to store energy in its electric field is spoken of as capacitance, §167.

All circuits have to a greater or lesser degree the ability to set up an electric field, and this means that they have capacitance. The effect of capacitance in many circuits is quite small in comparison with the effects of inductance and resistance, but in overhead lines, underground and submarine cables, and in communication circuits the effect of capacitance is very important.

Every condenser presents a certain opposition to an alternating current, and this effect may be regarded as similar to inductive reactance. It is called *capacitive reactance,* to distinguish this type of opposition from the other. Capacitive reactance is expressed in ohms, and its value depends upon both the capacitance of the condenser and the frequency of the current source to which it is connected.

Let

$C$ = capacitance of the circuit in farads (1 farad = $10^6$ microfarads),
$f$ = frequency of the power supply in cycles per second,
$X_c$ = capacitive reactance in ohms.

Then the capacitive reactance of the circuit is

$$X_c = \frac{1}{2\pi \times f \times C}$$

86

To find the capacitive reactance of a circuit:

*Multiply the capacitance of the circuit in farads by the frequency of the alternating e.m.f. and by $2\pi$; then divide this product into unity.*

**Problem 112.**—What would be the capacitive reactance of a 25-microfarad condenser to an alternating current of 60 cycles?

Since 25 microfarads $= 25 \times 10^{-6}$ or 0.000025 farad, the capacitive reactance of the condenser is given by Formula (86) as

$$X_c = \frac{1}{2\pi \times f \times C} = \frac{1}{2 \times 3.1416 \times 60 \times 0.000025} = \frac{1}{0.0094} = 106.1 \text{ ohms}$$

**Problem 113.**—It is desired to introduce a capacitive reactance of 2000 ohms in a circuit for operation at 500,000 cycles per second. What capacitance should a condenser have to accomplish this objective?

Transpose Formula (86) and solve for $C$; hence

$$C = \frac{1}{2\pi \times f \times X_c} = \frac{1}{2\pi \times 500,000 \times 2000} = \frac{10^{-8}}{20\pi} \text{ farad}$$

$$= 159 \text{ micromicrofarads}$$

To derive Formula (86), consider a sinusoidal potential wave of frequency $f$ to be impressed upon a condenser of capacitance $C$ farads. If the maximum value of the potential is $E$ volts, the charge on the capacitor will have a maximum value of $Q = C \times E$ coulombs, as given by Formula (76). This means that in a half cycle the charge will vary from $+Q$ to $-Q$, a change of $2Q$ coulombs. Since this change occurs in 1/2 of $1/f$ second, the *average* current will be the quantity of electricity divided by the time, §35, or

$$2Q \div \frac{1}{2 \times f} = 4 \times Q \times f \text{ coulombs per second (or amperes). The}$$

corresponding maximum current value is obtained by multiplying the foregoing expression by $\pi/2$ or 1.57, as explained in §174.

Therefore, the maximum value of the current will be $\dfrac{\pi}{2} \times 4 \times Q \times f$ or

$$I = 2\pi \times C \times E \times f \qquad\qquad 87$$

Since both $I$ and $E$ are expressed by maximum values, and since both are equally related to their effective values—namely, by the ratio $\sqrt{2}$ to 1—the foregoing equation also applies to *effective values* of both $I$ and $E$. If the equation is solved for $E$, the p.d. across the capacitor, say $E_c$, will be

$$E_c = \frac{1}{2\pi \times f \times C} \times I \qquad 88$$

Finally, by dividing through by the current, the capacitive reactance sought for becomes

$$X_c = \frac{E_c}{I} = \frac{1}{2\pi \times f \times C}$$

**Experiment 86.**—Connect a condenser having a capacitance of about 10 microfarads in series with a tungsten-filament lamp to the blades of a double-throw switch, as shown in Fig. 241. When the switch is thrown downward to the D.C. terminals, there will be a pulse of current through the circuit which causes the lamp to flash momentarily, but there will be no steady current because of the capacitor. When the switch is thrown upward to the A.C. terminals, the lamp will remain illuminated steadily as long as the switch is closed. The condenser is charged and discharged in such rapid succession that the current pulses through the lamp will not cause it to flicker appreciably.

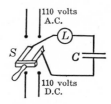

Fig. 241. Effect of capacitance

If a short-circuiting key were placed across the capacitor, then on closing the key the lamp would become brighter, because the capacitive reactance of the condenser would not then be effective.

## 183. Current and Potential Relations in Capacitive Circuits.—

In order to ascertain the phase relations between the potential and current in a capacitive circuit, such a circuit will be compared with a pipe line through which water is made to flow, first one way, then the other, by a pump located in one section of it. The pipe circuit corresponds to an electric circuit, the pump to a generator of alternating e.m.f., and the flow of water to an electric current. Imagine one section of the pipe to be enlarged, and to have placed in it a transverse elastic diaphragm; this pipe section serves as a good analog to a condenser.

Picture the diaphragm in its medial position and the piston of the pump in the middle of its travel, as shown at the left in Fig. 242. This middle position corresponds to zero pressure in the pipe line. When the piston is raised, the pressure in the region above the piston is increased, and this will be regarded as positive pressure. When the piston is elevated to the end of its stroke there is a maximum positive pressure in that region; when completely depressed, a maximum negative pressure. It is clear that the water will flow upward while the piston moves from its lowest to its highest position, and this direction of flow will be regarded as positive. Thus, the flow will be positive from the condition of maximum negative pressure to maximum positive pressure. The direction of flow remains unchanged when the piston passes through its middle position and the pressure is zero; these facts are noted in the figure.

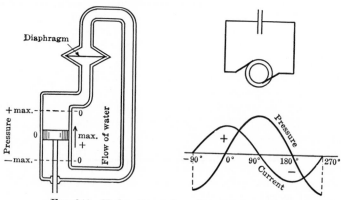

Fig. 242. Hydraulic analog of capacitive circuit

In the electric circuit shown at the right of the figure, the p.d. applied by the generator corresponds to pressure in the hydraulic analog, and the electric current corresponds to water flow. If a sinusoidal p.d. is impressed upon the circuit containing a condenser, the current will be sinusoidal. This current will be in the positive direction while the p.d. (pressure) changes from a maximum negative to a maximum positive value, and the current will be in a negative direction while the pressure changes from a maximum positive to a maximum negative value, as just described. These conditions require that the zero values of current occur at moments of maximum pressure values, and since the curves are both sinusoids, their relation may be plotted as in the figure. It is seen that the current *leads* the pressure or p.d. by 90 degrees.

The capacitor is fully charged at the instant of maximum positive pressure, discharged at the instant of zero pressure, fully charged again but in the opposite direction at the instant of maximum negative pressure, discharged at the next instant of zero pressure, and so on. Thus, the charge is zero when the current is a maximum, and the charge is a maximum when the current is momentarily zero and reversing in direction.

**184. Components of Impressed Potential Difference.**—When an alternating-current circuit contains resistance as well as either inductance or capacitance, it is convenient to view the impressed alternating e.m.f. as made up of two components. For a circuit having resistance $R$ and inductance $L$ connected in series, one component is required to overcome the resistance and the other is required to neutralize the counter e.m.f. of self-induction.

The first component of the impressed p.d. is determined from Ohm's Law to be $E_r = R \times I$, where $I$ is the current in the circuit. It will be remembered that the alternating current in a circuit having only resistance will be in phase with the impressed p.d., §179; consequently in an inductive circuit, that component of the impressed p.d. which is necessary to overcome resistance must be in phase with the current. This condition is shown in the vector diagram of Fig. 243, by

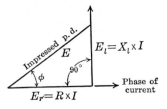

Fig. 243. Components of p.d. impressed on inductive circuit

drawing this component $E_r$ along the horizontal axis designated as the *phase of current*.

The other component of the impressed p.d., necessary to neutralize the counter e.m.f. of self-induction, will be equal to and in direct opposition to that counter e.m.f. The value of the latter has been determined in §180 as $E_l = X_l \times I = 2\pi \times f \times L \times I$, and its phase has been ascertained as lagging the current by 90 degrees. Consequently, the component of the impressed p.d. is located opposite to, or 180 degrees away from, the counter e.m.f. of self-induction, that is 90 degrees ahead of the current phase; it is shown as line $E_l$ in Fig. 243 drawn at right angles to $E_r$.

Both components of the impressed p.d. have been located in the figure, and their resultant will be the diagonal line $E$, forming the hypotenuse of a right-angled triangle. Since the square of the hypotenuse of a right triangle is equal to the sum of the squares of the other two sides, it follows that the impressed p.d. becomes

$$E = \sqrt{E_r^2 + E_i^2}$$ 89

If the symbols in this expression are interpreted as potential drops, then

$E$ = total drop of potential,
$E_r$ = resistance drop = $R \times I$,
$E_i$ = inductive reactance drop = $X_i \times I$.

The formula shows that the potential drop due to resistance and that due to inductance cannot be added arithmetically to obtain the total drop in the circuit, but must be added geometrically at right angles to each other.

**Problem 114.**—A lamp and a reactor are connected in series to a source of alternating current, and a voltmeter is used to measure the potential drops across them. The drop on the lamp is 46 volts and that on the reactor (resistance neglected) is 100 volts; what is the total drop in potential?

(89)    $E = \sqrt{E_r^2 + E_i^2} = \sqrt{46^2 + 100^2} = \sqrt{12{,}116} = 110.7$ volts

**Experiment 87.**—Connect an incandescent lamp in series with a coil to the blades of a double-throw switch in the manner shown in Fig. 240. First, make connection with alternating-current service mains, and measure the p.d. across the lamp, across the coil, and across the mains. Note that the arithmetical sum of the first two readings is greater than the third; this is always so in an inductive circuit because of the difference of phase between the two potential drops. Second, make connection with direct-current service mains, and measure the potential drops as before. Note that the sum of the drops across the lamp and the coil is equal to the p.d. across the mains.

The alternating p.d. impressed upon a circuit containing both resistance and capacitance may also be considered as composed of two components: the one required to overcome the resistance $R$, and the other required to overcome the capacitive reactance $X_c$. The first is in phase with the current and is equal to $E_r = R \times I$. The second lags the current by 90 degrees (Fig. 242) and has a magnitude of $E_c = X_c \times I$. These relations are indicated in the vector diagram of Fig. 244. The resultant of these components is

the impressed p.d.; its value can be found by extracting the square
root of the sum of the squares of the other two sides of the triangle, that is

$$E = \sqrt{E_r^2 + E_c^2} \qquad\qquad 90$$

Comparing Figs. 243 and 244, it is seen that the reactive component due to inductance is drawn upward from the horizontal
datum representing the phase of current, and that the component
due to capacitance is drawn downward. Generalizing, and representing the reactive component due to either inductance or capacitance as $E_x$, it follows that the impressed p.d. becomes

$$E = \sqrt{E_r^2 + E_x^2} \qquad\qquad 91$$

In an inductive circuit the reactance is $X = 2\pi \times f \times L$, while in
a capacitive circuit it is $X = \dfrac{1}{2\pi \times f \times C}$.

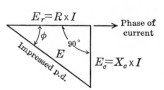

The following definitions may now be
given for resistance and reactance in an
alternating-current circuit:

FIG. 244. Components of p.d.
impressed on capacitive circuit

RESISTANCE is that quantity which
when multiplied by the current gives that
component of the impressed p.d. which is
in phase with the current.

REACTANCE is that quantity which when multiplied by the
current gives that component of the impressed p.d. which is at
right angles to the current.

**185. Impedance.**—The combined effect of resistance and reactance in a circuit is called *impedance* and expresses the total
opposition of the circuit to an alternating current. Impedance
is also measured in ohms; its symbol is $Z$. It is the impedance of
a circuit which when multiplied by the current through it gives
the impressed p.d.

To obtain the expression for the impedance of a circuit, regard
Formula (91) as an equation of potential drops, wherein the resistance drop is $E_r = R \times I$, the reactance drop is $E_x = X \times I$, and
the impedance drop is $E = Z \times I$. Since the current is common

to all the potential drops, it may be factored out, and the impedance of the circuit in ohms becomes

$$Z = \sqrt{R^2 + X^2}$$                              92

To FIND THE IMPEDANCE OF A CIRCUIT:

*Square the resistance of the circuit, and square the reactance of the circuit; add these products; then extract the square root of this sum.*

$$\text{Impedance} = \sqrt{\text{resistance}^2 + \text{reactance}^2}$$

**Problem 115.**—What would be the impedance of a coil of 4 ohms resistance and 8 ohms reactance?

For this coil $R = 4$ and $X = 8$; hence the impedance is

(92)      $Z = \sqrt{R^2 + X^2} = \sqrt{4^2 + 8^2} = \sqrt{16 + 64} = 8.94$ ohms

**186. Graphical Representation of Resistance, Reactance and Impedance.**—The relations expressed by Formula (92) may be represented by a right-angled triangle, as shown in Fig. 245. The ohmic resistance $R$ is laid off on a convenient scale to form the

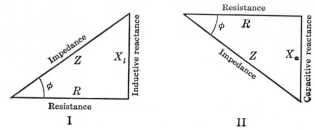

FIG. 245. Relation between resistance, reactance, and impedance
I—Inductive circuit; II—Capacitive circuit.

base line, the reactance $X$ is laid off also in ohms to form the perpendicular, and the impedance is then given by the hypotenuse of the triangle and its value may be scaled off in ohms. It will be observed that at I the line representing inductive reactance $X_l = 2\pi \times f \times L$ projects upward, and that at II the line representing capacitive reactance $X_c = \dfrac{1}{2\pi \times f \times C}$ projects downward. The angle between the lines representing resistance and impedance is indicated by $\phi$. Triangles are frequently used to indicate the relations between resistance, reactance and impedance, and to determine their relative values graphically.

When the reactance of a circuit is small compared with the resistance, it has very little effect, for then the impedance is not much larger than the resistance. When the reactance is large compared with the resistance, the impedance is much greater than the resistance. In circuits of large inductance the resistance may often be neglected, so that it might be correct to say that the current equals the p.d. divided by the reactance. If the fre‑ quency is doubled in such cases, the reactance is doubled and the current with the same p.d. is reduced one-half.

**Problem 116.**—A resistor of 12 ohms resistance is connected in series with a coil of 0.02 henry inductance to a 60-cycle source of alternating current. Calculate the impedance of the circuit.

The reactance of the coil is 7.54 ohms, as computed in Problem 109. Hence, the impedance of the circuit is

$$(92) \qquad Z = \sqrt{R^2 + X^2} = \sqrt{12^2 + 7.54^2} = \sqrt{200.8} = 14.2 \text{ ohms}$$

**Problem 117.**—A resistor of 150 ohms resistance is connected in series with a capacitor of 25 microfarads capacitance to a 60-cycle supply of alter‑ nating current. What is the impedance of the circuit?

The reactance of the capacitor is 106.1 ohms, as computed in Problem 112. Hence, the impedance of the circuit is

$$(92) \qquad Z = \sqrt{R^2 + X^2} = \sqrt{150^2 + 106.1^2} = \sqrt{33,757} = 183.7 \text{ ohms}$$

**187. Angle of Lag or Lead.**—In a circuit containing resistance and inductance or capacitance the current is not in phase with the impressed p.d.; the amount of lag or lead depends upon the relative magnitude of the resistance and the reactance. The lag or lead is measured as an angle and expressed in degrees.

The ratio of the length of one side of a right triangle to that of another is called a *trigonometric function* of an acute angle in the triangle. One such function is the *tangent* of an angle (ab‑ breviated tan) and this has no reference to the tangent of a circle. The tangent of the angle $\phi$ in Fig. 245 is the ratio of the vertical side of the triangle to the side which is horizontal. Tables of trigonometric functions are available which give the values of the functions for the various angles; thus, the following table lists the tangent values of angles from 0 to 89 degrees at 1 degree intervals. The table indicates, for example, that the tangent of an angle of 30 degrees is 0.5774, of 45 degrees is unity, of 60 degrees is 1.7321. Naturally, when the tangent of an angle is known, the angle can be determined from the same table; for example, if the tangent of an angle is 0.7, the angle is very nearly 35 degrees.

### TANGENTS OF ANGLES

| Angle | Tan | Angle | Tan | Angle | Tan | Angle | Tan | Angle | Tan |
|---|---|---|---|---|---|---|---|---|---|
| 0° | 0.0000 | 18° | 0.3249 | 36° | 0.7265 | 54° | 1.3764 | 72° | 3.0777 |
| 1 | 0.0175 | 19 | 0.3443 | 37 | 0.7536 | 55 | 1.4281 | 73 | 3.2709 |
| 2 | 0.0349 | 20 | 0.3640 | 38 | 0.7813 | 56 | 1.4826 | 74 | 3.4874 |
| 3 | 0.0524 | 21 | 0.3839 | 39 | 0.8098 | 57 | 1.5399 | 75 | 3.7321 |
| 4 | 0.0699 | 22 | 0.4040 | 40 | 0.8391 | 58 | 1.6003 | 76 | 4.0108 |
| 5 | 0.0875 | 23 | 0.4245 | 41 | 0.8693 | 59 | 1.6643 | 77 | 4.3315 |
| 6 | 0.1051 | 24 | 0.4452 | 42 | 0.9004 | 60 | 1.7321 | 78 | 4.7046 |
| 7 | 0.1228 | 25 | 0.4663 | 43 | 0.9325 | 61 | 1.8040 | 79 | 5.1446 |
| 8 | 0.1405 | 26 | 0.4877 | 44 | 0.9657 | 62 | 1.8807 | 80 | 5.6713 |
| 9 | 0.1564 | 27 | 0.5095 | 45 | 1.0000 | 63 | 1.9626 | 81 | 6.3138 |
| 10 | 0.1763 | 28 | 0.5317 | 46 | 1.0355 | 64 | 2.0503 | 82 | 7.1154 |
| 11 | 0.1944 | 29 | 0.5543 | 47 | 1.0724 | 65 | 2.1445 | 83 | 8.1443 |
| 12 | 0.2126 | 30 | 0.5774 | 48 | 1.1106 | 66 | 2.2460 | 84 | 9.514 |
| 13 | 0.2309 | 31 | 0.6009 | 49 | 1.1504 | 67 | 2.3559 | 85 | 11.430 |
| 14 | 0.2493 | 32 | 0.6249 | 50 | 1.1918 | 68 | 2.4751 | 86 | 14.301 |
| 15 | 0.2679 | 33 | 0.6494 | 51 | 1.2349 | 69 | 2.6051 | 87 | 19.081 |
| 16 | 0.2867 | 34 | 0.6745 | 52 | 1.2799 | 70 | 2.7475 | 88 | 28.636 |
| 17 | 0.3057 | 35 | 0.7002 | 53 | 1.3270 | 71 | 2.9042 | 89 | 57.290 |

When the resistance and inductive reactance of a circuit are known, it is possible to determine the angle of lag of current behind the impressed e.m.f. If the reactance $X_l$ in a particular circuit were 7 ohms and the resistance $R$ were 10 ohms, then the ratio of $X_l$ to $R$ would be $7 \div 10$ or 0.7, and this value represents the tangent of the angle $\phi$. For this value of the tangent the table indicates the angle to be 35 degrees of lag. In general, the tangent of the angle of lag is given by

$$\tan \phi = \frac{\text{reactance}}{\text{resistance}} = \frac{X_l}{R} = \frac{2\pi \times f \times L}{R} \qquad 93$$

The larger the inductive reactance compared with the resistance, the larger will be the angle of lag. On the other hand, if the reactance is small in comparison with the resistance, the angle of lag will be small, and the current will be nearly in phase with the impressed p.d.

**Problem 118.**—By what angle would the current lag the 25-cycle p.d. impressed on a circuit in which the resistance is 4 ohms and the inductance is 0.1 henry?

By Formula (84), $X_l = 2\pi \times f \times L = 2\pi \times 25 \times 0.1 = 15.7$ ohms. Then

(93) $$\tan \phi = \frac{X_l}{R} = \frac{15.7}{4} = 3.925$$

From the table, the angle having a tangent of 3.925 is almost 76 degrees; consequently the current lags the impressed p.d. by this angle.

The effect of capacitance in a circuit is exactly the opposite to that of inductance, for capacitance makes the current lead the impressed p.d. while inductance makes the current lag. The tangent of the angle of lead is the capacitive reactance divided by the resistance, hence, if the resistance $R$ and the capacitive reactance $X_c$ in a circuit are known, the angle of lead may be calculated from

$$\tan \phi = \frac{\text{reactance}}{\text{resistance}} = \frac{X_c}{R} = \frac{\dfrac{1}{2\pi \times f \times C}}{R} = \frac{1}{2\pi \times f \times C \times R} \qquad 94$$

**Problem 119.**—What is the angle of current lead in the circuit of Problem 117?

Here the capacitive reactance is 106.1 ohms and the resistance is 150 ohms. Then

(94) $$\tan \phi = \frac{X_c}{R} = \frac{106.1}{150} = 0.707$$

Whence $\phi = 35°$ approximately.

**188. Circuits Having Resistance, Inductance and Capacitance.**—The calculations of the previous sections can be extended to circuits containing both inductance and capacitance. In such circuits the net reactance $X$ is equal to the arithmetical difference between the inductive reactance $X_l$ and the capacitive reactance $X_c$, or

$$X = X_l - X_c \qquad 95$$

Therefore, the impedance of a circuit containing inductance, capacitance and resistance is equal to

$$\sqrt{\text{resistance}^2 + (\text{inductive reactance} - \text{capacitive reactance})^2}$$

or

$$Z = \sqrt{R^2 + (X_l - X_c)^2} \qquad 96$$

**Problem 120.**—What would be the total impedance of a circuit, having a coil of 50 ohms resistance and of 0.01 henry inductance in series with a capacitor of 30 microfarads capacitance, to an alternating current of 500 cycles?

(84)      $X_l = 2\pi \times f \times L = 6.28 \times 500 \times 0.01 = 31.4$ ohms

(86)      $X_c = \dfrac{1}{2\pi \times f \times C} = \dfrac{1}{6.28 \times 500 \times 0.00003} = 10.6$ ohms

The net reactance is

(95)      $X = X_l - X_c = 31.4 - 10.6 = 20.8$ ohms

Therefore, the impedance of the circuit is

(92)   $Z = \sqrt{R^2 + X^2} = \sqrt{50^2 + 20.8^2} = \sqrt{2500 + 433} = 54.2$ ohms

The procedure may also be shown by the diagram of Fig. 246, which depicts the relation between reactance, resistance and im-

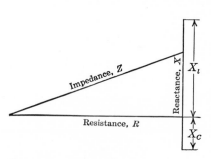

FIG. 246. Impedance of circuit containing resistance, inductance, and capacitance

pedance. The net reactance $X$ of the circuit is indicated as the *difference* between the lengths of the lines representing inductive and capacitive reactances. In the figure the capacitive reactance $X_c$ is one-third as great as the inductive reactance $X_l$; the net reactance $X$ is, therefore, two-thirds as great as the inductive reactance alone, and the impedance line is drawn from the left-hand end of the resistance line to a point two-thirds up along the line representing inductive reactance.

It is obvious that when $X_l$ and $X_c$ are equal, the difference between them is zero, and the impedance $Z$ becomes equal to $\sqrt{R^2}$, which of course is $R$. When this is the case the circuit operates as though there were neither inductance nor capacitance present, the current rising and falling in unison with the e.m.f. Such a circuit is said to be in *resonance* with the impressed alternating p.d.

**189. Ohm's Law for Alternating-Current Circuits.**—In dealing with direct-current circuits the relation existing between the e.m.f., current and resistance is fully expressed by Ohm's Law. This law cannot be applied directly to alternating-current circuits, since the current no longer depends simply upon the resistance and e.m.f., but also depends on the frequency $f$ of the source and the inductance $L$ and capacitance $C$ that may be contained in the circuit. The law can be modified, however, to include the effects of these factors, by phrasing it as follows:

*The current in any circuit is equal to the alternating electromotive force impressed upon it divided by the impedance of the circuit.*

Let

$E$ = e.m.f. in the circuit in volts,
$Z$ = impedance of the circuit, in ohms, as given by Formula (96),
$I$ = current in that circuit in amperes.

Then

$$I = \frac{E}{Z} \qquad\qquad 97$$

This modification of Ohm's Law bears the same relation and importance to alternating-current problems that the law itself does to direct-current problems. Naturally, it may be applied to a part of a circuit if $E$ is interpreted as the potential difference applied to that part.

TO FIND THE CURRENT IN AN ALTERNATING-CURRENT CIRCUIT:

*Divide the e.m.f. impressed upon the circuit by the impedance of that circuit.*

**Problem 121.**—(a) What current will there be through a coil of 7 ohms resistance and 24 ohms reactance when connected to a source of 60-cycle e.m.f. at 110 volts? (b) What would be the current if the coil were connected across a 110-volt direct-current supply circuit?

The impedance is

(96) $\qquad Z = \sqrt{R^2 + X_l^2} = \sqrt{7^2 + 24^2} = \sqrt{49 + 576} = 25$ ohms

With alternating current

(97) $\qquad\qquad I = \frac{E}{Z} = \frac{110}{25} = 4.4$ amperes (a)

With direct current

(18) $\qquad\qquad I = \frac{E}{R} = \frac{110}{7} = 15.7$ amperes (b)

**Problem 122.**—What e.m.f. would be required from a 1000-cycle alternator to provide a current of 0.3 ampere through a capacitive circuit formed of a 2000-ohm resistor and a 0.1 microfarad capacitor?

(86)    $$X_c = \frac{1}{2\pi \times f \times C} = \frac{10^6}{2\pi \times 1000 \times 0.1} = 1592 \text{ ohms}$$

(96)    $$Z = \sqrt{R^2 + X_c^2} = \sqrt{2000^2 + 1592^2} = \sqrt{6{,}534{,}500} = 2556 \text{ ohms}$$

(97)    $$E = I \times Z = 0.3 \times 2556 = 767 \text{ volts}$$

The similarity between Formula (97) and Ohm's Law is apparent. The value of the *resistance* of a circuit may be calculated merely from the physical dimensions of the conducting wires, but this is not so with *impedance* (the total opposition offered to an alternating current). Beside the frequency of the e.m.f., the two factors which determine the impedance, namely inductance and capacitance, both depend upon the shape of the circuit as well as upon its dimensions.

The impedance of a circuit or electrical device may be measured by the ammeter-voltmeter method in the same way that resistance is measured in a direct-current circuit (§133), using, of course, alternating-current instruments. It is calculated from the equation $Z = E \div I$. Knowing the ohmic resistance, the *reactance* can be calculated from Formula (92), and thereafter the inductance or capacitance can be found from Formulas (84) or (86), provided the frequency of the current is known.

## QUESTIONS

1. Why does inductance have such an important effect upon the strength of an alternating current?
2. What are the factors that determine the amount of inductive reactance in a circuit?
3. Derive the expression for inductive reactance.
4. What are some uses for reactors?
5. What effect has capacitance upon an alternating current?
6. Upon what factors does the capacitive reactance of a circuit depend?
7. Derive the formula for capacitive reactance.
8. Explain the phase relationships in inductive and capacitive circuits.
9. Give a graphical illustration of the relation existing between the impressed p.d. and its components.
10. What is the essential difference between capacitive and inductive reactance in their effect upon an alternating current?

11. Distinguish between resistance, reactance and impedance.
12. How would you represent graphically the relation existing between impedance, reactance and resistance?
13. What determines the angle of current lag or lead?
14. What is meant by the tangent of an angle? For what angle is the value of the tangent unity?
15. Knowing the values of resistance and inductance in a circuit, how would you determine the angle of lag for a current of given frequency.
16. Under what conditions can a current in a circuit lead the p.d. impressed upon it.
17. What circuit factors beside resistance must be taken into consideration in determining the strength of an alternating current, and what do those factors depend upon?
18. If the frequency of an alternating p.d. that is impressed upon an inductive circuit is doubled, how will the current be affected, assuming the p.d. to remain the same?
19. What is the form of Ohm's Law for alternating-current circuits?
20. How can the impedance of a circuit be measured?
21. Explain the difference in behavior of a capacitor when joined to a direct-current circuit and to an alternating-current circuit.

## PROBLEMS

1. How much inductive reactance does a coil having an inductance of 0.5 henry present to an alternating current of 25 cycles? *Ans.* 78.5 ohms.
2. At what frequency would a device having an inductance of 0.001 henry possess an inductive reactance of 10 ohms? *Ans.* 1590 cycles per second.
3. A 2-microfarad condenser is used in a telephone set. How much capacitive reactance does it have (a) for "ringing current" of $16\frac{2}{3}$ cycles and (b) for "speech current" averaging 1000 cycles per second? *Ans.* (a) 4780 ohms; (b) 79.6 ohms.
4. A capacitor is connected in series with a resistor to 240-volt alternating-current service mains, and a voltmeter connected across the resistor reads 100 volts. What should be the p.d. across the capacitor? *Ans.* 218 volts.
5. A circuit has 10 ohms resistance and 10 ohms reactance at a certain frequency. What is its impedance at that frequency? Check the result by plotting the given values to scale and then measuring the hypotenuse of the triangle. *Ans.* 14.1 ohms.
6. By what angle would the current in the circuit of Problem 5 lag the impressed e.m.f.? *Ans.* 45°.
7. The current in a coil of wire that has 5 ohms resistance lags the p.d. impressed upon it by 30 degrees at a frequency of 60 cycles. What is the inductance of the coil? *Ans.* 0.00766 henry.

8. A circuit has a capacitive reactance of 154 ohms and a resistance of 100 ohms. What is the angle by which the current in the circuit leads the impressed p.d.? *Ans.* 57 degrees.

9. What e.m.f. must a 60-cycle alternator supply to a circuit of negligible resistance and of 0.2 henry inductance in order to yield a current of 5 amperes? *Ans.* 377 volts.

10. Find the current produced by a 25-cycle alternating e.m.f. of 120 volts in a circuit having 250 ohms resistance and 30 microfarads capacitance. *Ans.* 0.366 ampere.

11. (a) What is the impedance of a circuit of 20 ohms resistance and 10 ohms inductive reactance? (b) What current would a 60-cycle p.d. of 110 volts produce in this circuit? (c) What is the inductance of the circuit? *Ans.* (a) 22.4 ohms; (b) 4.91 amperes; (c) 0.00266 henry.

12. A length of copper wire, having a sectional area of 2055 CM is wound to form a helix of 900 turns each 11.5 inches in diameter. It has an inductance of 0.404 henry. Determine the current in this coil when it is connected across 120-volt, 25-cycle service mains. *Ans.* 1.85 amperes.

13. (a) What would be the impedance of the circuit in Problem 11 if a 50-microfarad capacitor were inserted in series? (b) How much current would be produced? *Ans.* (a) 47.4 ohms; (b) 2.32 amperes.

# Lesson XVII

## NETWORKS AND POLYPHASE CIRCUITS

Impedances in series—Admittance and its components—Impedances in parallel—Resonance in a series circuit—Parallel resonance—Electric filters—Power factor—Power in single-phase circuits—Polyphase circuits—Power in polyphase systems—Questions and Problems.

**190. Impedances in Series.**—In alternating-current circuits the resistors, reactors and condensers are connected in a variety of ways in order to fulfill the particular objectives sought. The more common of these connections are the series and parallel groupings in single-phase circuits, and the wye and delta groupings in three-phase circuits. Networks comprising these groupings can be analyzed and solved for the total impedance.

When several reactive devices are connected in series in an alternating-current circuit, the total impedance of the group cannot be determined by adding the individual impedances arithmetically, as is done with resistances in direct-current work, because the potential differences causing the currents through these devices are not in phase with each other. Instead, the impedance of each device must be resolved into its component resistance and reactance, these components are then added separately, and thereafter the total impedance is determined from these sums.

Let

$R_1$ and $X_1$ be the resistance and reactance components of one device having an impedance $Z_1$,

$R_2$ and $X_2$ be the corresponding components of the next device of impedance $Z_2$, and so on.

Then the total impedance of the circuit is

$$Z = \sqrt{(R_1 + R_2 + \ldots)^2 + (X_1 + X_2 + \ldots)^2} \qquad 98$$

To find the total impedance of a number of devices connected in series:

*Find the sum of the resistances in the circuit, and the sum of the reactances; then square these sums separately and add the results; finally extract the square root of this total.*

**Problem 123.**—An incandescent lamp and two inductive devices are connected in series as illustrated in Fig. 247; lamp $B$ has resistance only and coils $A$ and $C$ have both inductive reactance and resistance. The values of the resistance, reactance and impedance in ohms for each part of the circuit are noted. What is the total impedance of the circuit shown?

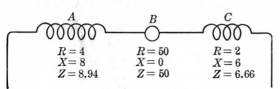

$A$    $B$    $C$

$R = 4$    $R = 50$    $R = 2$
$X = 8$    $X = 0$    $X = 6$
$Z = 8.94$    $Z = 50$    $Z = 6.66$

Fig. 247. Impedances in series

The lamp has no reactance, so its impedance is equal to its resistance. The total impedance is given by

$$(98)\ Z = \sqrt{(R_1 + R_2 + R_3)^2 + (X_1 + X_2 + X_3)^2}$$
$$= \sqrt{(4 + 50 + 2)^2 + (8 + 0 + 6)^2} = \sqrt{56^2 + 14^2} = 57.7 \text{ ohms}$$

If the impedances of the three devices in this problem had been added the result would have been 65.6 ohms; this result has no meaning whatever.

In problems of this type it is helpful to put the data in tabular form and solve in a systematic manner. Thus, the foregoing problem would be set up as follows:

| Quantity | Devices | | | Totals |
|---|---|---|---|---|
| | $A$ | $B$ | $C$ | |
| $R$ | 4 | 50 | 2 | 56 |
| $X$ | 8 | 0 | 6 | 14 |
| $Z$ | 8.94 | 50 | 6.66 | .. |

Total $Z = \sqrt{(56)^2 + (14)^2} = \sqrt{3332} = 57.7$ ohms.

**191. Admittance and Its Components.**—It will be recalled that in calculating the resistance of several resistors connected in parallel in a direct-current circuit, it was found convenient to deal with the reciprocal of resistance. In calculations of alternating-current circuits there is also need for the reciprocal, but it is applied to impedance rather than to resistance. The reciprocal of impedance is called *admittance*, and its symbol is $Y$. Thus, the admittance of the impedance $Z$ is

$$Y = \frac{1}{Z} \qquad\qquad 99$$

The admittance of an alternating-current circuit has two components, called *conductance* and *susceptance*, just as impedance has the components of resistance and reactance. The symbol to be used for conductance is $G$ and that for susceptance is $S$. Admittance and its components make up a triangle in the same way that

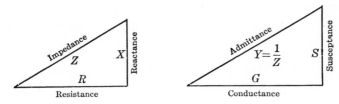

FIG. 248. Similarity between impedance and admittance triangles

impedance and its components form a triangle; the corresponding triangles are shown in Fig. 248 with the hypotenuse as impedance in the one and admittance in the other.

For any particular impedance, the two triangles are similar, and this means that the angles are alike and the corresponding sides bear the same ratio to each other. Thus, the ratio of resistance $R$ to impedance $Z$ in the impedance triangle is the same as the ratio of conductance $G$ to admittance $Y$ in the admittance triangle. Consequently,

$$\frac{R}{Z} = \frac{G}{Y}$$

Herefrom the conductance is

$$G = \frac{R \times Y}{Z} = \frac{R}{Z^2} = \frac{R}{R^2 + X^2}$$

Similarly in the triangles, the ratio of reactance $X$ to impedance $Z$ is the same as the ratio of susceptance $S$ to admittance $Y$, or

$$\frac{X}{Z} = \frac{S}{Y}$$

from which the susceptance is

$$S = \frac{X \times Y}{Z} = \frac{X}{Z^2} = \frac{X}{R^2 + X^2}$$

Finally, the sum of the squares of conductance and susceptance must be the square of the admittance; whence the admittance is

$$Y = \sqrt{G^2 + S^2} \qquad\qquad 100$$

The reader is cautioned that in an alternating-current circuit the conductance of a device *is not* the reciprocal of its resistance, except in the case of a non-inductive resistor. Further, the susceptance of a device *is not* the reciprocal of its reactance. Instead, the values of $G$ and $S$ are found by the procedure reviewed below.

To FIND THE CONDUCTANCE OF A DEVICE:

*Divide the resistance by the sum of the squares of the resistance and reactance.*

$$G = \frac{R}{R^2 + X^2} \qquad\qquad 101$$

To FIND THE SUSCEPTANCE OF A DEVICE:

*Divide the reactance by the sum of the squares of the resistance and reactance.*

$$S = \frac{X}{R^2 + X^2} \qquad\qquad 102$$

It is to be noted that the susceptance of condensers is conventionally regarded as positive, while that of reactors is taken as negative.

**192. Impedances in Parallel.**—When inductive devices are connected in parallel, the joint impedance of any given group of devices is determined by a method similar to that described in §190; but instead of dealing with the individual resistances and reactances, the calculation involves the corresponding quantities of *conductance* and *susceptance*.

Let

$G_1$ and $S_1$ be the conductance and susceptance of one device having an impedance $Z_1$ and admittance $Y_1$,

$G_2$ and $S_2$ be the corresponding components of the next device of impedance $Z_2$ and admittance $Y_2$, and so on.

Then the total admittance of the circuit is

$$Y = \sqrt{(G_1 + G_2 + \ldots)^2 + (S_1 + S_2 + \ldots)^2} \qquad 103$$

and the total impedance is the reciprocal of the admittance $Y$.

To FIND THE TOTAL IMPEDANCE OF A NUMBER OF DEVICES CON-
NECTED IN PARALLEL:

(1) *Find the conductances and susceptances of the individual devices*, (2) *obtain the sum of the conductances and the algebraic sum of the susceptances*, (3) *square these sums separately and add the results*, (4) *extract the square root of this total to get the admittance, and* (5) *take the reciprocal of this quantity.*

Problem 124.—What would be the joint impedance of the three devices in Fig. 247 if they were connected in parallel?

The conductance of coil $A$ is

$$(101) \qquad G_1 = \frac{R}{R^2 + X^2} = \frac{4}{16 + 64} = 0.05$$

and its susceptance is

$$(102) \qquad S_1 = \frac{X}{R^2 + X^2} = \frac{-8}{16 + 64} = -0.10$$

The negative sign is chosen because the susceptance corresponding to inductive reactance is taken as a negative quantity. Similarly, the conductance and susceptance for the non-inductive lamp $B$ of 50 ohms resistance are respectively

$$G_2 = \frac{50}{2500 + 0} = 0.02 \qquad\qquad S_2 = \frac{0}{2500 + 0} = 0$$

and these quantities for coil $C$ are respectively

$$G_3 = \frac{2}{4 + 36} = 0.05 \qquad\qquad S_3 = \frac{-6}{4 + 36} = -0.15$$

The rest of the solution follows the tabular procedure outlined in §190, with the admittance computed from Formula (100) and the impedance from Formula (99). The resulting impedance is 3.61 ohms as computed in the table below.

| Quantity | Devices | | | Totals |
|---|---|---|---|---|
| | $A$ | $B$ | $C$ | |
| $R$ | 4 | 50 | 2 | . . . |
| $X$ | 8 | 0 | 6 | . . . |
| $Z$ | 8.94 | 50 | 6.66 | . . . |
| $G$ | 0.05 | 0.02 | 0.05 | 0.12 |
| $S$ | —0.10 | 0 | —0.15 | —0.25 |

$$Y = \sqrt{(0.12)^2 + (-0.25)^2} = 0.277 \qquad Z = \frac{1}{0.277} = 3.61$$

**Problem 125.**—If coil $C$ of Fig. 247, referred to in the preceding problem, were replaced by a capacitor having a reactance of 3 ohms and a resistance of zero, what would be the impedance of the circuit in which the three devices are connected in parallel?

The conductance and susceptance of this capacitor are respectively

$$G_3 = \frac{0}{0+9} = 0 \qquad\qquad S_3 = \frac{+3}{0+9} = +0.33$$

and the following tabular solution shows the resulting impedance to be 4.12 ohms.

| Quantity | Devices | | | Totals |
|---|---|---|---|---|
| | $A$ | $B$ | $C$ | |
| $R$ | 4 | 50 | 0 | . . . |
| $X$ | 8 | 0 | 3 | . . . |
| $Z$ | 8.94 | 50 | 3 | . . . |
| $G$ | 0.05 | 0.02 | 0 | 0.07 |
| $S$ | —0.10 | 0 | +0.33 | 0.23 |

$$Y = \sqrt{(0.07)^2 + (0.23)^2} = 0.243 \qquad Z = \frac{1}{0.243} = 4.12$$

Circuits having series-parallel groupings of impedances can be solved by applying the methods so far considered in this lesson to the procedure used with direct-current circuits, §86. These groupings and other types of networks are reduced to the simpler forms and solved piecemeal until the total impedance is obtained.

**Experiment 88.**—Fig. 249 shows a series-parallel circuit that illustrates a peculiarity when used with alternating current. In the figure $L_1$, $L_2$ and $L_3$ are incandescent lamps of the same kind, $C$ is a capacitor, and $M$ is an adjustable reactor of negligible resistance made up of a coil with a movable iron core. If the entire circuit is connected to direct-current service mains of, say, 110 volts, there will be no current through the lower branch because the condenser is present; but if connected to alternating-current mains, there will be current through both branches. By adjusting the inductance of the reactor, the conditions may be made such that lamp $L_1$ would operate merely at a dull red heat while lamps $L_2$ and $L_3$ would be illuminated to full brightness. This means that the sum of the two currents through $L_2$ and $L_3$ is less than either current. Such a striking result would, of course, be impossible with direct currents.

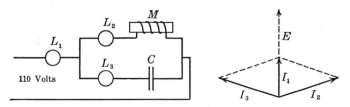

FIG. 249. Series-parallel alternating-current circuit

Inductance $M$ may be adjusted so that current in main circuit will be less than current in either branch circuit.

In this experiment the alternating current in lamp $L_1$ is the resultant of the currents in the two branch circuits. The current in the inductive circuit could lag the impressed p.d. $E$ up to one-quarter of a cycle; it is represented in the vector diagram at the right by line $I_2$. The current in the capacitive circuit will be nearly one-quarter of a cycle ahead of the impressed p.d.; it is represented by line $I_3$. The inductance is assumed to be adjusted so that the currents in lamps $L_2$ and $L_3$ become approximately equal. The current in lamp $L_1$ will be the vector sum of currents $I_2$ and $I_3$, and is represented by line $I_1$. It is seen that, because of the phase relations indicated, the total current $I_1$ may be smaller than either of the component currents $I_2$ or $I_3$.

**193. Resonance in a Series Circuit.**—If an alternating p.d. is impressed upon a circuit comprising a coil and a capacitor connected in series, the current produced will depend upon the resistance and inductance of the coil, upon the capacitance of the capacitor, and upon the frequency of the impressed p.d. This current value is expressed by Formulas (96) and (97) as

$$I = \frac{E}{\sqrt{R^2 + (X_l - X_c)^2}}$$

where $R$ is the resistance, $X_l$ is the inductive reactance, and $X_c$ is the capacitive reactance, all in ohms. If these reactances could be varied, the current in the circuit would attain a maximum value when the inductive reactance $X_l$ became equal to the capacitive reactance $X_c$, for then the total reactance would be zero and the impedance of the circuit would be merely $R$.

This condition, for maximum current in a series circuit, means that the inductive reactance $X_l = 2\pi \times f \times L$ (Formula 84) must equal the capacitive reactance $X_c = \dfrac{1}{2\pi \times f \times C}$ (Formula 86), or

$$2\pi \times f \times L = \frac{1}{2\pi \times f \times C}$$

The equality called for by this expression can be met by changing the frequency $f$ of the alternating p.d., or by changing one or both of the circuit constants—inductance $L$ or capacitance $C$. If the reactances have been equalized the circuit is said to be in *resonance* with the applied p.d.

The resonant frequency of the circuit is obtained from the foregoing equation by solving for $f$, yielding

$$f = \frac{1}{2\pi\sqrt{L \times C}} \qquad\qquad \textbf{104}$$

Thus, the condition of resonance is attained when the frequency of the impressed p.d. coincides with the resonant frequency of the circuit.

Consider a circuit having a resistance of 40 ohms, an inductance of 0.001274 henry and a capacitance of 0.002 microfarad. Its resonant frequency in cycles per second is

$$(104) \quad f = \frac{1}{2\pi\sqrt{0.001274 \times 0.000000002}} = \frac{1}{2\pi \times 0.00000159} = 100,000$$

The following table gives the inductive, capacitive, and total reactances of this circuit for several frequencies up to twice the resonant frequency:

| Frequency Cycles per Second | Inductive Reactance Ohms | Capacitive Reactance Ohms | Total Reactance Ohms |
|---|---|---|---|
| 30,000 | 240 | 2660 | −2420 |
| 40,000 | 320 | 2000 | −1680 |
| 60,000 | 480 | 1330 | −850 |
| 100,000 | 800 | 800 | 0 |
| 150,000 | 1200 | 530 | 670 |
| 200,000 | 1600 | 400 | 1200 |

At resonance the inductive reactance is 800 ohms and the capacitive reactance is also 800 ohms. At lower frequencies the capacitive reactance predominates over inductive reactance, while at higher frequencies the inductive reactance is the larger. Further, the resistance of the circuit (40 ohms in this illustration) is small in contrast with the reactance values and has a negligible effect upon the current value except at resonance.

These values of reactance are plotted in Fig. 250 against frequency in kilocycles (1 kilocycle = 1000 cycles). The straight line marked $X_l$ represents the inductive reactance and the curve marked $X_c$ represents the capacitive reactance; the sum of the two is shown by the curve marked Reactance, and this curve crosses the horizontal axis at the resonant frequency of 100 kilocycles.

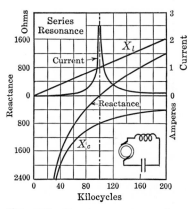

Fig. 250. Reactance curves of a series circuit and the curve of current

Another curve of importance is that which shows the variation of current with frequency; it is called a *resonance curve*. Such a curve for the circuit under discussion is also plotted in Fig. 250 and assumes that the impressed p.d. is 100 volts. This current curve would rise to infinity at the resonant frequency were it not for the resistance of the circuit.

The potential differences in a resonant circuit may greatly exceed the p.d. impressed upon it. In the numerical illustration, the p.d. across the condenser is $E_c = X_c \times I = 800 \times 100/40 = 2000$ volts, twenty times as great as the applied p.d. This pressure is balanced by the potential difference across the coil—namely, $E_l = X_l \times I$, which is also 2000 volts. Hence, when a series circuit becomes resonant with the alternating e.m.f. there may be potential differences set up in the circuit which are great enough to puncture its insulation. In radio circuits, on the other hand, the condition of resonance is sought for; this is done by adjusting the inductance or capacitance, a process called *tuning*.

**Problem 126.**—A solenoid has an inductance of 0.2 henry and a resistance of 10 ohms; it is connected in series with a 25-microfarad capacitor. (a) Determine the resonant frequency of the circuit. (b) What will be the impedance of the circuit at resonance? (c) How will the p.d. across the capacitor compare with the applied p.d. at resonance?

$$(104) \qquad f = \frac{1}{2\pi\sqrt{L \times C}} = \frac{1}{6.28\sqrt{0.2 \times 0.000025}} = 71.1 \text{ cycles (a)}$$

At resonance the impedance of the circuit is the same as the resistance, namely 10 ohms (b).

The reactance of the condenser at resonance is

$$(86) \qquad X_c = \frac{1}{2\pi \times f \times C} = \frac{1}{2\pi \times 71.1 \times 0.000025} = 89.6 \text{ ohms}$$

Hence, the potential drop across the capacitor, $X_c \times I$, will exceed the applied p.d., $R \times I$, at resonance in the ratio $X_c$ to $R$, or $89.6 \div 10 = 8.96$ (c).

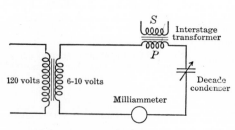

Fig. 251. Demonstration of resonance in a series circuit

**Experiment 89.**—Connect the high-potential side of a filament transformer to 120-volt, 60-cycle mains. To the low-potential side, which may be designed for 10, 7.5 or 6.3 volts, connect the primary winding of an interstage transformer, a variable condenser and an alternating-current milliammeter, as indicated in Fig. 251. It would be desirable to use a condenser of three decades with steps of 0.001, 0.01, and 0.1 microfarads. Use an interstage transformer such that, when the condenser is varied through its range, the current indicated on the milliammeter will rise, reach a peak value, and then decrease. Vary the condenser and note the corresponding values of capacitance and current. Plot a curve of current in milliamperes against capacitance in microfarads.

**194. Parallel Resonance.**—When a coil and a capacitor are placed in parallel connection with an alternator, the behavior is quite different from that of the series arrangement considered in the last section. Ignoring the resistance of the circuit, the conductance of each device becomes zero and the susceptances become the reciprocals of the reactances, §191. Then for the coil the inductive susceptance is

$$S_l = \frac{1}{X_l} = -\frac{1}{2\pi \times f \times L}$$

and for the condenser the capacitive susceptance is

$$S_c = \frac{1}{X_c} = +2\pi \times f \times C$$

where $X_l$ is the inductive reactance of the coil having inductance $L$, $X_c$ is the capacitive reactance of the condenser having capacitance $C$, and $f$ is the frequency of the applied p.d. Then the total susceptance of the two devices in parallel is

$$S = S_l + S_c$$

which is the same as the total admittance (since the resistance is neglected).

For the circuit having $L = 0.001274$ henry and $C = 0.002$ microfarad considered in the last section, and disregarding the resistance of 40 ohms, the susceptances at various frequencies are given in the following table:

| Frequency Cycles per Second | Inductive Susceptance | Capacitive Susceptance | Total Susceptance |
|---|---|---|---|
| 30,000 | —0.00416 | +0.00038 | —0.00378 |
| 40,000 | —0.00313 | +0.00050 | —0.00263 |
| 60,000 | —0.00208 | +0.00075 | —0.00133 |
| 100,000 | —0.00125 | +0.00125 | 0 |
| 150,000 | —0.00083 | +0.00188 | +0.00105 |
| 200,000 | —0.00063 | +0.00250 | +0.00187 |

At the frequency of parallel resonance—namely, 100,000 cycles—the inductive and capacitive susceptances are the same and have the value 0.00125.

The values of $S_l$ and $S_c$ are plotted separately in Fig. 252, and their total is shown by the curve marked Susceptance. By taking reciprocals of values along this curve there is obtained the two-branch dotted curve marked Reactance. Since the susceptance curve crosses the zero axis at the frequency of parallel resonance, both branches of the reactance curve go to infinity at that frequency. Consequently, the current in the main circuit at that frequency is zero. The curve of current would be similar to the curve of total susceptance except that the part below the axis would lie an equal distance above it.

In this parallel arrangement at resonance, relatively large currents may be set up in the inductive and capacitive branches and sometimes damage may result by the overloading and burning-out of the conductors in or between these branches. Parallel resonance is made use of in some communication circuits when current of definite frequency is to be suppressed.

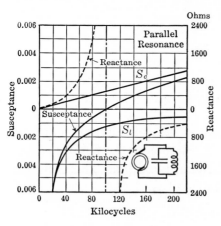

Fig. 252. Susceptance and reactance curves of a parallel circuit

### 195. Electric Filters.

—Circuits for augmenting and suppressing currents of a definite frequency were considered in the last two sections. Such series and parallel circuits containing elements having inductance and capacitance may be considered the simplest types of more complicated networks that are used for controlling the strength of currents having a definite *range* of frequencies; such networks are called *electric filters*.

A filter which transmits currents of the lower frequencies and eliminates those of the higher frequencies is termed a *low-pass filter;* it consists of several meshes having series-connected inductances and shunt-connected capacitors as shown at the top in Fig. 253.

A periodic network in which capacitors are the series-connected elements and inductance coils are the shunt elements, as indicated at the center of the figure, is called a *high-pass filter.* A combination of these two types (shown at the bottom) transmits currents above some predetermined frequency and below some higher selected frequency; they are called *band-pass filters.*

Filters are used to smooth out the varying currents produced by rectifiers, to select currents of definite frequencies in carrier-current and radio transmission, and for the elimination of harmonics generated by vacuum-tube oscillators.

The constants of a low-pass and a high-pass filter which, in combination, are used with a carrier-current

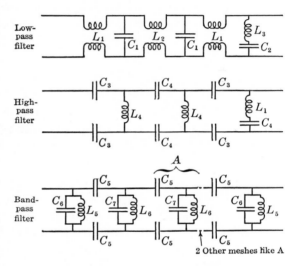

FIG. 253. Types of electric filters

telegraph set (as illustrated in Fig. 420), are given below for the symbols used in Fig. 253:

$$L_1 = 0.0532 \text{ henry} \qquad\qquad C_1 = 2C_4 = 0.1711 \text{ microfarad}$$
$$L_2 = 0.0658 \text{ henry} \qquad\qquad C_2 = 0.0529 \text{ microfarad}$$
$$L_3 = 2L_4 = 0.0329 \text{ henry} \qquad C_3 = 0.106 \quad \text{microfarad}$$

The design of these filters is based upon the assumption that the wires extending toward the left connect to lines of 600 ohms resistance, while those extending toward the right connect with terminal equipment also of 600 ohms resistance. The cut-off frequency is 3000 cycles.

The constants of the band-pass filter shown in the figure are as follows when it is designed to transmit only frequencies from 10,000 to 12,000 cycles between 600-ohm terminations:

$$L_5 = 0.00186 \text{ henry} \qquad C_5 = 0.048 \text{ microfarad}$$
$$L_6 = 0.00093 \text{ henry} \qquad 2C_6 = C_7 = 0.185 \text{ microfarad}$$

**196. Power Factor.**—With direct currents the power expended in a circuit is the product of the e.m.f. applied to the circuit and the current in it. In an alternating-current circuit containing resistance only, the current $I$ is in phase with the e.m.f. $E$, and the power in watts is also equal to $E \times I$. With inductance or capacitance in the circuit, the current will be out of phase with the impressed p.d., and the actual power expended is reduced.

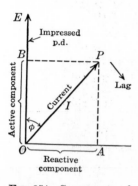

FIG. 254. Components of an alternating current

When the current in an alternating-current circuit is not in phase with the impressed p.d., the current may be looked upon as made up of two components located at right angles to each other. In Fig. 254 the current $I$ lags the e.m.f. $E$ by $\phi$ degrees. The current vector $OP$ is resolved into components by dropping perpendiculars from $P$ to the horizontal and vertical axes, and the two components are found to be: $OA$, at right angles to the impressed p.d., called the *reactive component* of the current; and $OB$, in phase with the p.d., called the *active component*. It is evident from the figure that the greater the angle of current lag the greater will be the reactive component and the smaller will be the active component.

As its name implies, the active component of the current is the one that determines the amount of power expended in the circuit. The ratio of the active component to the current itself is called the *power factor* of the circuit; thus, in Fig. 254

$$\text{power factor} = \frac{OB}{OP}$$

In the triangle $OBP$, the side $OB$ is adjacent to the angle $\phi$ and

$OP$ is the hypotenuse; the ratio of the adjacent side to the hypotenuse is the cosine of the angle, §170, and therefore

$$\cos \phi = \frac{OB}{OP}$$

Consequently, the power factor of a circuit is numerically equal to the cosine of the angle of the current lag or lead with respect to the applied potential difference, or

$$\text{power factor} = \cos \phi \qquad \qquad \textbf{105}$$

The power factor of a circuit is usually expressed in per cent. When the current and p.d. are in phase, $\phi = 0°$, and $\cos \phi = 1$; this condition is spoken of as unity power factor or 100 per cent power factor.

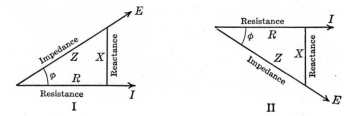

FIG. 255. Impedance triangles for lagging and leading currents

The power factor of a circuit may also be determined from its impedance triangle, involving the circuit constants: resistance $R$, reactance $X$, and impedance $Z$. In Fig. 255, triangle I represents an inductive circuit in which the current $I$ lags the impressed p.d. $E$ by the angle $\phi$, and triangle II represents a capacitive circuit in which the current leads the p.d. In both triangles the cosine of angle of lag or lead is the ratio of the adjacent side $R$ to the hypotenuse $Z$, or

$$\cos \phi = \frac{R}{Z}$$

By substituting this value in Formula (105), the power factor becomes

$$\text{power factor} = \frac{R}{Z} \qquad \qquad \textbf{106}$$

The active component of the current is the component which is in phase with the impresed p.d. In Fig. 254, this component of current $I$ (or $OP$) is $OB$, and since $OB/OP$ is the cosine of the angle $\phi$, it follows that the active component is

$$OB = I \times \cos \phi$$

The power expended in the circuit is the product of this active current component and the applied potential difference, consequently the power expended is

$$P = E \times I \times \cos \phi$$

From this expression, power factor can be defined as the ratio of the actual power expended in a circuit to the product of e.m.f. and current, that is

$$\text{power factor} = \frac{P}{E \times I} \qquad 107$$

Summarizing, three definitions of power factor are available; one in terms of the angle of current lag or lead, another in terms of resistance and impedance in the circuit, and the third in terms of the watts expended and volt-amperes supplied. These definitions are embodied in Formulas (105) to (107) respectively.

**Problem 127.**—An electromagnet takes a current of 8 amperes when connected to a 110-volt source of alternating current. A wattmeter, connected with its current coil in series with the magnet and its potential coil in parallel with the magnet is observed to read 616 watts. What is the power factor of the magnet? What is the phase difference between the current and the impressed p.d.?

The actual power expended is 616 watts and the apparent power is $8 \times 110$ or 880 volt-amperes.

$$(107) \qquad \text{power factor} = \frac{P}{E \times I} = \frac{616}{880} = 0.70 \text{ or } 70 \text{ per cent}$$

Referring to the table of trigonometric functions in the Appendix, the angle for which the cosine is 0.70 is found to be 45.5 degrees.

**197. Power in Single-Phase Circuits.**—It was pointed out in the preceding section that the power expended in an alternating-current circuit is not merely the product of the applied p.d. and the current, but the power factor must be included also. The only exception is the non-reactive circuit, because the current $I$ and the applied p.d. $E$ are in phase, and the power expended is $P = E \times I$, just as in a direct-current circuit.

The product of the effective values of current and p.d. is called the *apparent power*. The actual power expended in an alternating-current circuit is the apparent power multiplied by the power factor. Apparent power is expressed in volt-amperes (or kilovolt-amperes) while actual power is in watts (or kilowatts). Alternating-current apparatus is rated by the apparent power in kilovolt-amperes (abbreviated kv-a.); this practice is followed because the rating of such apparatus is determined by the limitation imposed by heat production, and the heat produced depends upon the actual current rather than by its active component.

To find the power in an alternating-current circuit:

*Multiply the effective value of e.m.f. by the effective value of current, and multiply this product by the cosine of the angle of lag or lead.*

Let

$E$ = applied potential difference in volts,
$I$ = current in the circuit in amperes,
$\cos \phi$ = power factor of circuit in per cent,
$P$ = power expended in circuit in watts.

Then

$$P = E \times I \times \cos \phi \qquad \textbf{108}$$

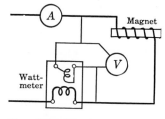

FIG. 256. Measurement of power in an alternating-current circuit

**Problem 128.**—A fluorescent lamp circuit of 70 per cent power factor takes 0.3 ampere when connected to 115-volt alternating-current mains. What power does the lamp take?

A power factor of 70 per cent means seventy hundredths, or 0.70; therefore the power taken by the lamp is

(108)          $P = 115 \times 0.3 \times 0.70 = 24.2$ watts

In measurements on single-phase circuits, the product of the readings of a voltmeter and an ammeter will yield the apparent power in the circuit or portion of the circuit to which these instruments are connected. To obtain the actual power from these readings, a knowledge is required of the power factor of the circuit or of the angle of current lag or lead. A wattmeter, however, measures directly the actual power expended. The connections of these instruments to the circuit of an alternating-current magnet are given in Fig. 256. The power factor of the magnet can be obtained by dividing the wattmeter reading by the product of the readings of ammeter $A$ and voltmeter $V$ (Formula (107)).

**Experiment 90.**—Provide an electromagnet with a laminated core, and connect it to single-phase alternating-current service mains with an ammeter, voltmeter and wattmeter joined in the circuit as shown in Fig. 256. Read the instruments and determine the power expended in the magnet and the power factor of the circuit. Then connect a resistor in series with the magnet and repeat the observations and calculations. It will be found that the current in the latter test is less than in the first, but the power factor is greater.

The effect of difference in phase on power consumption may be shown graphically by sine waves of e.m.f., current and power for several circuit conditions. Fig. 257 shows the current wave in

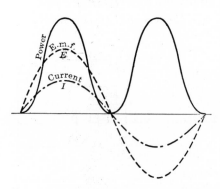

FIG. 257. Curves of e.m.f., current, and power in an alternating-current circuit containing only resistance

phase with that of e.m.f.; the power curve is the product of the other two and lies wholly above the horizontal axis. The power is positive at all times, since the products of negative values of e.m.f. and current as well as the products of their positive values are always positive. The amount of power is simply the product of the effective e.m.f. and the effective current, as read on a voltmeter and on an ammeter; that is, power $= E \times I$. This represents the condition for a circuit having resistance only.

Next, suppose that the circuit also contains inductance which causes the current to lag the e.m.f. by an angle $\phi$, as indicated in Fig. 258. The power curve is here constructed as before, but it is no longer wholly above the horizontal axis. This results from the fact that the current at times is positive while the e.m.f. is negative, and vice versa, making the product of current and e.m.f. at those times negative, and causing the corresponding points on the power curve to lie below the horizontal axis. This means that during the intervals of time, *ab* and *cd*, negative work is being done; better stated, instead of having work done upon it, the circuit during those intervals is returning energy to the power system to which it is connected. The net power supplied to the circuit is $E \times I \times \cos \phi$.

Fig. 259 shows the situation for an idealized inductive circuit, that is, one without resistance; the angle of lag is 90 degrees and the power curve lies equally above and below the horizontal axis. The circuit in this case returns as much energy as is expended in it; the negative power for time intervals $cd$ and $ef$ being equal to the positive power for intervals $bc$ and $de$. The total work done in this case, therefore, is zero,

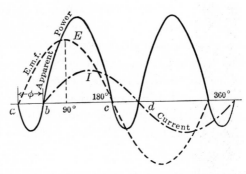

FIG. 258. Curves of e.m.f., current, and power in a circuit containing inductance

and although there is current in the circuit, the absence of resistance means that no energy is expended in it.

Although reactive currents do not represent a waste of power, they are objectionable for they load the generator and lines, and reduce the useful currents which they can accommodate within their rated capacities. For example, an alternator furnishing current to a network of low power factor may be delivering a small amount of power, and requiring little mechanical power to drive the machine, but the current is circulating through the lines and alternator armature, and both are heated unnecessarily. As the current output of the arma-

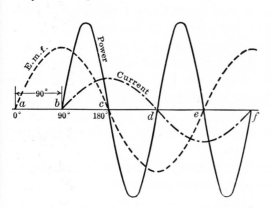

FIG. 259. Curves of e.m.f., current, and power in an inductive circuit of negligible resistance

ture is limited largely by this heating, it is clear that the useful current which may be taken from the alternator is cut down by the presence of the reactive current. In practice, alternating-current apparatus is designed to have as high a power factor as possible consistent with other requirements.

The power factor of the circuits of electric service companies may be improved by the use of condensers to counteract the effect of inductive reactance; when so used they are termed *static condensers* to distinguish this method of power-factor correction from the one which utilizes synchronous motors as so-called *synchronous condensers,* §245. Static condensers or capacitors are found to be more economical than synchronous condensers in sizes below about 500 kilovolt-amperes, and at frequencies from 40 to 125 cycles. They are available in units, and the number of units required depends upon the extent of the improvement in power factor desired.

**Problem 129.**—What is the rating of a capacitor for use on 60-cycle, 2300-volt lines, if its capacitance is 2.5 microfarads?

The current taken by the capacitor is

(87) $\quad I = 2\pi \times C \times E \times f = 2\pi \times 0.0000025 \times 2300 \times 60 = 2.17$ amperes

and its power rating is

(49) $\quad\quad P = E \times I = 2300 \times 2.17 = 5000$ volt-amperes

**198. Polyphase Circuits.**—Circuits that are supplied by two-phase and polyphase alternating-current generators have more than two line wires and receive two or more equal e.m.f.'s that are definitely related in phase. A two-phase alternator develops two alternating e.m.f's of the same value but which are always a quarter of a cycle apart. Such a generator may be looked upon as composed of two separate single-phase alternators of the same size, having e.m.f.'s that are maintained mechanically at a phase difference of 90 degrees. Let these alternators be denoted by 1 and 2 at the left of Fig. 260, and assume that the e.m.f. $E_2$ of alternator 2, lags that generated in alternator 1, namely $E_1$, by 90 degrees. These relations may be represented graphically by the arrows $E_1$ and $E_2$ on the diagrammatic representation of the two-phase alternator at the center of the figure, lag being clockwise.

Now consider the lower terminal of alternator 1 and the upper terminal of alternator 2 to be connected at $B$, thus forming a two-phase, three-wire system. The p.d. between terminals $A$ and $C$ is due to the e.m.f.'s produced in both alternators, and its value is determined by the vector diagram at the right in which $E_1$ and $E_2$ represent effective values. The addition of these equal e.m.f.'s of $E$ volts at 90 degrees difference in phase yields the diagonal $E_{AC}$ which has a value of $\sqrt{2}\,E$ volts. Thus, the p.d. across line wires $A$ and $C$ is $\sqrt{2}$ or 1.41 times the p.d. across lines $A$ and $B$ or across $B$ and $C$.

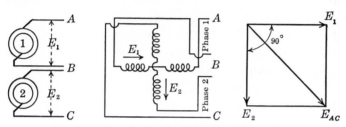

FIG. 260. E.m.f. relations in a two-phase system

Similarly, consider a three-phase alternator to consist of three single-phase generators having equal e.m.f.'s maintained at successive phase displacements of 120 degrees. At the left in Fig. 261, alternators 1, 2 and 3 are shown connected one to each line wire, and their other terminals joined to form the *neutral point* of the system. This so-called *Y*-connection is visualized at the center;

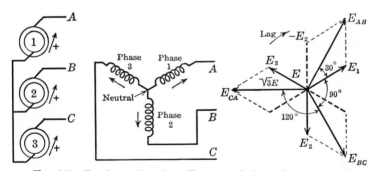

FIG. 261. E.m.f. relations in a Y-connected three-phase system

such a diagram is used to represent a *Y*-connected three-phase alternator. Let the directions of the e.m.f.'s in the three armature coils, as their axes successively pass a given fixed point, be positive, as shown by the arrows. Then, the phase relations of the armature electromotive forces will be represented as in the vector diagram at the right, in which $E_2$ lags $E_1$ by 120 degrees, and $E_3$

lags $E_2$ by 120 degrees.   The potential differences between the
three line wires may then be determined by graphical construction,
also included in the figure.

The p.d. between lines $A$ and $B$ is equal to vector $E_1$ *minus* vector $E_2$, minus because these e.m.f.'s are directed away from the
neutral point and partially oppose each other.   While $E_1$ and $E_2$
are equal numerically, their difference is not zero, because they
are directed at an angle to each other.   To subtract vector $E_2$ from
$E_1$, change the sign of $E_2$ (that is, reverse it so that it will assume
the dotted position marked $-E_2$) and then add $E_1$.   This process is
shown in the diagram and the result is $E_{AB}$ leading $E_1$ by 30 degrees.   Similarly, $E_{BC}$ equals $E_2$ minus $E_3$ and lags $E_1$ by 90 degrees, again $E_{CA}$ equals $E_3$ minus $E_1$ and lags $E_1$ by 210 degrees.
The magnitudes of the line p.d.'s for the $Y$-connected system may
be determined by scaling the diagram or by geometrical proof.   If
the e.m.f. generated in each armature coil is $E$ volts, the line p.d.'s
will be

$$E_{AB} = E_{BC} = E_{CA} = \sqrt{3}\,E = 1.73\,E \qquad\qquad 109$$

In Fig. 262 are indicated the corresponding conditions for the
delta ($\Delta$) connection of the alternators.   The e.m.f. across two line
wires is equal to that produced by one alternator only and is $E$

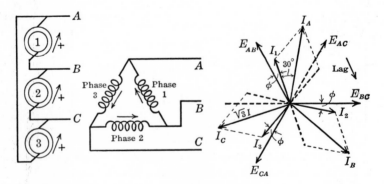

Fig. 262. E.m.f. relations in a $\Delta$-connected three-phase system

volts, and if all the other conditions remain unchanged, $E_{BC}$ will
lag $E_{AB}$ by 120 degrees, and $E_{CA}$ will lag $E_{BC}$ by 120 degrees.
Assume the three phases to be equally loaded, that is, the three
circuits (one across each pair of line wires) have the same resis-

tance and the same reactance. The arrows represent positive direction of current in the coils, as their axes successively pass a fixed point, and the values of the currents in the lines may be determined as shown in the vector diagram, where $\phi$ is the angle of lag. It is seen that $I_A$ is equal to $I_1$ minus $I_3$ and lags $E_1$ or $E_{AB}$ by $30° + \phi$. Similarly $I_B$ is equal to $I_2$ minus $I_1$ and lags $E_1$ by $150° + \phi$; again $I_C$ is equal to $I_3$ minus $I_2$ and leads $E_1$ by $90° - \phi$. If the current in each alternator or phase winding be represented by $I$, the magnitudes of the line currents in the $\Delta$-connection are

$$I_A = I_B = I_C = \sqrt{3}\,I = 1.73\,I \qquad\qquad 110$$

**199. Power in Polyphase Systems.**—The power expended in a single-phase circuit in which the e.m.f. is $E$ volts and the current is $I$ amperes, is given by Formula (108) as

$$P = E \times I \times \cos\phi$$

where $\phi$ is the angle of phase difference between the current and impressed p.d., and $\cos\phi$ is the power factor of the circuit. Both $E$ and $I$ are effective values and $P$ is the power in watts. This is also the basic expression for the determination of power expended in polyphase circuits.

The power delivered to the receiving circuits of a two-phase, four-wire system can be measured by two wattmeters, one connected in each phase. The sum of their readings is the total power supplied. If the load is balanced between the two circuits, one of the wattmeters may be dispensed with, and the total power is then double the reading of the other.

The power factor of a balanced two-phase load may be measured by a wattmeter; the derivation of the formula to be used in the determination requires a knowledge of two trigonometric facts. One, the sine of an angle is the same as the cosine of its complementary angle, thus, $\sin\phi = \cos(90° - \phi)$; and the other, the tangent of an angle is the ratio of its sine to its cosine, that is $\tan\phi = \sin\phi \div \cos\phi$. In making the measurement, the wattmeter is connected in the circuit of one phase, as shown at the left in Fig. 263, and the reading is

$$P_1 = E \times I \times \cos\phi$$

When the potential coil is transferred to the other phase, as shown at the right, leaving the connection of the current coil unchanged, the reading is

$$P_2 = E \times I \times \cos(90° - \phi) = E \times I \times \sin \phi$$

because of the 90-degree phase difference between the two e.m.f.'s. It follows from these equations that

$$\tan \phi = \frac{\sin \phi}{\cos \phi} = \frac{P_2}{P_1} \qquad\qquad \mathbf{111}$$

The angle $\phi$ is then determined by reference to a table of tangents, and thereafter $\cos \phi$ (power factor) may be read from a table of cosines.

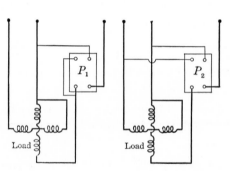
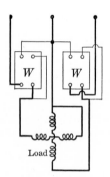

FIG. 263. Measurement of power factor of a balanced two-phase three-wire circuit

FIG. 264. Measurement of power in a two-phase circuit

Measurement of power in a two-phase three-wire system can be measured by two wattmeters $W,W$ connected as in Fig. 264 whether the load is balanced on the two phases or not. The total power expended is the sum of the instrument readings.

An accurate method for the determination of the power in unbalanced three-phase systems, avoiding the necessity of a neutral point, involves the use of two wattmeters connected as in Fig. 265 I. The load circuits may be connected either in $\Delta$ or $Y$. The algebraic sum of the instrument indications is, as before, the total power supplied. In some cases the lesser reading will be negative. To determine the correct sign of the readings, the wattmeters may be interchanged so that the wires shown in the figure will connect with like-numbered wattmeter terminals. Should the reading of either wattmeter be reversed by this change, then the original reading of that meter is negative.

Another method of measuring power in a *balanced* three-phase system, either Δ- or Y-connected, is based upon the assumption that both potentials and currents vary sinusoidally. No neutral point is required, and the con-
nections are shown in Fig. 265 II. The potential coil of the wattmeter is connected from the wire which includes the current coil first to one of the other wires, and then to the remaining wire. The readings of the instrument for the two positions are $P_1$ and $P_2$. The angular displacements between the current in any wire and the p.d.'s between it and the other line wires are $30° + \phi$ and $30° - \phi$, as will become evident from an inspection of Fig. 262. The power readings are then

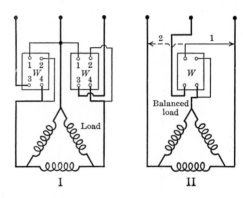

FIG. 265. Measurement of power in three-phase circuits

$$P_1 = \sqrt{3}\,E \times I \times \cos (30° + \phi)$$

and

$$P_2 = \sqrt{3}\,E \times I \times \cos (30° - \phi)$$

where $E$ is the e.m.f. generated and $I$ is the current in each armature coil of the alternator supplying the load circuit. The algebraic sum of the readings gives the total power delivered as

$$P_1 + P_2 = \sqrt{3}\,E \times I \times \Big[ \cos (30° + \phi) + \cos (30° - \phi) \Big]$$

and this can be simplified to be

$$P_1 + P_2 = 3\,E \times I \times \cos \phi$$

When $\phi$ is greater than 60 degrees, $P_1$ becomes negative; hence care is required to avoid confusion of signs at power factors less than 50 percent.

Represent the p.d. between any two line wires by $E_l$, and the current in each line by $I_l$. Since $E_l = \sqrt{3}\,E$ in the Y-connection and $I_l = \sqrt{3}\,I$ in the $\Delta$-connection, a division of the previous results by $\sqrt{3}$ yields the total power delivered with either connection as

$$P = P_1 + P_2 = \sqrt{3}\,E_l \times I_l \times \cos\phi \qquad\qquad 112$$

**Problem 130.**—A three-phase alternator is connected to a balanced receiving circuit of 80 per cent power factor. Determine the power supplied by the alternator when the p.d. across the line wires is 150 volts and the current in each line is 20 amperes.

(112) $P = \sqrt{3}\,E_l \times I_l \times \cos\phi = \sqrt{3} \times 150 \times 20 \times 0.80 = 4160$ watts

**Experiment 91.**—Procure three identical alternating-current magnets, such as those used in circuit breakers or contactors, and connect them to three-phase service mains to form a balanced $\Delta$-connected load. Measure the power supplied to this load by the 1-wattmeter method illustrated in Fig. 265 II. Repeat the test with the three magnets connected in $Y$. Show that the total power in the $\Delta$-connected load is three times that in the $Y$-connected one.

## QUESTIONS

1. Explain how to find the impedance of a number of devices connected in series to a source of alternating e.m.f.
2. Define admittance, conductance and susceptance of an alternating-current circuit.
3. The resistance, reactance and impedance of a circuit are respectively 12, 16 and 20 ohms. Plot the impedance and admittance triangles.
4. What is meant by the resonant frequency of a circuit and how is it expressed?
5. Upon what factors does resonance in a circuit depend?
6. Distinguish between series and parallel resonance.
7. What is an electric filter and for what purpose is it used?
8. Will the product of volts by amperes give the actual power expended in an alternating-current circuit? Why?
9. What is meant by power factor?
10. Why do you believe that alternating-current apparatus should be rated in kv-a. rather than in kw.
11. Prove that the actual power expended in a circuit is equal to the apparent power multiplied by the power factor.
12. What are the e.m.f. relations in two- and in three-phase circuits?
13. Explain the $Y$ and $\Delta$ methods of connecting alternator windings.
14. Show that the p.d. between terminals of a three-phase $Y$-connected alternator is $\sqrt{3}$ times the e.m.f. generated in the phase winding.
15. How can the power factor of a single-phase circuit be measured? How in a balanced two-phase system?

16. A three-phase alternator is connected to a balanced inductive load and the power is measured according to the method of Fig. 265 II. What is the total power delivered to the receiving circuits if the indications of the wattmeter are 2200 and 2900 watts?

17. Explain how the power supplied to an unbalanced three-phase load may be measured.

## PROBLEMS

1. (a) What would be the impedance of a circuit consisting of two coils, $A$ and $B$, connected in series; coil $A$ has a resistance of 2 ohms and a reactance of 1.5 ohms, while coil $B$ has a resistance of 4 ohms and a reactance of 7 ohms. (b) What would be the impedance of each part of the circuit? *Ans.* (a) 10.4 ohms; (b) $A = 2.50$ ohms, $B = 8.06$ ohms.

2. A device has a resistance of 4 ohms and a capacitive reactance of 3 ohms. Determine its admittance, conductance and susceptance. *Ans.* $Y = 0.20$, $G = 0.16$, $S = 0.12$.

3. What is the impedance at 1000 cycles of a circuit containing a resistor of 50 ohms resistance and a condenser of 2 microfarads capacitance that are connected in series? *Ans.* 94.0 ohms.

4. What would be the impedance of the circuit if the coils of Problem 1 were connected in parallel? *Ans.* 1.94 ohms.

5. (a) What is the resonant frequency of a series circuit having a capacitance of 10 microfarads and an inductance of 0.352 henry? (b) What will be the p.d. across the capacitor at resonance, when the current is 10 amperes? *Ans.* (a) 85 cycles per second; (b) 1880 volts.

6. The current leads the e.m.f. available in a certain capacitive circuit by 80°. (a) What is the power factor of the circuit? (b) What is the ratio of its capacitive reactance to its resistance? *Ans.* (a) 17.4 per cent; (b) 5.67 to 1.

7. A 15-microfarad capacitor is connected in series with an inductive circuit and causes the 60-cycle current in the circuit to shift in phase from 45 degrees lagging to 45 degrees leading. What is the inductance of the circuit? *Ans.* 0.235 henry.

8. What current will a 240-volt alternator produce in a circuit which has a power factor of 90 per cent and takes 1 kilowatt? *Ans.* 4.63 amperes.

9. Find the power taken by a coil having a resistance of 100 ohms and an inductance of 0.40 henry when connected across 110-volt, 60-cycle mains. *Ans.* 37 watts.

10. What is the phase displacement between sinusoidal waves of potential and current, respectively of 100 volts and 10 amperes maximum value, when the power expended in the circuit is 424 watts? *Ans.* 32 degrees.

11. An alternator generating an e.m.f. of 1100 volts at a frequency of 60 cycles per second supplies energy to a system that has a resistance of 125 ohms and an inductance of 0.5 henry. (a) Find the value of the

current. (b) Determine the power factor. (c) Find the angle of lag. (d) Calculate the apparent power and the actual power expended. *Ans.* (a) 4.86 amperes; (b) 55.3 per cent; (c) 56.5 degrees; (d) 5346 volt-amperes and 2950 watts respectively.

12. The e.m.f. generated in each armature winding of a three-phase alternator is 120 volts, and the maximum allowable current in each coil is 5 amperes. Determine the p.d.'s between the lines and the maximum allowable current in each line wire when the alternator is Y-connected and when it is Δ-connected. *Ans.* Y: 208 volts, 5 amperes; Δ: 120 volts, 8.67 amperes.

13. A balanced two-phase load is measured with a wattmeter as explained in §199, the readings being $P_1 = 1200$ and $P_2 = 800$ watts. What is the power factor of the load? *Ans.* 83 per cent.

# Lesson XVIII

## PRINCIPLES OF DYNAMO-ELECTRIC MACHINES

Dynamos—Classification of generators—Generation of electromotive force—Multi-coil armatures—Gramme ring armature—Drum armature—Armature resistance—Eddy current loss—Hysteresis loss—Other losses in a dynamo—Armature insulation—The commutator and brushes—Armature reaction in a generator—Commutation of an armature coil—Improvements in commutation—Causes of sparking—Questions and Problems.

**200. Dynamos.**—The term *dynamo* is applied to machines which convert either mechanical energy into electrical energy, or electrical energy into mechanical energy, by utilizing the principles of electromagnetic induction and electromagnetism. A dynamo is called a *generator* when mechanical energy supplied in the form of rotation is converted into electrical energy; it is called a *motor* when electrical energy is changed to mechanical energy of rotation. Thus, a dynamo is a reversible machine capable of operation as a generator or a motor, as desired.

When operated as a generator, the dynamo develops an electromotive force that is capable of producing current through electrical circuits connected to the machine. The amount of electrical energy delivered to these circuits depends upon the quantity of mechanical energy supplied to the generator. In the circuit *external* to the machine the e.m.f. causes the electricity to flow from a higher (or positive) potential to a lower (or negative) potential, just as water flows from a higher to a lower level. In the *internal* circuit of a generator the electricity is caused to flow from a lower potential to a higher potential, just as water is raised by a pump from a lower to a higher level. As pointed out earlier, the flow of elec-

413

tricity around a circuit is really the circulation of electrons through it, but it should be remembered that the direction of the current is regarded as opposite to the direction of the electrons.

The dynamo consists essentially of two parts: a *magnetic field structure* formed of electromagnets, and an *armature* formed of a number of coils of wire wound upon an iron core. One of these parts is arranged to move with respect to the other, and the motion is made uniform so as to produce a steady e.m.f. in the generator or a constant torque in the motor.

**201. Classification of Generators.**—Generators may be classified according to their design and construction into *direct-current generators* and *alternating-current generators,* the latter being also called *alternators.* The direct-current machine is fundamentally an alternator, for it actually generates an alternating current; its armature is provided with an appropriate commutating device and the current is rendered unidirectional in the external circuit, although it still alternates in direction within the armature winding.

In direct-current generators the field structure is stationary and the armature revolves within it. The field is constructed in the form of a ring with inwardly projecting poles, magnetized alternately north and south. In alternating-current generators the field structure may be made stationary or designed to revolve, the latter being the usual form.

A dynamo having only one N-pole and one S-pole in its field structure is called a *bipolar* dynamo. Machines having more than two poles, that is, four or any other even number, are called *multipolar* dynamos. The greater the number of poles on a generator the lower will be its speed of operation for the production of a given e.m.f. If a bipolar direct-current generator is required to rotate at 1200 revolutions per minute to generate an e.m.f. of 125 volts, then under otherwise equal conditions a four-pole dynamo need operate at only 600 revolutions per minute.

The flux paths in bipolar and multipolar revolving-armature dynamos are indicated in Fig. 266. There are two flux paths in a bipolar machine, four in a four-pole machine, and so on. The magnetic lines in any flux path leave the N-pole, pass through a part of the armature, enter the adjacent S-pole of the field structure, and complete their paths through the ring frame. The presence of the iron core of the armature between the field poles reduces the reluctance of the flux paths and yields vastly more magnetic flux through those paths for the same current through the field circuit.

Generators are usually of multipolar design, but in describing the action it is customary to assume bipolar construction because of the greater simplicity in treatment.

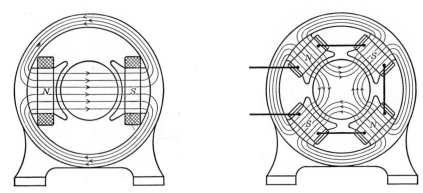

Fig. 266. Flux paths in bipolar and four-pole dynamos

**202. Generation of Electromotive Force.**—The production of an e.m.f. in a loop of wire that is rotated in a magnetic field was described in Lesson XV. To make use of an e.m.f. produced in this way it is necessary to have continuous electrical connection between the revolving loop and a stationary circuit in which current is established. Fig. 267 shows the two collecting devices used for this purpose. At I the shaft is equipped with *slip rings* that connect to the ends of the loop *ABCD,* and at II the shaft has a *commutator* of two segments that connect to the loop. Brushes *X* and *Y* press upon these devices and lead to the external circuit consisting of several lamps. The rotation of the loop in the bipolar field is continually in one direction; this is indicated by the curved arrows.

As inductor *AB* moves down and inductor *CD* moves up in the magnetic field directed from N to S, the e.m.f.'s induced in them will be directed around the loop and produce a current through the external circuit, as shown by the small arrows. A brief period later, when $AB$ moves up and $CD$ moves down, the current around the loop will be in the reverse direction. In diagram I, terminal $A$ of the loop is always in contact with brush $X$ and terminal $D$ is always in contact with brush $Y$, and it is clear that the current through the lamps will reverse every time the current in the loop reverses. Thus, an alternating current is maintained in an external circuit supplied with e.m.f. from a rotating coil through collector rings.

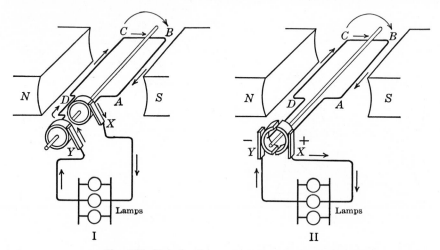

Fig. 267. Rotating loop with collecting devices
I—Slip rings for alternating current; II—Commutator for direct current.

In diagram II, the two brushes and the slot between the two segments of the commutator are so oriented that, whenever the e.m.f. changes its direction in the loop, the terminals $A$ and $D$ will simultaneously change connection with brushes $X$ and $Y$. Consequently, while the current reverses in the coil, the current in the lamp circuit remains unchanged in direction, and brush $X$ will always be positive and brush $Y$ negative. Thus, a direct current is maintained in an external circuit supplied with e.m.f. from a rotating coil through a commutator.

The graphs of the currents through the external circuit are shown in Fig. 268 for the two arrangements. The scales indicate that one complete revolution of the loop takes 2 seconds, and that the current has a peak value $AE$ of 5 amperes. The lobes $PAB$ and $BCD$ of the curves are sinusoidal. In diagram I the lobes are in opposite directions about the base line to indicate an alternating current, in diagram II the lobes are in the same direction to indicate a direct current. This direct current is a pulsating one and fluctuates in value from 0 to 5 amperes. Means are available for

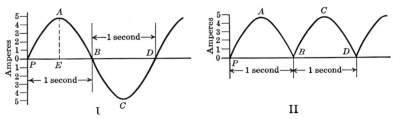

FIG. 268. Character of current supplied by a rotating loop

I—Alternating current through slip ring; II—Pulsating unidirectional current through commutator.

reducing the fluctuation so that the direct current produced by coils revolving in magnetic fields may be rendered uniform in strength.

**Experiment 92.**—Make up an elementary generator with an electromagnet as a field structure and a coil of 50 turns or more as an armature, patterned after the diagrams of Fig. 267. The coil can be wound around a flat bobbin of wood and the shaft can be placed through the bobbin lengthwise. Equip the coil with two slip rings and also a two-section commutator. Place the brushes upon the slip rings and connect the brushes to a low-range direct-current voltmeter having its zero mark at the center of the scale. With the field magnets energized, turn the coil by hand and observe that the instrument swings one way and then the other, because the current developed alternates in direction. Then place the brushes upon the commutator and note that the deflection of the voltmeter is in one direction because the current in this instrument is now unidirectional.

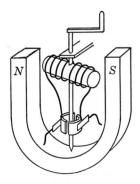

FIG. 269. Model of direct-current generator

**Experiment 93.**—Replace the slip rings of the generator model of Experiment 82 by a two-section commutator as shown in Fig. 269. Connect a direct-current voltmeter to the brushes and observe that this instrument always deflects in one direction as the generator is turned. The deflection will increase as the speed is raised. Then rotate the brush assembly slowly and locate the positions which yield the maximum and minimum e.m.f.'s.

**203. Multi-Coil Armatures.**—A direct-current generator with only one coil on its armature and a two-segment commutator would produce a current composed of a series of positive lobes as illustrated in part II of Fig. 268. To produce a steadier current, imagine another coil to be put upon the same armature, located with its plane at right angles to that of the first coil, and equipped with its own two-segment commutator. The current that the second coil alone would produce in the external circuit is just like the one previously mentioned, except that its zero values will occur at moments $A$ and $C$ when the current in the first coil has its maximum values. Finally, suppose that the two coils are joined in series to the same load circuit through their respective commutators; then the generated e.m.f. will be the sum of those contributed by each coil and the current will be correspondingly increased.

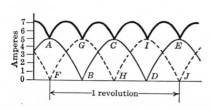

FIG. 270. Representation of direct current from a two-coil armature

The process of determining the current in the circuit is illustrated in Fig. 270, where the light full-line curve $ABCDE$ represents the current wave from one coil and the dotted curve $FGHIJ$ that from the other one. The heavy line at the top is the sum of the two curves, obtained by adding their heights at each point along the base line; it shows the character of the current produced by the two coils acting together in the same circuit. The current in the circuit still varies in strength but never falls to zero as it does when supplied by a single-coil armature. In the particular example, it varies from a minimum value of 5 amperes to a maximum of about 7 amperes. When the number of coils on the armature is increased the current fluctuation becomes less and less.

The armatures of dynamos are wound with many coils of wire, so that the current in the external circuit will be almost free from fluctuation. These coils are angularly disposed on the iron core and cover its entire cylindrical surface. The greater the subdivision of the armature winding the larger will be the number of segments required in the commutator.

**204. Gramme Ring Armature.**—An early type of direct-current armature, known as a *Gramme* ring armature, is illustrated in Fig. 271. The coils are wound upon an iron ring and the ending of each coil is joined to the beginning of the adjacent coil, so that the armature winding itself forms a closed circuit. From each junction of a coil with its neighbor a wire leads to a commutator segment. On a four-coil armature there will be four junctions and the commutator will have four segments. As the number of coils is increased the number of commutator segments is increased correspondingly.

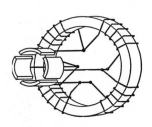

FIG. 271. Four-coil Gramme-ring armature

A ring armature with eight coils is depicted in Fig. 272, rotating clockwise in a bipolar field. The magnetic flux issuing from the N-pole passes through the upper and lower halves of the ring to the S-pole; hardly any lines of flux cross the air space inside the ring. Consequently, only the conductors on the outside of the ring cut the flux; these are often called *inductors* to distinguish them from conductors which do not cut magnetic flux. The direction of the e.m.f. induced in any inductor is found by the right-hand rule, §146. The e.m.f.'s in all the inductors on the left half of the armature are directed into the page, and those in all the inductors on the right half are directed out of the page. The directions of the e.m.f.'s in the coils are indicated.

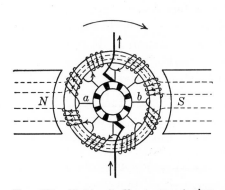

FIG. 272. Eight-coil direct-current ring armature in a bipolar field

When the external circuit of the armature is closed the current produced by the e.m.f. in each half of the winding is directed toward the upper or positive brush. The current path extends from the positive brush to the external circuit (not shown), from that circuit to the negative brush at the lower part of the figure, and from this point the path divides through both halves of the armature.

As each coil passes from under the influence of the N-pole and comes into action under the S-pole, the direction of current through it reverses; this accounts for the fact that the directions of the currents in the two uppermost coils are opposed to each other. During the rotation of the armature each brush will momentarily span the gap between adjacent segments of the commutator and cause the coil connected between them to be short-circuited. These periods of short-circuit are brief, but nevertheless it is necessary to locate the brushes so that the short-circuiting of coils occurs at instants when there is little e.m.f. induced in them.

To appreciate how the e.m.f.'s induced in the coils of a ring armature add up to produce the p.d. available at the brushes, consider the two left and the two right coils in Fig. 272 momentarily in the position of developing the maximum e.m.f., and the two top and the two bottom coils to be momentarily developing only half that e.m.f. For definiteness assume these values to be 40 volts and 20 volts respectively. Since the four coils on the left are in series, the total e.m.f. developed in this half of the ring will be 20 + 40 + 40 + 20 or 120 volts; the same e.m.f. will be developed in the right half also. The windings of the two halves are in *parallel,* and consequently the e.m.f. at the brushes will be 120 volts. The current in the external circuit will be the sum of the currents in each half of the winding. If the current supplied to that circuit is 10 amperes, there will be 5 amperes through the coils on each side of the ring armature.

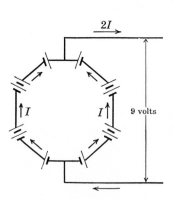

FIG. 273. Battery analogy of a ring armature

**Experiment 94.**—Using a dozen No. 6 dry cells, arrange them in groups as shown in Fig. 273 to represent the eight coils of the ring armature depicted in Fig. 272. With 1.5 volts per cell, the p.d. available between the upper and lower terminals should be 9 volts; check this value with a voltmeter. Connect the terminals to a' suitable resistor and measure the current through it with an ammeter; then verify the fact that half this current comes from each side of ring circuit.

Fig. 274 shows a Gramme-ring machine that is made for demonstration purposes. The field structure and armature are designed so that their upper surfaces are flush and level to permit the mapping of their magnetic fields. The commutator and brushes are located on the under side of the armature.

**Experiment 95.**—Place a sheet of glass or cardboard horizontally upon a demonstration Gramme-ring machine and sprinkle iron filings upon the surface to study the character of the magnetic field: first, with the armature removed and the field excited: second, with the armature in place and no current through it; third, with current in the armature but none in the field; and fourth, with current in both parts of the machine but rotation of the armature prevented. Make sketches to show the flux distribution for the conditions stated.

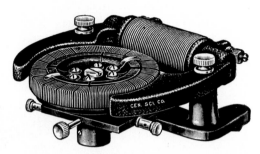

FIG. 274. Demonstration generator with Gramme-ring

Central Scientific Company

**205. Drum Armature.**—In the ring armatures already considered the wire forming the coils is wound in and out around the core as shown in Figs. 271 and 274. Only that part of the wire which is located on the outside of the ring cuts the magnetic lines of force and is active in developing e.m.f.; this part, made up of inductors, is collectively termed the *active wire*. The wire on the ends and inside of the ring is necessary, of course, to connect one inductor to the next. In the *drum armature* both sides of each coil are made effective in producing e.m.f. by placing them on the cylindrical surface of the core. The construction is illustrated in Fig. 275. In this way each loop of wire in a coil comprises two inductors.

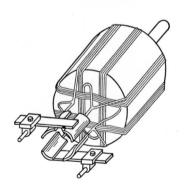

FIG. 275. Four-coil drum armature

The inductors of each coil on a drum armature are so located that when one side of a coil is under a N-pole, its other side will be under the next adjacent S-pole. In a bipolar field this means that the coil sides are about diametrically opposite, as shown in the figure. The coils of a drum armature cover its entire surface.

The electromotive forces induced in the two sides of each armature coil are cumulative, and the coils are connected to form a closed winding with commutator taps at the junctions. Both halves of the drum winding are in parallel in supplying the external circuit. Thus, the e.m.f. available in that circuit is the e.m.f. generated in one-half of the total number of inductors on the armature, and each half of the winding delivers one-half of the

FIG. 276. Armature and commutator mounted on spider or quill
Allis Chalmers Manufacturing Company

current in the external circuit, just as in the ring armature. Drum armatures are used almost to the exclusion of the ring type.

There is no necessity in drum armatures for employing iron cores that are complete cylinders, except in armatures of small diameter. In larger armatures the core extends inward back of the winding slots just far enough to allow an adequate cross section of iron for the magnetic flux. Such cores are assembled on a mechanical support, called a *spider*, which is mounted on the shaft. This type of construction affords splendid cooling facilities, and is economical in iron. While the general form is that of a ring, drum armature cores of such construction should not be confused with the practically obsolete ring armature. Fig. 276 depicts a drum armature of a large generator.

In medium-sized multipolar machines the armature windings consist of a number of formed coils, each coil being composed of several conductors of round or rectangular wire individually insulated and then fastened together with cotton, linen or varnished cloth tape. The coils are varnished and impregnated with insulating compound to expel all moisture. They are inserted in slots in the armature core and kept in place by retaining wedges, while the end connections are held by banding wire. Formed coils possess superior insulation and permit of speedy removal in case of repair.

In large-sized generators, the inductors are solid copper bars with appropriate insulation, and these are placed in the armature slots, which are first lined with mica formed tubes. The bars are then connected at each end with properly shaped jumpers to form the coils of the winding.

**206. Armature Resistance.**—The resistance of an armature is usually measured by taking current and potential readings at the brushes of the dynamo with the armature at rest and using an outside source of electricity. Since the two halves of the winding of a bipolar armature are in parallel, the resistance of the armature as measured between brushes is one-half the resistance of each half of the winding.

The heat developed in an armature winding is the product of its resistance $R$ and the square of the current $I$ through it; thus, the copper loss in the armature is given by Formula (52) as $I^2 \times R$. The current and resistance values must apply to the same path.

**Problem 131.**—The resistance of a bipolar armature between brushes is 0.25 ohm. What is the resistance of all the wire upon the armature? What is the copper loss in the armature when it supplies 10 amperes to the external circuit?

Since there are two current paths in parallel through the armature, and their combined resistance is 0.25 ohm, the resistance $R'$ of each path is found by Formula (31), using $n = 2$, $R = 0.25$ ohm; whence

$$R' = R \times n = 0.25 \times 2 = 0.5 \text{ ohm}$$

This is the resistance of one-half the winding; therefore, the total resistance of the wire upon the armature is $0.5 \times 2 = 1$ ohm.

Using the resistance between brushes and the current in the external circuit, the armature copper loss is $I^2 \times R = (10)^2 \times 0.25 = 25$ watts. Using the resistance of the entire winding and the current in it, the copper loss is $(5)^2 \times 1 = 25$ watts, as before.

Armature resistance should be considered in determining the current that a generator can produce in a circuit connected to it. The p.d. available at the brushes of the machine will be less than the e.m.f. generated in the armature by the p.d. necessary to maintain the current through the armature resistance, §75.

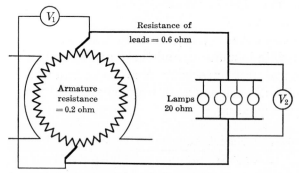

FIG. 277. Distinction between e.m.f. generated in armature and p.d. available at brushes

**Problem 132.**—A generator supplies current to a group of lamps having an equivalent resistance of 20 ohms. The e.m.f. generated in the armature is 125 volts, the resistance of the armature is 0.2 ohm, and the resistance of the leads from the brushes to the lamps is 0.6 ohm. What current will the lamps receive? What p.d. will a voltmeter indicate when placed across the brushes? and when connected across the lamps?

The circuit is shown in Fig. 277. If $R$ and $r$ be respectively the external and internal resistances of the generator, the current supplied by the machine is

$$(23) \qquad I = \frac{E}{R + r} = \frac{125}{20 + 0.6 + 0.2} = 6.0 \text{ amperes}$$

The p.d. required to maintain 6.0 amperes through the armature will be

$$(24) \qquad E_d = I \times r = 6.0 \times 0.2 = 1.2 \text{ volts}$$

consequently, the p.d. across the brushes will be $V_1 = 125 - 1.2 = 123.8$ volts. Similarly, the p.d. across the lamps will be $V_2 = 125 - 6.0 \times 0.8 = 120.2$ volts.

**207. Eddy Current Loss.**—When the armature is rotated in the magnetic field of a dynamo there will be currents induced not only in the winding but also in the iron core of the armature. The latter currents do not appear in the external circuit, but are localized in the core itself, thereby heating it. These currents are called eddy currents (§151), and the loss of energy represented by them is termed the *eddy current loss*. A section of a solid armature core and the paths of the eddy currents are shown in Fig. 278. The direction of current in these paths is determined by the right-hand rule.

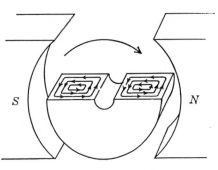

FIG. 278. Eddy current paths in solid armature core

Eddy current losses may be diminished considerably by building the armature of a series of thin disks of soft sheet iron or steel, and insulating each disk from its neighbors. A coat of varnish, or merely a thin layer of oxide between the sheets, will serve to separate them electrically from each other. The effect of laminating the core is indicated in Fig. 279, which shows the eddy currents confined to each lamination. The resistance of the entire path of eddy currents is greatly increased and, therefore, the intensity of these currents is diminished. The eddy current loss in the 4-disk core of Fig. 279

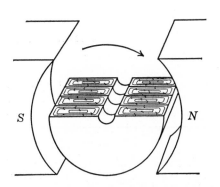

FIG. 279. Eddy-current paths in laminated armature core

The thickness of disks is magnified.

is only $\frac{1}{16}$ of that in the solid core of Fig. 278 for otherwise identical conditions. To reduce this loss still further a great many disks are used to make up the armature core; indeed, the laminations are punched from metal as thin as 0.014 inch. The appearance of a lamination for a slotted armature is shown in Fig. 280.

It was pointed out in §205 that the conductors in large machines are generally straight bars of rectangular cross section which are individually insulated, inserted in each slot, and joined by jumpers to form coils. It is not advisable to use bars of very large cross section because of the eddy currents set up in them when one side of a conductor happens momentarily to be in a stronger field than the other. Instead, several smaller conductors of equivalent total cross section are used and these are connected in parallel at the commutator.

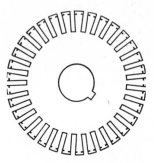

FIG. 280.  Sheet iron armature lamination

**208. Hysteresis Loss.**—Another source of energy loss in the iron or steel parts of electrical machinery is called *hysteresis* (pronounced hister-eé-sis). This occurs in those parts which are subjected to rapid changes in magnetization. In magnetizing a piece of iron, work must be done upon its molecular magnets in order to align them in any definite direction, and when they are aligned first one way and then the other many times per second the work done is considerable and the iron is heated in the process. This waste of energy in the iron due to cyclic magnetization is called *hysteresis loss*.

**Experiment 96.**—Connect the winding of an electromagnet to a source of alternating current. First use a solid iron core and note that it will get quite hot because of the eddy currents induced in it and because of magnetic hysteresis. Replace the solid core by a bundle of iron wires to increase the resistance of the core to eddy currents; the electromagnet will not heat up nearly as much as before. Apply an alternating current of lower frequency, if one is available, and observe that the heating is less than before because both the eddy current and hysteresis losses are reduced.

The armature core of a direct-current generator is subject to reversals in magnetization as it revolves. Consider the armature of a bipolar generator shown in Fig. 281 with flux directed through it from left to right. The core itself will exhibit N-polarity on the right and S-polarity on the left side. After a half revolution of the armature from the position shown, the flux will enter the iron at the place where it emerged before; consequently, the polarity of the core has been reversed. If the armature speed is 1800 revolutions per minute, then the core will have 3600 reversals of magnetism per minute. The energy needed in this process is regarded as a loss because it does not appear as useful electrical work. Thus, part of the energy required to drive the armature is wasted in heating the core by hysteresis.

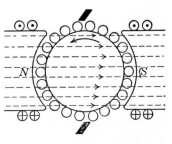

Fig. 281. Armature revolving between a pair of field poles

**209. Other Losses in a Dynamo.—** —The losses described in the last three sections are those that occur in the armature of a dynamo. They are the $I^2 \times R$ copper loss in the winding and the eddy current and hysteresis losses in the iron core. The heat generated in the armature by these losses raises the temperature of the armature winding and increases its resistance, thereby augmenting the $I^2 \times R$ loss.

In addition to these losses in a dynamo there are the $I^2 \times R$ losses in the field winding and at the brush contacts, and the mechanical losses associated with the rotation of the armature. The latter include the friction between the armature shaft and its bearings, the friction of the brushes upon the commutator, and air friction or windage. Losses in the field rheostat are included in the generator losses where there is a field rheostat in series with the field magnets of the generator.

To summarize, the losses of a dynamo may be classified into electrical and mechanical losses, as follows:

| *Electrical Losses* | *Mechanical Losses* |
|---|---|
| Armature copper | Bearing friction |
| Field copper | Brush friction |
| Brush contact | Windage |
| Eddy current | |
| Hysteresis | |

The core losses (eddy current and hysteresis) and the mechanical losses are the same at all loads. Usually 10 per cent or less of the energy supplied to a dynamo is accounted for by the losses enumerated; the rest is available for useful purposes.

**210. Armature Insulation.**—The armature winding of a dynamo is wedged into the slots of the armature core but must be thoroughly insulated from it. Windings may be insulated with micanite, pressboard, paper, cotton, varnished cloth, and others, the amount and quality depending upon the potential to be developed by the armature.

The quality of an insulating material is tested by subjecting it to high potentials and ascertaining the p.d. at which it "breaks down," or conducts electricity. The specimen to be tested is interposed between two plates connected to a source of high potential, and the p.d. is increased until a spark passes from plate to plate through the specimen, thereby puncturing it. The following table lists some insulating materials and the p.d.'s at which an average specimen failed under test:

INSULATION TEST

| Material | Thickness in Inches | "Break Down" Potential |
|---|---|---|
| Dry cotton tape | 0.013 | 250 |
| Soft gray wrapping paper | 0.010 | 1,000 |
| Asbestos paper | 0.015 | 1,500 |
| Varnished cloth | 0.010 | 7,500 |
| Red sheet fiber | 0.037 | 7,000 |
| Press board or fuller board | 0.022 | 5,000 |
| Micanite | 0.018 | 14,000 |

The insulation of electrical machinery is usually tested by applying a greater p.d. than the apparatus is required to stand in normal operation; for example, a 1000-volt armature may be subjected to 3000 volts applied between the core and the winding. If there is any defect in the insulation upon application of the high potential, the indicating instruments in the testing circuit will reveal it. The standard test for many classes of apparatus is twice the normal potential of the circuit to which the apparatus is connected, plus 1000 volts.

**211. The Commutator and Brushes.**—A commutator consists of a number of segments of hard-drawn copper, assembled around an iron hub and thoroughly insulated from the hub and from each other. Mica is used for the insulation, its thickness usually varying from 0.02 to 0.15 inch, depending upon the e.m.f. of the machine. In the construction of a commutator, the segments and mica strips are assembled and clamped together by an external temporary steel ring. Grooves are then turned into the inner surface to receive a commutator sleeve and clamping ring, and these parts are securely clamped together by cap screws. The external steel ring is then removed and the outside surface of the commutator is machined into a true cylinder.

Fig. 282 gives a sectional view of a direct-current generator and shows the location of the field coils, armature winding and

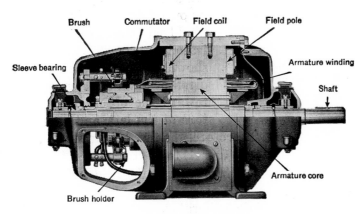

FIG. 282. Sectional view of 40-kw. direct-current generator
General Electric Company

commutator. The manner of locking the commutator bars without short-circuiting them will be understood from the figure.

The current is conducted to and from the armature by means of brushes which are pressed against the commutator by springs. Brushes are generally made of hard graphitic carbon, although in low-potential dynamos brushes of copper gauze are used to advantage because of their lower resistance. Copper brushes are also used in some turbine-driven generators. The brushes are supported by brush holders which are designed to avoid vibration of the brushes, a common cause of sparking. All the holders of a machine are securely bolted to a rocker ring or brush-holder yoke, which serves to move all the brushes upon the commutator to the positions which result in the least sparking. In older designs these yokes were of metal and the brush holders had to be individually insulated from them; in more recent designs the yokes are molded of insulating material.

**212. Armature Reaction in a Generator.**—The current in the winding of an armature produces magnetic poles in the core and

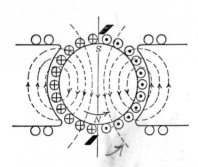

FIG. 283. Magnetic field produced by current through armature alone

these set up a magnetic field apart from that developed by the field magnets. If a current from some outside source is established through the armature of a bipolar dynamo with its own field magnets unenergized, it would set up a magnetic field as illustrated in Fig. 283. The winding is shown located on the surface of the armature and the current is directed toward the observer in the conductors at the left, and away from him in those at the right. Therefore, the flux has an upward direction through the armature core from S to N. This magnetic flux extends across the main flux directed between the field poles and is aptly termed *cross flux*.

In the operation of the generator, both the main field and the cross field exist at the same time, consequently the actual magnetic field through the armature is the resultant of the two components. A combination of the fields shown in Figs. 281 and 283 results in the one depicted in Fig. 284. In the upper half of the right pole the direction of the cross flux (Fig. 283) is the same as that of the main

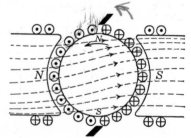

FIG. 284. Distortion of magnetic field due to cross-magnetizing effect of armature current

field (Fig. 281), causing the resultant field intensity there to be strong; in the lower half of that field pole the two fluxes are opposed, causing the resultant field to be weak. These conditions are represented in Fig. 284 by the closeness of the lines of force. The distribution of these lines through the generator field poles and armature is seen to be non-uniform, and the cause of this departure from uniform flux distribution is called *armature reaction.*

In view of the fact that the main field is distorted by the armature flux, the brushes should not be set in a line perpendicular to the field axis. This is indicated in Fig. 285, wherein the field axis is marked *neutral plane.* The position of minimum inductive action in the armature coils will be along a line somewhat in advance of the neutral plane, in the direction of armature rotation. This is shown as line *ab,* and is perpendicular to the resultant flux axis of Fig. 284. Commutation of an armature coil should, therefore, take place as the coil passes the line *ab,* which is accordingly called the *commutating plane.*

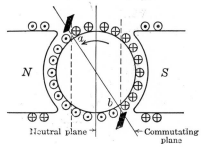

FIG. 285. Shifting brushes from neutral plane because of armature reaction

In practice, the brushes should be set at diametrically opposite points (in a bipolar dynamo) and then shifted jointly by the rocker arm to a position corresponding to the commutating plane. The angle of advance of this plane from the neutral position will depend upon the current in the armature, the brushes being shifted forward for an increase, and backward for a decrease in armature current. When the brushes are not set to correspond with the commutating plane, sparking at the brushes may result.

**213. Commutation of an Armature Coil.**—The process of commutation means the passage of one armature coil after another from the influence of one field pole to that of the other. During this passage each coil is short-circuited by the brush for a brief period, and in that period the current must be reduced to zero and again brought to full value in the opposite direction.

Consider an armature coil during its commutation at the positive brush of a generator. The coil is shown at *B* in Fig. 286 passing the commutating plane *ab.* While at position *A,* a definite amount of magnetic flux encircles the coil because of the current in it. This flux should disappear and be reestablished in the reverse direction before the coil is transferred to the other side of the brush at $C$. The changing flux develops in the coil an e.m.f. of self-induction, §157, which in this case is commonly called the *reactance voltage*. The presence of this e.m.f. in the short-circuited coil is undesirable for it produces an unusually large current in the coil during the period of commutation. Suppose the reactance voltage is 1 volt in a coil having 0.01 ohm resistance, including the toe of the brush; then the current through that coil and brush would be $I = \dfrac{E}{R} = \dfrac{1}{0.01} = 100$ amperes. The interruption of currents of this magnitude would produce considerable sparking at the brushes.

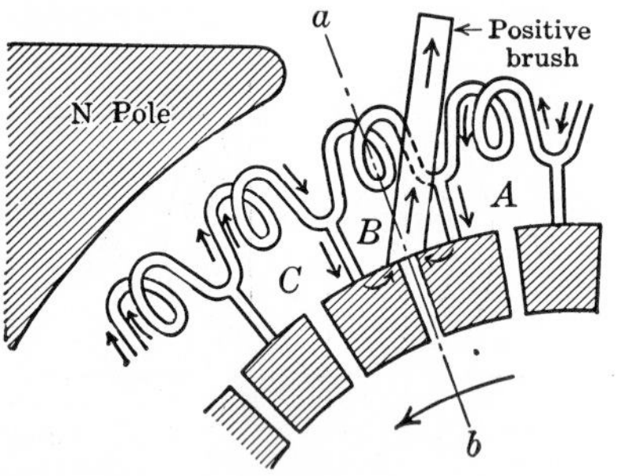

FIG. 286. Commutation of an armature coil

At instant shown coil B is short-circuited by brush.

The current through a short-circuited coil may be reduced (1) by adding resistance to the coil circuit, or (2) by introducing an e.m.f. opposing the reactance voltage into the coil at the time of commutation. The increase of resistance may be effected by the use of carbon rather than copper brushes or by the use of high-resistance leads from armature winding to commutator; the former method being more usual. An opposing e.m.f. may be obtained by so placing the brushes that the coil will cut a small amount of flux from that field magnet pole toward which the coil is moving. That is, the plane of commutation may be shifted so that the coil, while short-circuited at a brush, will pass through a magnetic field of opposite direction and of such strength that an e.m.f. will be induced in the coil sufficient to reverse the direction of the initial current in spite of the reactance voltage. If the current strength in the coil after reversal is identical with its original intensity, then the coil may be transferred to the other side of the brush without disturbance, and sparkless commutation will be achieved.

The tendency of a dynamo to spark can be greatly reduced if, in construction, the armature winding is divided into many coils.

Each coil will then have relatively few turns and its inductance will be small, for the inductance of a coil is proportional to the square of the number of its turns (Formula 70); in consequence, the reactance voltage will be small. This e.m.f. in modern dynamos seldom exceeds 3 volts per segment, and splendid commutation is obtained. Many dynamos, however, do spark at the brushes, but the fault lies in the manner of adjustment, rather than in the design of the machine. Some specific causes of sparking are considered in §215.

The greater the current output of a generator the greater must be the e.m.f. induced in the short-circuited coil to effect the reversal of its current. This means that with increasing load the coil undergoing commutation must be brought into a more intense field. This is accomplished in older machines by shifting the brushes through a movement of the rocker arm. Fig. 287 shows in exaggerated fashion the relative positions of the brushes of a bipolar generator operating at full load, half load, and no load. The brushes are rocked forward from position 3 to position 1 as the load on the machine is increased, and rocked backward as the load is diminished.

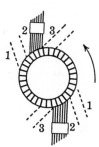

Fig. 287. Shifting position of brushes

1—Full load; 2—Half load; 3—No load.

### 214. Improvements in Commutation.—The current in the armature of a dynamo is responsible for the cross flux which produces distortion of the magnetic field and necessitates a shift of the brush axis to attain sparkless commutation. If the magnetomotive force which sets up this cross flux were always neutralized by an equal amount oppositely directed, there would be no transverse flux, and shifting of the brushes would be unnecessary when the load on the machine changes. Such neutralization means that the armature coils undergoing commutation would have e.m.f.'s induced in them which would balance the reactance voltage, §213, at all loads and reverse the direction of current in these coils. Then the brushes might be permanently and centrally located for all loads and for either direction of rotation, with satisfactory commutation.

The neutralizing magnetomotive force mentioned may be provided by a so-called *compensating winding* embedded in the field poles and traversed by the armature current. This construction is illustrated in Fig. 288, which shows the field frame of a generator having eight main poles and a compensating winding.

Fig. 288. Field frame of generator showing compensating winding in pole faces
Large outer coils constitute the main field winding, small outer coils comprise the interpole winding.
Elliott Company

The field poles and ring are entirely of laminated steel, and the compensating winding occupies slots in the pole faces.

The use of auxiliary poles between the main field poles of dynamos is another method for reducing armature reaction by producing a magnetomotive force approximately balancing that of the armature. These poles are called *interpoles* or *commutating poles,* and provide in the region between the main poles a field of such strength and direction to set up the proper e.m.f. in the coils undergoing commutation for the reversal of current. The coils on the interpoles are traversed by the entire armature current, or by a definite part of it. The generator field structure shown in Fig. 288 has commutating poles as well as a compensating winding.

Fig. 289.  Field frame of interpole machine
Shows relative positions of main (large) and commutating poles.

Electro Dynamic Company

Interpoles are especially used on shunt motors for variable speed service and in series motors for railways; the field of an interpole motor is illustrated in Fig. 289. Successful commutation of high peak loads is obtained at any speed

Fig. 290.  Frame of compensated interpole motor
Showing construction of main and interpoles, compensating coils embedded in main poles, and the other coils in place.

General Electric Company

within a range of 100 per cent to 400 per cent of its minimum speed in either direction.

Fig. 290 shows the field windings of a 16-pole mill-type direct-current motor.

**215. Causes of Sparking.**—In properly designed and constructed dynamos, sparking may occur for a number of reasons. The chief causes are as follows:

Brushes are not set at the commutating plane. They should be rocked until the position of minimum sparking is found. Brushes should be equally spaced on the commutator so that the same number of commutator bars will be subtended between them.

Brushes are set with insufficient pressure against the commutator.

Brushes are not set to utilize the full area of contact with the commutator.

Brushes vibrate or chatter in the brush holder.

High, low, or loose commutator bars, causing poor contact with the brush.

Loose connection between armature coil and commutator bar, as evidenced by a peculiar snappy spark when this particular bar passes under a brush.

Commutator is worn in ridges, causing an uneven surface for brush contact.

Collection of dirt and grease on the commutator. Carbon or copper particles may short-circuit some commutator segments, and oil may prevent good brush contact.

Armature winding is partially short-circuited by a breakdown in the insulation or is open-circuited. A defective coil should be disconnected, its ends taped, and a wire of adequate size used as a bridge to connect the commutator bars that were joined to the detached coil. This will maintain the continuity of the armature circuit, and the machine may be run temporarily until the coil can be rewound.

Dynamo is excessively loaded. This condition can be recognized by reading the ammeter in the circuit or by noting the increased operating temperature of the machine.

In some cases the methods of correction are indicated, in others the remedial measures will suggest themselves.

## QUESTIONS

1. Distinguish between the functions of a generator and of a motor.
2. How does a generator differ from a primary battery as a source of electricity?
3. How does an alternator differ from a direct-current generator?
4. Make a sketch of the e.m.f. generated in a loop that is revolved in a magnetic field (a) when equipped with slip rings, and (b) when provided with a commutator.
5. What is a commutator, what is it used for, and how is it connected?
6. Since a two-part commutator is so simple in construction, why are armature windings subdivided into many coils, thus necessitating many bars on the commutator?
7. Make a sketch of a 12-coil bipolar ring armature for a direct-current generator with two turns per coil. Indicate the direction of current in the armature coils and in the external circuit.
8. What is the difference between a drum armature and a ring armature? Which is more commonly used?
9. What is meant by laminating an armature core? Why is this done?
10. Explain what is meant by hysteresis loss.
11. State three ways in which energy is wasted in a dynamo armature.
12. A piece of mica subjected to an insulation test is said to have broken down at 4500 volts. What is meant by this?
13. What is meant by cross flux and by armature reaction?
14. Distinguish between the neutral plane and the commutating plane of a dynamo?
15. Why should a coil be commutated as it passes from the influence of one field pole to that of the next one?
16. What is meant by reactance voltage and how is it neutralized?
17. In some generators it is necessary to change the position of the brushes for changes in the current output of the machine. Why is this?
18. What is the function of interpoles or compensating windings in the structure of the field magnets?
19. State some causes for sparking at the brushes of a dynamo.
20. An armature contains a defective coil. How would you remedy the trouble temporarily so that the machine could be operated?

## PROBLEMS

1. If the conductors employed in the winding of the armature of Fig. 272 have a safe current-carrying capacity of 100 amperes, what maximum current may be drawn from the armature with safety? *Ans.* 200 amperes.
2. The resistance of all the wire on a bipolar armature is 0.3 ohm. What is the armature resistance as measured between brushes? *Ans.* 0.075 ohm.

3. The armature in Problem 2 generates an e.m.f. of 60 volts. What will be the current through some lamps connected across it if the lamps have an equivalent resistance of 4 ohms? Assume the total resistance of the lead wires to be 0.2 ohm. *Ans.* 14.0 amperes.

4. What will be the p.d. indicated by a voltmeter, in Problem 3, when placed (a) across the lamps? (b) across the brushes? *Ans.* (a) 56.0 volts; (b) 58.95 volts.

5. The resistance of the armature of a generator measured between brushes is 0.1 ohm, and that of the field winding measured between terminals is 10 ohms. The currents through the armature and field windings are respectively 50 amperes and 5 amperes. Compute the copper losses in these windings. *Ans.* 250 watts each.

# Lesson XIX

## DIRECT-CURRENT GENERATORS

Classification of dynamos by field excitation—Self-exciting process in direct-current generators—The shunt generator—The series generator—Compound-wound generators—Compound-wound machines in parallel—The three-wire system—Three-wire generators—Capacity and rating—Efficiency of a generator—Questions and Problems.

**216. Classification of Dynamos by Field Excitation.**—The current for magnetizing the field magnets of direct-current generators may be supplied in a number of ways, and these lead to a classification of dynamos according to the method of excitation. These methods are, of course, independent of the construction of the magnetic flux path, and depend only upon the windings and their connections.

A direct-current generator may be excited by itself or by a separate machine; accordingly the machine is styled a *self-excited* generator or a *separately-excited* generator. The connection diagrams of these machines are illustrated in Fig. 291. In the diagrams numbered from I to VI, $A$ represents the generator armature, $E$ an auxiliary armature, $Se$ the series field winding, $Sh$ the shunt field winding, $R$ the field rheostat, and $X$ the external circuit. The individual descriptions follow:

I. *Series Machines*—The field magnets are connected in *series* with the armature; they are wound with a few turns of heavy wire having a low resistance and are traversed by the main current. Series generators are generally used as series boosters and also in a European system of high-potential direct-current power transmission.

II. *Shunt Machines*—The field magnets are connected in parallel or *shunt* with the armature; they are wound with many turns of relatively small wire, have a high resistance compared with the armature, and are traversed by only a small portion of the main current.

III and IV. *Separately-Excited Machines*—Current for the field magnets is supplied from an auxiliary generator. At III this generator forms a part of the main machine by having a

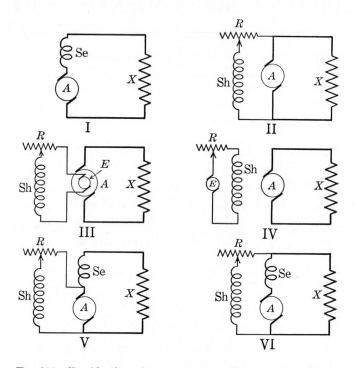

Fɪɢ. 291. Classification of generators according to field excitation

separate armature on the same shaft, while at IV the field is supplied by a distinct machine called an *exciter*.

V and VI. *Compound-Wound Machines*—Each field core of the machine has two independent coils. One is wound with a few turns of heavy wire, forming the *series coil*, and connected in series with the main circuit; the other, with many turns of smaller wire, forming the *shunt coil*, and connected in parallel with the armature. Generator V is called a *short-shunt machine* and generator VI is called a *long-shunt machine;* this distinction is made because the shunt field in the former bridges only the armature while in the latter it bridges the armature as well as the series field.

The series generator (I) is generally operated as a constant-current machine, while the other generators (II to VI) are operated as constant-potential machines. Most generators are of the constant-potential type.

The field circuit of all dynamos except those of small size should not be broken suddenly, because the e.m.f. of self-induction may rise to such value as to injure the insulation. A resistor and a special field switch are generally used so that the magnetic energy of the field may be converted into heat in the resistance.

**217. Self-Exciting Process in Direct-Current Generators.**—If the soft iron or steel field cores of a generator have once been magnetized they retain permanently a small amount of their magnetism. An armature revolving in even so weak a field as that due to residual magnetism will cut some lines of force, and as a result a small e.m.f. is maintained at the brushes without any excitation. This e.m.f., often spoken of as the *residual volts,* can be read upon a voltmeter connected to the brushes, when the field circuit is open and the armature revolves at its proper speed. It may amount to several volts or more, depending upon the quality of the iron and the number of armature conductors. When the field circuit is closed, the residual volts will establish a current through the field magnets; this current will augment the number of lines of force and cause a larger e.m.f. to be induced in the armature and this in turn increases the field excitation and produces a still higher p.d. at the brushes. Such action continues until the normal e.m.f. of the machine is attained.

The process of building up the field of a shunt generator may be observed when the machine is started by having a *pilot lamp,* or a voltmeter connected to the brushes. Ten to twenty seconds may be required from the time the field switch is closed until the armature generates its rated e.m.f. If a machine does not build up, owing to the loss of its residual magnetism, it is necessary to re-magnetize the field cores.

A shunt generator with its field properly connected and with sufficient residual flux may not build up its e.m.f. if the field-circuit resistance is too high or if the armature speed is too low. Consequently, such a machine should be started with the resistance of the field rheostat entirely cut out, and if the machine still does not build up, the speed of the armature should be raised to its rated value.

**Problem 133.**—The resistance of the armature of a shunt dynamo is 0.80 ohm and that of the field magnets is 100 ohms. With the field circuit open the armature generates 6 volts, due to the residual magnetism. What will be the current in the field winding to start the building-up process when the field circuit is closed?

Since the armature and field magnets form a series circuit, the current is

$$(23) \qquad I = \frac{E}{R+r} = \frac{6}{100 + 0.80} = 0.0595 \text{ ampere}$$

**218. The Shunt Generator.**—In a shunt dynamo the field coils have many turns and their resistance is high compared with that

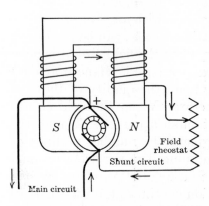

FIG. 292. Shunt generator with field rheostat to regulate e.m.f.

of the armature. Only a relatively small field current is needed to provide the magnetization necessary to produce the magnetic flux. The e.m.f. generated in the armature can be adjusted to the desired value by changing the current through the field coils; this is done by adjusting the resistance of the field rheostat in series with the coils. The connections are shown in Fig. 292. Decreasing the resistance of the field rheostat increases the current in the field coils, thereby increasing the flux cut by the armature inductors, and raising the e.m.f. generated in the armature winding. Adding resistance in the field rheostat lowers the e.m.f. of the machine.

The current and potential relations in the shunt generator are determined by Ohm's Law. The current through the shunt field is equal to the potential difference at the brushes divided by the combined resistance of field winding and field rheostat. The current through the armature of a shunt generator is the sum of the currents in the field circuit and external circuit. The potential drop in the armature is equal to its resistance multiplied by the current through it.

**Problem 134.**—A shunt generator maintains 110 volts across a number of lamps joined in parallel which require a total current of 50 amperes. The lamps are located some distance from the generator and the resistance of the leads to them is 0.02 ohm. The resistance of the armature is 0.03 ohm and of the field coils is 37 ohms. Find: (a) the p.d. at the brushes; (b) the total e.m.f. generated.

The potential drop in the leads is

(20) $$E = I \times R = 50 \times 0.02 = 1 \text{ volt}$$

In consequence the p.d. at the brushes is $110 + 1 = 111$ volts. (a)

The current through the field winding is

(18) $$I = \frac{E}{R} = \frac{111}{37} = 3 \text{ amperes}$$

The current through the armature is $50 + 3 = 53$ amperes. Hence the drop in the armature is

(20) $$E = I \times R = 53 \times 0.03 = 1.59 \text{ volts}$$

The e.m.f. generated is $111 + 1.59 = 112.59$ volts. (b)

The resistance of the armature is somewhat higher when the machine is carrying a load than when running idle because of the rise of temperature in operation. Armature resistance is usually measured by the ammeter-voltmeter method (§133) directly after a load test on the machine.

In starting a shunt generator, the machine is brought up to rated speed and the p.d. at the brushes is adjusted to the required value by manipulating the field rheostat; then the main switch connecting the generator with the external circuit is closed. After closing the switch so that the armature can supply current to the load, the p.d. at the brushes will be found somewhat lower even if the speed is the same as before. Two causes for this drop in potential are: first, an increased drop in the armature due to the additional current through it, and second, since the potential difference at the brushes has been lowered, because of the increased armature drop, there will be less current in the field winding, which means a reduction in the magnetic flux that is cut by the armature.

The p.d. available at the brushes of a shunt generator changes a little with each change in load, *increasing as the load decreases and decreasing as the load increases.* The manufacturer usually supplies a statement of the p.d. at the terminals of a generator at no load and when carrying full load. These values of p.d. permit the operator to determine an important factor of the machine which is known as *voltage regulation.* The regulation of a generator is the ratio of the change in potential between no load and full load to the potential difference available at full load, for a fixed and stated armature speed. The regulation changes somewhat with speed.

To FIND THE REGULATION OF A GENERATOR:

*Obtain the difference between the no-load and full-load p.d.'s of the machine and divide by the full-load p.d.*

$$\text{percentage regulation} = 100 \times \frac{\text{no-load p.d.} - \text{full-load p.d.}}{\text{full-load p.d.}} \qquad \textbf{113}$$

The regulation of modern generators amounts to a few per cent. The fact that the p.d. of such machines does change a little with load variations does not jeopardize the classification of shunt machines as constant-potential generators.

**Problem 135.**—The p.d. of a shunt generator, operating at 1000 revolutions per minute, is 112 volts at no load and 108 volts at full load. Find its regulation at this speed.

$$(113)\ \text{Percentage regulation} = 100 \times \frac{112 - 108}{108} = \frac{400}{108} = 3.7 \text{ per cent}$$

If the current fluctuations are wide and quite frequent, it would be necessary to have an attendant on hand to manipulate the field rheostat or else employ some automatic device in order to keep the p.d. constant. Therefore, shunt generators are adapted only to service where the load is fairly constant, in which service they will require very little attention after the field rheostat has been once adjusted.

Shunt generators of the same p.d. may be joined in parallel by connecting all the positive brushes and connecting all the negative brushes, as shown in Fig. 293 for two machines. To connect a generator with other generators already in service, its p.d.

should first be adjusted equal to or a little higher than that of the others, after which adjustment the machine can be connected to the common circuit. If an attempt is made to parallel two generators with crossed polarities, i.e., connect the positive terminal of either machine with the negative terminal of the other, the machines will short-circuit each other and serious damage will result unless the fuse or circuit breaker in the system functions quickly.

The p.d.'s of the machines operated in parallel should be carefully controlled so that the total load will be properly apportioned

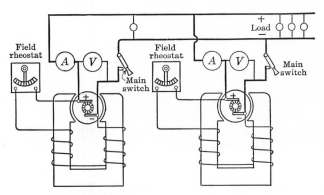

FIG. 293. Two shunt generators connected in parallel

The p.d. is the same for both machines and the current supplied to the load is the sum of the generator currents.

among them. To take load off a machine that is running in parallel with others, add resistance gradually in its field circuit until the ammeter in the armature circuit reads practically zero, then disconnect the machine by opening the switch. Shunt generators can also be operated in series; if the machines are of different ratings, the current in the external circuit is limited to the capacity of the smaller machine.

The polarity of the brushes of a shunt generator may be changed by reversing the field connections to the brushes and reversing the direction in which the armature rotates; the brush holders may have to be inclined in the opposite direction to conform with the new direction of rotation.

**Experiment 97.**—Operate a small shunt-wound generator at its rated speed and connect a voltmeter across the brushes. Adjust the field rheostat so that the voltmeter will read the normal p.d. across the brushes at no load. Connect a number of lamps in parallel to the generator and place an ammeter in the circuit to read the load current. Switch on more and more lamps and note the instrument readings, *leaving the field rheostat at the same setting.* Maintain constant armature speed throughout the test. Plot a curve of p.d. as ordinates against load current as abscissas.

A test on a certain 1-kilowatt shunt generator, operated at 1980 revolutions per minute, gave the following results:

| Load current ....... | 0 | 3 | 6 | 9 | 12 amperes |
|---|---|---|---|---|---|
| Brush potential ..... | 110 | 108 | 106 | 103 | 97 volts |

**Experiment 98.**—Excite the field magnets of a shunt generator from a separate source and prepare to operate the machine at different speeds.

FIG. 294. Dissectible motor-generator having armature equipped with commutator and slip rings
Evans equipment made by Central Scientific Company

Adjust the field rheostat so that the p.d. across the brushes will be below normal at the slowest speed. Connect a voltmeter across the brushes and operate the machine at different speeds without load. Take readings of the voltmeter and observe a proportional increase of induced e.m.f. with increased speed of rotation.

A test on the generator mentioned in Experiment 97 gave the following readings:

| Speed ......... | 1800 | 2020 | 2290 | 2470 rev. per min. |
|---|---|---|---|---|
| Brush potential .. | 100 | 112 | 127 | 137 volts |

A dynamo for demonstrating the generation of direct and alternating currents is shown in Fig. 294. The armature has a commutator at one end for direct-current operation as a generator or motor, and it has six collector rings at the other end for single-phase, two-phase, or three-phase operation. The field coils may be connected so that the machine may be operated as a shunt, series, or compound generator.

**219. The Series Generator.**—In a series generator the field coils are in series with the armature and carry the entire current supplied by the machine; consequently, they are designed to have relatively few turns and a low resistance. With the armature revolving at a constant speed, the current and e.m.f. of a series generator will vary with every change in the resistance of the external circuit, for each change of current alters the field magnetization and thereby the e.m.f. induced in the armature. The connections of the machine are shown in Fig. 295.

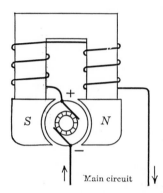

FIG. 295. Series generator

Present day series generators are usually employed as *series boosters* to maintain constant p.d. at certain points on a transmission system over which there is an appreciable and variable potential drop. For example, series boosters in a traction system form

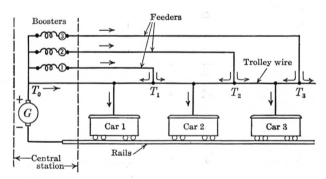

FIG. 296. Series boosters in an electric railway system

part of the central station equipment in order to maintain constant potential along the trolley wire through the use of individual feeders.

In Fig. 296 is shown a 600-volt generator $G$ with three series boosters 1, 2, and 3 supplying current through the distributing system to the traction motors. The fields of the boosters are so adjusted that the e.m.f.'s generated in their armatures are just equal to the potential drops in the associated feeders and in the boosters themselves. In this way the effective potential drop over each feeder, from the central station to the tap on the trolley wire, is zero. Thus, points $T_0$, $T_1$, $T_2$, and $T_3$ are at the same potential, and the p.d. between these points on the trolley wire and the rails is maintained at 600 volts, assuming that the drop in the rail return system is negligible. The feeders are heavy copper cables strung on poles or carried in conduits underground. These cables are permanent while the trolley wire must be renewed periodically because of wear.

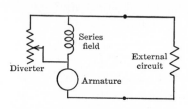

FIG. 297.  Series generator with diverter

The e.m.f. developed by a series generator is usually controlled by means of a *diverter;* this is an adjustable resistor connected across the field winding as shown in Fig. 297. The diverter by-passes some of the current which normally would traverse the field, consequently, the e.m.f. generated by the armature is reduced.

**Problem 136.**—A series generator, having a field winding and an armature respectively of 0.01 and 0.02 ohm resistance, is connected in a feeder circuit in which the current is 100 amperes. The resistance of the feeder is 0.035 ohm. What should be the value of the e.m.f. generated in the armature in order that the p.d. across the entire feeder circuit may be zero?

The required e.m.f. must equal the total potential drop in the circuit. Since the total resistance is

(27)          $R = 0.010 + 0.020 + 0.035 = 0.065$ ohm

and the current in the feeder is 100 amperes, the generator e.m.f. should be

(20)          $E = I \times R = 100 \times 0.065 = 6.5$ volts

**Problem 137.**—If the series generator of Problem 136 develops an e.m.f. of 10 volts when there is a current of 100 amperes through its field winding, what must be the resistance of a diverter so that the armature will develop the desired e.m.f. as stated in that problem? Assume that the iron of the magnetic circuit of the machine is not saturated so that the e.m.f. generated in the armature may be regarded as proportional to the field current.

The field current on the basis of this assumption would be $\dfrac{6.5}{10} \times 100 =$
65 amperes; therefore, the current in the diverter must be

$$I = 100 - 65 = 35 \text{ amperes}$$

Since the diverter and the field winding are in parallel, the p.d. across them must be the same. The resistance of the series field is 0.01 ohm and that of the diverter will be taken as $R$, then

(20) $$E = 65 \times 0.01 = 35 \times R$$

whence the resistance of the diverter is

$$R = \frac{65 \times 0.01}{35} = 0.0186 \text{ ohm}$$

If the machine in this problem is operated well above the knee of its magnetization curve the resistance of its diverter would be smaller. Diverters are made adjustable so that they may be changed readily to meet different operating conditions.

**220. Compound-Wound Generators.**—The compound-wound generator has both shunt and series field windings and possesses the characteristics of both types of direct-current dynamos. It is designed to give automatically a better voltage regulation on constant-potential circuits than is possible with a shunt machine. The connections are shown in Fig. 298, and it will be observed that the directions of current in the two windings around the field cores are the same. With no current in the external circuit, the magnetic field is pro-

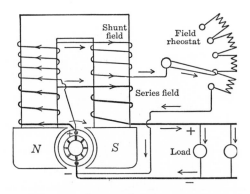

Fig. 298. Compound-wound generator

The series and shunt fields assist each other.

duced by current only in the shunt winding. When there is current in the external circuit, the series winding tends to strengthen the magnetic field; thus it counteracts the tendency of the shunt generator to develop a lower p.d. at the brushes when it delivers current to the load. By a proper selection of the number of turns on the series winding, the potential at full load may be made identical with that at no load. Such a machine is said to be *flat compounded*.

If a greater number of turns are used in the series coil of the generator than are required for flat compounding, the potential at full load will be increased; in this way it could make up for the loss on transmission lines, so that a constant p.d. might be maintained at some point distant from the generator. The machine is then said to be *over-compounded*. Over-compounded generators for lighting service may be arranged to yield a full-load potential from 3 to 5 per cent higher than the no-load potential. Generally their series field coils are wound with a somewhat larger number of turns than are actually required, and the amount of compounding is determined later by a load test. The adjustment is made by placing a diverter across the series field winding so that the main current will divide between the two paths, and then regulating the resistance of the diverter to produce the desired compounding. When a compound generator is adjusted to yield a full-load potential lower than that at no-load, the machine is said to be *under-compounded*.

**Experiment 99.**—Make a test on a compound generator by operating it at constant speed and changing the output from no-load to 25 per cent overload. Keep the shunt field rheostat unchanged throughout the test and take readings of load current and p.d. at the brushes.

The following readings were taken on a particular 1-kilowatt compound generator:

| Load current ...... | 0 | 3 | 6 | 9 | 12 amperes |
|---|---|---|---|---|---|
| Brush potential ....| 110 | 111 | 112 | 111 | 109 volts |

In a short-shunt compound-wound generator the shunt field is subjected to a somewhat higher potential than with the long-shunt connection. Reference to Fig. 291 V and VI shows that the p.d. applied to the shunt field in the latter case for any particular load is equal to the p.d. at the brushes minus the drop on the series field. The operating characteristics of short-shunt and long-shunt compound machines are very nearly alike.

A short-circuit on a compound-wound generator overloads the machine, since the excessive current through the series field tends to keep the p.d. at its normal value. To prevent damage to the machine the line should be opened automatically under such conditions, either by fuse or circuit breaker. Compound-wound direct-current generators are extensively used in electric lighting and power stations and in electric railway stations where the load is fluctuating.

**Problem 138.**—A compound-wound generator supplies 100 amperes at 112 volts to a group of lamps located at a distance from the generator. The resistances of the circuit and machine are: leads 0.02 ohm, armature 0.01 ohm, series winding 0.02 ohm, shunt winding 40 ohms. Find: (a) p.d. at the brushes; (b) total e.m.f. generated; (c) power loss in the leads; (d) loss in the series winding; (e) loss in the shunt winding; (f) loss in the armature; (g) power supplied to the external circuit.

The drop in the leads as well as in the series winding is

$$(20) \qquad E = I \times R = 100 \times 0.02 = 2 \text{ volts}$$

The p.d. at the generator terminals is $112 + 2 = 114$ volts, and that at the brushes is $114 + 2 = 116$ volts. (a)

The current through the shunt field is

$$(18) \qquad I = \frac{E}{R} = \frac{116}{40} = 2.9 \text{ amperes}$$

The total current through the armature is $100 + 2.9 = 102.9$ amperes. The drop in the armature is

$$(20) \qquad E = I \times R = 102.9 \times 0.01 = 1.029 \text{ volts}$$

Consequently, the e.m.f. generated in the armature is

$$112 + 2 + 2 + 1.029 = 117.03 \text{ volts} \qquad (b)$$

The losses are obtained from Formula (52) as follows:

$$P = I^2 \times R = 100 \times 100 \times 0.02 = 200 \text{ watts in the leads} \qquad (c)$$
$$P = 100 \times 100 \times 0.02 = 200 \text{ watts in the series winding} \qquad (d)$$
$$P = 2.9 \times 2.9 \times 40 = 336.4 \text{ watts in the shunt winding} \qquad (e)$$
$$P = 102.9 \times 102.9 \times 0.01 = 105.9 \text{ watts in the armature} \qquad (f)$$

The power supplied to the external circuit is

$$(49) \qquad P = E \times I = 114 \times 100 = 11{,}400 \text{ watts} = 11.4 \text{ kilowatts} \qquad (g)$$

**221. Compound-Wound Machines in Parallel.**—The connection of compound generators for parallel operation involves more care than is required for the paralleling of shunt generators and makes use of a supplementary connection between the machines, called an *equalizer bar*. The purpose of the equalizer is to enable each machine to take its share of the load and to make the division of load on the machines independent of slight changes in speed. The equalizer bar connects the brushes to which the series fields are attached, as shown in Fig. 299. These brushes are, of course, of the same polarity and have the same potential when the machines operate at the same p.d.

Suppose compound generator 1 to be supplying a load and that it is desired to have generator 2 share the load. The latter machine is brought up to speed and its p.d. is regulated by shunt field rheostat $F_2$ until it is equal to that of generator 1. Although the

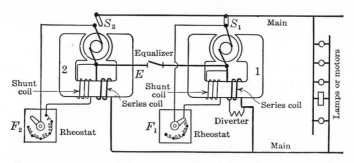

Fig. 299. Two compound-wound generators connected in parallel

loaded and idle machines now have the same p.d. across their terminals, the p.d. at the brushes of the loaded machine will be higher than that of the other, by an amount equal to the drop on the series field of generator 1. Consequently, there is a slight difference of potential between the two ends of the equalizer bar and, when its switch $E$ is closed, a current is established through the equalizer, around the series field of machine 2, and through the external circuit. The line switch $S_2$ of generator 2 is now closed and that machine will take some portion of the load; then its shunt field rheostat is regulated further so that there will be no current in the equalizer.

If the speed of either machine falls, thereby lowering its generated e.m.f., current from the other machine supplied through the equalizer will strengthen its series field, thus increasing the e.m.f. Sometimes there will be no current in an equalizer while at other times there will be some, directed one way or the other. To reduce the $I^2 \times R$ loss in the equalizer, it should be as short as possible and of the same size as the main generator cables.

A triple-pole switch is generally used for coupling a compound generator with others, the middle blade of which is connected to the equalizer. This blade is somewhat longer than the others so that, when the switch is closed, the equalizer is connected first and the main terminals a little later. In shutting down a generator so connected in parallel with others, the main line terminals are first disconnected and then the equalizer is opened. The e.m.f. is then lowered by inserting all the resistance of the shunt field rheostat, after which the field circuit may be opened, and the speed reduced to zero.

Any number of compound-wound generators may be operated in parallel, provided that their p.d.'s are the same, and that the resistances of the series fields are inversely proportional to the current capacities of the several machines. Each machine will then take load in proportion to its capacity.

**222. The Three-Wire System.**—Most central stations supplying direct current utilize the *three-wire system* to distribute electrical energy for lighting and power so that lamps can be operated at one potential and motors at the same or twice this potential. One way to form a three-wire system is to connect two 110-volt generators in series, and then connect the lamps between the middle wire that

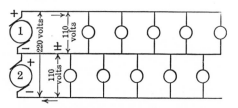

Fig. 300. Lamps supplied by three-wire system

leads to the junction of the machines and either outside wire, as shown in Fig. 300. When the lamps are divided evenly between the two sides of the system, assuming the lamps to have the same rating, there will be no current through the middle wire; the same is true for any other balanced load. Under such conditions, the middle wire could be disconnected at the generators without affecting the operation.

When the load on the two sides of a three-wire system is unbalanced, the middle wire carries a current equal to the difference between the currents in the outer wires. The middle wire may, therefore, have no current through it, or have current in either direction, the amount depending upon how closely the load on the two sides of the system is balanced; for this reason the middle wire is called the *neutral wire*. Motors wound for 220 volts are connected to the two outside wires and do not interfere with the load balance.

The chief advantage of the three-wire system is the saving in copper. Considering first only the outside wires, the p.d. across them is double that of the two-wire system, so that the current required for any given load is reduced to half. With the same percentage potential drop on the lines, the drop in volts is twice as great. Consequently, to transmit half the current at twice the drop, means that the outer lines may have four times as much resistance. Therefore, each of the two outer lines of the three-wire system need be only one-quarter as heavy as each in two-wire distribution. But since an extra wire is required to provide the lower p.d. and since this neutral line is usually the same size as the others, the three-wire system takes three-eighths (37.5 per cent) as much copper as the two-wire system for the same power and percentage drop.

**223. Three-Wire Generators.**—There are direct-current machines available for use on three-wire systems which generate within a single dynamo the two potentials required for the system; they are called *three-wire generators*. In one arrangement a 220-volt generator is equipped with slip rings as well as a commutator, and an iron-core reactor is connected across the rings in order to establish a tap for the neutral wire; the connection plan is illustrated in Fig. 301 for a bipolar machine. The reactor, of high inductance and low resistance, is bridged across the armature at points on the winding that are diametrically opposite each other; consequently, the center tap of the reactor will have a potential midway between the potentials of the brushes on the commutator. The e.m.f. across the reactor is alternating but the alternating current through this winding is small, because of its high reactance. If the load is balanced on the two sides of the system, there will be no direct current in the neutral wire nor in the reactor; but if the loads are unbalanced, there will be direct current in one direction or the other through the neutral wire and through half of the reactor. The p.d. across the reactor, due to direct current, is small because of the low resistance of the reactor.

In another type of three-wire generator, the reactor is mounted on the armature shaft and revolves with it or its winding is embedded in the same slots with the armature winding; in either arrangement only one slip ring is needed. In still another type a second armature winding, developing half the e.m.f. of the main winding, is utilized to provide the connection with the neutral wire through a slip ring.

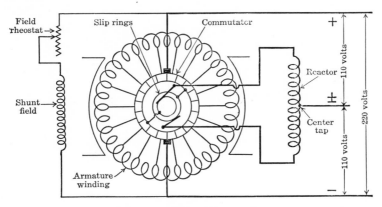

FIG. 301. Three-wire generator

Compounded three-wire generators have their series field coils divided into two equal sections, one being connected in series with one outer wire and the other section in series with the other outer wire.

**224. Capacity and Rating.**—The capacity or rating of a generator depends very largely upon its heating when in service, and also upon commutating conditions. Eddy-current and hysteresis loss in the core, together with copper loss in the armature and field windings, produce heat in the generator, and its temperature continues to rise until the heat is dissipated as fast as it is produced. Since the copper loss increases very rapidly with load (the loss increases four-fold when the current is doubled), a limit is reached beyond which the machine could not be run without speedy deterioration of its insulating materials. This limit is imposed by the type of insulation employed. The American Institute of Electrical Engineers in its Standardization Rules gives the limits for *hottest-spot temperatures* of insulations as follows:

O.— Cotton, silk, paper and similar materials, when neither impregnated nor immersed in oil—90° C. or 194° F.

A.— Cotton, silk, paper and similar materials, when so treated or impregnated as to increase the thermal limit, also enameled wire—105° C. or 221° F.

B.— Mica, asbestos and other materials capable of resisting high temperatures, in which any Class A material or binder is used for structural purposes only—125° C. or 257° F.

If these maximum temperatures be exceeded, not only may the insulation be endangered, but the excess load may lead to injury by exceeding other limits, such as commutation, stalling load, and mechanical strength.

In determining the temperature of different parts of a machine a thermometer is applied to the hottest accessible part of the completed machine, and the hottest-spot temperature for the winding is estimated by adding a correction of 15° C. (27° F.) to the highest temperature observed, in view of the practical impossibility of locating the thermometer at the hottest spot. When the thermometer is applied directly to the surfaces of bare windings, such as an edgewise-wound strip conductor or a cast copper winding, a correction of 5° C. instead of 15° C. is made. For commutators, collector rings, or bare metallic surfaces not forming part of a winding, no correction is applied. Thermometers used for taking temperatures of machines should be covered by felt pads cemented or puttied on. Measurements of temperature of windings may also be made by means of their increase in resistance or by the use of embedded thermocouples.

In testing a generator for operation in locations where the ambient air temperature will not exceed 40° C. (104° F.), the permissible rise of temperature as observed by thermometer would be $221 - 27 - 104 = 90°$ F. for Class A insulating materials, and $221 - 104 = 117°$ F. for the commutator. To determine the continuous rating of a machine it is operated under load conditions until a constant temperature difference between the machine and the surrounding air is reached. Under full load this may require from 6 to 20 hours, according to the size and construction of the machine.

Direct-current generators are rated in size, according to the number of kilowatts which they are capable of maintaining in the circuit external to their terminals within the limit of permissible heating. For example, a generator rating of 50 kilowatts and 110 volts means that the machine will deliver without excessive heating 50 kilowatts to the circuit external to its terminals, and that a p.d. of 110 volts will be maintained at this output across the terminals. The current, therefore, at full load will be $50 \times 1000 \div 110 = 455$ amperes.

The potential differences at the brushes and at the terminals of a shunt generator are practically the same, but in a series or compound generator the potential at the brushes is higher than that at the terminals on account of the drop in the series field winding.

**225. Efficiency of a Generator.**—The term *efficiency* as applied to any machine is the ratio of the power *delivered by* it to the power *supplied to* it. Thus, the efficiency of a generator is the ratio of the electrical power output to the mechanical power input, or

$$\text{efficiency} = \frac{\text{output}}{\text{input}} \qquad \textbf{114}$$

When the efficiency of a machine is stated without specific reference to load conditions, full or rated load is always understood.

To obtain the efficiency of a generator:

*Divide the output of the generator by the input, both expressed in the same units.*

Let
$P$ = output of generator in watts,
$p$ = total losses of generator in watts,
$e$ = efficiency of the generator expressed as a decimal.

Then the input to the machine is $P + p$, and the efficiency becomes

$$e = \frac{P}{P + p} \qquad \textbf{115}$$

The efficiency to be expected of a generator depends upon the size of the machine and the relative load it is supplying. For example, a 5-kilowatt dynamo may have an efficiency as low as 80 per cent; a well-designed 40-kilowatt machine, 90 per cent; and a 500-kilowatt generator, 94 per cent. Again, a certain 200-kilowatt generator has an efficiency at full load of 93 per cent, at ¾ load of 92 per cent, at ½ load of 90 per cent, and at ¼ load of 84 per cent.

**Problem 139.**—Determine the efficiency of a 25-kilowatt generator if 37.5 horsepower are required to drive the machine at full load.

The power delivered at full load is $25 \times 1000 = 25,000$ watts, and the power supplied is $37.5 \times 746 = 27,975$ watts (§96); it follows that the efficiency of the machine is

$$(114) \qquad \text{efficiency} = \frac{\text{output}}{\text{input}} = \frac{25,000}{27,975} = 0.894 = 89.4 \text{ per cent}$$

**Problem 140.**—A 15-kilowatt generator has the following losses at full load:

Armature copper loss ..... 820 watts    Core losses ......... 450 watts
Field copper losses ....... 500 watts    Friction losses ..... 210 watts

Compute the full-load efficiency of this machine.

The sum of the losses is $p = 820 + 500 + 450 + 210 = 1980$ watts, while the output of the generator is $P = 15,000$ watts. Therefore, the efficiency of the machine is

$$(115) \qquad e = \frac{P}{P + p} = \frac{15,000}{15,000 + 1980} = 0.883 = 88.3 \text{ per cent}$$

## QUESTIONS

1. Distinguish between a shunt-wound generator, a series-wound generator, and a compound-wound generator.
2. What is an exciter, and for what is it used?
3. Make diagrammatic sketches of the connections for four methods of field excitation.
4. Since the field magnets of a self-exciting generator are not supplied with current from any external source, how is it possible for the machine to generate an e.m.f.?

5. What is meant by the term "residual volts"?

6. A large number of lamps on a circuit connected to a shunt generator are suddenly switched off. Name two actions that occur at the generator as a result of the load reduction, and state how you would counteract them?

7. The circuit of a shunt generator is closed and then the machine is started up, but it refuses to "build up." Why?

8. Give two reasons for the fall of potential at the brushes of a shunt generator when the current taken from the machine is increased.

9. What will be the effect of joining two shunt generators in series if one machine is rated at 50 and the other at 100 kilowatts? Assume both machines to have the same e.m.f.

10. What is the difference in the method of regulating the field magnetizing force in a series and in a shunt machine?

11. Explain why a series generator is a variable potential machine.

12. What is a diverter? what is its purpose? and in what type of machine is it employed?

13. Describe the use of a series generator as a booster in a railway distribution system.

14. What is the advantage of a compound-wound generator over a shunt machine?

15. A generator is compounded for 10 per cent of its rated e.m.f. What is meant by this statement, and how is the objective accomplished?

16. What is meant by an over-compounded generator?

17. What is an equalizer bar, and for what purpose is it used?

18. How would you proceed to parallel a compound-wound direct-current generator that has been "shut down" with two others that are carrying load?

19. How would you disconnect and shut down one of the machines in Question 18?

20. What advantage has three-wire direct-current distribution over two-wire distribution?

21. How may a generator be designed to supply current to both sides of a three-wire distribution circuit?

22. The neutral wire of a three-wire system is accidentally broken off between the load and the generator. What effect will this have on the system?

23. Explain what determines the capacity of a dynamo.

24. What is meant by the efficiency of a generator?

## PROBLEMS

1. A shunt generator supplies a load of 150 amperes at 120 volts. The resistance of the armature is 0.02 ohm and of the field magnets is 22 ohms; the resistance of the leads may be neglected. (a) Find the e.m.f

generated by the machine. (b) What is the field current? *Ans.* (a) 123.11 volts; (b) 5.45 amperes.

2. The e.m.f. of a shunt-wound railway generator rises from 500 volts at full load to 590 volts upon disconnecting the load. What is the regulation of the machine? *Ans.* 18 per cent.

3. It requires 58 horsepower to drive a 40-kilowatt generator when delivering is rated output. What is its efficiency? *Ans.* 92.5 per cent.

4. A series generator supplies 14 amperes to the external circuit which has a resistance of 4 ohms. The resistance of the armature is 0.03 ohm, while the combined resistance of the field and diverter is 0.01 ohm. The resistance of the lead wires to the load is 0.4 ohm. The generator requires 1.5 horsepower to drive it. Calculate : (a) total e.m.f. generated; (b) p.d. at the brushes; (c) efficiency of the generator. *Ans.* (a) 62.16 volts; (b) 61.74 volts; (c) 77 per cent.

5. A compound-wound short-shunt generator is connected to 700 incandescent lamps in parallel, each having a resistance of 220 ohms and requiring 110 volts. The resistances are as follows: leads 0.02 ohm; shunt field 40 ohms; series field 0.015 ohm; armature 0.02 ohm. It requires 63 horsepower to drive the machine under the load stated. Find the following: (a) e.m.f. generated; (b) p.d. at the brushes; (c) drop on series field; (d) power loss in shunt field; (e) power loss on the line; (f) efficiency of the machine. *Ans.* (a) 129.31 volts; (b) 122.25 volts; (c) 5.25 volts; (d) 374 watts; (e) 2450 watts; (f) 87 per cent.

6. A direct-current distribution system requires 10 tons of copper when carrying a certain load operated at 115 volts with two wires. What amount of copper will be required to operate the system at 230 volts with three wires, assuming the same load and the same percentage potential drop. *Ans.* 3.75 tons.

7. The efficiency of a 175-kilowatt generator is 87.5 per cent. How much energy is supplied to the machine? *Ans.* 200 kilowatts.

# Lesson XX

## DIRECT-CURRENT MOTORS

Comparison between generators and motors—Principle of the motor—Direction of rotation—Effect of armature reaction—Counter electromotive force—Current taken by a motor—Torque and mechanical power—Efficiency of a motor—Starting a shunt motor—Speed control of the shunt motor—Speed regulation—The series motor—Characteristic curves—Motor wiring calculations—Questions and Problems.

**226. Comparison between Generators and Motors.**—A generator is a machine for developing electrical energy by moving conductors in a magnetic field, the torque necessary to maintain the motion being supplied by a steam engine or other source of mechanical power. An electric motor is just the opposite; it is a machine for converting electrical into mechanical power. When the field magnets of a direct-current dynamo are excited and its armature is traversed by current from an outside source, the armature will revolve due to the interaction between the magnetic field of its current-carrying wires and that produced by the field magnets.

Any direct-current generator will run as a motor when supplied with electric power, and conversely, a motor, when driven by mechanical power, will supply electrical energy to the circuit connected to it. In fact, the terms generator and motor are applied to a dynamo to indicate the direction of energy conversion, whether from mechanical to electrical, or vice-versa.

Direct-current motors are constructed in bipolar or multipolar form in the same manner as direct-current generators, and the description of such machines given in the two preceding lessons applies equally well to electric motors. The general appearance of a direct-current motor is seen from Fig. 302. The housings of motors are designed to suit their surroundings, as to the presence of moisture, facilities for cooling, and protection against dust and foreign particles. Direct-current motors are classified with respect to field excitation in the same manner as generators; they are *shunt wound, series wound,* or *compound wound.*

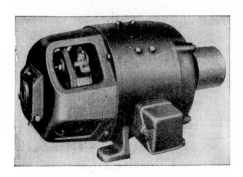

FIG. 302. A 5-hp. direct-current motor
Century Electric Company

**227. Principle of the Motor.** —The principles involved in the movement of current-carrying conductors located suitably in a magnetic field were discussed under the subject of electromagnetism in Lesson X. It was also shown in §130 how a loop of wire could be rotated continuously by commutating the current through it at the proper instants during its revolution in the field, and how the torque could be increased and made more uniform by adding more loops to form coils and arranging these at different angles to form an armature. Further, it was pointed out that the direction of rotation of each coil is such that the magnetic flux set up by the current in it will be the same as that of the field. These are the basic ideas of motor action, and it is desirable to review them briefly.

In Fig. 303 the loop *ABCD* and a commutator of two sections are mounted on a shaft centrally located

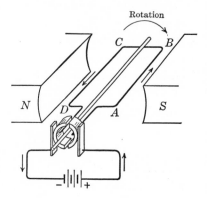

FIG. 303. Loop armature rotating in a magnetic field

in the field structure *NS*. Current is supplied to the loop from a battery, and it is directed momentarily from *A* to *B* in the right-hand inductor and from *C* to *D* in the left-hand one. A force will act on each inductor and its strength will depend on the current in the loop, the length of the inductor, and the intensity of the field between the poles. The force on conductor *AB* will be downward and that on conductor *CD* will be upward; consequently, each will aid the other in producing rotation in a clockwise direction.

The flux developed by the current in the loop is directed upward for the position shown, and clockwise rotation of the loop will tend to align this flux with that of the field. When the loop arrives at the position of flux alignment, 90° from the position depicted, the torque would cease because the forces on conductors *AB* and *CD* are then vertically down and up on "dead center" with the shaft. At this position of the loop, the commutator will reverse connections with the brushes, so that the current will be directed around the loop in the opposite direction; the forces on these inductors will now produce further rotation in the clockwise direction until the fluxes of the loop and field are again aligned. These reversals of current at the commutator occur automatically with every half revolution of the loop in a bipolar field, and in this way continuous rotation is obtained.

In a generator, the direction of current induced in the armature is such as to oppose the motion necessary to produce that current, and the opposition increases as the current increases, thereby requiring additional mechanical power to drive the armature as the load increases. Thus, the force action developed by the induced current in a generator armature is opposed to the direction of rotation of the armature. In a motor, the motion of the conductors in the magnetic field induces e.m.f.'s in them and these tend to oppose the current supplied to the machine. As will be explained later in more detail, §230, the greater the mechanical load applied to the pulley of a motor, the lower will be the speed of the machine and the lower will be the induced e.m.f. in the armature. Consequently, the greater will be the current taken by the motor from the supply mains.

Experiment 100.—Using the generator of Experiment 92 as a motor, first adjust the brushes on the slip rings and place the coil so that its plane will lie in the direction of the magnetic field. When current from an outside source is established through the coil, it will turn until its plane becomes perpendicular to the flux, at which position rotation ceases, according to the principle outlined. Incline the coil at any other angle and close the circuit; it will rotate only to the position aligning its flux with the field.

Second, adjust the brushes upon the commutator and again supply current to the coil. The coil will now rotate continuously in one direction, the current in it being reversed by the commutator at each half revolution. Determine the polarity of the field magnets with a compass, and note whether the direction of rotation is according to the left-hand rule.

**228. Direction of Rotation.**—The direction of rotation of a motor can be found by the left-hand rule, §113, when the polarity of the field magnets and the direction of current through the armature are known. The direction of rotation of a motor can be changed by reversing the current either through the armature or through the fields, but not through both. If both are changed, the motor will run in the same direction as before.

In a series motor, if the current traverses the field and armature windings in the same relative direction as when the machine is operated as a generator, the armature will revolve in the opposite direction to its rotation as a generator. Reversing the connections to the source of electricity at the terminals of the motor will not change its direction of rotation, since this change will reverse the current through both the armature and the field. It is necessary to reverse *either* the armature or field connections to change the direction of motion.

A shunt dynamo turns in the same direction when used as a motor as when used as a generator. For example, if current is supplied to the dynamo of Fig. 292 from an external source and is so directed that the polarity of the field structure is unchanged, then the current through the armature will be opposite in direction to the current supplied by the machine when it is operated as a generator. Again, comparing the loop of Fig. 267 II revolving as a generator with the loop of Fig. 303 revolving as a motor, it will be observed that the currents through the loop are opposite but the field polarity and the direction of rotation are the same.

**Experiment 101.**—Connect and operate the elementary generator of Experiments 92 and 100 as a shunt motor. Reverse the current at the motor terminals and the direction of rotation will be found the same as before. (a) Verify the left-hand rule for the direction of rotation of the armature. (b) Reconnect the machine so as to reverse the direction of rotation.

**Experiment 102.**—Connect the two field coils of the motor used in Experiment 101 in parallel, but be sure that the poles have the proper polarity, N and S. Then connect the armature in series with the field to form a series motor. (a) Verify the left-hand rule for the direction of rotation. (b) Reverse the direction of rotation.

**229. Effect of Armature Reaction.**—The reaction of the armature current upon the field of a motor distorts that field just as in a generator, §212, except that the lines of force in this case are crowded together in the leading pole tips and lessened in the trailing tips. Consequently, the flux distribution is just opposite to that illustrated in Fig. 284, and the commutation plane is shifted in the other direction to that shown in Fig. 285.

To allow for armature reaction in a motor, the brushes are *rocked backward against the direction of rotation* until the non-sparking position is found. The angle of brush shift against the direction of rotation should be increased as the current taken by the motor increases (or as its mechanical output increases), and the amount of shift should be decreased as the load is lessened. In motors with interpoles or compensating windings, §214, the brushes may be retained in the same position regardless of variations in load. The conditions and remedies for sparking at the brushes of a motor are the same as those previously given for generators.

**230. Counter Electromotive Force.**—The conductors on the armature of a motor, rotating in its own magnetic field, cut the lines of force just as if the machine were being driven as a generator by mechanical power, and consequently, an e.m.f. is induced in those conductors. Consider the loop in the bipolar field of Fig. 303 to be set in rotation clockwise by current from the battery shown; the arrows indicate the direction of this current around the circuit. As conductor $AB$ moves down in the magnetic field, there will be induced in it an e.m.f. directed from $B$ to $A$, as determined by the right-hand rule, §146. At the same time inductor $CD$ moves up in this field and there will be induced in it an e.m.f. directed from $D$ to $C$. These induced e.m.f.'s add up and are directed around the circuit oppositely to the arrows. The resultant of the e.m.f.'s induced in the loops of a motor armature is called the *counter electromotive force* of the motor, because it opposes the p.d. that is applied to the machine to make it rotate.

The presence of a counter e.m.f. may be observed by connecting a lamp across the brushes of a shunt motor, and then disconnecting the machine from the service mains. The lamp will not be extinguished at once but will gradually become dim as the speed of the motor decreases. If a voltmeter is used instead of the lamp in such a test, it will indicate, by the direction of deflection of its pointer, that the counter e.m.f. is opposed to the p.d. of the supply circuit.

The counter e.m.f. of a motor operating at any speed will be the same as the e.m.f. developed by it when run as a generator at the same speed, provided the field strength is the same in both cases. Consequently, to measure the counter e.m.f. of a motor at any speed, drive it as a generator at this speed and observe the induced e.m.f. on a voltmeter connected across the brushes.

The counter e.m.f. of a motor depends upon the same factors as those governing the induced e.m.f. in a generator, §148, and is directly proportional to the following: the flux density of the magnetic field, the number and length of conductors on the armature, and the speed at which the lines of force are cut. The counter e.m.f. will always be less than the p.d. applied to the motor by an amount equal to the potential drop in the motor armature.

Because of the counter e.m.f. developed in a motor, the current through the armature is *not* equal to the applied p.d. divided by the armature resistance. To determine the value of this current, let

$E$ = potential difference applied to the motor brushes,
$\varepsilon$ = counter e.m.f. developed by the motor,
$r$ = internal resistance of the armature,
$I$ = current through the armature.

Then the net p.d. across the armature is $E - \varepsilon$ ; consequently, the armature current will be given by

$$I = \frac{E - \varepsilon}{r} \qquad\qquad 116$$

To FIND THE CURRENT THROUGH THE ARMATURE OF A MOTOR:

*Subtract the counter e.m.f. from the p.d. applied across the armature, and divide this result by the armature resistance.*

**Problem 141.**—A small motor connected to a 110-volt circuit develops a counter e.m.f. of 105 volts at a particular speed. The resistance of the armature is 2 ohms. (a) What current is being supplied to the armature at that speed? (b) What current would the armature take if it could not revolve and generate a counter e.m.f.?

The armature currents are respectively:

(116) $$I = \frac{E - \varepsilon}{r} = \frac{110 - 105}{2} = 2.5 \text{ amperes} \qquad \text{(a)}$$

(18) $$I = \frac{E}{R} = \frac{110}{2} = 55 \text{ amperes} \qquad \text{(b)}$$

The speed which any motor attains is such that the sum of the counter e.m.f. developed in the armature and the potential drop due to its resistance is exactly equal to the total p.d. applied to its terminals. This result is derived from Formula (116) by transposition. The potential drop in the armature of a motor is a small portion of the applied p.d., perhaps between 2 and 7 per cent, so that the counter e.m.f. is not much different from the applied potential difference.

**231. Current Taken by a Motor.**—The current taken by a motor depends upon the mechanical load that it carries; the larger the load, the greater the current. This accommodation of current to load results in economical operation, and is due entirely to the development of counter electromotive force.

No counter e.m.f. is induced in a motor armature until it begins to revolve; so the current through it, when stationary, would be very large (see Problem 141). As the armature gains speed, the counter e.m.f. rises, and the current through it gradually diminishes. Thus, the counter e.m.f. automatically decreases the current as the speed increases.

If the load upon a motor is increased, the torque that it has been developing is no longer sufficient to overcome the larger load, and consequently, its speed falls. The reduction of speed lessens the counter e.m.f. and permits a greater current to be accommodated through the armature, which greater current produces the larger torque needed. The automatic adjustment of the current to the load is shown in the following experiment.

**Experiment 103.**—Connect a small shunt motor to direct-current service mains with an ammeter of suitable range in series with it. Measure the speed of the armature with a speed indicator and watch, or with a tachometer. Take readings of current and speed, first with the motor uncoupled to its load, and then with the load applied. The load may be a lathe that is belt-connected to the motor, and the work on the lathe may be a metal rod that is being turned down in size by a V-shaped cutting tool. As the cut of the tool is varied, the load will change and the instrument readings will permit a correlation between current and speed. Any other machinery that is at hand could be coupled to the motor pulley instead of the lathe.

The following readings were taken on a particular motor that rotates at 1800 revolutions per minute at no load and 1680 at full load:

| Speed .....1800 | 1770 | 1730 | 1680 | 1650 rev. per min. |
|---|---|---|---|---|
| Current ... 4 | 9 | 15 | 25 | 30 amperes |

The speed falls from 1800 to 1680, a reduction of 120 revolutions per minute, over the range from no load to full load, while the current rises from 4 to 25 amperes. Thus, a 6.6 per cent reduction in speed causes a current rise of 525 per cent.

The difference between a dynamo operating as a generator and as a motor may be summarized as follows:

*Generator.* The armature is driven by an engine, or other source of mechanical power, and revolves in a magnetic field; as a result an e.m.f. is induced in the armature which sets up a current in the external circuit. The presence of this current in the armature conductors as they revolve in the magnetic field develops a torque which opposes the motion of the armature. The work done by the engine in overcoming this opposition is the work which maintains the current in the circuit connected to the generator.

*Motor.* The armature is supplied with current from an outside source of electrical power and the forces developed on its conductors in the magnetic field produce rotation of the armature. Because of the motion of these conductors in the field, a counter e.m.f. is induced in them, and this opposes the current supplied to the armature. The work done by the outside electrical source in overcoming this counter e.m.f. is the work which appears as mechanical energy at the motor pulley.

**232. Torque and Mechanical Power.**—The mechanical power developed by a motor depends upon two factors, the speed and the torque, and is equal to the product of these factors. The effect of torque in producing rotation is explained in §92, and it was pointed out that the twisting tendency is proportional to the force and to the distance at which it acts from the center of rotation. Thus, a pull of 50 pounds acting with a lever arm of 2 feet constitutes a torque of 100 pound-feet.

The most common method of testing the mechanical output of a motor is with the prony brake, one form of which is shown in Fig. 304. The brake con-sists of a lever of wood hollowed out to

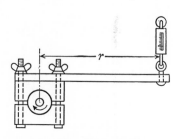

FIG. 304. Prony brake

fit the pulley and clamped around it by bolts passing through a wooden block on the other side of the pulley. The bolts are fitted with wing nuts, by means of which the pressure of the wood on the surface of the pulley can be adjusted, thus altering the force due to friction. By measuring the pull at the end of the lever, the length of the lever, and the speed of rotation of the pulley, it is possible to calculate quite readily the amount of power developed.

The rotation of the motor tends to turn the brake lever and this tendency is counteracted by a spring balance. It is important to have the balance arranged at right angles to the brake lever. The work done by the motor in making one revolution is equal to the force $F$ indicated by the spring balance multiplied by $2\pi \times r$, where $r$ is the lever arm, or the perpendicular distance between the line of action of the force and the axis of the motor shaft. If $r$ is expressed in feet and $F$ is in pounds, then the work done per revolution of the motor shaft is $2\pi \times r \times F$ foot-pounds. If the motor makes $n$ revolutions per minute, the time rate of doing work is $2\pi \times r \times n \times F$ foot-pounds per minute. To reduce this result to horsepower, it is necessary to divide by 33,000, since one horsepower equals 33,000 foot-pounds of work per minute, §94. Hence, the power developed by the motor in horsepower is

$$P = \frac{2\pi \times r \times n \times F}{33,000} \qquad 117$$

Since the product of $F$ and $r$ is the torque exerted by the motor, say $T$, the power developed can also be expressed as

$$P = \frac{2\pi \times n \times T}{33,000} \qquad \textbf{118}$$

**Problem 142.**—A prony brake having a lever arm of 3 feet is used to measure the power of an electric motor. The spring balance at the end of the lever reads 14.5 pounds when the shaft makes 1200 revolutions per minute. What is the output of the machine?

$$(117) \; P = \frac{2\pi \times r \times n \times F}{33,000} = \frac{2\pi \times 3 \times 1200 \times 14.5}{33,000} = 9.94 \text{ horsepower}$$

In testing the output of a large motor in a factory where a generator of suitable size is available, the two machines are coupled together and the motor is arranged to drive the other machine. The output of the generator is absorbed by resistors and the amount of power supplied to them can be regulated by varying their resistance. If the generator happens to develop the same e.m.f. as the p.d. of the circuit supplying the motor, the current from the generator may be returned to the supply circuit, thereby saving considerable power. In this method, called the *loading back method*, the power output is regulated by altering the strength of the generator field.

The mechanical power developed by a motor, including that required for mechanical friction losses and for eddy currents and hysteresis, may be determined from the counter e.m.f. and armature current.

To FIND THE MECHANICAL POWER DEVELOPED BY A MOTOR:

*Multiply the counter e.m.f. by the current through the armature.*

Let

$\varepsilon$ = counter e.m.f.,
$I$ = armature current only.

Then the mechanical power developed in watts is

$$P = \varepsilon \times I \qquad \textbf{119}$$

**Problem 143.**—(a) What power is developed by a 110-volt motor having an armature resistance of 2 ohms and revolving at a speed such as to develop a counter e.m.f. of 100 volts? (b) What power is supplied to the armature?

The motor current and the power developed by the machine are respectively:

(116) $$I = \frac{E - \varepsilon}{r} = \frac{110 - 100}{2} = 5 \text{ amperes}$$

(119) $$P = \varepsilon \times I = 100 \times 5 = 500 \text{ watts} \qquad (a)$$

Since 746 watts = 1 horsepower, the power developed may also be expressed as $500 \div 746 = 0.67$ horsepower. The power supplied to the armature is

(49) $$P = E \times I = 110 \times 5 = 550 \text{ watts} \qquad (b)$$

**233. Efficiency of a Motor.**—The capacity of a motor to perform useful work is limited by the same conditions as those governing the capacity of a generator, §224. A motor is rated commercially according to the amount of power it will maintain at full load within the limit of permissible heating. For example, a 10-kilowatt motor will develop at rated potential and without overheating 10 kilowatts or 13.4 horsepower at the pulley.

The efficiency of a motor, as in the case of the generator, is the ratio of the output to the input. Therefore, as expressed by Formula (114),

$$\text{efficiency} = \frac{\text{output}}{\text{input}}$$

The input to a motor can be obtained from voltmeter and ammeter readings, and the output can be measured by a prony brake.

It is often convenient to estimate the efficiency of a motor from a knowledge of its losses. Let

$P$ = input to motor in watts,
$p$ = total losses of motor in watts,
$e$ = efficiency of the motor expressed as a ratio.

Then the output is $P - p$, and the efficiency becomes

$$e = \frac{P - p}{P} \qquad 120$$

The losses are divided into two classes: the copper losses in the armature and fields, and the stray power loss; the latter includes friction, eddy currents, and hysteresis.

**Problem 144.**—A 25-horsepower, 220-volt shunt-wound motor, having an armature resistance of 0.1 ohm and a field resistance of 80 ohms, is to operate under heavy load. Its speed at this load is such as to develop a counter e.m.f. of 210 volts. Assuming the stray power loss as 600 watts, calculate the output and efficiency of the motor.

The drop in the armature is the difference between the applied p.d. and the counter e.m.f., or $220 - 210 = 10$ volts. The armature current is $10 \div 0.1 = 100$ amperes, and the field current is $220 \div 80 = 2.75$ amperes. The power consumed in copper loss is $10 \times 100 = 1000$ watts in the armature, and $2.75 \times 220 = 605$ watts in the shunt field. Then the total loss in the machine is $1000 + 605 + 600 = 2205$ watts.

The input to the motor is $100 \times 220 = 22,000$ watts for the armature, and 605 watts for the field, or a total of 22,605 watts. The motor output is $22,605 - 2205 = 20,400$ watts or $\dfrac{20,400}{746} = 27.4$ horsepower. Whence the efficiency of the motor is

$$(120) \qquad \text{efficiency} = \frac{20,400}{22,605} = 0.903 = 90.3 \text{ per cent}$$

**Experiment 104.**—Attach a prony brake to the pulley of a direct-current motor of, say, ½ to 2 horsepower rating. Bridge a voltmeter across the motor terminals and connect an ammeter in series with the motor to the service mains. Adjust the brake so the current taken by the motor is approximately that for full load. Read the meters and also the scale associated with the prony brake. Measure the speed of the motor with a revolution counter and a watch. From these observations, calculate the electrical input and the mechanical output of the motor, and determine its efficiency.

## 234. Starting a Shunt Motor.

—The armatures of motors are designed to have a low resistance in order that the potential drops in them may be kept small. Motors of large size naturally have lower armature resistances than small machines. These facts are of importance in the starting of motors from rest. When a motor is connected directly to the supply mains it takes a very large current at first, but this falls quickly to normal operating values as the machine speeds up and develops counter e.m.f. To avoid this current peak during the starting period, it is customary to use a *starting box* with the motor to limit the initial current to an appropriate value. Such a device comprises a group of resistors which can be cut out of circuit progressively by moving an arm over the resistor contacts; it also has other protective features.

Fig. 305 shows the connections of a starting box used with a shunt motor to limit the current in the armature before it attains normal speed. It has four resistors connected with contacts 1 to 5, and a pivoted arm $S$, which can sweep over these contacts. The total resistance of the resistors should be such that, when added to the armature resistance, the starting current will be reduced to about 1.5 times its full-load value. The box also has an electromagnet $R$ which can attract a small piece of iron $P$ attached to arm $S$, when that arm is on contact 5. The terminals of the box marked $L$, $F$, and $A$ connect respectively to the line, field winding, and armature.

In starting the motor, the switch is closed and the arm is moved to the right from the "off position" shown. On reaching contact 1, the arm closes the field circuit of the motor through the electromagnet $R$; it also closes the armature circuit through all the starting resistors. The arm is then moved over contacts 2, 3, 4, and 5 in order to cut out resistors as the motor gains speed and develops more and more counter e.m.f. The electromagnet holds the arm in the "operating position" on contact 5 against a retractable spring (not shown). To stop the motor, it is merely necessary to open the switch; this action deprives the electromagnet of current, the iron piece is no longer held attracted, and the arm springs back to the off position.

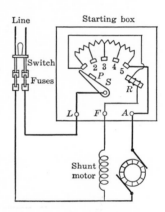

FIG. 305. Connections of three-point starting box to a shunt motor

Should the power supply be interrupted while the motor is in operation, the electromagnet $R$ in the field circuit will release the arm and permit the spring to return it to the off position automatically. This accounts for the designation of this electromagnet as the *no-field release coil*. Upon resumption of electric service, the motor will not start until the arm is moved manually to the right over the contacts.

In Fig. 305 the electromagnet is in series with the field winding, and any variation of the field current will affect the strength of this magnet. Since the speed of most shunt motors is adjusted by means of a field rheostat, §235, the pull of the magnet will vary with the field current. Consequently, the potential at which the magnet releases the starter arm will depend on the setting of the field rheostat. In order to remove this uncertainty, the electromagnet is connected directly across the line in the four-point starting box shown in Fig. 306. With this connection scheme the electromagnet can be designed to release the starter arm at a definitely-specified minimum line potential independently of the field rheostat setting.

Controlling devices are available which provide for starting and stopping motors merely by pressing push buttons. When the "on-button" is pressed, the resistors in series with the motor armature are cut out of circuit progressively by *magnetic switches* or *contactors;* these devices are basically relays, §110, so designed that the large motor currents can be accommodated at the contacts. When the "off-button" is pressed the resistors are restored to the armature circuit by similar means.

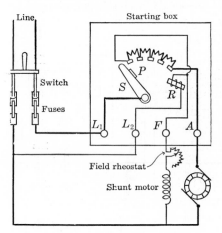

FIG. 306. Connections of four-point starting box to a shunt motor

*In starting a shunt motor always be sure that the field windings are energized,* for without field excitation the armature, in building up its counter e.m.f., would speed up to a dangerously high value and possibly be wrecked.

**235. Speed Control of the Shunt Motor.**—In the operation of many industrial machines it is necessary to alter the speed of the driving motor. This could be accomplished in shunt motors by introducing a variable resistance in the armature circuit, but this method of speed control is wasteful of energy and results in changes of speed with variations of load. Another method of speed control involves the application of different p.d.'s upon the motor armature; this method is employed in machine shops for driving lathes, planers, drill presses, etc., and requires multi-potential supply circuits.

The most usual method of speed control is the variation of magnetic field intensity in the motor. The stronger the field intensity of a motor the lower will be the speed of its armature for the development of the counter e.m.f. needed for a given load. To make a shunt motor rotate faster it is necessary to weaken its field. The strength of the magnetic field may be varied: 1, by altering the current in the field coils; and 2, by altering the magnetic reluctance of the flux path.

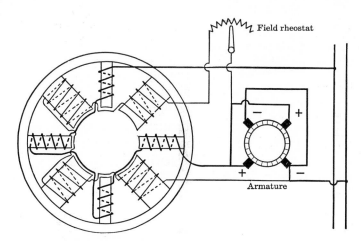

FIG. 307. Wiring diagram of four-pole interpole motor
Interpole coils are in series with armature.

(1) The current in the field coils can be varied by placing a rheostat in the field circuit. Increasing its resistance lessens the current and weakens the field, consequently, the motor will speed up. The control of speed by varying the field strength is limited in range of action, since with high field strengths the saturation of the magnetic circuit requires large field currents and these cause undue heating, and with low field strengths the armature reaction produces a considerable demagnetizing and distorting effect on the field flux and occasions sparking. However, the range can be widened considerably by neutralizing the effects of armature reaction through the use of compensating windings and interpoles, §214.

Fig. 307 shows the connections of an interpole (or commutating-pole) motor. Such interpole or compensated motors afford sparkless commutation under wide ranges of speed and load, and are splendidly adapted for individual motor drive of machine tools, for elevator operation, for driving printing presses, and for many other applications.

FIG. 308. Combined starting box and field-regulating rheostat Cutler-Hammer, Inc.

A combined starting and field-regulating rheostat is shown in Fig. 308. The movable arm has two parts which wipe over separate sets of contacts; the larger part connects with the starting resistance in the armature circuit and the smaller one with the field resistance units. The motor is started by moving the arm to the extreme right, where the magnet will hold the larger part. The other part of the arm is then moved back and adds resistance to the field circuit, thus increasing the speed of the motor to any desired value. With this arrangement it is impossible to start the motor under weakened field excitation.

(2) The reluctance of the flux path in a shunt motor may be varied by altering the length of the air gap between the armature and the field poles. Increasing the gap length, decreases the flux and produces a higher speed. This method of speed con-

FIG. 309. Motor of the armature shifting design
Reliance Electric & Engineering Company

trol was utilized in motors made by the Stow Manufacturing Company, in which all the poles were simultaneously moved through hollow field cores by turning a single hand wheel. It is also utilized in motors made by the Reliance Electric and Engineering Company, in which the width of the air gap is different at the two ends of the machine, and speed variation is accomplished by an axial movement of the armature with respect to the field. Fig. 309 shows an adjustable-speed motor with a hand wheel for shifting the armature endwise.

**236. Speed Regulation.**—The speed of a shunt-motor under constant impressed p.d. and fixed excitation is roughly constant. The speed will fall somewhat as the load on the machine is increased because of the increased potential drop in the armature. This change of speed, with a definite setting of the field rheostat, occurring from full load to no load, expressed as a percentage of the speed at no load, is called the *speed regulation* of the motor. Thus,

$$\text{speed regulation} = \frac{\text{no-load speed} - \text{full-load speed}}{\text{full-load speed}} \qquad \textbf{121}$$

Speed regulation concerns itself with changes in speed inherent in the machine, whereas speed control signifies deliberate external adjustment to attain various desired speeds; care should be exercised not to confuse these terms.

**Problem 145.**—A motor when operating at full load runs at 1710 revolutions per minute and when the load is removed its speed is 1800. What is its speed regulation?

$$(121) \quad \text{speed regulation} = \frac{1800 - 1710}{1710} = 0.053 = 5.3 \text{ per cent}$$

When the numerical value of the speed regulation of a motor is small, as in the foregoing problem, the motor is said to possess good speed regulation.

**237. The Series Motor.**—As the name indicates, the series direct-current motor has its armature and field windings connected in series. When such a motor is operated from the usual constant-potential service mains its speed is high under light loads and low under large loads. If the load were accidentally removed from a series motor it would speed up tremendously and perhaps be ruined; consequently, such motors are solidly coupled to their loads by gears, rather than by belts. The series motor is particularly well suited for car propulsion and for the operation of cranes and hoists at varying speeds, because the energy taken from the supply circuit fluctuates less than it would with shunt motors. Fig. 310 depicts a series-wound totally-enclosed motor; its frame is split horizontally so that the armature may be removed readily.

Fig. 310. Series-wound direct-current motor
General Electric Company

Series motors are used for railway work because they best fulfill the requirements—namely, powerful torque at starting, variable speed, and economical operation at varying loads. It is common practice to use two motors on a railway or trolley car. When the car is started the motors are first connected in series with each other and with a controller across the mains. As the car gains speed, the motorman turns the controller handle and thereby cuts resistance out of circuit until the motors operate in series across the full p.d. of the mains. Then the controller places the motors in parallel with a resistor in series with both, and finally, it gradually cuts out this resistance step by step until each motor is connected directly across the mains. The mains in electric railway operation are the two track rails for the negative line wire, and the third rail or overhead conductor for the positive line wire.

**238. Characteristic Curves.**—In selecting a motor for a definite service it is necessary to know its performance characteristics at various loads. This information is usually embodied in curves plotted on cross-section paper and supplied by the manufacturer. The characteristics for a shunt motor are speed, current, torque, and efficiency for various outputs. Fig. 311 shows the characteristic curves of a 7.5-horsepower, 230-volt commutating-pole shunt motor.

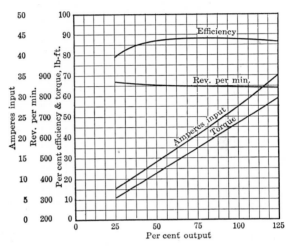

FIG. 311. Characteristic curves of a shunt motor

Readings of current and torque values from this curve for three particular loads show the following:

| Per Cent Full Load | Amperes | Pound-Feet |
|---|---|---|
| 25 | 7.7 | 11 |
| 50 | 14.1 | 23 |
| 100 | 27.5 | 47 |

It will be observed that both current and torque values increase almost proportionally to the load. Per ampere of current there is produced a torque of $11/7.7 = 1.4$ pound-feet at $\frac{1}{4}$ load, $23/14.1 = 1.6$ pound-feet at $\frac{1}{2}$ load, and $47/27.5 = 1.7$ pound-feet at full load; showing that the torque exerted by the motor is very nearly proportional to the current taken. The curve for speed shows a drop from 870 to 845 revolutions per minute over the range from 25 to 100 per cent of full load. Over the same range the motor has efficiency values between 79 and 88 per cent.

The series motor has quite different characteristics and the performance curves are usually plotted against current input. Fig. 312 gives the speed, torque, and efficiency curves of a 40-horsepower, 600-volt commutating-pole series railway motor. The horsepower rating of a railway motor is the mechanical output at the car axle which causes a temperature rise above the surrounding air, as measured by thermometer, not exceeding 90° C. at the commutator and 75° C. at any other normally accessible part after 1 hour's continuous run at rated potential on a stand with the motor covers arranged to secure maximum ventilation without using an external blower.

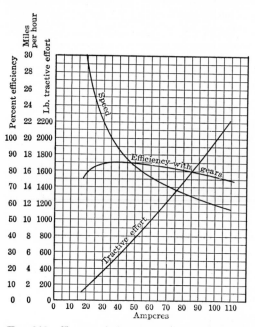

FIG. 312. Characteristic curves of a series railway motor.

The torque exerted by a railway motor is expressed in terms of the *tractive effort* produced on the car in the direction of its motion. The relation between tractive effort in pounds and torque in pound-feet, neglecting losses in gears, is given by

$$\text{tractive effort} = \frac{24 \times \text{gear ratio} \times \text{torque}}{\text{wheel diameter in inches}}$$

The relation between car speed in miles per hour and motor speed in revolutions per minute is given by

$$\text{miles per hour} = \frac{\text{torque} \times \text{motor speed}}{14 \times \text{tractive effort}}$$

Readings of tractive effort and speed from the curve for three current values follow:

| Amperes | Pounds | Miles Per Hour |
|---|---|---|
| 25 | 250 | 24.9 |
| 60 | 1000 | 15.2 |
| 90 | 1700 | 12.5 |

The figures show that a small torque is exerted by a series motor at high speed and a large torque at low speed. Since power output equals the product of torque and speed, §232, it is evident that the energy taken by a series motor does not fluctuate as much as that taken by a shunt motor. Thus, from the foregoing table, while the tractive effort varies from 250 to 1700 pounds, a 7-fold increase, the product of tractive effort and speed increases from $250 \times 24.9 = 6230$ to $1700 \times 12.5 = 21,200$, a 3.5-fold increase of power. In contrast, a shunt motor would demand about a 7-fold increase of power, since the speed is practically constant. For this reason the series motor is particularly well suited for car propulsion and for the operation of cranes and hoists where the speeds vary over wide ranges.

Compound-wound motors in which the series and shunt fields assist each other are frequently used for heavy intermittent loads, such as in operating elevators and rolling mills. They exert a powerful starting torque and yet the speed is not excessively variable under load changes.

**239. Motor Wiring Calculations.**—The determination of wire size for the installation of a motor requires a knowledge of the current needed, the potential drop allowable, the length of the run, and the current-carrying capacity of commercial insulated wire. The current is found from the rating of the machine, the p.d. of the supply lines, and the efficiency of the motor.

Let

$E$ = p.d. required by the motor in volts,
$I$ = current taken by the motor in amperes,
kw. = kilowatt rating of the motor,
hp. = horsepower rating of the motor,
$e$ = efficiency of the motor expressed as a decimal, that is, the ratio of its output to its input.

A rearrangement of Formulas (50), (51) and (114) gives the current through the motor as

$$I = \frac{1000 \times \text{kw.}}{E \times e} = \frac{746 \times \text{hp.}}{E \times e} \qquad \textbf{122}$$

To FIND THE CURRENT REQUIRED BY A MOTOR WHEN ITS OUTPUT, EFFICIENCY, AND POTENTIAL DIFFERENCE ARE KNOWN:

*Multiply the kilowatt rating by 1000 and divide by the p.d. at the motor and by its efficiency; or multiply the horsepower rating by 746 and divide by the p.d. at the motor and by its efficiency.*

Two steps are involved in deciding upon the appropriate wire size for supplying electric power to a motor. The first is a calculation of the size required to transmit the current needed without exceeding the desired potential drop, and the second is to refer to a table of allowable current capacities, §77, and select a size wire which will carry the current without overheating and be *no smaller* than the size calculated in the first step.

Let

$L$ = total length of both line wires in feet,
$E_d$ = allowable potential drop over the line in volts,
CM = cross-sectional area of the line wire in circular mils,
$\rho$ = resistivity of the wire material in ohm-CM per foot.

Then a combination of Formulas (25) and (122) gives the expression for wire size as

$$CM = \frac{746 \times \text{hp.} \times L \times \rho}{E \times E_d \times e} \qquad \textbf{123}$$

To FIND THE SIZE OF WIRE NECESSARY TO TRANSMIT ENERGY TO A PARTICULAR MOTOR OVER ANY DISTANCE, WHEN THE POTENTIAL DROP ON THE LINE WIRES IS STIPULATED:

*Multiply the rated horsepower of the motor by 746, then by the length of the circuit in feet, and then by the resistivity of the conductor material; divide this result by the product of the p.d. required at the motor, the drop on the line, and the efficiency of the motor.*

**Problem 146.**—What size of copper wire is required to conduct current to a 10-horsepower, 220-volt motor located 150 feet from service mains?

The drop on the line is to be 5 volts and the efficiency of the motor is 85 per cent. What current does the motor take?

Take the resistivity of copper wire to be 10.4 ohm-CM per foot, §63. Then

$$(123) \qquad CM = \frac{746 \times hp. \times L \times \rho}{E \times E_d \times e} = \frac{746 \times 10 \times 300 \times 10.4}{220 \times 5 \times 0.85} = 24{,}900$$

A No. 6 A.w.g. wire having a sectional area of 26,300 circular mils will be required.

The current supplied to the motor will be

$$(122) \qquad I = \frac{746 \times hp.}{E \times e} = \frac{746 \times 10}{220 \times 0.85} = 40 \text{ amperes}$$

A No. 6 wire will take this current without overheating.

## QUESTIONS

1. How does a motor differ from a generator?
2. Distinguish between a shunt and a series motor.
3. Explain the operating principle of a motor.
4. A certain series generator rotates clockwise. Leaving the direction of the current in the field and armature unchanged, what will be the direction of rotation when it is used as a motor?
5. A shunt generator rotates in a counterclockwise direction. How will it run when driven as a motor and with the directions of the current in the field and armature unchanged?
6. What change is necessary in order to reverse the direction of any direct-current motor?
7. Since the torque exerted by a motor depends on the current through the armature, and since the counter e.m.f. tends to reduce the armature current, of what advantage is the counter e.m.f.?
8. How can you demonstrate that a motor develops a counter e.m.f.?
9. Upon what factors does the counter e.m.f. of a motor depend?
10. Why is it impossible for the counter e.m.f. of a motor to attain a value equal to the applied p.d.?
11. Explain how it is possible for a shunt motor to take amounts of current from the supply circuit in proportion to the power developed by the motor.
12. What is meant by torque?
13. What factors determine the mechanical power which can be exerted by a motor? How does this power differ from the mechanical power output of the machine?
14. Describe the prony brake and loading-back methods of measuring the output of a motor.

15. Compare Formula (115) for the efficiency of a generator with Formula (120) for the efficiency of a motor.
16. Explain the function of a starting box.
17. Explain two methods of speed control of shunt motors. Illustrate.
18. Distinguish between speed control and speed regulation of a motor.
19. State the conditions of torque and speed that motors are required to develop in commercial work, and the kind of motor adapted to each case.

## PROBLEMS

1. The counter e.m.f. of a motor is 230 volts when the current through the armature is 25 amperes. The resistance of the armature is 0.4 ohm. What is the applied p.d.? *Ans.* 240 volts.
2. A shunt motor, having an armature resistance of 0.4 ohm and a field resistance of 125 ohms, is connected to 250-volt mains and develops a counter e.m.f. of 230 volts when operating on a certain load. What current is taken from the line? *Ans.* 52 amperes.
3. What mechanical power is developed by the motor in Problem 2? *Ans.* 15.4 horsepower.
4. If 1500 watts are lost in mechanical friction, hysteresis and eddy currents in the motor of Problem 2, what useful power can the motor develop? *Ans.* 13.4 horsepower.
5. A small shunt motor is connected to a 220-volt circuit and rotates at 1500 revolutions per minute when coupled to a lathe. When the machine is driven as a generator and the field current is the same as before, it develops an e.m.f. of 220 volts at a speed of 1650 revolutions per minute. What counter e.m.f. is developed in the motor when driving the lathe? *Ans.* 200 volts.
6. The armature resistance of the motor in Problem 5 is 1.45 ohms. What is the armature current when the machine is run as a motor at 1500 revolutions per minute? *Ans.* 13.8 amperes.
7. The field winding of the motor in Problems 5 and 6 receives 1.2 amperes. If the mechanical losses alone amount to 300 watts, what is the efficiency of the motor? *Ans.* 74.6 per cent.
8. In making a brake test with a lever arm 3 feet long, a motor exerts a pull of 25 pounds when revolving at 1150 revolutions per minute. (a) What is the motor torque? (b) What power is developed? *Ans.* (a) 75 pound-feet; (b) 16.4 horsepower.
9. Determine the speed regulation of a shunt motor having the characteristic curves given in Fig. 311, taking the no-load speed as 895 revolutions per minute. *Ans.* 5.9 per cent.
10. With 6 volts drop on the line, what size wire is required to supply current to a 15-horsepower, 220-volt motor located 250 feet from the source of power? The motor efficiency is 86 per cent. *Ans.* No. 3 A. w. g.

# Lesson XXI

## SYNCHRONOUS MACHINERY

Classification of alternators—Revolving-armature alternators—Revolving-field alternators—Armature windings—Rating of alternators—Synchronous motors—Starting of synchronous motors—Changing alternating to direct current—Rotary converters—Motor-generator sets—Questions and Problems.

**240. Classification of Alternators.**—In generating an alternating e.m.f. there must be relative motion between the inductors of the armature and the flux from the field coils, and it does not matter which revolves. This leads to a classification of alternators into two types; in one the field winding is stationary and the armature revolves, and in the other the armature winding is stationary and the field structure revolves. With either type slip rings are used to conduct the current to and from the rotating member.

All alternators must have direct current for field excitation, and this current is usually derived from a separate generator that is used for field excitation only. Some revolving-armature alternators have two distinct windings on the armature, one winding for generating the alternating e.m.f.'s that are supplied to the load through slip rings, and the other winding for furnishing the direct current to its own field coils through a commutator; such alternators are said to be self-exciting.

Alternators may also be classified according to the design and connection of their armature windings. In a *single-phase alternator* all the armature inductors are included in one winding and generally connected in series so that their individual e.m.f.'s will add together; the alternator mentioned in §170 is necessarily one of this type since it has only one loop in the armature wind-

485

ing. In a *polyphase alternator* there are two or more distinct windings properly distributed over the armature surface and appropriately connected to the terminals of the machine, §198. Each winding develops the same e.m.f. but there are definite phase angles between the windings.

The *two-phase alternator* has two independent armature wind ings, which in a bipolar machine would be placed at right angles to each other. Upon driving such a machine, each winding generates the same alternating e.m.f. but, because of the relative positions of its inductors, the e.m.f.'s are 90 degrees apart in phase. These are shown in Fig. 235 plotted with respect to time.

Fig. 313. Armature of a 3.75-kv-a. single-phase self-exciting alternator
General Electric Company

The *three-phase alternator* consists of three like windings symmetrically placed on the armature so as to produce three equal e.m.f.'s that are 120 degrees apart in phase, as shown in Fig. 236.

The connections of the windings in two- and three-phase alternators are shown in Figs. 260 to 262. The two-phase machine has four terminals and the three-phase machine has three terminals. In all types, the frequency of the e.m.f.'s produced is obtained by multiplying the number of pairs of poles by the number of revolutions per second made by the revolving member.

**241. Revolving-Armature Alternators.**—Alternating-current generators which have the armature as the revolving member resemble direct-current generators. The armature has copper windings in the slots of an iron core and connections are made from these windings to the slip rings. The cores are laminated to keep down the losses due to eddy currents. Fig. 313 illustrates the revolving armature of an alternator with the exciter winding embedded in the same slot as the main winding.

The poles of the stationary field project inwardly from a ring-shaped frame. The magnet cores are cylindrical or rectangular in form and usually constructed of cast mild steel containing a very small percentage of carbon, the magnetic quality of which is nearly equal to that of wrought iron. These cores are bolted or welded into the cast or fabricated steel field ring. In the larger machines the field ring is divided into two parts, for convenience in handling. The pole faces or shoes are generally constructed of laminated sheet steel, and in many machines the entire field cores are so made.

**242. Revolving-Field Alternators.**—It is common practice in alternators to have the field magnets revolve inside a stationary armature. With such construction the armature windings can be more easily insulated to withstand high potentials, and there is no need for collecting current at high potentials from the slip rings. The design of the field structure for this type of alternator is determined by the speed at which it is to be driven; a high-speed turbine-driven alternator has two or four poles, and a slow-speed engine-driven machine may have as many as thirty poles.

The revolving field consists of laminated iron cores surrounded by their coils and bolted to a ring of hot-rolled or cast steel; this ring is joined to the hub by a steel disk or by "spider" arms. The field coils are wound with cotton-covered copper wire, usually of rectangular cross section. The wire is either put on spools which may be slipped over the poles or is wound directly on them after they have been wrapped with layers of insulating material and provided with end collars. Varnish is applied as each layer is wound and the completed coils are impregnated with insulating compound.

Fig. 314 shows at the left the field structure for an alternator driven by a Diesel engine. Each pole face carries a damper winding to keep the field revolving at a steady speed despite the pulsating character of the torque developed by this type of engine. The damper winding consists of copper bars embedded in parallel slots in the pole face and these bars are soldered to connecting straps at both ends.

The stationary armature consists of an iron core and a copper winding supported by a circular cast-iron or fabricated-steel frame. The core is formed of sheet-steel laminations stacked together and held rigidly in place by clamping fingers, ducts being provided at intervals in stacking to allow for ventilation. The inner surface of the laminated core has slots to receive the wind-

FIG. 314. Details of revolving field and stationary armature
Westinghouse Electric Corporation

ings, and these consist of carefully-insulated form-wound coils. The method of assembling the armature coils is illustrated at the right in Fig. 314; the coils are held in the slots by suitable wedges.

In alternators that are driven at high speed by steam turbines, the diameter of the rotating member is less and the axial length of the machine is greater than in slow-speed alternators. The rotating field of such a machine is constructed of a steel forging integral with the shaft, and radial slots are machined in it for the winding. The field winding is formed of flat copper strap, wound on edge, with the flat surface parallel to the bottom of the slot.

Strips of mica and molded mica are used for insulation between the layers and around the complete coils. Fig. 315 illustrates the winding for a two-pole turbo-alternator before the coil ends were enclosed by retaining rings.

FIG. 315. Revolving field of a turbo-alternator
Westinghouse Electric Corporation

**243. Armature Windings.**—The armature windings of alternators may be illustrated diagrammatically in two ways, as in Fig. 316 for a single-phase four-pole machine. At the left the winding is unrolled and viewed against the field poles, and at the

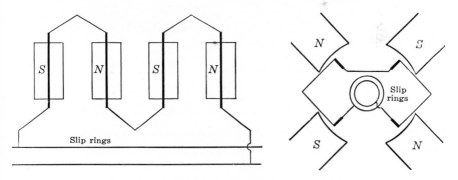

FIG. 316. Representations of single-phase winding

right it is shown radially within the field structure. The heavy lines represent the inductors and the light lines the connecting wires. Where only one inductor is shown, in practice there would be a number of them placed in one slot or distributed over several slots. Fig. 317 shows a two-phase winding at the left and a three-phase Y-connected winding at the right for a four-pole machine.

The angular spread of the entire armature winding represents 360 degrees as measured mechanically around the pole face area.

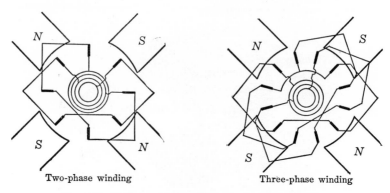

Two-phase winding                    Three-phase winding

Fɪɢ. 317. Radial representation of polyphase windings

However, it is convenient to designate the angle between like-named poles as 360 degrees, because in moving through that angle each armature inductor develops a complete cycle of e.m.f. values. To distinguish between these angles, the complete span around the

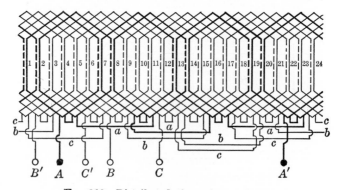

Fɪɢ. 318. Distributed three-phase winding

pole face area is called 360 *mechanical degrees,* and the angle between like-named poles is called 360 *electrical degrees.* In a four-pole machine 360 mechanical degrees correspond to 720 electrical degrees.

Modern alternators have six or more slots per pole so that the windings can be distributed and better ventilated. With such windings the e.m.f.'s developed in the various series-connected inductors which form one phase winding are not in phase with each other, and the total e.m.f. of the winding will be the vector sum rather than the arithmetical sum of the e.m.f.'s developed in the individual inductors. Fig. 318 shows the layout of a three-phase, four-pole distributed winding with two slots per pole per phase. Herein the three windings are lettered $AA'$, $BB'$ and $CC'$. and the connecting wires are marked with corresponding lower-case letters.

**Problem 147.**—The windings of a three-phase bipolar alternator are in 18 slots located 20 degrees apart. Assuming each inductor to generate 1 volt, what e.m.f. would be developed by three inductors in adjacent slots when connected in series?

The e.m.f.'s induced in the outer inductors must be projected to the phase of the central one as indicated in Fig. 319. Since the angle between inductors is 20 degrees, the resolution of the e.m.f. in each outer conductor gives as the horizontal component 1 volt $\times \cos 20° = 1 \times 0.940 = 0.94$ volt. Therefore, the e.m.f. of the three inductors in series is $0.94 + 1.00 + 0.94 = 2.88$ volts.

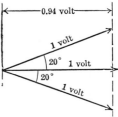

Fig. 319. Adding e.m.f.'s developed in several conductors

**244. Rating of Alternators.**—Alternating-current generators are rated in kilovolt-amperes (kv-a.) instead of kilowatts, because the capacity of an alternator depends on the current, and the power factor of the circuits to which it would furnish power is not known in advance. The actual energy output in kilowatts is equal to the apparent power in kilovolt-amperes multiplied by the power factor of the circuit. An alternator having a rating of 100 kilovolt-amperes would deliver under full-load conditions 100 kilowatts at unity power factor; if the power factor were 0.8 the output of the machine would be reduced to 80 kilowatts, for the current and the consequent heating of the armature would be approximately the same as if it were delivering 100 kilowatts at unity power factor.

Most alternators are three-phase machines, and the windings are connected either $Y$ or $\Delta$ as illustrated in Fig. 320. In the

$Y$-connection the current in any line $A$, $B$, or $C$, is the same as that in the corresponding armature winding 1, 2, or 3. The e.m.f. between lines $A$ and $B$ is found by combining the e.m.f.'s in windings 1 and 2; these differ in phase by 120 degrees but, since one is reversed with respect to the other, the two vectors representing their e.m.f.'s must be added at 60 degrees and this brings their total to $\sqrt{3} = 1.732$ times either one. The e.m.f. acting between any two lines is $\sqrt{3}$ times the e.m.f. developed in one of the armature windings (Formula 109).

In the $\Delta$-connection, the e.m.f. acting between any two lines $AB$, $BC$, or $CA$, is the same as the e.m.f. in one of the phase windings 1, 2, or 3; the line currents will be $\sqrt{3}$ times the currents in the armature windings (Formula 110).

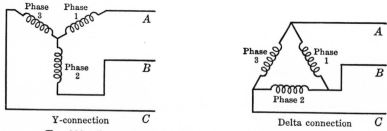

Fig. 320. Connections of windings in three-phase alternators

The distribution circuit supplied by a three-phase generator can be placed across any pair of wires, but a balanced condition should be sought by dividing the load equally across the three pairs of wires. Many loads, such as the three-phase induction motor, contain three equal parts joined either in $Y$ or in $\Delta$, as in the phase windings of an alternator. Such a machine is connected to all three wires of the circuit and forms a balanced load.

**Problem 148.**—A three-phase $Y$-connected alternator delivers 100 kilowatts to a balanced load of 65 per cent power factor. The p.d. across the line wires is 208 volts. Determine the p.d. across each phase winding and the current in it.

The power supplied to the load is given by Formula (112) as $P = \sqrt{3} \times E_l \times I_l \times \cos \phi$, where $E_l$ is the p.d. between the line wires, $I_l$ is the current per line, and $\cos \phi$ is the power factor. Since $P = 100$ kilowatts, $E_l = 208$ volts, and $\cos \phi = 0.65$, it follows that

$$I_l = \frac{P}{\sqrt{3} \times E_l \times \cos \phi} = \frac{100 \times 1000}{1.73 \times 208 \times 0.65} = 428 \text{ amperes}$$

The p.d. and current for each phase winding of this $Y$-connected alternator are, therefore, $208/\sqrt{3} = 120$ volts and 428 amperes respectively.

To determine the relative ratings of an alternator obtainable from a given winding, let $E$ be the p.d. per phase winding and let $I$ be the limiting current through its coils, in both cases effective values of sine-wave quantities are assumed. Then for either $\Delta$- or $Y$-connected three-phase windings the capacity is $3E \times I$ kilovolt-amperes. If either winding is used to supply only a single-phase load by connecting that load to two of the three alternator terminals, the capacity will be reduced. In the $\Delta$-wound armature the current will be $I$ in one winding and $\frac{1}{2} I$ in the other two, making the current per terminal $\frac{3}{2} I$; consequently, the single-phase rating is $\frac{3}{2} E \times I$, which is 50 per cent of its three-phase rating. In the $Y$-wound armature the current will be $I$ in two windings and zero in the third, and the p.d. across the load is $\sqrt{3}E$; therefore, the single-phase rating is $\sqrt{3}E \times I$, which is 58 per cent of the three-phase rating.

**245. Synchronous Motors.**—Any single or polyphase alternator will run as a motor if it is connected to a source of alternating electric power of the same frequency and e.m.f. as it produces as a generator, provided it is first brought up to proper speed before the full p.d. is applied. The proper speed is determined from Formula (82) to be

$$V = \frac{60 \times f}{P}$$

where $f$ is the frequency of the alternating current supplied to the motor, and $P$ is the number of pairs of field poles on the motor. This speed is spoken of as the *synchronous speed*.

TO FIND THE SYNCHRONOUS SPEED OF AN ALTERNATING CURRENT MOTOR:

*Multiply the frequency of the power supply by 60 and divide by the number of pairs of field poles on the motor.*

A synchronous motor is an alternator with its field winding excited from a source of direct current, and its armature supplied from a source of alternating current; it requires in addition some means to bring the moving member or *rotor* to synchronous speed before the motor can assume its load. The term synchronous applied to any machine means that its driven element is in step or unison with the driving one; in a synchronous motor, it means the rotor revolves at a speed determined by the number of field poles and by the frequency of the alternating current supplied to the motor. For example, a synchronous motor having 24 poles and supplied with 60-cycle current would rotate at a speed of exactly 300 revolutions per minute.

To explain the operation of the synchronous motor, assume that an alternating current is supplied to the armature loop of the simple alternator located as shown in Fig. 224. During a half-cycle when current is directed around the loop from B to A, the loop sets up magnetic flux in a direction opposed to that of the field coils and, consequently, the loop tends to turn so that these fluxes may be aligned. However, before the loop turns appreciably, the current through it is reversed and the flux set up is in the same direction as that of the field, thus tending to turn the armature in the opposite direction. The alternations in the current occur with such rapidity that the force acting on the loop in either direction does not persist long enough to produce any rotation of the armature, with the result that it appears at rest but actually is vibrating over a narrow range. If, however, the armature loop is first brought to a speed corresponding with the frequency of the alternating current supplied to it, then the current reversals will be in unison with the motion of the loop and it will continue to revolve. At synchronous speed the magnetic fluxes of field and loop are always in the same relative position.

While the single-phase synchronous motor has no starting torque the polyphase type when operated without load is self-starting because there is always some torque exerted on the rotor. As the current in the armature coils of one phase reaches zero, the current is increasing in the coils of the other phase or phases, and the net result is a magnetic field which circulates around the surface of the armature, §250. With the field circuit open, this rotary flux sets up eddy-currents in the faces of the field poles and reacts with them to develop torque. To improve the starting of such motors, the pole faces of revolving-field rotors have copper bars imbedded in them, and these are connected to end rings to form an auxiliary *cage winding* similar to the rotor winding of a squirrel-cage induction motor, §251. A rotor constructed in this manner is shown in Fig. 321. Such motors are started by applying the alternating p.d.'s to the armature windings, leaving the direct-current field circuit open.

Another advantage of the cage winding on the rotor is its action as a damper to prevent *hunting* of the motor. This term as applied to synchronous motors means the periodic fluctuations in rotor speed, or the periodic surging of current between a motor and its source of power. If, due to a sudden increase in load, the rotor is slightly retarded, the armature takes more current from the source and the rotor accelerates so as to shift the phase of its counter e.m.f. with respect to the impressed e.m.f. It will shift the phase too much, however, and the driving torque will be lessened and become in-

FIG. 321. Revolving field of 800-horsepower, 2300-volt synchronous motor

General Electric Company

sufficient for the motor load, whereupon the rotor will again lag, and so on. This oscillation of the rotor about its mean speed, that is, hunting, is effectively reduced by the cage or damping coils of the rotor; see also Fig. 314.

Synchronous motors are used where starting under load is not necessary; they are available in large sizes. The chief advantages of the synchronous motor are: its speed is constant at all loads and the power factor of the circuit on which it is operated can be controlled by varying the field strength of the motor. The current can be made to lead the impressed p.d. merely by a change of excitation, thereby neutralizing the lagging current taken by induction motors that may be connected to the same circuit. Synchronous motors are frequently connected in transmission lines for the purpose of regulating their phase relations, the motor being run without load and the field excitation being adjusted to suit the conditions. In such cases, where the synchronous motor operates only to correct power factor, the machine is termed a *synchronous condenser,* for the reason that its action on a circuit is the same as that of a condenser, §196.

**246. Starting of Synchronous Motors.**—Generally a synchronous motor does not have sufficient starting torque to come up to speed under load and, therefore, it requires an auxiliary source of power. After the motor has been brought to synchronous speed, the e.m.f. induced in its armature winding must have a phase difference of about 180 degrees with the line potential before the motor can be connected to the mains. A device, known as a *synchronizer,* is used to determine both speed and phase so that the motor can be put into service.

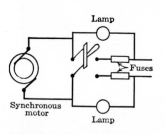

FIG. 322. Synchronizing by means of lamps

The simplest form of synchronizer consists of incandescent lamps connected across a switch that is inserted in the motor circuit, as shown in Fig. 322. The lamps will be brightest when the phase difference between the service and motor potentials is zero, and will be dark when this phase difference is 180 degrees, the lamps being alternately bright and dark as the motor comes up to synchronism. When synchronism is approached, the alternations in the brilliancy of the lamps become less rapid and finally become so slow as to permit closing of the main switch at an instant when the lamps are dark.

An instrument known as a *synchroscope* is extensively used to determine when synchronism has been reached; its appearance is shown in Fig. 323. The pointer of the instrument rotates at a speed proportional to the difference in frequency between the e.m.f. of the motor and the p.d. of the service to which the motor is being synchronized. When the machine is in synchronism and the pointer comes to rest at the top of the scale, the main switch may be closed, thus connecting the motor to the supply circuit.

The plan of one form of synchroscope is given in Fig. 324. A laminated iron structure $M$ is magnetized by current from the service mains in winding $f$, and a laminated core $C$ is pivoted between the pole pieces. The core has two windings placed at right angles to each other; these are connected by slip rings (not shown) to the synchronous motor. The circuit of winding 1 includes a resistor $R$ and that of winding 2 includes a reactor $X$. The current in $f$ is in phase with the impressed p.d.; the current in 1 is in phase with the motor e.m.f. and that in 2 lags this e.m.f. by 90 degrees. At synchronism, the currents in windings $f$ and 1 will be in phase and the core will take the position shown. When the motor e.m.f. lags or leads the p.d. across the line by 90 de-

FIG. 323. Synchroscope
General Electric Company

grees, the current in winding 2 will be in phase with that in $f$ and cause the core to assume a position at right angles to that shown, bringing coil 2 horizontal. For other phase relations the core will take corresponding positions, and the pointer attached to it will show the angular position. Thus, the pointer shows firstly whether the motor is revolving too fast or too slow, and secondly, when the phase relations between motor and line potentials are such that the motor switch may be closed. Synchronous moto/ having rotors co

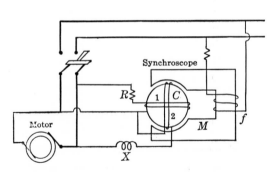

FIG. 324. Construction of a synchroscope

structed with self-starting auxiliary cage windings are sta/ with reduced alternating potentials on the armature and witl field circuit open. When such a motor has nearly reached chronous speed, the full p.d. is applied to the armature and current is supplied to the field windings. When starting/

manner precaution must be taken against puncturing the insulation of the field coils, due to the high e.m.f. produced in them by the alternating flux. This is usually done by placing a resistance, high or low depending upon the torque desired, across the entire field winding to take care of the induced e.m.f. A less practical method of opening the field circuit at several points with a multi-blade switch would require many slip rings.

**247. Changing Alternating to Direct Current.**—The economical operation of electricity supply systems requires that the electrical energy generated in the central stations be transmitted at high potentials to points where the energy is to be used, and that at these points the potential be lowered to values suitable for the apparatus to be operated. The ease with which the potential of alternating currents can be changed has resulted in the almost universal use of such currents in transmission systems. But alternating current cannot be used to perform all the services in which electricity takes part; for example, the electroplating of objects, the electrolytic refining of metals, the charging of storage batteries, the functioning of electrical communication systems, and the operation of urban electric railways, all require direct current. In consequence, there is frequent need for changing the alternating current generated into direct current for use in particular applications.

One method employed for the conversion of alternating to direct current makes use of a machine called a *synchronous converter* or more commonly a *rotary converter*. Many are used in the substations of electric railway systems for supplying direct current to the standard traction equipments so well suited for local transportation purposes. Another machine for current conversion is the *motor-generator set* and it consists, as its name implies, of a motor permanently coupled to a generator. In both, the electrical energy supplied as alternating current is first changed to mechanical energy of rotation and then changed again to electrical energy as direct current.

There are a number of other devices for changing alternating to direct current which do not involve the intermediate development of mechanical energy of rotation; such devices are called *rectifiers.* Many of these are used in combination with electron tubes or other electronic devices, and are described in Lesson XXV.

**248. Rotary Converters.**—The rotary converter is essentially an alternator and a direct-current generator combined in one machine, the general appearance of which is similar to that of a direct-current generator. It has, in addition, suitable collector rings connected to the armature winding at points having the proper angular relation, the number of rings depending on the number of phases on which the machine is operated.

It has been shown in Lesson XVIII that the armature coils of a direct-current generator have alternating currents in them and that, by using a commutator, the alternating current is changed to direct current for use in the external circuit. Therefore, if a commutator is placed on the revolving armature of an alternator and its segments are connected to appropriate points of the winding, a direct current can be delivered to the load circuit through brushes on the com-

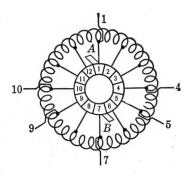

Fig. 325. Taps on rotary converter armature to permit single-, two-, or three-phase operation

mutator. The machine is driven by supplying alternating current of proper potential to the armature winding through brushes on the slip rings. In this way an alternator can be changed into a rotary converter, a machine which performs the functions of both motor and generator.

Fig. 325 represents the armature winding of a bipolar converter with the connections to the commutator segments numbered from 1 to 12. If the converter is to operate on a single-phase circuit, the alternating current is led to and from the armature winding through slip rings connected to taps 1 and 7. For two-phase operation two more rings are added to the machine and connected to taps 4 and 10, which are 90 degrees away from the other taps, thus making four slip rings on the alternating-current side of the machine. If the armature is to be used on a three-phase circuit it is provided with three slip rings connected to taps 1, 5 and 9, which are 120 degrees apart. Whether the machine operates from a single-phase or a polyphase supply circuit, the direct current is available between brushes $A$ and $B$. In practice rotary converters have multipolar field frames and drum-wound armatures, but their connections are explained more simply by reference to a ring-wound armature shown in a bipolar field.

The direct e.m.f. produced by a converter bears a fixed ratio to the impressed alternating p.d. In a single-phase machine,

FIG. 326. Three-phase, 150-kilowatt, 6-pole synchronous converter

General Electric Company

the direct e.m.f. is equal to the maximum value of the impressed alternating e.m.f., which means 1.41 times its effective value. In polyphase converters the ratio of conversion will depend upon the number of phases and the method of connecting the windings; for example, in a two-phase machine the ratio of the alternating to the direct e.m.f. for each phase is 0.71, and in a three-phase converter this ratio is 0.62 for each phase. Rotary converters are mostly of the polyphase type; a three-phase machine is shown in Fig. 326.

Rotary converters may be started and be brought up to synchronous speed by the same methods that are employed with synchronous motors, §246. They may also be started from the direct-current side when direct current is available; this is done by operating the machine as a shunt motor, then shutting off the direct-current and applying a reduced alternating p.d. to the armature, and finally raising the potential until the machine is in synchronism.

If a direct current is supplied to a rotary converter through the brushes and commutator, it will run as a shunt motor and alternating current may be taken from the slip rings; when operated under these conditions the machine is termed an *inverted converter*.

Rotary converters of large capacity, or those that may be required to carry large momentary overloads, have commutating poles which fulfill the same functions as they do in direct-current generators and motors, §214, that is, insuring sparkless commutation from no load to heavy load with a fixed brush position. Machines of this type that are started from the alternating-current side are provided with a mechanical brush raising device, for the brushes must be raised from the commutator during starting in order to prevent sparking. Another use that is made of commutating poles in rotary converters is to adjust the ratio between the potentials of the direct and the alternating current by varying the excitation of the commutating poles by means of a rheostat inserted in series with the pole windings; converters having this form of regulation are termed *regulating-pole* rotary converters.

Regulation of converters is also accomplished by means of reactors connected in the leads to the slip rings of the machines. The field excitation is adjusted so that the converter takes a lagging current at light load, and a leading current at heavy load. This phase shift causes the alternating p.d. of the converter, and likewise the direct e.m.f., to rise automatically as the load on the machine increases.

A *synchronous booster converter* consists of an ordinary converter mounted on the same shaft with an alternator serving as a booster. This has the same number of poles as the converter and its armature winding is included in the taps from the converter winding to the slip rings, as shown in Fig. 327. By varying or reversing the field excitation of the booster, it is possible to increase

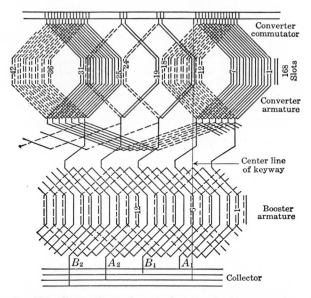

FIG. 327. Connections of a synchronous booster converter

or decrease the alternating p.d. impressed upon the converter element, and thereby to control the direct e.m.f.; this may be varied from 15 to 30 per cent above and below normal.

**249. Motor-Generator Sets.**—A motor-generator set consists of a motor mechanically coupled to one or more generators, with all machines usually mounted on the same bed plate. Motor-generator sets may comprise: (1) direct-current machines, (2) alternating-current machines, and (3) both direct- and alternating-current machines.

A motor-generator set of the first type converts from a direct current at one potential to a direct current at another. Such units are used for battery charging, electrolytic work, and potential boosting; also with machines of equal e.m.f. as a *balancer* for maintaining the potential of the middle wire of three-wire systems.

A balancer associated with a three-wire distribution circuit is shown in Fig. 328 with its two dynamos connected in series across the generator leads. If the circuit is unbalanced and supplies a heavier load on the upper branch, the p.d. on the lower branch tends to become greater than on the other and causes the lower dynamo of the balancer to operate as a motor and drive the upper

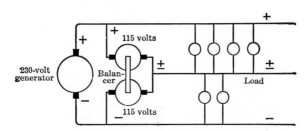

FIG. 328. Motor-generator used as balancer on a three-wire circuit

one as a generator; that machine then assists in supplying current to the greater load on the upper branch. This action takes place automatically in either direction. Balancers have shunt or compound excitation and are rated by the current in the neutral wire.

**Experiment 105.**—Make up a motor-generator set of two direct-current dynamos and drive one machine as a motor. Connect the generator to a suitable load and measure the p.d. at the load and the current supplied to it. Measure the input similarly, and determine the efficiency of the motor-generator set.

A motor-generator set of the second type is used chiefly for changing alternating current of one frequency to another of different frequency, with or without a change in the number of phases or in potential; this type, known as a *frequency changer,* is used to interlink power systems operated at different frequencies.

The third type of motor-generators is employed, like rotary converters, to change alternating current to direct current. This type is the most common and some of its principal uses are as follows: (a) to obtain direct current for charging storage batteries, using the power furnished by alternating current service mains, in connection with garage service, railway signal systems, and telephone circuits; (b) to furnish direct-current for operating arc lamps for motion-picture projection, for searchlights, and for similar work where the flicker of alternating-current arcs is objectionable; and (c) to supply low-potential direct currents for electrolytic work. Fig. 329 shows a motor-generator set driven by a 60-horsepower induction motor and the direct-current generator supplies 40 kilowatts at 100 volts.

FIG. 329. Motor-generator set

General Electric Company

## QUESTIONS

1. Distinguish between a single-phase and a polyphase alternator.
2. What are the advantages of a revolving-field alternator over one of the revolving-armature type?
3. Is the three-phase alternator armature of Fig. 318 connected in Δ or Y?
4. Make up a radial diagram of a Δ-connected armature winding for a four-pole alternator.
5. Why are alternators rated in kilovolt-amperes?
6. What is a synchronous motor and how does it operate?
7. To what uses are synchronous motors limited?
8. How are synchronous motors started and what simple means would you use to determine when the motor is running in synchronism?
9. Explain the operation of a synchroscope.
10. What are rotary converters and for what purpose are they used?
11. Explain how the taps on the armature of a rotary converter are located for two-phase and for three-phase operation.
12. What is a regulating-pole converter? a synchronous booster converter? an inverted converter?
13. State the purpose of cage or damper windings on alternators and converters.
14. Mention some of the uses of motor-generator sets.
15. Explain the operation of a balancer on a three-wire direct-current distribution system.

## PROBLEMS

1. What is the frequency of an alternator having 30 poles and revolving at 240 revolutions per minute? *Ans.* 60 cycles.

2. A three-phase Δ-connected alternator supplies current to a balanced receiving circuit of 80 per cent power factor. The p.d. across the line wires is 220 volts and the current in each line is 20 amperes. (a) What power is supplied by the machine? (b) Determine the potential difference across each phase winding and the current in it. *Ans.* (a) 6.09 kilowatts; (b) 220 volts, 11.6 amperes.

3. If the limiting current through the armature winding of the alternator of Problem 2 is 15 amperes, what would be the rating of the machine when supplying current over only one phase? *Ans.* 4.95 kilovolt-amperes.

4. It is desired to have a simple three-phase converter deliver direct current at 600 volts. What alternating p.d. should be applied to the slip rings? *Ans.* 372 volts.

5. A motor-generator set delivers 160 kilowatts of direct current at 250 volts and is driven by a 550-volt three-phase synchronous motor. Under these conditions the current in each line wire to the motor is 200 amperes at unity power factor. Calculate the efficiency of the set. *Ans.* 84.2 per cent.

6. What would be the highest speed for which a 25 to 60 cycle frequency changer could be designed? *Ans.* 300 revolutions per minute.

# Lesson XXII

---

# INDUCTION MOTORS

---

Polyphase induction motors—Squirrel-cage and wound-rotor motors—Direction of rotation—Starting of polyphase induction motors—Single-phase induction motors—Split-phase motor—Capacitor motor—Shading-pole motor—Single-phase series motors—Repulsion motors—Questions and Problems.

**250. Polyphase Induction Motors.**—There are three general types of alternating-current motors: Synchronous motors, single-phase and polyphase induction motors, and single-phase commutator motors. The first was described in the preceding lesson and the others will be considered in this one. Of these types, the polyphase induction motor is the simplest and most common form for industrial use.

The induction motor was invented in 1888 by Nikola Tesla (1856-1943); it is a constant-speed machine which behaves like the direct-current shunt motor. The stationary member of the induction motor that corresponds to the field structure of the shunt motor is called the *stator,* and the rotating member that corresponds to the armature of that motor is called the *rotor.* The machines differ in that the current in the armature windings of the direct-current motor is conducted to them by brushes through a commutator, while the current in the rotor windings of the induction motor is induced in them by the alternating magnetic fields set up by currents in the stator windings. The operating principle of the induction motor is based on a *rotating magnetic field.*

The idea of a rotating magnetic field can be illustrated by suspending a horseshoe magnet from its midpoint with its poles extending downward, and placing a compass a short distance below the magnet. The needle will immediately take up a position parallel to the magnetic flux passing from one pole of the magnet to the other. If the magnet is now rotated, its magnetic field moves with it and causes the needle to follow. In the induction motor a revolving magnetic field is developed without moving the magnetic structure itself, and this moving field sets the pace for the rotor.

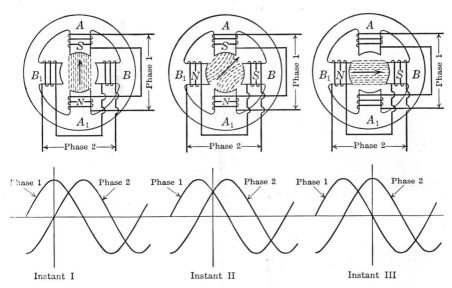

FIG. 330. Production of rotating field by two-phase currents

A rotating magnetic field can be produced by alternating currents through two or more groups of coils wound on a circular iron ring. The action will be explained by the aid of Fig. 330, which shows a four-pole ring with two windings that receive current from a two-phase alternator, §243. Phase 1 of this machine supplies current to the coils on poles $A$ and $A_1$ of the ring, while phase 2 supplies current to the coils on poles $B$ and $B_1$. The sinusoidal currents from the alternator are shown along the lower part of the figure. The three diagrams of the ring represent the magnetization at three different instants during a cycle.

At instant I, the current of phase 1 has its maximum value and the poles of coils $AA_1$ are fully magnetized, while the current of phase 2 is zero and the poles $BB_1$ are not magnetized; consequently, the magnetic flux will be directed between poles $A$ and $A_1$ and a compass needle placed at the center of the ring will assume the vertical position as shown by the arrow. At instant II, the current in phase 1 has decreased to the same value as that to which the current in phase 2 has increased, and the four poles are now equally magnetized, drawing the needle to the 45-degree position indicated. At instant III, the current of phase 1 has decreased to zero, while the current of phase 2 has reached its maximum value; consequently, the flux will be directed between poles $B$ and $B_1$, drawing the needle into a horizontal position. The above action is repeated during successive instants and the field and needle continue to revolve in the same direction as long as the two-phase currents are supplied to the coils. If the compass needle is replaced by a rotor, consisting of an iron core wound with copper conductors, there will be currents induced in these conductors, and they will produce a magnetic field about the rotor; this field will react with the rotating magnetic field of the stator and cause rotation.

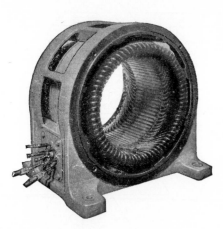

FIG. 331. Stator of induction motor
General Electric Company

The torque that would be exerted by the rotor, revolving in a field frame constructed with projecting poles as illustrated in Fig. 330, would not be uniform, for the magnetic flux would vary in strength from instant to instant and cause the pull on the rotor to be pulsating. Commercial induction motors have multipolar stator frames without such projecting poles; their appearance is shown in Fig. 331. The structure is formed of laminated iron or steel plates having slots in which the windings are imbedded, and the completed stator resembles the stationary armature of a revolving-field alternator or synchronous motor. The coils of the stator winding are distributed symmetrically over the entire face of the core and are connected to form distinct circuits, two for a two-phase motor and three for a three-phase motor, and these circuits are supplied with current respectively from a two- or three-phase alternator.

The speed of the revolving field is determined by the frequency of the alternating current supplied to the motor and by the number of poles on the stator; the speed is not influenced by the number of phases. The expression for the synchronous speed of an induction motor in revolutions per minute is the same as that given for a synchronous motor in §245, or

$$\text{synchronous speed} = \frac{60 \times \text{frequency}}{\text{pairs of poles}}$$

**Problem 149.**—What are the three highest possible synchronous speeds for 60-cycle induction motors?

The foregoing equation shows that the synchronous speed is inversely proportional to the number of poles; therefore, the highest speed will be that for a motor with the fewest poles, namely, one pair. For a' two-pole motor the speed is $60 \times 60 \div 1 = 3600$ revolutions per minute. The synchronous speed of a four-pole motor is 1800, and that of a six-pole motor is 1200 revolutions per minute.

The speed at which the rotor revolves is always less than that of the revolving field, for if the rotor revolved at the same speed as the rotating field there would be no cutting of the field by the rotor conductors, hence no induced current in the rotor conductors nor reactions of the rotating field to yield mechanical power by the rotor. The ratio of the difference in speed of the rotor and the rotating field to the speed of the rotating field is known as the *slip* and is usually expressed as a percentage; thus

$$\text{slip} = \frac{\text{synchronous speed} - \text{rotor speed}}{\text{synchronous speed}} \qquad \textbf{124}$$

As the load on the motor is increased, the speed of the rotor decreases almost in proportion to the load over a certain range; the slip of a modern motor does not usually exceed a few per cent at full load.

**251. Squirrel-Cage and Wound-Rotor Motors.**—The usual type of rotor for induction motors consists of a laminated steel core having slots in which conductors are imbedded, and these conductors are connected to metal collars, placed one at each end of the rotor, and called *end rings*. This type of rotor is styled a *squirrel-cage rotor* because of the appearance of the conducting structure; this may be of copper bars soldered to the rings, or of aluminum cast in one piece. A squirrel-cage rotor is illustrated in Fig. 332; it shows the end rings. The current induced in the rotor conductors is in a direction parallel to the rotor axis, and the reaction of the magnetic flux of these conductors against the rotating field is, therefore, in a direction to produce the maximum torque.

FIG. 332. Rotor of squirrel-cage motor
Westinghouse Electric Corporation

The polyphase induction motor with squirrel-cage rotor is simple and rugged in construction, self-starting under load, capable of exerting a powerful torque, and operated at practically constant speed for all loads. This type of motor can be used in places where there is inflammable material, for the motor requires no collector rings nor brushes from which sparks are likely to arise.

A type of rotor frequently used in large induction motors has polar windings similar to the winding on the stator. The rotor is connected only to an adjustable resistor and the resistance of this device is gradually reduced as the motor speeds up; at full speed it operates as a squirrel-cage motor with its rotor windings short-circuited. The maximum torque which a given induction motor can exert is found to be the same for different resistances in the rotor circuit, but the speeds when it exerts this maximum torque are different. A high rotor resistance means that the torque will be large at low speed, and a low rotor resistance means a large torque at operating speed. Therefore, resistance is inserted in the rotor winding when the motor is put into operation in order to insure a high torque and a relatively small current when starting under load.

In one design of wound rotor the resistor is carried on the rotor spider and its resistance is changed by pushing a knob on the end of the rotor shaft. In another design, Fig. 333, the terminals of the winding are brought out to slip rings, and the starting resistance, located outside of the motor, is connected with the rotor windings by means of brushes. When the motor reaches its proper speed, the resistance is gradually cut out so that a large torque is secured within the operating speed range.

Fig. 333. Wound rotor of induction motor

Allis-Chalmers Manufacturing Company

**252. Direction of Rotation.**—The direction of rotation of an induction motor is the same as that of the rotating field. In order to reverse the direction of rotation of a polyphase induction motor it is necessary to reverse the direction of the field, and this is done by changing the phase sequence of the stator windings. For example, the two-phase motor of Fig. 330 can be reversed by changing the connections of one winding (either phase 1 or phase 2) in coupling the motor to the source of alternating current supply.

In a two-phase three-wire motor, the rotation can be reversed by interchanging the outer wires from the motor to the switch.

as shown at the center of Fig. 334. It can also be reversed by interchanging the internal connections of one phase winding of the stator, as shown at the right in the figure.

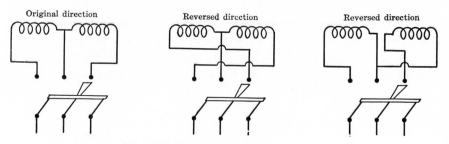

FIG. 334.  Reversing a two-phase motor

A three-phase motor can be reversed by interchanging any two leads coming from the motor to the switch; in Fig. 335 leads 1 and 2 are reversed. The same result would be achieved by reversing leads 2 and 3, or leads 1 and 3.

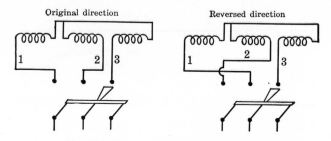

FIG. 335.  Reversing a three-phase motor

**253. Starting of Polyphase Induction Motors.**—If the rotor of an induction motor is at rest, and its stator windings are connected directly to the supply circuit to start the machine, these windings would draw very large currents. As the rotor acquires speed the currents fall rapidly and assume their operating values.

Induction motors of small size may be connected directly to the supply line through fuses and a switch, but the momentary rush of current at the start may be five to eight times that of the full-load current; consequently, a fuse that would protect a motor from an injurious overload might be blown whenever the motor is started. This condition can be met by an arrangement which employs two sets of fuses, one set having a current-carrying capacity that would accommodate the starting current without blowing, and the other set having a lower capacity sufficient to carry the full-load current of the motor; in case of an overload on the motor the latter fuses will be blown and so protect the machine. Such an arrangement is shown in Fig. 336. The double-throw switch is thrown downward to start the motor, thus connecting it directly to the line through the starting fuses; then, when the motor has acquired full speed, the switch is quickly thrown upward, thus putting the running fuses in series with the motor.

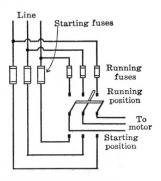

FIG. 336. Use of two sets of fuses for starting small induction motors

The method of starting squirrel-cage induction motors having outputs, say, of 50 horsepower and more, is to reduce the potential applied to the motor at starting; this is accomplished through a *starting compensator* or *auto-starter*. The auto-starter first connects the motor to the line through an auto-transformer, §264, to keep the current drawn from the line within moderate limits; naturally the starting torque is reduced. After the rotor has increased in speed sufficiently, the motor terminals are connected directly across the line. An external view of a Westinghouse auto-starter is shown in Fig. 337. The switch is operated by the handle at the right, and the mechanism is such that the handle must be moved to the starting position before it can be moved to the running position, thus insuring proper operation.

FIG. 337. Auto-starter

A connection diagram of a three-phase motor starter appears in Fig. 338. It has two auto-transformers $T$, connected in open $\Delta$, and both ends of the transformers are disconnected from the lines when the starter is in the "off" position. In the "starting" position all switches marked $A$ are closed, causing either 65 or 80 per cent of full potential to be impressed on the motor; in the "running" or full-potential position only switches marked *B* are closed, thereby removing the compensators from the circuit. The starter is also equipped with overload coils *O,* an overload trip *C,* and a low-potential release coil *L.*

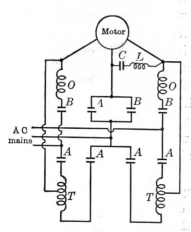

FIG. 338. Connections of a three-phase auto-starter

Although only one tap of an auto-transformer is used in motor starting service, three taps are usually provided to meet different conditions. For example, a motor that draws a starting current 500 per cent of normal, on full potential, would take a starting current of only 210 per cent of normal on the 65-per cent tap of an auto-transformer.

Another method of starting induction motors is to change the resistance of the rotor circuit; naturally, this method is applicable only to motors having wound rotors. The resistors may be mounted directly on the shaft inside the rotor and controlled by a switch on the rotor shaft, as explained in §251. With the slip-ring type of rotor, the starting resistor is external to the motor and in a form that corresponds to the starting box for a direct-current motor. Fig. 339 shows the internal connections of such a starter for a three-phase slip-ring motor, the resistors for the three phases being simultaneously controlled by the three-pronged rheostat arm. To start the motor, the stator windings are first connected to the three-phase supply circuit, and then the rheostat handle is moved in a direction to decrease the resistance in the three rotor circuits.

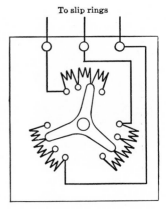

To slip rings

FIG. 339. Starter for a three-phase slip-ring induction motor

**254. Single-Phase Induction Motors.**—The single-phase induction motor differs from the polyphase type principally in the character of its magnetic field. An ordinary single-phase winding will not produce a field that is rotating but will set up one that is periodically varying in strength, and the induced currents and poles developed in the rotor by this field will tend to produce equal torque in opposite directions; therefore, the rotor cannot start to revolve. However, if the rotor can be brought to synchronous speed in some manner, then the reaction of the stator and rotor flux will be so timed as to produce a steady torque that will keep the rotor revolving.

The starting of single-phase induction motors is accomplished by three general methods applicable to small-sized motors only. These are the split-phase, the capacitance, and the shading-pole methods. The first two involve an extra winding and the third utilizes short-circuited turns for producing a magnetic flux that is out of phase with the flux set up by current in the main winding. All of them utilize squirrel-cage rotors. Motors of these types will be described in the next three sections.

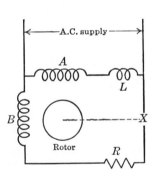

FIG. 340. Split-phase motor

**255. Split-Phase Motor.**—One method of making single-phase induction motors self-starting is to develop a second phase within the motor itself. This is accomplished by having two windings on the stator, and connecting one through a reactor and the other through a resistor, as shown in Fig. 340. With this arrangement, the single phase supply is virtually split into two phases; one may be called the running phase, and the other one, the starting phase.

In the figure, $A$ represents the winding for the power or running phase, $B$ the winding for the starting phase, $L$ the reactor, and $R$ the non-inductive resistor. The power phase is connected to the supply circuit as long as the motor is in operation, but the starting phase is disconnected automatically, by means of a centrifugal switch $\times$ as the rotor is brought up to speed. With the starting winding cut out of circuit, the motor continues operation purely as a single-phase machine.

The two windings are located approximately 90 electrical degrees apart on the stator frame. Further, the currents in these windings during the starting period are almost 90 degrees apart in phase, because the circuit of $A$ is largely inductive while that of $B$ is almost wholly resistive. Because of these facts, a rotating field is established during the starting period, and a torque is developed to get the motor under way. The reactor and resistor are generally incorporated in their respective windings. This is done by having more turns of wire on the power winding and using smaller wire on the starting winding. If the resistor and reactor were interchanged, the continuous loss of power in $R$ would greatly reduce the efficiency of the motor.

The split-phase motor has a low power factor and its starting torque is relatively small. Because of these disadvantages this type of machine is limited to the fractional horsepower class.

**256. Capacitor Motor.**—The development of inexpensive condensers of large capacitance and small volume has made possible the capacitor motor. This type of single-phase machine is equipped

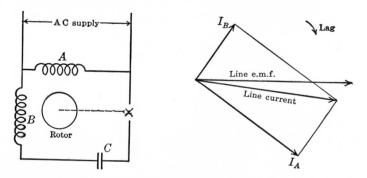

Fig. 341. Capacitor motor and its vector diagram

with a two-phase winding, that is, it has two windings placed 90 electrical degrees apart. The connections of the capacitor motor are shown at the left of Fig. 341; winding $A$ is connected directly across the service mains and winding $B$ is joined to them through a condenser $C$. Capacitor motors are generally available only in sizes below 1 horsepower.

Because of the inductive reactance of winding $A$, it draws a current which lags the e.m.f. of the line. The inductive reactance of the other winding is offset by the capacitive reactance of the condenser. With sufficient capacitance, the net reactance of circuit $B$ will be capacitive and the current in it will lead the line e.m.f. These currents are indicated by $I_A$ and $I_B$ in the vector diagram at the right of the figure, and can be made to differ in phase by exactly 90 degrees, as shown. Such currents set up a rotating field, and the resulting characteristics of the motor approach those of a two-phase machine. The absence of a resistor makes it possible to use both phases for normal operation as well as for starting.

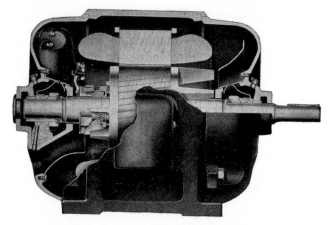

Fig. 342. Capacitor motor, Type KC
General Electric Company

Capacitor motors may be divided into three classes, depending upon the use of the condenser. In the first class, the capacitor is used for starting service only; the circuit of winding $B$ is opened by a centrifugal switch located at $X$ when the rotor reaches its normal operating speed. The condensers employed are often of the electrolytic type, §166. Motors in this class are characterized by relatively high torque and power factor during the starting period. The cost of such machines is the lowest of the three classes and accounts largely for their popularity. However, the operating torque and power factor of these machines are no better than for split-phase motors.

In the second class of capacitor motors, the condenser is permanently connected in the circuit and there is no need for a centrifugal switch. Condensers with paper dielectric are generally used. The motors are very desirable because they have high power factor during normal running as well as while starting; they are the most expensive of capacitor motors.

In the third class of capacitor motors condensers of large capacitance are used during the starting period, and others of smaller capacitance for normal running. The characteristics and costs of these machines are intermediate between those of capacitor motors in the other classes.

Fig. 342 shows a cut-away section of a single-phase capacitor motor with the capacitor mounted in the left endshield.

**257. Shading-Pole Motor.**—A machine which is gaining prominence among small single-phase induction motors is the so-called *shading-pole motor*. The arrangement of this motor is shown at the left in Fig. 343. There are slots in the polar structure to admit a single loop of heavy copper in each pole; these are shown in cross section at $S$. The loops are called *shading coils,* and the parts of the poles encircled by them are termed *shading poles.*

The field structure of the motor resembles a transformer, §260, in that there are separate windings around the iron core; the main winding connected to the source of electric power corresponds to the primary winding of a transformer, and each shading coil corresponds to a secondary winding that is short-circuited upon itself. With alternating current in the primary, currents are induced in each shading coil and these set up a magnetic flux in the shading poles that is out of phase with the flux from the main field poles. The shading poles are effective during normal operation as well as in starting.

The operation of the shading-pole motor is best explained by means of the vector diagram in Fig. 343. The main vector $\Phi_m$ represents the alternating flux produced by the stator winding. Some of this flux passes through coils $S$ and induces in them an e.m.f. by transformer action. This is marked $e_s$ and lags $\Phi_m$ by 90°, as indicated. Since each coil consists of only one short-circuited turn its inductance is low, and the current $I_s$ established in it lags $e_s$ by only a small angle. The flux $\Phi_s$ established by the current in the shading coils is in phase with $I_s$ and so is practically 90 degrees away from $\Phi_m$. Further, the axis of the shading poles is roughly at right angles to the axis of the main poles. Consequently, the conditions for establishing a rotating field have been

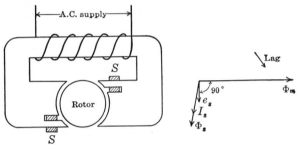

FIG. 343. Shading-pole motor and its vector diagram

met and a starting torque is assured. However, the torque produced by shading-pole motors is small, because the flux $\Phi_s$ is small compared with $\Phi_m$, and therefore such motors are built only in fractional horsepower sizes.

**258. Single-Phase Series Motors.**—In addition to induction motors for single-phase operation there are also motors with wound rotors and commutators. These are of three general types, namely: the single-phase series motor, the plain repulsion motor, and the repulsion-induction motor.

The series motor for operation on single-phase circuits is about the simplest form of alternating-current commutator motor, and in general design is practically the same as a direct-current series motor, except that all the iron used for the magnetic circuit is laminated and that a compensating field winding is often used. Since the direction of rotation of a direct-current series motor remains unchanged if the current through it is reversed, §228, it follows that any direct-current series motor will operate on alternating current.

The armature of a series motor, revolving in an alternating magnetic flux, will have several e.m.f.'s set up in its winding; these are as follows: First, an e.m.f. is induced in the armature as a result of the periodic reversals of flux from the field magnets; this is set up by transformer action whether the armature is revolving or stationary. Second, an e.m.f. is generated in the armature coils as they revolve and cut the field flux. Third, a reactive e.m.f. is set up in both the armature and field circuits due to their self-inductance. The impressed p.d. must be high enough to overcome this reactive e.m.f. and also the e.m.f. generated by the rotating armature conductors in cutting the flux, the latter being the same as the counter e.m.f. in a direct-current motor. Hence, the impressed alternating p.d. must be greater than would be applied to a corresponding direct-current motor in order to overcome the opposing effects mentioned, and produce a current equal to that produced by the direct-current pressure. The inductive action of the armature and field windings causes the current to lag the impressed p.d. considerably; consequently, a series motor has a very low power factor. A further analysis of this motor shows that it has a starting torque but little greater than the torque at normal speed.

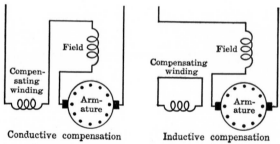

Conductive compensation          Inductive compensation

Fig. 344. Connections of compensated single-phase series motor

In order to improve the power factor and starting torque of the series motor some means must be taken to neutralize the armature reactive e.m.f., for this is not essential to the operation of the motor. This neutralization is accomplished by the use of a compensating field winding, having turns sufficient to set up a magnetic field equal and opposite to that due to the current in the armature coils. The compensating winding may be energized by either of two methods: *conductive* or *forced compensation,* in which the winding is connected in series with the main field winding and armature, or *inductive compensation,* in which the compensating winding, short-circuited upon itself, is activated by transformer action. Both methods of connection are illustrated in Fig. 344. Conducive compensation can be used with either alternating or direct current, while inductive compensation can be used only when the motor operates on alternating current.

The objectionable sparking at the brushes of single-phase series motors is caused by the local currents produced by the e.m.f. induced in the armature coils which are short-circuited by the brushes, and brought about by the periodic reversals of the field flux. The spark occurs as the short-circuit is opened when the commutator bars, to which the short-circuited coil is connected, leave from under the brushes. This sparking is minimized by constructing the armature of many coils of but few turns each, thus reducing the e.m.f. induced in each coil, and by the use of resistance leads between the armature conductors and the commutator segments.

Compensated series motors are well adapted for traction service, for they exert a large torque at starting and less torque at high speeds. They have come into quite considerable use for operating locomotives on electric railways; in several installations the motors are operated over some parts of the road with direct current.

An important commercial application of the principle of the series commutator motor is to be found in a small-sized motor that will operate on either alternating or direct current, and for this reason termed a "universal" motor. This type of motor is widely used for operating vacuum cleaners, fans, electric drills and other small electrical appliances.

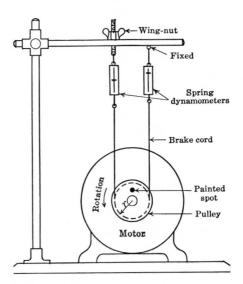

FIG. 345. Measuring the output of a motor

**Experiment 106.**—Mount a fractional horsepower 2-pole, 60-cycle single-phase series motor on a suitable stand, and adjust two spring dynamometers as shown in Fig. 345 so that the brake cord connecting them will be held taut around the motor pulley. The left-hand spring scale can be moved vertically by the wing-nut in order to vary the tension in the cord; the other scale is fixed. Put a spot of paint on the pulley and illuminate it with a fluorescent lamp that is operated from the same power supply system as is used for the motor.

When power is supplied to the motor, the machine comes up to speed and two spots will be seen on the pulley; these will be observed to move in a direction opposite to that of the rotation of the rotor. Two spots appear because the lamp flashes twice per cycle. Count the speed of the spots in revolutions per minute and subtract the value from the synchronous speed of 3600 to get the speed of the motor. Read the spring scales and subtract the lesser reading from the other in order to get the net force applied by the brake cord at the pulley. Measure the radius $r$ of the pulley. Calculate the output by means of Formula (117).

Adjust the wing-nut to yield different tensions in the cord and determine the speed and output for each; then plot the output as ordinates against speed as abscissas.

**259. Repulsion Motors.**—A motor in which a rotor exactly like a direct-current armature is placed in a magnetic field produced by an ordinary single-phase stator winding, and in which the armature remains short-circuited in a line at a predetermined

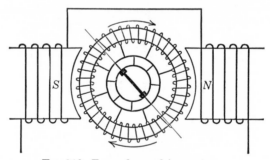

Fig. 346. Two-pole repulsion motor

angle with the stator field flux, is called a repulsion motor. The short-circuiting is accomplished through brushes which rest on the commutator and are joined by a low-resistance connector. Fig. 346 shows a simple diagram of the stator and rotor windings for a two-pole repulsion motor as well as the position of the short-circuited brushes.

The pulsating flux produced by the alternating current in the stator winding may be considered to have two components, one in the direction of the brush axis and the other perpendicular to this axis. The former component produces an electromotive force in the armature conductors and sets up a current in them, while the latter flux component reacts upon this armature current to develop torque. It is necessary, therefore, that the brush axis be located on a line inclined at an angle to the axis of the field. The operating characteristics of the repulsion motor have been improved by the use of a second set of brushes connected with a compensating field winding.

The greatest application of the repulsion motor principle has been to improve the starting performance of the ordinary single-phase induction motor, and the compensating winding is often embodied as well. The motor is then called a repulsion induction motor. The stator field is built of steel laminations and the main and compensating windings are fitted into the slots. The rotor is the same as the armature of a direct-current series motor.

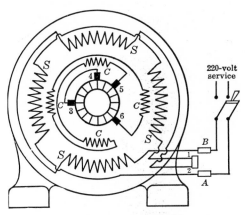

Fig. 347. Connections of four-pole compensated single-phase motor

The connections of this motor are shown in Fig. 347. There are two parts to the four-pole main stator windings $S$. The two parts may be connected in series for 220-volt operation, by joining terminals 1 and 2 as indicated, or may be connected in multiple for 110-volt operation by joining terminals $A$ to 2 and 1 to $B$. The compensating field winding $C$ is connected with a set of brushes (5 and 6) termed the "compensating brushes," which are placed 90 electrical degrees from the main short-circuiting brushes (3 and 4); the latter brushes are referred to as the "energy brushes," and these have about the same angular relations to the stator field as have the brushes of a plain repulsion motor.

The compensating winding, which derives its current from the induced e.m.f. in the armature, serves to reduce the phase angle between the motor current and the applied p.d., thus pro-

ducing high power factor at all loads. The compensating field
also serves to restrict the maximum no-load speed and to lessen
the variation of speed which usually accompanies changes of load.
This type of compensated repulsion-induction motor possesses
heavy starting torque at all loads and, after starting, operates
practically as an induction motor. The speed may be adjusted
by inserting a rheostat in series with brushes 3 and 4, which brushes
are normally short-circuited.

Another type of compensated repulsion-induction motor has
a rotor with two windings, a squir-
rel-cage winding consisting of copper bars placed in the bottom of the
rotor slots, and above these bars,
a regular direct-current armature
winding connected with the commutator. The connections of the
main and compensating stator windings of this motor are shown in
Fig. 348. The motor is provided
with a centrifugal switch $S$, which
keeps the compensating winding
open-circuited during the starting
period, but places it in series with
the main stator winding when the
motor has acquired the proper
speed.

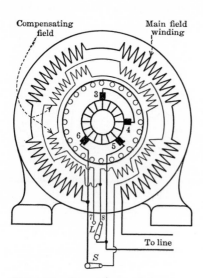

Fig. 348. Connections of compensated single-phase motor
Rotor has both squirrel-cage and regular
winding.

In operation, the squirrel-cage
winding produces practically all
the torque, and very little of the load current is carried by the
brushes and commutator. The amount of compensation can be
varied by lead $L$; when joined to point 7 it affords maximum compensation, giving a leading current at light loads, and when
connected to point 8 it affords normal compensation, giving nearly
unity power factor at rated load. The particular advantages of
this type of motor are good power factor and practically constant
speed at all loads, and a starting torque of approximately twice
the full-load torque with the motor taking about three times full-
load current.

## QUESTIONS

1. Name four general types of alternating-current motors.
2. Describe how a rotating magnetic field can be produced?
3. What are some of the advantages of the polyphase induction motor of the squirrel-cage type over a shunt-wound direct-current motor?
4. Explain the meaning of the terms synchronous speed and slip.
5. How would you reverse the direction of rotation of a three-phase motor?
6. What is the function of an auto-starter such as is used with polyphase induction motors?
7. How does a single-phase induction motor differ in behavior from a polyphase induction motor?
8. How is a rotating field produced in a split-phase motor?
9. When the centrifugal switch of a split-phase motor fails to operate, the machine overheats. Can you explain why?
10. Describe three classes of capacitor motors. Does a capacitor motor excel a split-phase motor?
11. How is a rotating field produced in a capacitor motor?
12. Describe the construction of a shading-pole motor.
13. Explain how a rotating field is produced in a shading-pole motor.
14. Name all the characteristics common to split-phase, capacitor and shading-pole motors. Which of these motors operate continuously on two phases?
15. Name three general types of single-phase commutator motors; state briefly how they operate.
16. Distinguish between conductive and inductive compensation in single-phase series motors.

## PROBLEMS

1. Determine the synchronous speed of an 8-pole, 25-cycle induction motor. *Ans.* 375 revolutions per minute.
2. What is the speed of a 6-pole, 60-cycle induction motor which has a slip of 5 per cent? *Ans.* 1140 revolutions per minute.
3. A 60-cycle induction motor rotates at 840 revolutions per minute. (a) Estimate the synchronous speed and the slip. *Ans.* 900 revolutions per minute; 6.7 per cent.
4. The following observations are made on a 4-pole, 60-cycle universal motor in Experiment 106: Diameter of pulley = 4 inches, spring scale readings—61 ounces and 11.8 ounces, speed of the painted spots = 50 revolutions per minute. Determine the output of the motor under the conditions stated. *Ans.* 0.17 horsepower.

# Lesson XXIII

## TRANSFORMERS AND RECTIFIERS

Transformers—Accommodation to load—Efficiency and regulation—
Transformers on polyphase circuits—Auto-transformers and current trans-
formers—Mercury arc rectifier—Multi-anode rectifier—Ignitron rectifier—
Tungar rectifier—Vibrating rectifier—Copper oxide and selenium recti-
fiers—Electrolytic rectifier—Half- and full-wave rectifiers—Questions and
Problems.

**260. Transformers.**—A transformer is a device for changing
electrical energy at one potential into electrical energy at another
potential, and consists usually of two electrically-distinct windings which are so arranged that the magnetic flux associated with
one winding also threads through the other. If there is an alternating current in one winding, the magnetic flux rises to full
value in one direction, falls to zero, rises again to a maximum
value in the opposite direction, and falls again to zero, and so on
as long as the current is maintained; this varying magnetic flux
induces an alternating e.m.f. in the other winding. The greater
the number of turns on that winding the greater will be the e.m.f.
induced in it.

The operation of a transformer is somewhat like that of an
induction coil, §152, except that there is no need for a make-and-
break device or interrupter. Such a device is included in the
circuit of one winding of the induction coil in order to vary the
strength of the magnetic field and thus make it possible to develop
an e.m.f. in the other winding; this is necessary because the coil
is operated on direct current. If alternating current is supplied
instead, the change of flux is accomplished by the current itself
and no interrupter is required.

The two windings of a transformer are termed the *primary*
and the *secondary* winding, the primary being the winding which

receives the energy from the supply circuit, and the secondary the one which receives the energy by induction from the primary. In most transformers the two windings are magnetically linked by a closed core of laminated steel.

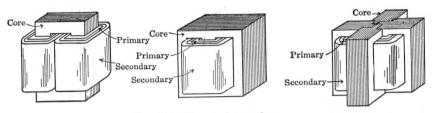

FIG. 349. Types of transformers
Left—core type; center—shell type; right—composite type.

The construction of transformers for single-phase circuits is shown in Fig. 349. The cores are built up from annealed punchings of thin silicon sheet steel with the joints staggered so as to yield a core of low reluctance. The turns and layers of each winding are insulated from each other by suitable materials and the windings are usually subjected to a vacuum-drying and filling process which removes all moisture and then impregnates them with insulating compound. In many transformers one or both windings are divided into two or more coils, each coil being individually insulated. The high-potential coils are naturally insulated more thoroughly than the low-potential ones, and the two sets are well insulated from each other.

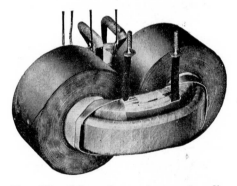

FIG. 350. Coils and wound-core of a distribution transformer
General Electric Company

In a newer design of a shell-type transformer, the core consists of two continuous strips of high-quality steel wound by machine into compact spirals around the insulated coil assembly and spot-welded at the ends to maintain tightness. This construction is shown in Fig. 350 for a transformer which steps the p.d.

down from 2400 volts to either 240 or 120 volts. A different method of forming the core is employed by another company. The strip is wound on a rectangular mandrel to the desired thickness and the resulting core is annealed, bonded and impregnated; it is then cut into two U-shaped pieces, the cuts are accurately machined, and the parts of the core are placed around the insulated copper windings.

If both windings of a transformer have the same number of turns, the p.d. produced by the secondary will be the same as that

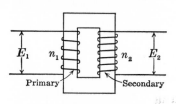

FIG. 351. Ratio of transformer windings

impressed upon the primary. To change the potential difference from one value to another, it is necessary to place more turns on one winding than on the other. Thus, a transformer with 200 turns on the primary and 1000 turns on the secondary winding will make available at the secondary terminals a p.d. 5 times as great as that impressed upon the primary. For the more general case depicted in Fig. 351, let

$E_1$ = p.d. impressed upon the primary winding,
$E_2$ = e.m.f. developed by the secondary winding,
$n_1$ = turns in primary winding,
$n_2$ = turns in secondary winding.

Then the ratio of turns is

$$\frac{n_2}{n_1} = \frac{E_2}{E_1} \qquad \textbf{125}$$

When the transformer is used to deliver energy at a higher potential than that at which energy is received it is called a *step-up* transformer, and when it lowers the potential it is called a *step-down* transformer. Any desired alternating e.m.f. may be procured with a transformer by properly proportioning the number of turns on its windings.

If there were no losses in a transformer, its power output would be the same as its power input, and the product of volts and amperes would be the same for both windings. Under these conditions,

$$E_1 \times I_1 = E_2 \times I_2$$

where $I_1$ and $I_2$ are respectively the currents in the primary and secondary windings. Rearranging this equation yields

$$\frac{E_2}{E_1} = \frac{I_1}{I_2} \qquad 126$$

which shows that the ratio of the currents is the inverse ratio of the e.m.f.'s in the two windings. Thus, for the transformer having a turn ratio of 5 mentioned ahead, the primary current would be 5 times the value of the secondary current. Specifically, if the primary winding takes 50 amperes at 120 volts, the secondary winding will supply 10 amperes at 600 volts.

All transformers have losses—eddy-current and magnetization losses in the core and heat losses in the primary and secondary windings; consequently, Formula (126) is not entirely correct. However, transformers have very high efficiencies, over 95 or even over 98 per cent for those of large capacity, and so the equation may be used for most calculations without significant errors.

Transformers are utilized in transmitting electrical energy over long distances, and high potentials are employed in order to reduce the line losses. At the power station the potential is raised by step-up transformers to the value found economical for transmission, and at the receiving substations the potential is lowered by step-down transformers to values suitable for the distribution circuits. These in turn supply energy for the operation of lamps, motors or other electrical apparatus through so-called distribution transformers.

**Problem 150.**—The primary winding of a transformer receives energy from a 2200-volt distribution circuit and supplies 90 amperes to 110-volt lamps. What is the ratio of this transformer, and what current does it take from the high-potential circuit?

In this step-down transformer, $E_1 = 2200$ volts, $E_2 = 110$ volts, $I_2 = 90$ amperes; therefore the ratio of turns is

(125) $$\frac{n_1}{n_2} = \frac{E_1}{E_2} = \frac{2200}{110} = 20$$

and the primary current is

(126) $$I_1 = \frac{E_2}{E_1} \times I_2 = \frac{110}{2200} \times 90 = 4.5 \text{ amperes}$$

The energy lost in the operation of transformers is converted into heat, and this must be dissipated to keep their temperatures within safe limits. Small transformers are placed in tanks filled with oil, and the heat generated is conveyed by the oil to the tank, and from there it is dissipated by radiation and natural air circulation. The tank for such *self-cooled* transformers is of cast iron or pressed steel of the form shown in Fig. 352. Larger transformers require increased radiating surface and, therefore, the

FIG. 352. 50 kilovolt-ampere transformer, 2400/4160 Y to 120/240 volts

General Electric Company

FIG. 353. 13,800/2400-volt self cooled transformer

General Electric Company

housing is made in the form of corrugated steel tanks. For still larger sizes, external radiators or oil-circulating tubes are used on the tanks, the latter type being shown in Fig. 353. Large transformers may also be cooled by placing coiled pipes in the oil at the top of the transformer tank and passing air or water through these pipes; the latter are called *water-cooled* transformers. Transformers which are not submerged in oil may be cooled by air circulated past the windings and core by means of a blower; these are called *air-blast* transformers.

**261. Accommodation to Load.**—When an alternating potential difference is applied to the primary winding of a transformer, a current is established in that winding which produces an alternating magnetic flux in the iron core. This flux not only induces an e.m.f. in the secondary winding, but also induces one in the primary winding; the latter e.m.f. is in direct opposition to the p.d. impressed upon the primary and is called a counter e.m.f. With the secondary circuit open, the primary current is small because the counter e.m.f. is almost as large as the impressed p.d.; this current is called the *exciting current* and is responsible for the flux in the core.

When the secondary winding of the transformer is connected to a load, the induced e.m.f. establishes a current in this winding and its associated load circuit. This current circulates around the core oppositely to the primary current and its effect is to decrease the magnetic flux. Any decrease of this flux would reduce the counter e.m.f. in the primary winding and permit of a larger primary current. The decrease in magnetic flux and in primary counter e.m.f. in commercial transformers between rated load and no load is very small, since a very small decrease of counter e.m.f. greatly increases the difference between the applied and counter potentials; as a result the primary current is considerably increased.

The increase of primary current due to loading the transformer is just great enough to balance the demagnetizing action of the current in the secondary winding; consequently, the flux in the core is maintained approximately constant by the primary current whatever value the secondary current may have. When the load on a transformer is increased, the primary of the transformer automatically takes more current and power from the line and these are in direct proportion to the load on the secondary winding.

**262. Efficiency and Regulation.**—The efficiency of a transformer is the ratio of the power output at the secondary terminals to the power input at the primary terminals. A determination of the efficiency of a transformer, made by measuring the input and the output, does not yield an accurate result when the efficiency is high. It is more satisfactory to compute the input by measuring the losses separately, and to add their total to the output of the transformer.

The core loss is measured by placing a wattmeter in the primary circuit with the secondary open; it is the same at all loads. The copper loss at full load is measured with the wattmeter similarly connected but with the secondary winding short-circuited through an ammeter, applying just enough p.d. to the primary winding to produce the full-load current in the secondary circuit. The sum of the core and copper losses gives the total loss at the stated load. With the losses known, the efficiency at full load can be found by applying Formula (115). Let

$P$ = rated output of a transformer in watts,
$p$ = core loss plus the copper losses at full load in watts,
$e$ = full-load efficiency.

Then the input is $P + p$, and the efficiency of the transformer at full load becomes

$$e = \frac{P}{P + p}$$

The efficiency at other loads may be determined in a similar manner.

To find the efficiency of a transformer when the losses are known:

*Divide the output by the sum of the output and losses, each expressed in watts.*

**Problem 151.**—A transformer has a core loss of 150 watts, and a copper loss of 175 watts when delivering its rated output of 10 kilowatts. What is the full-load efficiency of the transformer?

The losses add up to 325 watts and the output is 10,000 watts. Hence the efficiency is

$$e = \frac{P}{P + p} = \frac{10,000}{10,000 + 325} = \frac{10,000}{10,325} = 96.9 \text{ per cent}$$

In every well-designed constant-potential transformer, the secondary p.d. will be practically the same at all loads if the p.d impressed on the primary winding is kept unchanged. There is, however, a slight falling off in secondary p.d. as the load is increased because of the resistance and reactance drops in the windings themselves. This drop in p.d. over the output range from no load to full load varies almost directly as the load, provided the power factor remains constant.

The ratio of the drop in p.d. at the secondary terminals of a transformer from no load to rated load (at the specified power factor) to the secondary p.d. at rated load is called its *regulation,* it being assumed that the primary p.d. is kept unchanged. Compare this statement with Formula (113). The regulation of constant-potential transformers may be from 1 to 5 per cent depending upon their electrical and magnetic characteristics.

**Problem 152.**—The p.d. at the secondary terminals of a transformer rises from 220 to 228 volts upon the removal of its rated load. What is the regulation of this transformer?

The drop in potential from no load to full load is $228 - 220 = 8$ volts; therefore, the regulation is $8 \div 220 = 0.036$ or **3.6 per cent.**

**263. Transformers on Polyphase Circuits.**—The connection of transformers to polyphase circuits may be accomplished in many ways, but only a few of the simpler methods will be considered here. Fig. 354 shows the connection diagrams of single-phase transformers applied to two- and three-phase circuits; for all except the lower transformer at (V) the ratio of turns is assumed as 10. Numerical values are assigned to the potentials and currents for definiteness. At (I) are shown the connections of two transformers to a four-wire, two-phase system in order to yield a three-wire two-phase circuit. With 1000 volts across phases $A$ and $B$, the p.d. between the outer low-tension terminals is $100\sqrt{2}$ or 141 volts.

On three-phase circuits the three transformers may have their windings connected in Y as shown at (II) in the figure, or in $\Delta$ (delta) as shown at (III). With 1000 volts between any pair of line wires, the p.d. across each primary winding is $1000 \div \sqrt{3}$ or 580 volts for the Y-connection and is 1000 volts for the $\Delta$-connection. The primary and secondary windings of the transformers may both be connected Y, both $\Delta$, or one set of windings Y and the other $\Delta$. At (IV) are shown the connections of three single-phase transformers with their primary windings connected in Y and their secondary windings connected in $\Delta$. Instead of using three single-phase transformers in a three-phase transformation it is possible to use a single three-phase transformer; such a transformer has three sets of windings on connecting iron cores.

A scheme devised by the American engineer, Charles F. Scott (1864-1944), for the transformation from a two-phase, four-wire system to a three-wire, three-phase system is shown at (V);

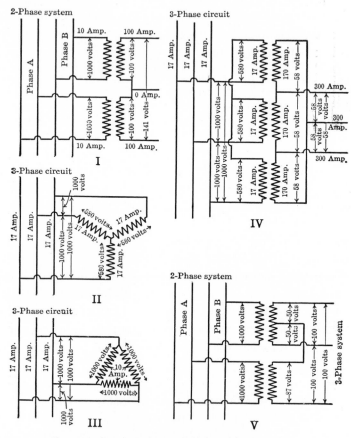

Fig. 354. Connections of single-phase transformers

| | |
|---|---|
| I | 4-wire 2-phase to 3-wire 2-phase transformation. |
| II | 3-phase Y-connection. |
| III | 3-phase Δ-connection. |
| IV | 3-phase transformation from Y to Δ. |
| V | 2-phase to 3-phase Scott transformation. |

the upper transformer has a tap at the middle point of its secondary winding and the lower transformer has a ratio of 10 to $\frac{1}{2}\sqrt{3}$.

**264. Auto-Transformers and Current Transformers.**—Transformers in which a part of the winding is included in both the primary and secondary circuits is called an *auto-transformer*.

The turn ratio of such a device is the ratio of the number of turns included between the high-potential terminals and the number between the low-potential terminals, as indicated in Fig. 355. Such transformers are used in starting devices for induction motors, as compensators for varying the e.m.f. of alternating-current circuits over limited ranges, and for other purposes where small transformation ratios are required. Auto-transformers for starting service are designed for high current and high magnetic flux densities because they are in service for relatively short periods of time.

The transformers considered so far are those used on constant-potential circuits and most transformers are for this purpose. Another type which is used in connection with electrical measuring instruments is called a *current transformer*. The primary winding is connected in series with the circuit in which the current is to be measured, and the secondary winding is connected directly with the terminals of the ammeter. The current

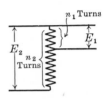

Fig. 355. Connections of an auto-transformer

through this instrument will then be proportional to but much less than the main current and the instrument will not be subjected to the high potentials of the main circuit. In using a current transformer be sure to short-circuit the secondary winding when connecting or breaking the connection between the transformer and the ammeter.

**265. Mercury Arc Rectifier.**—The device that first became available for changing alternating current to direct current without mechanical motion is the mercury arc rectifier. It is an electronic device consisting of a small pool of mercury that serves as a cathode and one or more positive electrodes of graphite, all within a glass or metal enclosure filled with mercury vapor. In operation, a *hot spot* is formed on the surface of the mercury which emits large numbers of electrons, and these are drawn to the anodes and flow through the load circuit in one direction.

The electrons, emitted by the hot spot, collide with the mercury vapor molecules with sufficient force to liberate one or more electrons at each collision, and thus ionize the vapor; this condition is indicated by the greenish-blue glow of the rectifier, §287. Each collision between a rapidly moving electron and a neutral mercury molecule results not only in the liberation of more electrons, which join the stream to the anode and thereby add to the current, but also renders the striken molecule a positive ion. Such positive ions are drawn to the hot spot on the cathode, but move there quite slowly because they are much heavier than electrons. The kinetic energy of these ions is converted to heat upon striking the mercury pool, and it is this heating effect which maintains the hot spot when once it is formed.

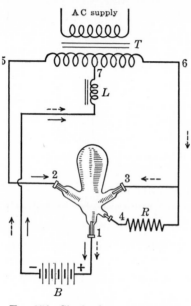

FIG. 356. Single-phase mercury arc rectifier

The relatively slow motion of the positive ions causes them to remain in the space between an anode and the cathode for a much longer period than do the electrons liberated by the ionization process. Consequently, each positive ion neutralizes the charge of many negative electrons in this space. It is this neutralization of the *space charge* of the electrons which makes possible the operation of mercury arc rectifiers at very low anode potentials. The p.d. between an anode and the cathode, called the *arc drop*, varies from 15 to 20 volts, depending on the structure of the rectifier tube, but is practically independent of the current supplied to the load.

Fig. 356 shows a single-phase mercury arc rectifier of the glass-bulb type employed in charging storage batteries. Any other load requiring direct current might be substituted for the battery *B*. The bulb has four electrodes. The mercury pool cathode is joined to electrode 1, and the graphite anodes are indicated by 2 and 3. Electrode 4 is an auxiliary or starting anode, the current to which is limited by the starting resistor *R*. The transformer *T*, with a center-tapped secondary winding 5-7-6, supplies the rectifier with alternating current. Coil $L$ is an iron-core reactor for improving the operation of the rectifier.

The rectifier is started by tilting the bulb momentarily to the right, allowing the mercury of the cathode pool to spill over and make contact with electrode 4. The starting circuit is closed by this action and alternating current is established by part 6-7 of the transformer through the resistor and battery. As the bulb is brought to its normal upright position, the interruption of the mercury path causes an arc between electrodes 4 and 1; this arc initiates the hot spot on the mercury pool.

If, at the instant when the hot spot is formed on the cathode, point 5 is positive to point 6, anode 2 will be positive to center tap 7, and current is established in circuit 5, 2, 1, $B$, $L$, 7 in the direction named and indicated by full arrows. At the termination of the half-cycle, terminal 6 becomes positive to 5, causing the current path to be 6, 3, 1, $B$, $L$, 7, as indicated by the dotted arrows. The events just described are repeated with each half-cycle and the arc shifts from one anode to· the other. It will be observed that the direction of the current in the battery is always from 1 to 7; this is the correct direction to charge the battery.

This explanation of rectifier action shows that the direct current through the battery or other load is in reality the alternating current which is established first in one half of the secondary winding and then in the other half. The reactor $L$ shifts the phase between the potential and current waves in the halves of the secondary winding so that they do not pass through zero at the same time. In this way, when the current through one anode drops to zero, the potential of the other is sufficiently positive for the arc to be maintained, so that current can be reestablished through the load before the hot spot on the cathode has the opportunity to cool. The reactor also assists in smoothing the current through the load.

The mercury arc rectifier has the advantage over rectifiers with filamentary cathodes, §268, that the number of electrons emitted by the hot spot increases almost without limit as the load increases. Therefore, the maximum current taken from a mercury arc rectifier is always determined by other considerations than the limitation of the emitter. The reverse of this is generally true of rectifiers which do not employ mercury pool cathodes. A disadvantage of the mercury arc rectifier is the fact that it ceases to function whenever the load circuit is opened, and must be restarted each time the circuit is closed. Therefore, such rectifiers are not readily adaptable to service where the direct-current circuit is interrupted frequently.

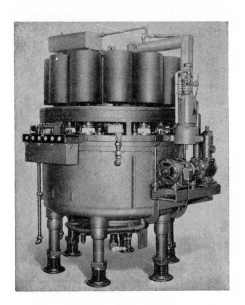

FIG. 357. Water-cooled 2000-kw. mercury arc rectifier

Allis-Chalmers Manufacturing Company

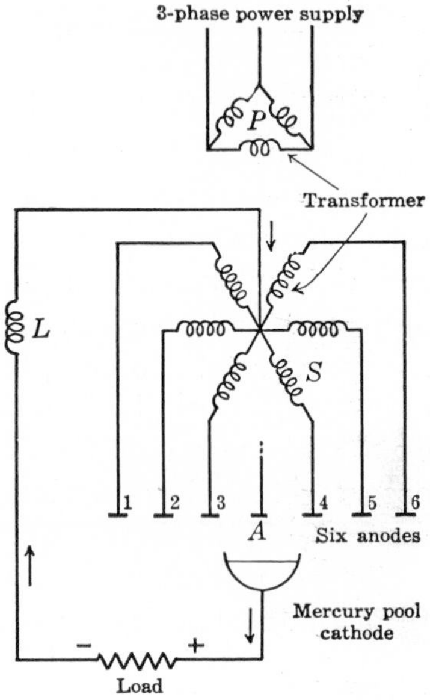

FIG. 358. Circuit of 6-anode mercury-arc rectifier

**266. Multi-Anode Rectifier.**—Mercury arc rectifiers with a number of anodes for operation on polyphase circuits were introduced some years ago. They are now so highly developed and efficient that many converters and motor-generator sets are being replaced by them, especially in direct-current urban railway service. Fig. 357 shows an exterior view of a multi-anode water-cooled rectifier for railway work, having a rated output of 4000 amperes at 500 volts. The rotary and high vacuum pumps are shown at the right for maintaining the proper low pressure in the steel tank, and the cylindrical anode radiators are shown at the top.

Fig. 358 shows one of a number of circuits employed with a 6-anode rectifier. Three-phase power is supplied to the Δ-connected primary windings $P$ of the transformer, and the secondary windings $S$ are arranged as a 6-phase star. The starting anode $A$ is supplied with power from a separate transformer, not shown. As soon as current is established in its circuit, this anode is lifted by means of a solenoid and an arc is drawn from the mercury pool. A hot spot is produced on the cathode and then the anodes 1 to 6 take up their operation in turn. Each anode carries current for approximately one sixth of a cycle.

The p.d. applied to each anode by its corresponding transformer winding is approximately sinusoidal. As the potential on anode 1 falls from its maximum positive value, that on anode 2 is rising, and when this potential is just slightly greater than the diminishing potential on anode 1, the arc snaps to anode 2. This process continues from anode to anode. The reactor $L$ provides a phase shift between the applied alternating potentials and the resulting currents, and also serves to smooth the direct current supplied to the load.

The operation of this multi-anode rectifier is, thus, basically the same as the older glass-bulb type with two anodes. However, it is much more efficient and produces a direct current with decidedly less ripple than the two-anode rectifier of the same output. Neither type is adapted to intermittent operation.

**267. Ignitron Rectifier.**—A modification of the mercury arc rectifier utilizes, in addition to a graphite anode and a mercury pool cathode, a third electrode or *ignitor;* this rectifier is called an *ignitron.* The tip of the ignitor, which is partly submerged in the mercury pool, is made of silicon carbide, a high-resistance refractory material of irregular surface.

When a p.d. is applied between the terminals of the ignitor and the mercury pool, so as to make the ignitor positive, minute arcs are formed between the ignitor tip and the mercury. If the anode is also positive when these arcs are initiated, a hot spot develops on the mercury cathode, and the current is established through the load circuit. Ionization takes place in the mercury vapor of an ignitron just as it does in the operation of a mercury arc rectifier.

Fig. 359 shows an ignitron used as a half-wave rectifier in conjunction with a thyratron, §296. Power is received from a single-phase supply circuit through transformer *T*. When terminal *a* of its secondary coil *ab* reaches a sufficiently high positive value, the thyratron permits current through itself and through the ignitor and the load. Tiny arcs at the ignitor start a hot spot on the mercury and, since the anode is positive at the time, current starts through the ignitron from anode to cathode. This current continues until the potential on the anode approaches zero. No current is passed by either the ignitron or the thyratron when terminal *a* and the anodes of the two tubes are negative. The thyratron is employed to assure that current is directed only from the ignitor to the cathode, so as to prevent damage that a reversed current might cause to the ignitor.

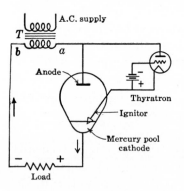

FIG. 359. Circuit of ignitron with controlling thyratron

Ignitrons are built in single-anode units; this construction makes possible a closer spacing of anode and cathode, and brings the arc drop down to about 12 volts. This low value for the arc drop accounts in part for the high efficiency of the ignitron. Ignitrons are also used in banks of 3, 6 and 12 units for operation as multi-anode rectifiers.

Since the hot spot on the mercury pool of an ignitron is initiated by electronic means almost instantly, the device is particularly useful in services that involve frequent and accurately-timed starting and stopping. For this reason ignitrons are almost exclusively used in electric welding where large currents are employed for very short and definite intervals.

**268. Tungar Rectifier.**—A rectifier that is widely used for charging storage batteries consists of a graphite anode and a closely-coiled tungsten filament that serves as a cathode, both mounted within a glass enclosure that contains an inert gas at low pressure. In this device, called a *tungar rectifier*, the heated filament emits electrons which ionize the enclosed gas in the same manner as in mercury arc rectifiers. The emission of electrons from heated filaments is considered in Lesson XXV.

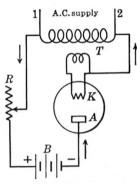

The connections of a tungar rectifier used as a battery charger are shown in Fig. 360. The transformer $T$ supplies power at a low potential to the filamentary cathode $K$ and heats it. Rheostat $R$ is in the circuit of anode $A$ and controls the current which charges battery $B$. When terminal 1 of the supply circuit is positive with respect to terminal 2, anode $A$ is positive to cathode $K$, and current is established as indicated by the arrows; during this half-cycle the battery receives a charge. When

FIG. 360. Circuit of a Tungar rectifier

the polarity of terminals 1 and 2 is reversed, no electrons proceed to $A$, ionization ceases, and no current traverses the tube; during this half-cycle the battery does not charge.

FIG. 361. Tungar battery charger
General Electric Company

Fig. 361 shows a tungar rectifier rated at 6 amperes and from 7.5 to 75 volts; it can be used for charging from three to thirty lead storage cells or an equivalent number of Edison cells.

**269. Vibrating Rectifier.—** A mechanical device for changing an alternating current to a direct current is called a *vibrating rectifier*. Its chief application is for charging three-cell storage batteries, such as are used on automobiles, from alternating-current lighting circuits. The rectifier consists of a transformer to secure a lower potential difference, and an electrically-operated switching mechanism to rectify the reduced e.m.f. The circuits of the rectifier are shown in Fig. 362. Alternating current is supplied to stationary magnets $M, M$ and its strength is regulated by rheostat $R$. The armature $m$ for these magnets is pivoted at the center, has a winding for its magnetization, and carries a spring for making contacts at $C, C$. The other resistors are for regulating the load current, and the condensers are for eliminating sparking at the contacts.

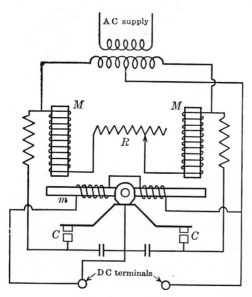

FIG. 362. Circuits of a vibrating rectifier

The rectifier is essentially a polarized relay with its armature vibrating in synchronism with the alternations of the supply current. The armature is magnetized from the battery connected to the D.C. terminals so that one end is north and the other south permanently. The alternating-current magnets are connected so that the lower ends have like polarity during each half-cycle. With the alternating current in one direction, the armature is drawn to one side and one of the contacts closes; during the next half cycle the other contact closes, and so on. The direction of current through the output circuit remains unchanged.

**270. Copper Oxide and Selenium Rectifiers.**—It is known that when different metals are placed in contact with each other they assume slightly different potentials. This effect is explained on the electron theory by considering that the free electrons within the metals move about in haphazard fashion with varying speeds, and that they pass across their mutual boundary more readily in one direction than the other; as a result one metal becomes negative and the other one positive. The resulting difference of potential, spoken of as *contact potential,* depends upon the metals used and upon the temperature. The establishment of different contact potentials at the two junctions of a thermocouple is the basic principle of its operation, §143.

The greater mobility of electrons in one direction than the other across a boundary between a pair of substances is made use of extensively in rectifying alternating currents. One of the substances is a good conductor and the other is distinctly inferior in conductivity and may be styled a semi-conductor. The two substances are separated by what is termed a *barrier layer,* a thin insulating "film" which, however, allows electrons to pass through in either direction. The conductor possesses many free electrons while the semi-conductor has only a few of them. When a difference of potential is applied from one substance to the other, an electric field is set up across the barrier layer, and since this layer is exceedingly thin, even a comparatively small p.d. will produce a strong field. If the polarity is such that the conductor is negative and the semi-conductor is positive, then the free electrons are speeded sufficiently to enable them to pass through the barrier layer; when the polarity is reversed the same action takes place, but since the number of free electrons in the semi-conductor is very much less than in the conductor, only a few get across the barrier. Consequently, the current established in one direction through such a device is vastly greater than in the other. When an alternating p.d. is applied to it, the current through it will be practically unidirectional, and so the device constitutes a *dry-contact rectifier.*

The copper oxide rectifier consists of copper disks or plates that have been oxidized on one side by heating to a high temperature. These are stacked in order and firmly pressed together. Electrons pass through the pile of disks readily in the direction from copper to oxide.

The selenium rectifier consists of disks of nickel-plated steel or aluminum that have a thin coating of selenium on one side. When the selenium is first applied it has a black polished surface but this is changed to the gray crystalline form by a series of heat treatments. This selenium surface is then sprayed with an alloy to form the "front electrode," and it is between this electrode and the selenium where the barrier layer is formed. The sprayed alloy is the good conductor and the selenium the semi-conductor; consequently, electrons pass through the barrier readily in the direction from the alloy to the selenium. A sectional view of a selenium unit is shown at the left in Fig. 363 and the assembled rectifier is illustrated at the right.

Dry-contact rectifiers are used principally for the charging of storage batteries, the operation of low-current control circuits, and the supply of power to direct-current motors, relays and solenoids, as well as to low-potential electrochemical processes.

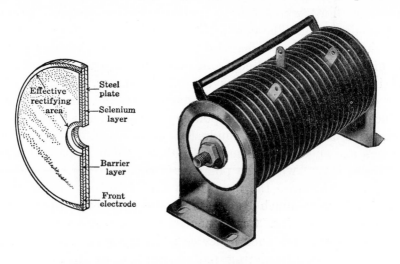

FIG. 363. Selenium rectifier in section and assembly
International Telephone and Radio Manufacturing Corporation

**271. Electrolytic Rectifier.**—To obtain relatively small amounts of direct-current power from alternating-current circuits, use may be made of the fact that certain pairs of metals, when immersed in particular solutions, permit more electrons to travel in one direction than in the other. A cell consisting of a plate of aluminum (Al) and a plate of lead (Pb) immersed in a solution of ammonium phosphate has been found to give good results. A film of aluminum hydroxide is formed on the surface of the aluminum plate, and it is this layer which permits current through the solution only when directed from the lead to the aluminum. As a result, half of each alternating current wave is suppressed.

Another form of electrolytic rectifier, known as a Balkite cell, employs electrodes of lead and tantalum in a dilute solution of sulfuric acid. Current is directed from the lead to the tantalum plate.

**272. Half- and Full-Wave Rectifiers.**—A single rectifying unit, such as those described in the last few sections, is a *half-wave* rectifier, because only lobes of alternating e.m.f. which are in one direction can produce a current through it. The circuit of such a rectifier is shown in diagram I of Fig. 364, wherein the solid triangle represents the rectifying unit. The alternating e.m.f. $E$

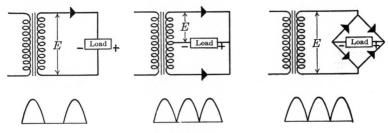

FIG. 364. Rectifier circuits for single-phase operation
I—Half-wave rectifier; II—Two-unit full-wave rectifier; III—Four-unit full-wave rectifier.

is supplied by a transformer and the direct current produced is directed through the load from $+$ to $-$. The character of this current is designated by the graph below the diagram; there are equal periods of current and no current, since only every other half-wave of the alternating e.m.f. is effective.

A full-wave rectifier comprises two or four units connected as shown in the other diagrams of the figure; in either scheme, direct current is maintained continuously through the load, although it does fluctuate between zero and a maximum value as shown by the corresponding graphs. In the connection plan at II, there are two rectifier units and the secondary winding of the transformer has a center tap. When the e.m.f. in this winding is directed upward, there is a current through the upper unit, through the load from right to left, and back to the transformer by means of the center tap. When the e.m.f. is directed downward, there is current through the lower rectifier unit, through the load from right to left, and back via the tap. Thus, the load current will be unidirectional; its fluctuation in value can be reduced by using filters, §195, with the rectifier units. A diode, §291, having two anodes virtually consists of two rectifier units within one enclosure, and operates in the fashion described.

The four-unit rectifier is connected in a "bridge" circuit as shown at III and does not require a center tap on the transformer. During one half-cycle the current is directed through the upper right unit, the load, and the lower left unit; during the other half-cycle the current is directed through the lower right unit, the load, and the upper left unit.

Experiment 107.—Make up four electrolytic cells with electrodes of aluminum and lead, and solutions of ammonium phosphate. Connect the cells in a bridge circuit to the low-potential terminals of a suitable transformer, as shown in Fig. 364, in order to form a full-wave rectifier. Use a three-cell lead storage battery as the load, and charge the battery from an alternating-current supply through the rectifier. Trace the directions of current during each half cycle, remembering that each cell conducts only from lead to aluminum through the solution.

## QUESTIONS

1. What is the function of a transformer and how does it accomplish its purpose?
2. Name three types of transformer construction; mention three methods used for cooling transformers.
3. Describe the action of a transformer and explain how its current intake accommodates itself automatically to the output.
4. How would you determine the efficiency of a transformer?
5. Explain the expression: regulation of a transformer.
6. How can three-phase alternating current be obtained from a two-phase supply circuit by means of transformers.
7. What is meant by an auto-transformer? by a current transformer?
8. Make a sketch of a mercury arc rectifier circuit and describe its operation.
9. Why are multi-anode mercury arc rectifiers employed?
10. What is an ignitron? State its advantages over the mercury arc rectifier.
11. Describe the tungar rectifier.
12. Describe the action of a selenium dry-contact rectifier.
13. Name the active elements of two types of electrolytic rectifiers.
14. Explain the operation of a full-wave rectifier.
15. Make a sketch of a rectifier circuit for half-wave and for full-wave rectification.

## PROBLEMS

1. What are the full-load currents in the two windings of a 20-kilovolt-ampere transformer that is used to supply electricity to a number of 110-volt lamps? The primary potential is 2200 volts, the ratio of turns is 20, and the efficiency of the transformer is 97 per cent. *Ans.* 9.1 amperes in the primary, and 182 amperes in the secondary winding.
2. The copper and iron losses of a 25-kilovolt-ampere transformer are 400 watts and 350 watts respectively when the transformer is delivering full load at unity power factor. (a) What is its efficiency? (b) If the secondary potential is 112 volts and the ratio of turns is 10, what will be the primary current? *Ans.* (a) 97.1 per cent; (b) 22.3 amperes.
3. Electrical energy of 5000 kilowatts is to be delivered at 2200 volts from transformers located in a substation that is situated 25 miles from a hydroelectric generating plant. The efficiency of the step-down transformers in the substation is 98 per cent, and their ratio of turns is 10. (a) What is the potential at the primary windings of the step-down transformers? (b) What is the potential at the secondary windings of the transformers located in the generating station if there is a potential drop of 10 per cent on the transmission line? (c) What power is delivered to the secondary windings of the transformers in the generating station? (d) What would be the cross-sectional area of the transmission line wires. *Ans.* (a) 22,000 volts; (b) 24,400 volts; (c) 5670 kilowatts; (d) 306,000 circular mils.
4. If the arc drop across the ignitron of Fig. 359 is 12 volts and the load resistance is 10 ohms, calculate the value of the rectified current when the p.d. across the secondary winding *ab* of the transformer is 250 volts. *Ans.* 23.8 amperes.

# Lesson XXIV

# ELECTRIC LIGHTING

Production of light—Incandescent lamps—Arc lamps—Mercury vapor lamps—Neon lamps—Sodium vapor lamps—Fluorescent lamps—Luminous intensity and light flux—Rating and efficiency of lamps—Illumination of a surface—Classes of illumination—Calculation of lighting systems—Electric light circuits—Questions and Problems.

**273. Production of Light.**—The practical utilization of electrical energy for the production of light dates back to 1880, and the electrical lighting art has developed steadily since. The types of electric light sources used today are the incandescent lamp, the arc lamp, and several kinds of gaseous conduction lamps. The latter includes low-pressure and high-intensity mercury vapor lamps, neon and other gas lamps, sodium lamps, and fluorescent lamps.

The production of light is attributed physically to actions taking place within the atoms of a glowing source. When an atom in its neutral (uncharged) state is hit by other atoms or charged particles (ions), it receives energy through the collision and as a result its electrons assume higher energy levels. The subsequent return of these electrons to their normal energy levels causes the atom to lose energy through radiation. The radiation emitted from the atom takes the form of waves in space, and the lengths of these waves from crest to crest cover a wide range. The long waves are perceived as heat, shorter ones as light, and still shorter ones as ultraviolet light and X-rays. The waves that are within the range of human vision form a spectrum of colors: red, orange, yellow, green, blue, and violet. The wavelength within this spectrum is longest for red and shortest for violet light.

548

The colors of the spectrum and their wavelength ranges are indicated in Fig. 365. The wavelengths could be expressed in inches or centimeters, but since light waves are so very short the numbers would be inconveniently small. It is customary to designate them in microns, the micron being one-thousandth of a millimeter, or one-millionth of a meter.

Different kinds of light sources emit radiations which differ in energy distribution over the various colors. An incandescent solid produces a *continuous spectrum* which extends from color to color with all hues included, but with more energy in some color regions than in others, depending upon the temperature. Luminous gases and vapors, in contrast, yield spectra consisting of

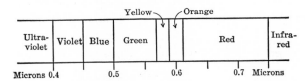

FIG. 365. Spectrum of visible light and adjacent radiations

one or more colors, each representing a definite wavelength. These discrete wavelengths are known as *lines* of the spectrum, and so the spectra of gases and vapors are called *line spectra*. The line spectrum of one gas differs from that of another. For example, sodium vapor yields two bright lines in the yellow part of the spectrum averaging 0.5893 micron in wavelength; again, magnesium has three lines in the green region averaging 0.5174 micron in length. Thus, glowing solids produce a blend of colors approaching white light, while gases produce characteristic colored light.

**Problem 153.**—The waves of green light that issue from a mercury vapor lamp are so small that 46,500 of them measure only 1 inch in length. What is the wavelength of the green line of the mercury spectrum?

If 46,500 waves in a row measure 1 inch, then the length of each wave is $1 \div 46,500 = 0.0000215$ inch. Since 2.54 centimeters are equivalent to 1 inch, the wavelength of this green light is $0.0000215 \times 2.54 = 0.0000546$ centimeter $= 0.000546$ millimeter $= 0.546$ micron.

**274. Incandescent Lamps.**—The incandescent lamp consists essentially of a conducting filament enclosed within a glass bulb and heated so intensely by the electric current that its atoms emit light. The original lamp of this type, brought out by Edison in 1880, used a filament of carbonized bamboo, mounted within an evacuated bulb to prevent oxidation. From this starting point, continued research has brought about numerous improvements in filament materials and treatment, vacuum production, and construction techniques. Tungsten-filament lamps are now commonly used for the illumination of streets and highways as well as for all sorts of interiors, and generally operate on 115-volt service mains.

The filament of the early tungsten lamp was operated in a vacuum at a higher temperature than carbon filaments and, as a consequence, the tungsten lamp proved more efficient. While it lasted just as long, the bulb suffered a gradual blackening due to deposition upon it of tungsten evaporated from the hot filament. Subsequent development brought about the gas-filled tungsten lamp, in which the bulb is filled with an inert gas, such as nitrogen, under a pressure approximately the same as the atmosphere. The presence of the gas retards the evaporation of the filament, but it introduces undesirable cooling of the filament through convection currents. To offset the latter effect, the filament is usually coiled in the form of a closely wound helix. Modern projection lamps, as well as most general-purpose lamps in the larger sizes, have doubly-coiled filaments; this concentration of the filament into a small zone localizes the heat and produces a light of great brilliancy.

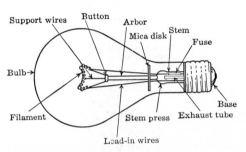

FIG. 366. Parts of an incandescent lamp

Fig. 366 shows the principal parts of a typical incandescent lamp. The bulb is of glass and may be clear, colored, inside frosted, or coated with diffusing or reflecting materials. The filament is of tungsten wire and is formed in a variety of straight-sided loops or coils. It is supported by molybdenum wires stuck into a glass button at the end of an arbor. The lead-in wires for conducting the current to the filament are made of a series of materials: nickel from filament to "stem press," Dumet wire through the glass at this point, and copper from stem press to the base. Dumet wire consists of a core of nickel-iron alloy and a sleeve of copper; this combination has substantially the same coefficient of expansion as glass. The base is of brass in various sizes and usually has a screw thread for insertion into a socket. The air is removed from the bulb through an exhaust tube which projects beyond the bulb during manufacture, then the bulb is filled with a mixture of nitrogen and argon, and the tube is finally sealed off short enough for the base to fit over it. The mica disk reduces the convection of hot gases into the neck of the bulb and protects the stem, base and socket against excessive temperatures. The fuse opens the circuit if the filament should arc across on failure; thus it avoids the sputtering of metal and the cracking of the bulb.

Because of the relatively low resistivity of tungsten, a lamp requires a long filament of very small diameter. For example, the filament of a 40-watt, 115-volt lamp is about 15 inches long and 0.0014 inch in diameter; that of a 500-watt lamp is about 32 inches long and 0.0074 inch in diameter. The filament temperatures for these two lamp sizes are respectively 2600° and 2730° C. When an incandescent lamp is operated on alternating current, the temperature of the filament fluctuates as the current changes between its maximum values and zero; the variation in light output with 60-cycle current is too rapid to be observed, but a flicker is noticeable with 25-cycle current.

**275. Arc Lamps.**—An electric arc is produced by a direct current through two carbon rods with their ends in contact when these ends are separated to form a gap of about one-quarter inch. To have the arc serve as a steady source of light, it is necessary to have a resistor in series with the carbon electrodes across the usual supply circuits, so that the p.d. across the arc will be in the neighborhood of 50 volts. As the arc is continued across the gap, disintegration of the carbon takes place, and a cup-shaped depression, termed the *crater*, is formed in the *positive carbon*, while the tip of the negative carbon assumes a conical form, as indicated in Fig. 367. These shapes are maintained as the carbons gradually waste away.

Most of the light produced by a direct-current arc lamp comes from the crater at the positive carbon, and relatively little from the arc itself. In an alternating-current arc lamp, the crater alternates from one carbon to the other with each reversal of current, and light is emitted from both carbon tips with equal intensity. On direct current the consumption of the positive carbon is about twice as rapid as that of the negative; on alternating current both carbons are consumed equally. The arc pro-

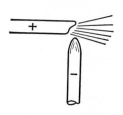

FIG. 367. Electrodes of direct-current arc lamp

vides an intense source of light and is used nowadays chiefly for motion picture projectors and searchlights.

In the *flaming arc* lamp, the carbon electrodes have a core impregnated with mineral salts. The vapors of these substances are present in the arc and the temperature of the carbons is reduced; in consequence they produce very little light and nearly all of it comes from the arc flame. The arc is enclosed in a glass globe to which the supply of air is limited by an air-circulation chamber, and the solid matter from the fumes is deposited in a condensing chamber.

**Experiment 108.**—Mount two electric light carbons on separate ring stands to form an arc lamp, and connect a rheostat or lampboard in series with it to 110-volt direct-current service mains. Regulate the gap length from about ⅛ to ¼ inch, and adjust the current to about 10 amperes. Use deeply colored glass in observing the arc. If a reading glass is handy, place it between the arc and the wall and adjust the distances so that the glass lens will produce an image of the arc on the wall. Observe that most of the light comes from the positive crater. Replace the carbons with impregnated ones and note that most of the light now comes from the arc itself.

In former years, arc lamps were extensively used in the lighting of streets, highways, and in large indoor areas. Automatic devices were used to feed the carbons as they were consumed in order to maintain the proper length of arc; this was accomplished by mechanical movements actuated with series- and parallel-connected electromagnets.

**276. Mercury Vapor Lamps.**—The early form of mercury vapor lamp known as the Cooper-Hewitt lamp was developed by the American inventor, Peter Cooper Hewitt (1861-1921). It was a glass tube several feet long with electrodes at the ends, the positive electrode being of iron and the negative one of mercury. The tube contained mercury vapor at low pressure, approximately

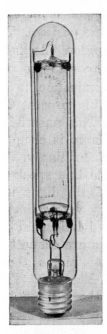

Fig. 368. High-intensity mercury vapor lamp

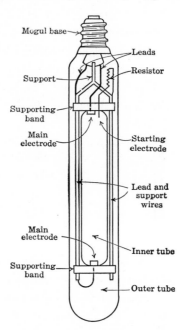

Fig. 369. Construction of mercury vapor lamp

1/30,000 that of the atmosphere. In starting the lamp the tube had to be tilted so that mercury could flow to the iron electrode; the spark formed on breaking the mercury thread initiated ionization. The present form of mercury vapor lamp is of different construction and operates at pressures ranging from ½ to 6 atmospheres; it is called the high-intensity mercury vapor lamp and is illustrated in Fig. 368.

The high-intensity mercury lamp has two glass bulbs, one inside the other, as shown in Fig. 369; this arrangement assures that changes in outdoor temperatures will not affect the inner tube too quickly. The inner or arc tube contains the two main electrodes, each consisting of a coiled barium oxide-coated tungsten wire, as well as a starting electrode. The latter is connected to the lower main electrode through a resistor so that the starting current can be kept to the proper value. A small amount of argon is added to the mercury vapor to facilitate starting.

When the lamp is connected to alternating-current service wires, electrons are drawn from the upper main electrode by the starting electrode whenever the latter is positive. This stream of electrons ionizes the argon and a blue glow fills the tube. The discharge serves to heat the mercury vapor to the point where its ionization is produced, and then conduction is established between the main electrodes. This heating process takes about 10 minutes. This unsatisfactory feature of the lamp is compensated for by its great brilliancy. The radiation is of the line spectra type and the color of the light is greenish. Such mercury vapor lamps are used for street and industrial lighting.

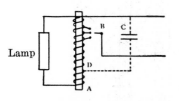

FIG. 370. Connection of mercury vapor lamp

The lamps are connected to alternating-current mains through individual auto-transformers as shown in Fig. 370. The winding has several taps at $B$ to accommodate the p.d. available at the mains, and the section $AD$ serves as a reactor in series with the lamp. Such reactors are necessary with all discharge lamps to control the currents which they take. A capacitor $C$ may be connected as indicated if it is desired to improve the power factor of the individual lamp units.

**277. Neon Lamps.**—Long tubes containing gas at low pressures are widely used for sign and display lighting. The principal gas used in these tubes is neon and this produces an orange-red light; a combination of argon and mercury produces bluish light, and helium produces a pinkish light. Colored tubes used with these gases yield other color effects.

Each tube has an electrode at both ends and is operated at from 8,000 to 12,000 volts through transformers supplied from 115-volt alternating-current supply lines. When the low potential circuit is closed, the gas becomes ionized first at the electrodes and then by collision of atoms throughout the tube. The light emitted shows a line spectrum which is characteristic of the gas used. Typical neon tube units have tubes 0.45 and 0.60 inch in diameter, operating at gas pressures of 10 to 24 millimeters of mercury, and taking currents of 15 to 50 milli-amperes.

Another type of neon lamp is the glow lamp, so named because it emits a pale blue-violet light. It is made in large numbers for use as signals and for pilot and night lights; one form is shown in Fig. 371. Glow lamps of present-day sizes take from 0.04 watt to 3 watts on 115-volt alternating-current lines.

FIG. 371. Glow lamp

**278. Sodium Vapor Lamps.**—The sodium va-por lamp delivers most of its radiation in the yellow region of the spectrum and is useful in those applications where this color of light is not objectionable. Since the lamp is available only in large sizes, either 150 or 180 watts, its greatest use is in highway illumination, flood lighting, and beacons.

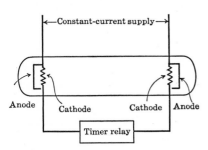

FIG. 372. Sodium vapor lamp and its connections

Fig. 372 shows the construc-tion and circuit of a sodium lamp used on a 6.6-ampere constant-current alternating-current series lighting circuit. The tube has at each end an electrode comprising an anode of molybdenum and a cathode formed of a coiled tung-sten filament coated with barium oxide.

When the lamp is connected to the line, a current is established through the filaments and through the timer relay associated with each lamp. The electrons liberated by the filament at one end of the tube are collected by the anode at the other end. When the direction of the current reverses, the other cathode supplies the electrons which are then collected by the opposite anode. This passage of electrons through the lamp during the starting period ionizes a small amount of neon gas contained in the tube. The lamp then glows with the characteristic orange-red color of neon. This discharge serves to heat the pure metallic sodium contained in the tube in order to furnish the sodium vapor. Gradually this vapor is ionized and the arc changes color to an orange-yellow. Full brilliancy is attained in about half an hour, but reasonably good lighting is available after a heating period of about 10 minutes. The timer relay opens the circuit of the cathodes after the heating period, whereupon the cathodes are maintained at operating temperature by the ionic bombardment, just as with fluorescent lamps.

The sodium vapor lamp has several glass envelopes. The inner tube has a layer of high boro-silicate glass which can resist the corrosive action of the hot sodium vapor. A second tube encloses the first and protects it mechanically. Over this one is an evacuated flask which acts as a heat insulator. This assures a proper temperature and, therefore, a proper pressure for the sodium vapor regardless of outdoor temperatures.

**279. Fluorescent Lamps.**—A fluorescent lamp is a long, slender glass tube filled with a mixture of mercury vapor and argon gas. At each end is located an oxide-coated cathode. The inside of the tube is coated with a phosphorescent compound, known as a *phosphor*, which glows when irradiated with ultraviolet light; a phosphor should not be confused with the element phosphorus. Recently fluorescent tubes have been produced in circular form for use in floor and table lamps.

When a fluorescent lamp is operating normally, the mercury vapor is ionized and ultraviolet light is produced. This light is intercepted by the phosphor which transforms these short waves into the longer ones of the visible spectrum. The color of the light emitted is characteristic of the particular phosphor used. By altering the chemical composition of the phosphor, lamps are produced yielding a variety of colors.

Fig. 373 shows the circuit of a single fluorescent lamp operated on alternating currents and controlled by a *glow starter*. This device has a bimetallic strip which, when heated, unbends and makes contact with the other or fixed electrode. When the lamp is turned on, the potential of the tube circuit is stepped up by an auto-transformer to a value sufficient to cause a discharge across the gap in the glow starter. Current is then established through the reactor, the two cathodes, and the glow starter. The glow discharge heats the bimetallic strip and causes it to make contact, thereby quenching the glow discharge. This action increases the current through the starter circuit so much that the cathodes emit electrons copiously. The absence of the glow discharge permits the strip to cool and break the contact within the starter. As the current in the reactor falls off, an e.m.f. is induced in it which acts across the terminals of both the starter and the lamp tube. Many electrons will have been liberated from the hot cathodes by this time and the additional potential pulse from the reactor sets up the ionization of the vapor throughout the tube. As the polarity changes the

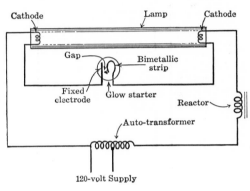

FIG. 373. Circuit of a fluorescent tube lamp

two filaments are repeatedly bombarded, alternately by electrons and by positive ions, and this action keeps the open-circuited filaments sufficiently hot for normal operation of the lamp. The reactor also serves to stabilize the current taken from the line after the starting period has ended. The starting process takes only a few seconds.

Fig. 374 shows two fluorescent tubes operated as a pair from one transformer. Tube 2 has a capacitor in series with its reactor so as to make the current lead that in tube 1 by about 90 degrees. Thus, when the current through tube 1 passes through zero and that tube is momentarily dark, the current is a maximum through tube 2 and that tube is fully bright. This arrangement reduces the flicker and consequent stroboscopic effect on moving objects which results when fluorescent tubes are operated singly. The compensator in the circuit of tube 2 limits the current in the starting circuit. This device is necessary because the series combination of a condenser and reactor results in a lowered circuit reactance.

Since the reactors used in conjunction with fluorescent lamps have considerable inductance, the current drawn by these lamps usually lags the impressed e.m.f. by a large angle and causes a low power factor. For this reason an installation having many fluorescent lamps generally requires some power factor correction.

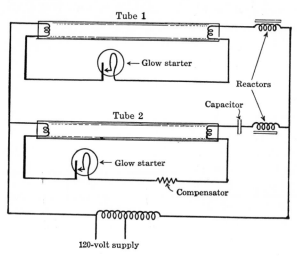

FIG. 374. Two fluorescent tubes operated as a single lamp
The capacitor helps to correct power factor and reduce flicker.

This is usually accomplished by bridging a condenser of proper capacitance across the mains to the whole installation.

**Problem 154.**—A certain 120-volt fluorescent lamp takes a current of 0.36 ampere and a power of 25 watts. What is the power factor of the lamp?

The input in volt-amperes is $120 \times 0.36 = 43.2$, while the input in watts is 25. Therefore, the power factor of the lamp is

$$(107) \qquad \text{p.f.} = \frac{P}{E \times I} = \frac{25}{43.2} = 0.58, \text{ or } 58 \text{ per cent}$$

**280. Luminous Intensity and Light Flux.**—The intensity of any source of light can be expressed in terms of a luminous source selected as a standard. For many years the flame of a spermaceti candle burning at the rate of 120 grains per hour has been used as the standard; this so-called international candle is taken as having an intensity of 1 *candlepower* when viewed in a horizontal plane. The candle is inconvenient in the measurement of light sources and, consequently, use is made of secondary standards; these are carefully calibrated incandescent lamps preserved in the national laboratories.

A 1-candlepower source will produce a certain illumination on a surface near it. Any other source substituted for this one and which produces the same illumination at the same distance is also rated 1 candlepower; if it produces twice as much illumination it is rated 2 candlepower, and so on. Such measurements depend upon the response of the observer's eye, and are influenced considerably by the color of the source.

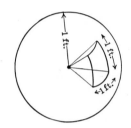

FIG. 375. A unit solid angle; measured by 1 square foot on spherical surface 1 foot from center

Radiant energy streams outward from a light source in all directions. The rate at which the source emits this energy, evaluated in terms of its visual effect, is spoken of as *light flux*. To arrive at a suitable unit for light flux, imagine a sphere of 1 foot radius with an area marked off on its surface of 1 square foot, as shown in Fig. 375. Then assume a source having a luminous intensity of 1 candlepower to be placed at the center of the sphere and to radiate light energy equally in all directions. Under these conditions the light flux which passes through the 1 square foot area is said to be a unit of light flux; this amount is called the *lumen*. To rephrase, a lumen is the amount of light flux radiating from a uniform 1-candlepower source through a solid angle of such size as to surround a unit area at a unit distance from the source.

Most light sources have different luminous intensities along different directions. The average of the candlepowers measured in all directions about the source as origin is called the *spherical candlepower*. If a source of 1 spherical candlepower be placed at the center of a sphere of 1-foot radius, every square foot on the spherical surface will receive 1 lumen of light flux. Since the entire area of this surface measures $4\pi = 4 \times 3.1416 = 12.57$ square feet, it follows that the *total light flux emitted by the 1-candlepower source is 4π or 12.57 lumens.*

Let

$I_s$ = spherical candlepower of a light source,
$F$ = light flux from that source.

Then since a source of 1 spherical candlepower emits 4π lumens of light flux, the total flux in lumens emitted by a source of spherical candlepower $I_s$ is

$$F = 4\pi \times I_s \qquad\qquad 127$$

To FIND THE LIGHT FLUX EMITTED BY A LAMP OF KNOWN CANDLE-POWER:

*Multiply the spherical candlepower of the lamp by 4π or 12.57.*

**Problem 155.**—How much light flux issues from a 40-watt incandescent lamp if its spherical candlepower is 37?

Since 1 candlepower emits 12.57 lumens, 37 candlepower will emit $12.57 \times 37 = 465$ lumens, or

(127) $$F = 4\pi \times I_s = 4\pi \times 37 = 465 \text{ lumens}$$

**281. Rating and Efficiency of Lamps.**—It has been the custom for many years to express the rating of lamps by the electrical input rather than the light output. They are rated by the power input in watts at the designated potential difference. The output of lamps is expressed in lumens; in the case of tube lamps it is often expressed in lumens per inch length of tube.

The output of incandescent lamps is noticeably affected by a change in the applied p.d. For example, if a 120-volt lamp is operated at 115 volts, its normal light output is reduced 13 per cent; at 110 volts it is reduced 26 per cent, at 105 volts 37 per cent, and at 100 volts 48 per cent.

The output of a lamp is generally measured by placing it within a sphere having a diffusing inner surface and comparing the brightness of a translucent window located on the surface with the illumination produced by a traveling calibrated lamp. Fig. 376 shows a 60-inch sphere photometer, complete with voltmeter and rheostat, for the measurement of lamps up to 1000-watt sizes. The revolvable double door supporting the two lamp sockets enables the measurement of one lamp to be made while another is being changed in the socket then on the exterior of the sphere.

Fig. 376. Integrating sphere photometer
Electrical Testing Laboratories, Inc.

The following tables give the inputs and outputs of incandescent and gaseous conduction lamps; the latter tables also include some other characteristics of importance.

OUTPUT OF INCANDESCENT LAMPS
110-120 Volts, Inside Frosted

| Rating of Lamp Watts | Output Lumens | Rating of Lamp Watts | Output Lumens |
|---|---|---|---|
| 6 | 38 | 100 | 1,650 |
| 10 | 79 | 150 | 2,600 |
| 15 | 150 | 200 | 3,700 |
| 25 | 270 | 300 | 6,000 |
| 40 | 465 | 500 | 10,000 |
| 50 | 660 | 750 | 14,000 |
| 60 | 835 | 1,000 | 21,500 |
| 75 | 1,100 | | |

TYPICAL CHARACTERISTICS OF VAPOR LAMPS

| | Mercury Vapor | | | | |
| | Low Pressure | | | | |
| | D.C. | A.C. | High-Intensity | Neon | Sodium Vapor |
|---|---|---|---|---|---|
| Input to lamp, watts ..... | 250 | 275 | 400 | 36 | 150 |
| Input to auxiliary, watts .. | 135 | 175 | 25 | 4 | 15 |
| Diameter of tube, inches.. | 1.0 | 1.0 | 1.3 | 0.45 | 2.50 |
| Length of tube, inches ... | 50 | 50 | 6 | 100 | 7 |
| Lamp current, amperes.... | 3.5 | 3.7 | 2.9 | 0.03 | 5.0 |
| Lamp p.d., volts ......... | 71 | 74 | 160 | 2,050 | 20 |
| Output, lumens .......... | 6,000 | 6,700 | 13,500 | 5,800 | 6,000 |

CHARACTERISTICS OF FLUORESCENT LAMPS

| | | | | | |
|---|---|---|---|---|---|
| Rating of lamp tube, watts... | 6 | 8 | 15 | 20 | 30 |
| Diameter of tube, inches..... | 0.625 | 0.625 | 1.0 | 1.5 | 1.0 |
| Length of lamp, inches...... | 9 | 12 | 18 | 24 | 36 |
| Input to unit, watts........ | 8 | 10.8 | 19.5 | 24.5 | 37.2 |
| Lamp current, amperes...... | 0.15 | 0.18 | 0.30 | 0.35 | 0.34 |
| Lamp p.d., volts........... | 45 | 54 | 56 | 62 | 103 |
| Life, hours ............... | 750 | 750 | 2500 | 2500 | 2500 |
| Output, lumens, for lamp of various colors: | | | | | |
|   Daylight ............... | 155 | 250 | 495 | 730 | 1200 |
|   White ................. | 180 | 300 | 615 | 900 | 1450 |
|   Soft white ............. | ... | ... | 435 | 640 | 1050 |
|   Gold ................... | ... | ... | 375 | 540 | 930 |
|   Green .................. | ... | ... | 900 | 1300 | 2250 |
|   Blue ................... | ... | ... | 315 | 460 | 780 |
|   Pink .................. | ... | ... | 300 | 440 | 750 |
|   Red ................... | ... | ... | 45 | 60 | 120 |

Lamp efficiency is expressed as the ratio of the light output in luminous flux to the electrical power input, and is accordingly expressed in lumens per watt. Let

$F$ = light output in lumens,
$P$ = power input in watts.

Then the efficiency of a lamp is

$$\text{efficiency} = \frac{F}{P} \qquad \textbf{128}$$

TO DETERMINE THE EFFICIENCY OF A LAMP:

*Divide the output in lumens by the input in watts.*

When the spherical candlepower is known, the output in lumens is given by Formula (127) as the product of 12.57 and the candle-power.

**Problem 156.**—What is the overall efficiency of the low-pressure alter-nating-current mercury vapor lamp?

The foregoing table gives the input as 275 watts to the lamp and 175 watts to the auxiliary equipment, and also lists the output as 6700 lumens. Therefore, the efficiency of the entire unit is

$$(128) \qquad \text{efficiency} = \frac{6700}{275 + 175} = 14.9 \text{ lumens per watt}$$

From the early days of electric lighting the aim has always been to produce lamps which will yield as much light as possible for each watt of electrical energy supplied to them. The early Edison lamp gave only 1.4 lumens per watt, while the present large incandescent lamps have efficiencies of about 20 lumens per watt. The sodium and fluorescent lamps have still higher efficiencies.

**282. Illumination of a Surface.**—The illumination produced by a source of light on a nearby surface is defined as the amount of light flux it receives per unit of area. To find the illumination, assume the light rays from the source to be perpendicularly inci-dent upon the surface.

Let

$A$ = area of the surface illuminated,
$F$ = light flux incident upon that surface,
$E$ = illumination on the surface.

Then the average illumination on the surface is

$$E = \frac{F}{A} \qquad\qquad 129$$

$$\text{illumination} = \frac{\text{light flux}}{\text{area illuminated}}$$

Since the light flux is expressed in lumens and the surface area in square feet, the unit of illumination is naturally the *lumen per square foot*.

The illumination produced by a light source upon a given surface is also determined by the luminous intensity of the source and its distance from the surface, assuming the rays of light strike the surface perpendicularly. Upon increasing the intensity of the source, a proportional increase will occur in the light flux falling upon the surface. Upon increasing the distance from the source, the illumination of the surface will be reduced; its value will be found to vary inversely with the square of the distance. The truth of this statement is verified by Fig. 377, which shows that a given flux through the same solid angle falls upon a unit square at a distance of 1 foot, upon 4 unit squares at 2 feet, upon 9 unit squares at 3 feet, and so on. Consequently, by Formula

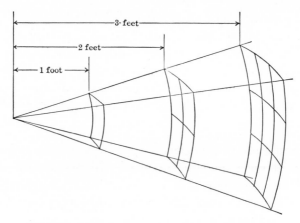

FIG. 377. Demonstration of inverse square law

The squares marked off on the curved surfaces are all of the same size.

(129), the illumination will be in the ratio of 1 to 1/4 to 1/9, that is, inversely as the square of the distance.

Let

$I$ = intensity of the light source,
$r$ = distance between the source and surface,
$E$ = illumination on the surface.

Then

$$E = \frac{I}{r^2}$$  130

$$\text{illumination} = \frac{\text{candlepower}}{(\text{feet})^2}$$

The illumination produced at a distance of 1 foot from a 1-candle-power source is commonly called a *foot-candle*.

The numerical value of illumination is the same whether expressed in foot-candles or in lumens per square foot. For example, a surface that is everywhere 8 feet away from a 256 candlepower lamp has an illumination of

$$(130) \qquad E = \frac{I}{r^2} = \frac{256}{(8)^2} = 4.0 \text{ foot-candles}$$

To compute the illumination of this surface in lumens per square foot, consider the total light flux issuing from the lamp to be distributed uniformly over a sphere of 8-foot radius. The total flux is $4\pi \times 256$ lumens, and the spherical surface has an area of $4\pi \times (8)^2$ square feet; consequently the illumination becomes

$$(129) \qquad E = \frac{F}{A} = \frac{4\pi \times 256}{4\pi \times 64} = 4.0 \text{ lumens per square foot}$$

as before.

**Problem 157.**—A 100-watt incandescent lamp yields about 1600 lumens, 600 of which fall on a table 5 by 3 feet. What is the average illumination on this table?

The luminous flux available is 600 lumens and the surface area is $5 \times 3 = 15$ square feet. Consequently, the illumination is

$$(129) \qquad E = \frac{F}{A} = \frac{600}{15} = 40 \text{ foot-candles}$$

There are several methods for measuring illumination. One instrument for this purpose is the *illuminometer;* it is virtually a portable photometer for comparing the illumination of the surface under measurement with that produced by a small incandescent lamp of known candlepower. The lamp is mounted within a light-tight enclosure and can be moved until it produces the same illumination as that existing upon the surface. Its value is then known to be $E = I/r^2$, $I$ being the candlepower of the standard lamp, and $r$ its distance from the surface. A scale may be provided on the instrument to give the result in foot-candles, since each position of the standard lamp corresponds to a particular value of illumination.

A recent development in such measurements is the *photovoltaic cell* (§298), which generates an e.m.f. under exposure to light. A plate of copper covered with a semi-transparent layer of copper oxide is exposed at the point where the illumination value is desired. Electrons pass to the copper electrode and the cell develops an e.m.f. which is proportional to the illumination. The current is indicated on a microammeter, the scale of which usually is calibrated directly in foot-candles. No external source of e.m.f. is necessary.

FIG. 378. Foot-candle meter
Weston Electrical Instrument Corporation

The "Photronic" cell shown with indicating instrument in Fig. 378 is of this general type. The cell has a diameter of about 1.5 inches. Its sensitivity to light varies with color and is about 1.4 microamperes per foot-candle or 120 microamperes per lumen.

**Experiment 109.**—Connect a Weston photronic cell to a 0-50 direct-current microammeter having a resistance not exceeding 200 ohms. This combination may be used as a foot-candle meter. Avoid exposing the cell to the sun, for light of such intensity may damage both the cell and the meter.

Carry the foot-candle meter about the laboratory and record the indications of the microammeter and the locations at which the readings were taken. Make certain that you do not cast a shadow over the cell while taking the readings. Sketch the outline of the laboratory and indicate by small crosses the points at which the observations of illumination were made. At each cross mark in small numbers the illumination observed for that location. To convert readings to foot-candles, divide the instrument readings in microamperes by 1.4.

**283. Classes of Illumination.**—The purpose of artificial lighting is to provide adequate illumination for seeing the objects intended for view and to keep the cost of the installation reasonable. In designing a lighting system care should be taken to avoid glare, for this fatigues the eye without aiding vision. Glare may be caused by light entering the eye directly from a bright source, or indirectly by reflection from a non-diffusing surface. This effect may be avoided by choosing the proper number of lighting units, by keeping them out of possible lines of vision, and by using devices which diffuse the light. There are four general classes of illumination: direct, semi-direct, semi-indirect, and indirect. The characteristics of these classes of illumination are given in the following paragraphs.

*Direct illumination* employs the light from the lamps directly without diffusing devices. Such lighting makes use of lamps equipped with reflectors or shades for directing the light to a definite area. Direct lighting with incandescent lamps is generally accompanied by glare and the production of deep shadows. However, such lighting with vapor or fluorescent lamps gives satisfactory light diffusion without noticeable glare, and incidentally the cost is less than is possible with incandescent lamps. While vapor and fluorescent lighting has so far been restricted generally to business and industrial installations, the use of this type of illumination is now finding favor in the home.

*Semi-direct* lighting usually involves the use of an incandescent lamp in a concentrating transparent or translucent shade which directs the light downward to the working plane.

*Semi-indirect* lighting generally employs incandescent lamps wholly or partially enclosed in diffusing fixtures or *luminaires*. In this class of illumination, the luminaire is translucent, transmitting a relatively small part of the light directly to where it is required and the rest is directed to the ceiling and walls where it is reflected and diffused. A room with an appropriate number of luminaires properly located will be illuminated uniformly and be free from sharp shadows. Semi-indirect lighting is used widely for home, business, and industrial illumination.

*Indirect lighting* employs opaque luminaires enclosing incandescent lamps, either of clear glass or with silvered bowls, and all the light is reflected to the walls or ceiling and none reaches the working plane directly. Indirect lighting is used wherever freedom from glare and shadow is desired. It is used in lighting art galleries, fine homes, important display rooms, and offices. The cost of maintaining such lighting is the highest of the four classes, since the larger part of the light generated is absorbed by the reflecting surfaces.

Fig. 379 illustrates typical lighting fixtures of all classes of illumination from direct to indirect. Eighteen groups of fixtures are shown, each with a *distribution curve* to indicate the relative light intensities in different directions. The length of any radial line to the curve represents the candlepower available along that particular direction. It will be noted that direct and semi-direct luminaires reflect their light downward, semi-indirect fixtures direct most of their light upwards and to the sides, while indirect luminaires distribute all their light upward or to the sides.

**284. Calculation of Lighting Systems.**—For correct interior lighting a sufficient amount of light should be provided to give the desired illumination, and the lighting units should be so designed and placed as to make it reasonably uniform, without glare. A large amount of light from the units is absorbed by the walls and ceiling, particularly if these are dark colored, and this makes it necessary to generate more light at the lamps than is received at the working plane. This is particularly true for small rooms, where wall surfaces are relatively large in comparison with the surface to be illuminated.

The usual method of determining the size of lamps to be installed is as follows: First, choose an illumination value which is suitable to the operations performed in the room. Second, calculate the number of lumens which must reach the working plane to produce the desired illumination. Third, determine the type of lighting units to be installed. Fourth, consider the relative wall and floor areas and determine a *room index* on the basis of the room dimensions. Fifth, ascertain a *coefficient of utilization* suitable for the installation. Sixth, calculate the number of lumens of light flux that must be developed by the lamps. Finally, knowing the efficiency of the lamps, determine the size and number of lighting units to be used.

The following table lists a few values of illumination which illuminating engineers now regard as satisfactory for the types of interiors indicated. The values are much higher than those recommended a few years ago.

TYPICAL ILLUMINATION VALUES

| Use | Foot-candles |
|---|---|
| Ordinary manufacturing | 10-20 |
| Precision manufacturing | 30-70 |
| School rooms | 20-25 |
| Drafting rooms | 30-50 |
| Commercial offices | 10-20 |
| Stores | 15-20 |
| Store display windows | 50-200 |
| Library or reading rooms | 20-25 |
| Residences | 10-20 |

The room index is based on the width and length of the room together with the ceiling height or the mounting height of the fixtures. Its value may be obtained from the following table which gives the index as a letter from A to J for the four classes of lighting fixtures previously described.

The coefficient of utilization is the proportion of the light produced by the lamps which reaches the working plane; its value varies with the type of lighting unit, the color of walls and ceiling, and the size and shape of the room. Such coefficients have been measured under a wide variety of conditions, and some for all sorts of lighting fixtures are given in the table on pages 572-573. If the ceiling reflects 75 per cent of the incident light and the walls reflect 30 per cent in a specific case, then choose a value for the coefficient from the first column of figures for the particular type of lighting unit and the appropriate room index. The types of lighting units numbered from 1 to 18 refer to those illustrated in Fig. 379.

The procedure for determining the illumination of a room can be summarized in the form of an equation, as follows. Let

$E$ = desired illumination in foot-candles,
$A$ = area of room in square feet,
$C$ = coefficient of utilization,
$F$ = required light flux in lumens.

Then the amount of light flux required is

$$F = \frac{E \times A}{C} \qquad\qquad 131$$

## ROOM INDEX

CEILING HEIGHT—FEET

| For Semi-Indirect and Indirect Lighting | 9 and 9½ | 10 to 11½ | 12 to 13½ | 14 to 16½ | 17 to 20 | 21 to 24 | 25 to 30 | 31 to 36 | 37 to 50 |
|---|---|---|---|---|---|---|---|---|---|

MOUNTING HEIGHT ABOVE FLOOR—FEET

| For Direct and Semi-Direct Lighting | 7 and 7½ | 8 and 8½ | 9 and 9½ | 10 to 11½ | 12 to 13½ | 14 to 16½ | 17 to 20 | 21 to 24 | 25 to 30 |
|---|---|---|---|---|---|---|---|---|---|

| Room Width (Feet) | Room Length (Feet) | | | | ROOM INDEX | | | | | |
|---|---|---|---|---|---|---|---|---|---|---|
| | 8-10 | H | I | J | J | | | | | |
| | 10-14 | H | I | I | J | | | | | |
| 9 | 14-20 | G | H | I | J | J | | | | |
| (8½-9½) | 20-30 | G | G | H | I | J | J | | | |
| | 30-42 | F | G | H | I | J | J | J | | |
| | 42-up | E | F | G | H | I | J | J | | |
| | 10-14 | G | H | I | J | J | | | | |
| | 14-20 | G | H | I | J | J | J | | | |
| 10 | 20-30 | F | G | H | I | J | J | | | |
| (9½-10½) | 30-42 | F | G | G | H | I | J | J | | |
| | 42-60 | E | F | G | H | I | J | J | | |
| | 60-up | E | F | F | H | H | I | J | | |
| | 10-14 | G | H | I | I | J | J | | | |
| | 14-20 | F | G | H | I | J | J | | | |
| 12 | 20-30 | F | G | G | H | I | J | J | | |
| (11-12½) | 30-42 | E | F | G | H | I | J | J | | |
| | 42-60 | E | F | F | G | H | I | J | | |
| | 60-up | E | E | F | G | H | I | J | | |
| | 14-20 | F | G | H | H | I | J | J | | |
| | 20-30 | E | F | G | H | I | J | J | | |
| 14 | 30-42 | E | F | F | G | H | I | J | J | |
| (13-15½) | 42-60 | E | E | F | F | H | I | J | J | J |
| | 60-90 | D | E | E | F | G | H | J | J | J |
| | 90-up | D | E | E | F | F | G | I | J | J |
| | 14-20 | E | F | G | H | I | J | | | |
| | 20-30 | E | F | F | G | H | I | J | | |
| 17 | 30-42 | D | E | F | G | H | H | J | J | J |
| (16-18½) | 42-60 | D | E | E | F | G | G | I | J | J |
| | 60-110 | D | E | E | F | G | G | I | J | J |
| | 110-up | C | D | E | E | F | G | H | I | J |
| | 20-30 | D | E | F | G | H | I | J | J | |
| | 30-42 | D | E | E | F | G | H | I | J | J |
| 20 | 42-60 | D | D | E | E | F | G | I | J | J |
| (19-21½) | 60-90 | C | D | E | E | F | G | H | J | J |
| | 90-140 | C | D | D | E | F | F | H | I | I |
| | 140-up | C | D | D | E | F | F | H | H | I |

## ROOM INDEX—Continued

### Ceiling Height—Feet

| For Semi-Indirect and Indirect Lighting | 9 and 9½ | 10 to 11½ | 12 to 13½ | 14 to 16½ | 17 to 20 | 21 to 24 | 25 to 30 | 31 to 36 | 37 to 50 |
|---|---|---|---|---|---|---|---|---|---|

### Mounting Height Above Floor—Feet

| For Direct and Semi-Direct Lighting | 7 and 7½ | 8 and 8½ | 9 and 9½ | 10 to 11½ | 12 to 13½ | 14 to 16½ | 17 to 20 | 21 to 24 | 25 to 30 |
|---|---|---|---|---|---|---|---|---|---|

| Room Width (Feet) | Room Length (Feet) | Room Index | | | | | | | | |
|---|---|---|---|---|---|---|---|---|---|---|
| 24 (22-26) | 20-30 | D | E | E | F | G | H | I | J | J |
| | 30-42 | C | D | E | F | G | G | I | J | J |
| | 42-60 | C | D | D | E | F | G | H | I | J |
| | 60-90 | C | D | D | E | F | F | H | I | J |
| | 90-140 | C | C | D | E | E | F | G | H | I |
| | 140-up | C | C | D | E | E | F | G | H | I |
| 30 (27-33) | 30-42 | C | D | D | E | F | G | H | I | J |
| | 42-60 | C | C | D | D | F | F | H | H | I |
| | 60-90 | B | C | C | D | E | F | G | H | I |
| | 90-140 | B | C | C | D | E | E | F | G | H |
| | 140-180 | B | C | C | D | E | E | F | G | H |
| | 180-up | B | C | C | D | E | E | F | G | H |
| 36 (34-39) | 30-42 | B | C | D | E | F | F | H | I | I |
| | 42-60 | B | C | C | D | E | F | G | H | I |
| | 60-90 | A | C | C | C | E | E | F | H | H |
| | 90-140 | A | B | C | C | D | E | F | G | H |
| | 140-200 | A | B | C | C | D | E | F | F | G |
| | 200-up | A | B | C | C | D | E | F | F | G |
| 42 (40-45) | 42-60 | A | B | C | C | E | F | G | H | I |
| | 60-90 | A | B | B | C | D | E | F | G | H |
| | 90-140 | A | B | B | C | D | D | E | F | G |
| | 140-200 | A | A | B | C | D | D | E | F | G |
| | 200-up | A | A | B | C | D | D | E | F | F |
| 50 (46-55) | 42-60 | A | A | B | C | D | E | F | G | H |
| | 60-90 | A | A | B | C | C | D | F | F | G |
| | 90-140 | A | A | A | C | C | D | E | F | F |
| | 140-200 | A | A | A | C | C | D | E | E | F |
| | 200-up | A | A | A | C | C | D | E | E | F |
| 60 (56-67) | 60-90 | A | A | A | B | C | D | E | F | G |
| | 90-140 | A | A | A | B | C | C | D | E | F |
| | 140-200 | A | A | A | B | C | C | D | E | E |
| | 200-up | A | A | A | B | C | C | D | E | E |
| 75 (68-90) | 60-90 | A | A | A | A | B | C | D | E | F |
| | 90-140 | A | A | A | A | B | C | D | E | F |
| | 140-200 | A | A | A | A | B | B | C | D | E |
| | 200-up | A | A | A | A | B | B | C | D | E |

## COEFFICIENTS OF UTILIZATION

| Type of Unit | Room Index | Ceiling 75% / Walls 30% | Ceiling 50% / Walls 30% | Ceiling 30% / Walls 30% |
|---|---|---|---|---|
| 1 | J | .38 | .38 | .39 |
|   | I | .46 | .46 | .46 |
|   | H | .51 | .50 | .50 |
|   | G | .54 | .52 | .52 |
|   | F | .56 | .55 | .55 |
|   | E | .59 | .58 | .57 |
|   | D | .61 | .60 | .60 |
|   | C | .63 | .62 | .60 |
|   | B | .64 | .62 | .62 |
|   | A | .65 | .63 | .62 |
| 2 | J | .27 | .27 | .28 |
|   | I | .33 | .32 | .32 |
|   | H | .36 | .36 | .36 |
|   | G | .39 | .38 | .38 |
|   | F | .40 | .39 | .39 |
|   | E | .42 | .42 | .41 |
|   | D | .44 | .43 | .42 |
|   | C | .45 | .44 | .43 |
|   | B | .46 | .44 | .44 |
|   | A | .46 | .45 | .44 |
| 3 | J | .16 | .16 | .17 |
|   | I | .20 | .20 | .20 |
|   | H | .22 | .21 | .21 |
|   | G | .23 | .23 | .22 |
|   | F | .24 | .23 | .23 |
|   | E | .25 | .25 | .25 |
|   | D | .26 | .26 | .26 |
|   | C | .27 | .26 | .26 |
|   | B | .27 | .27 | .26 |
|   | A | .28 | .27 | .27 |
| 4 | J | .29 | .29 | .28 |
|   | I | .38 | .37 | .37 |
|   | H | .43 | .42 | .42 |
|   | G | .47 | .46 | .45 |
|   | F | .50 | .49 | .48 |
|   | E | .55 | .54 | .53 |
|   | D | .59 | .58 | .58 |
|   | C | .61 | .60 | .60 |
|   | B | .65 | .64 | .63 |
|   | A | .67 | .66 | .65 |
| 5 | J | .28 | .28 | .27 |
|   | I | .36 | .35 | .35 |
|   | H | .39 | .39 | .39 |
|   | G | .43 | .43 | .43 |
|   | F | .45 | .45 | .45 |
|   | E | .50 | .49 | .49 |
|   | D | .54 | .53 | .53 |
|   | C | .55 | .54 | .54 |
|   | B | .58 | .57 | .57 |
|   | A | .59 | .58 | .58 |
| 6 | J | .24 | .24 | .23 |
|   | I | .32 | .31 | .30 |
|   | H | .36 | .35 | .34 |
|   | G | .39 | .38 | .37 |
|   | F | .42 | .40 | .39 |
|   | E | .46 | .45 | .43 |
|   | D | .50 | .48 | .47 |
|   | C | .52 | .50 | .48 |
|   | B | .55 | .52 | .51 |
|   | A | .56 | .54 | .52 |
| 7 | J | .22 | .22 | .21 |
|   | I | .29 | .28 | .28 |
|   | H | .32 | .32 | .31 |
|   | G | .35 | .35 | .34 |
|   | F | .37 | .36 | .36 |
|   | E | .41 | .40 | .40 |
|   | D | .44 | .43 | .43 |
|   | C | .46 | .45 | .44 |
|   | B | .48 | .47 | .46 |
|   | A | .49 | .48 | .47 |
| 8 | J | .16 | .16 | .16 |
|   | I | .21 | .20 | .20 |
|   | H | .23 | .23 | .23 |
|   | G | .25 | .25 | .24 |
|   | F | .27 | .26 | .26 |
|   | E | .30 | .29 | .29 |
|   | D | .32 | .32 | .31 |
|   | C | .33 | .32 | .32 |
|   | B | .35 | .34 | .34 |
|   | A | .36 | .35 | .34 |
| 9 | J | .10 | .10 | .10 |
|   | I | .13 | .13 | .13 |
|   | H | .15 | .14 | .14 |
|   | G | .16 | .16 | .15 |
|   | F | .17 | .16 | .16 |
|   | E | .19 | .18 | .18 |
|   | D | .20 | .20 | .20 |
|   | C | .21 | .20 | .20 |
|   | B | .22 | .21 | .21 |
|   | A | .22 | .22 | .22 |

COEFFICIENTS OF UTILIZATION—Continued

| Type of Unit | Room Index | Ceiling 75% / Walls 30% | Ceiling 50% / Walls 30% | Ceiling 30% / Walls 30% |
|---|---|---|---|---|
| 10 | J | .24 | .23 | .22 |
|  | I | .31 | .29 | .28 |
|  | H | .35 | .33 | .31 |
|  | G | .39 | .36 | .34 |
|  | F | .42 | .39 | .37 |
|  | E | .46 | .43 | .40 |
|  | D | .49 | .46 | .43 |
|  | C | .52 | .48 | .45 |
|  | B | .56 | .50 | .47 |
|  | A | .58 | .52 | .49 |
| 11 | J | .20 | .18 | .16 |
|  | I | .25 | .23 | .21 |
|  | H | .29 | .26 | .24 |
|  | G | .33 | .29 | .27 |
|  | F | .36 | .32 | .29 |
|  | E | .41 | .36 | .32 |
|  | D | .44 | .39 | .35 |
|  | C | .47 | .41 | .37 |
|  | B | .51 | .44 | .40 |
|  | A | .53 | .46 | .41 |
| 12 | J | .12 | .09 | .06 |
|  | I | .16 | .12 | .09 |
|  | H | .19 | .14 | .11 |
|  | G | .23 | .17 | .12 |
|  | F | .25 | .19 | .14 |
|  | E | .30 | .22 | .17 |
|  | D | .33 | .25 | .19 |
|  | C | .36 | .27 | .21 |
|  | B | .41 | .31 | .23 |
|  | A | .44 | .33 | .25 |
| 13 | J | .14 | .10 | .07 |
|  | I | .18 | .13 | .09 |
|  | H | .21 | .15 | .11 |
|  | G | .25 | .18 | .12 |
|  | F | .27 | .20 | .13 |
|  | E | .31 | .22 | .15 |
|  | D | .34 | .25 | .17 |
|  | C | .37 | .27 | .18 |
|  | B | .42 | .30 | .20 |
|  | A | .44 | .32 | .22 |
| 14 | J | .12 | .08 | .04 |
|  | I | .15 | .10 | .06 |
|  | H | .18 | .12 | .08 |
|  | G | .21 | .14 | .08 |
|  | F | .24 | .16 | .09 |
|  | E | .27 | .18 | .10 |
|  | D | .30 | .20 | .12 |
|  | C | .33 | .22 | .13 |
|  | B | .37 | .25 | .14 |
|  | A | .39 | .26 | .16 |
| 15 | J | .10 | .07 | .04 |
|  | I | .13 | .09 | .05 |
|  | H | .16 | .10 | .06 |
|  | G | .19 | .12 | .07 |
|  | F | .20 | .14 | .08 |
|  | E | .24 | .16 | .09 |
|  | D | .26 | .18 | .10 |
|  | C | .29 | .19 | .11 |
|  | B | .32 | .21 | .12 |
|  | A | .34 | .23 | .14 |
| 16 | J | .09 | .06 | .03 |
|  | I | .11 | .08 | .04 |
|  | H | .13 | .09 | .06 |
|  | G | .16 | .10 | .06 |
|  | F | .17 | .12 | .07 |
|  | E | .20 | .13 | .08 |
|  | D | .22 | .15 | .09 |
|  | C | .24 | .16 | .09 |
|  | B | .27 | .18 | .10 |
|  | A | .29 | .19 | .12 |
| 17 | J | .06 | .04 | .02 |
|  | I | .08 | .06 | .03 |
|  | H | .10 | .06 | .04 |
|  | G | .11 | .08 | .04 |
|  | F | .13 | .08 | .05 |
|  | E | .15 | .10 | .06 |
|  | D | .16 | .11 | .06 |
|  | C | .18 | .12 | .07 |
|  | B | .20 | .13 | .08 |
|  | A | .21 | .14 | .08 |
| 18 | J | .04 | .03 | .02 |
|  | I | .05 | .04 | .02 |
|  | H | .06 | .04 | .02 |
|  | G | .07 | .05 | .03 |
|  | F | .08 | .06 | .03 |
|  | E | .09 | .06 | .04 |
|  | D | .10 | .07 | .04 |
|  | C | .11 | .07 | .04 |
|  | B | .12 | .08 | .05 |
|  | A | .13 | .09 | .05 |

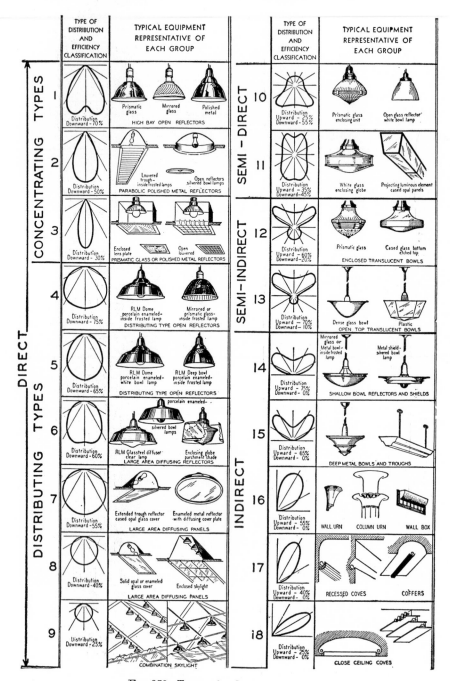

Fig. 379. Types of reflectors and bowls

*Multiply the desired foot-candle intensity by the floor area of the room in square feet, and divide by the coefficient of utilization.*

The lighting fixtures should be arranged in a room to yield a uniform light distribution. In addition, the placement of these fixtures should present a pleasing appearance and should permit economical operation of the lighting system. It is desirable to place the lighting units in several circuits so that all the lamps need not be turned on when only few are needed.

**Problem 158.**—Lay out a lighting plan for a factory measuring 60 by 30 feet and having a ceiling height of 14 feet. Assume that the ceiling and walls are such as to reflect respectively 50 and 30 per cent of the incident light, and that semi-indirect lighting is desired.

Choosing an illumination for this factory of 15 foot-candles, the light flux required on the working plane will be 15 lumens per square foot. For an area 60 by 30 feet, this means that $60 \times 30 \times 15 = 27,000$ lumens must be brought to that plane. The room index for a ceiling height of 14 feet and with semi-direct lighting is found to be letter D from the table. Choosing fixtures like Type 12 of Fig. 379, the coefficient of utilization would be 0.25 for the kinds of ceiling and walls specified. This means that only 25 per cent of the light produced at the lamps would reach the working plane in this factory. Therefore, the lighting units must produce $27,000 \div 0.25 = 108,000$ lumens.

The dimensions of the room suggest the division of the ceiling into 18 squares measuring 10 feet on a side, and the placement of a lighting unit at the center of each. Every lighting unit would then be required to produce $108,000 \div 18 = 6000$ lumens. Reference to the tables in §281 indicates that this is just the output of 300-watt incandescent lamps. Consequently, eighteen 300-watt lamps would provide the desired illumination in the factory under consideration.

Aging of the lamps and the accumulation of dust upon them affect the maintenance of illumination. Allowance for these factors should be made in the original planning of a lighting system.

**285. Electric Light Circuits.**—Electric lamps for indoor lighting in this country are operated at 110 to 120 volts from constant-potential circuits. Two- and three-wire distribution systems, either direct current or single-phase alternating current, are widely used for lighting installations. These systems of distribution are illustrated in Fig. 380, and show both lamp and motor loads connected in parallel between the constant-potential lines. The three-wire system, §223, provides twice the p.d. between the outside wires than it does between either of these and the central or *neutral* wire; this makes it possible to operate the larger motors

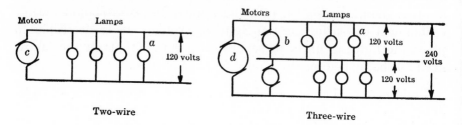

FIG. 380. Direct-current two- and three-wire distribution circuits

at 240 volts while the lamps and smaller motors operate at 120 volts. When the load is unbalanced there will be a current in the neutral wire corresponding to the difference in current taken by the two sides. A balance of load is sought in laying out the wiring for lighting installations.

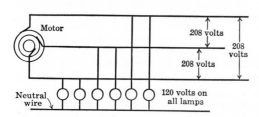

FIG. 381. Three-phase, four-wire distribution circuit

With three-phase alternating-current supply, the customary arrangement for providing lighting circuits is shown in Fig. 381. The lamps are connected from the neutral wire to any of the main wires and receive 120 volts, while three-phase motors are connected to the mains and receive $\sqrt{3} \times 120 = 208$ volts between terminals.

In all constant-potential supply circuits the potential drop in the lines is an important factor. In order to have the p.d. the same across all the lamps of an installation, *centers of distribution* are planned in wiring construction and lamps are supplied in groups by branch circuits from these centers. Feeders and sub-feeders extend from the centers to the service mains entering the building.

The potential drop on the branch circuits should not exceed 2 per cent.

In electric railways operated at 600 volts, the lamps are grouped in multiple series; for example, five 120-volt incandescent lamps are connected in series across the mains. For street lighting both constant-potential and constant-current circuits are used. In the latter, now less common, the lamps are connected in series and naturally all of them must have the same current rating. Each lamp socket is provided with an automatic cut-out which short-circuits the lamp filament in case it breaks or burns out.

Wiring should be protected from mechanical injury. While there are many ways of doing this, two methods of protection are more commonly employed than others. The first of these is the armored cable called "BX." This cable contains two or more rubber-insulated conductors which are covered by a wrapping of impregnated-paper insulation; the outer covering is a flexible steel armor. The second type of protection is the rigid steel conduit, either galvanized or cadmium-plated for outdoor wiring and black-enamelled for indoors. BX cable is used for most house wiring jobs and rigid conduit for industrial circuits.

## QUESTIONS

1. Give a brief physical explanation of the production of light.
2. Mention the parts of an incandescent lamp and state the purpose of each.
3. From what part of an arc lamp is most of the light emitted?
4. Name and describe two types of mercury vapor lamp.
5. Contrast a neon gas lamp and a sodium vapor lamp in both construction and operation.
6. What is the purpose of a phosphor in a fluorescent tube lamp?
7. Explain the starting of a fluorescent lamp equipped with a glow starter.
8. Why are fluorescent lamps often operated in pairs?
9. Summarize the difference between incandescent, arc, and gaseous conduction lamps.
10. Distinguish between luminous intensity and light flux.
11. What is the relation between the candlepower of a light source and its output in lumens?
12. How may the output of incandescent lamps be measured? How are they rated?
13. What is meant by the efficiency of a lamp? How is it expressed? Does it conform to the usual concept of efficiency?

14. In what units is illumination reckoned?

15. Explain why the illumination on a surface produced by a single lamp varies inversely as the square of the distance between the lamp and the illuminated surface.

16. Show that the foot-candle means the same thing as the lumen per square foot.

17. How can the illumination on a surface be measured?

18. Define the foot-candle and the lumen. Are they units of the same quantity?

19. Name and describe the various classes of illumination.

20. Suggest a suitable class of illumination for lighting (a) a living room, (b) a store, and (c) a church.

21. Sketch a light distribution curve of a semi-indirect lighting unit.

22. What would you choose as appropriate illumination values for the following premises: (a) a study hall in a school; (b) a work bench where fine detail must be observed; (c) a display window of a small merchant?

23. Upon what factors does the coefficient of utilization depend?

24. Mention the steps that you would follow in planning the lighting installation of a classroom or school auditorium.

25. What might be the effect on a three-wire lighting circuit if the fuse on the neutral wire were to burn out?

26. What are the principal methods of protecting electric light wiring against mechanical injury?

## PROBLEMS

1. The red line in the spectrum of hydrogen has a wavelength of 0.656 micron. Express this length in inches. *Ans.* 0.0000258 inch.

2. A 40-watt, 115-volt tungsten lamp has a filament 15 inches long and 1.4 mils in diameter. Calculate the resistances of this lamp when cold and when illuminated. Refer to §63 for the resistivity of tungsten at 20° C. *Ans.* 21.1 and 330 ohms respectively.

3. How much does it cost to operate 2 dozen 425-watt high-intensity mercury vapor lamps for an 8-hour working day in a plant where electrical energy costs 2 cents per kilowatt-hour? *Ans.* $1.63.

4. A 25-watt incandescent lamp has an efficiency of 10.8 lumens per watt. Determine its light output. *Ans.* 270 lumens.

5. A 100-watt, 115-volt tungsten lamp produces 1650 lumens. What is its spherical candlepower and its efficiency? *Ans.* 131 candlepower; 16.5 lumens per watt.

6. A 225-watt sodium vapor lamp operates on a 6.6-ampere constant-current circuit and produces 10,000 lumens. The power factor of the lamp is 65 per cent. Determine (a) the potential drop across the lamp, and (b) the efficiency of the lamp. *Ans.* (a) 52.4 volts; (b) 44.4 lumens per watt.

7. A 100-watt, 32-volt incandescent lamp yields 1800 lumens. Find (a) the current taken by the lamp, (b) its resistance, and (c) its efficiency. *Ans.* (a) 3.12 amperes; (b) 10.26 ohms; (c) 18 lumens per watt.

8. The illumination on a work bench measuring 12 by 5 feet is everywhere 20 foot-candles. What is the total luminous flux incident upon this bench? *Ans.* 1200 lumens.

9. The surface of a small desk is 6.5 feet vertically below a 150-watt tungsten lamp and this surface is 2.5 feet above the floor. What is the illumination on the desk and on the floor nearby? *Ans.* 4.9 and 2.6 foot-candles respectively.

10. A display room 30 feet long and 25 feet wide is to be illuminated by direct lighting, employing distributing luminaires like Type 6 in Fig. 379. The desired illumination is 35 foot-candles. The ceiling and walls reflect 50 per cent of the light, and the fixtures are to be hung 10 feet from the floor. Determine the coefficient of utilization for this installation. *Ans.* 0.43.

11. Six tungsten lamps are to be used for lighting the display room of Problem 10. Compute the total light flux which the lamps must produce and determine the size of lamp necessary. *Ans.* 61,000 lumens; 500-watt lamps.

12. A system of illumination employs 60 daylight fluorescent lamps 1.5 inch in diameter and 24 inches long. Calculate (a) the total light flux generated, (b) the total power required, and (c) the efficiency of illumination. *Ans.* (a) 43,800 lumens; (b) 1470 watts; (c) 29.8 lumens per watt.

13. Calculate the rating of eight incandescent lamps that would be needed to give a room, measuring 20 by 40 by 12 feet, an illumination of 13 foot-candles. Use a Type 13 fixture (Fig. 379) and assume the ceiling to reflect 50 per cent and the walls 30 per cent of the incident light. *Ans.* 300 watts.

14. What size of rubber-covered wire should be used to carry current from the electric service to the lamps of Problem 11 if the distance is 70 feet? Allow a potential drop of 2 per cent and allow for a possible increase of 50 per cent in the lighting load in the future. Electricity is supplied at 120 volts. *Ans.* No. 6 A.w.g.

# Lesson XXV

## ELECTRONICS

Conduction of electricity through gases—Geissler and Crookes tubes—Corona, spark discharge, and lightning—The Edison effect—Thermionic emission—Vacuum diodes—Gas diodes—Three-element vacuum tubes—Amplification factor of a triode—Other characteristics of triodes—Gas discharge tubes—Photo-tubes—Photovoltaic cells—X-ray tubes—Fluoroscope—Piezo-electric effect—Questions and Problems.

**286. Conduction of Electricity through Gases.**—The molecules of gases are relatively far apart and move about unceasingly throughout an entire region to which they have been admitted. They continually strike each other and strike the walls of the containing vessel. At a given instant some molecules are moving one way and some another, some are traveling rapidly and others slowly, while some are even at rest; but any appreciable volume of a gas contains so many molecules that their *average speed* is the same from moment to moment.

When heat is applied to the container the molecules of the gas rebound from its walls with greater speed, and very soon the speed of the molecules within the container will be increased. In this way the average molecular speed will rise with increase of temperature. Further, the molecules of the gas will strike the walls of the container oftener because of their increased speed and, as a result, exert a greater pressure upon the container. At any stated temperature and pressure, the molecules will have a definite average speed and also a definite average separation from each other, which spacing is called the *mean free path*. At 0° C. and atmospheric pressure the average speed of hydrogen molecules, for example, is about 6000 feet per second, and a molecule travels, on the average, less than 0.00001 inch between collisions. Such high molecular speeds and such minute free paths are typical of all gases.

The electrical behavior of a gas or air at various pressures can be studied in a glass tube container fitted with sealed-in electrodes and joined to a vacuum pump, as shown in Fig. 382. With a small potential difference between the anode $A$ and the cathode $C$, the current through the tube is practically zero when the gas is at atmospheric pressure. This means that there are relatively few electrons in a unit volume of gas at this pressure and that any free electron on its way

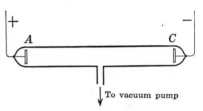

FIG. 382. Gaseous discharge tube

toward electrode $A$ encounters so many relatively heavy gas molecules in its path that its motion is greatly retarded. This motion is pictured in Fig. 383, wherein the neutral gas molecules are indicated by circles marked $N$ and a possible electron path is shown by the dotted line. Thus, at atmospheric pressure all gases are practically insulators.

On removing some of the gas from the tube with the pump, the number of molecules is reduced and an electron can travel longer distances between collisions. Its attraction by electrode $A$ then enables an electron to acquire higher speeds between impacts. As the pressure is reduced further by continued pumping, the speed becomes great enough for the electron to dislodge one or more

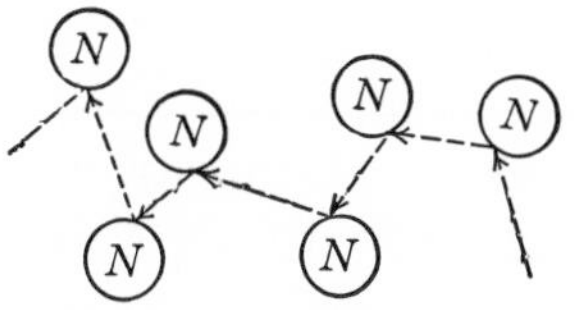

FIG. 383. Progress of an electron through a gas

electrons from a gas molecule with which it collides. The collision not only sets these electrons free, which then add to the electron flow, but the molecule itself has an excess positive charge and is attracted by electrode $C$, thus adding further to the motion of electricity through the gas. Such disruption of neutral molecules into *electrons* and *positive ions* by impact is called *ionization by collision*.

The action described becomes cumulative; the electrons liberated from one molecule acquire speeds high enough to dislodge electrons from another. While the amount of electricity transferred between the terminals depends upon the p.d. applied to them, it is also true that the resulting current will not be proportional to the p.d. as it is in metallic conductors. In other words, Ohm's Law does not apply to gaseous paths in electrical circuits.

When a positive ion in the course of its travel combines with one or more electrons to re-establish itself as a neutral atom or molecule, light is given off, §273. Such recombinations take place not only at the negative electrode, but throughout most of the gas as well, and luminous effects are observed. The orange glow of neon sign lamps, the greenish blue light from mercury vapor lamps, and the yellow light from sodium vapor bulbs are all examples of light produced as an aftermath of the ionization of gases.

**287. Geissler and Crookes Tubes.**—When there are relatively large distances between the molecules of a gas there is greater likelihood for an electron to acquire a speed between collisions that is sufficient for ionization; consequently, there is more conduction of electricity in gases at low pressures than at atmospheric pressure under like potential differences. The appearance of the discharge tube changes as the gas pressure in it becomes less. When a sufficiently large p.d. is maintained between the terminals of a tube filled with air and the pressure is gradually lowered, the discharge at first takes the form of a purplish wavy thread between the electrodes; later this broadens and fills the entire cross section of the tube, and then a glow makes its appearance near the cathode. At still lower pressures the glow moves away from the cathode, leaving a dark space between, and a second comparatively dark space forms beyond the glow; the remainder of the tube is then occupied by a luminous column in which striations of luminosity often appear. When the exhaustion is carried to about 0.001 millimeter of mercury, the luminous column disappears and the walls of the tube exhibit a fluorescent glow.

Tubes of various shapes containing gases at low pressure are available for showing the discharges described. They are called Geissler tubes, and are often made in sections of different kinds of glass and sometimes contain liquids. A simple form is shown in Fig. 384. Upon connecting the terminals of a Geissler tube to a small-sized induction coil, the gases glow and the glasses and liquids fluoresce with brilliant colors, both effects resulting from their violent bombardment by positive ions and electrons.

Tubes somewhat similar to Geissler tubes, but more highly evacuated, are known as Crookes tubes. In them, the discharge is in the nature of a radiation directed away from the cathode, to which

FIG. 384.  Geissler tube

the name *cathode rays* is given. The rays are really high-velocity electrons and they cause certain substances on which they fall to fluoresce. Conduction through the tube is explained by supposing that the bombardment of positive ions knocks electrons out of the cathode, particularly at reduced pressure, and that these electrons have sufficient energy to ionize the air within the tube by collision.

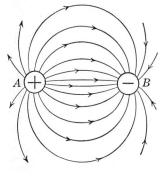

FIG. 385.  Electric field between charged conductors

**288. Corona, Spark Discharge, and Lightning.**—When conduction t a k e s place through a gas under such conditions that ionization occurs only in the immediate vicinity of the terminals, the conduction is called a *corona discharge*. This type of discharge is of red-violet color but is often so subdued as to be visible only in partial or complete darkness.

Fig. 385 shows the distribution of the lines of electric force about two conductors which are electrically charged, conductor $A$ being at a higher potential than conductor $B$. The field intensity is greatest near the surfaces of the conductors, where the lines are closest, consequently, electrons or other ions in these regions will move with high speeds, §164. If the potential difference between the conductors is large enough, the velocity of the ions near the conductor surfaces may reach values sufficiently high to product ionization by collision and corona may be observed. This occurs in air when the electric field intensity is about 78,000 volts per inch.

When the p.d. between two charged bodies is raised further, the electric field between them causes the electrons and positive ions in the region to be hurled along so violently that they produce more charged particles by collision; these in turn produce still more, and the cumulative ionizing action renders the air highly conducting almost instantly. As a result, a *spark discharge* takes place in the gap between the conductors and this is accompanied by a sharp snap or a loud report depending on the length of the gap. Under sufficiently intense fields, such discharges may also take place in liquid and solid dielectrics, in which case the insulating property of the materials will be impaired or ruined.

Corona is sometimes visible on high-tension transmission lines. By considering *A* and *B* of Fig. 385 as the cross sections of two wires of a single-phase transmission line, this diagram will represent correctly the electrostatic field around such a line. A transmission line is usually operated at an e.m.f. less than the *critical value* at which corona appears in order to avoid the accompanying energy loss. The critical value depends upon the diameter, surface, and separation of the wires and is also influenced by weather conditions.

The upper atmosphere comprises a layer of ionized air, apparently produced by sunlight, which is positive with respect to the earth. This layer and the surface of the earth may be regarded as a vast condenser, with the lower atmosphere as the dielectric between them. Through this region in fair weather there is a constant leakage due to ionization. But in a rapidly-developing rainstorm, clouds become charged and raindrops serve as carriers to develop intense electric fields between clouds or between clouds and the earth's surface. Huge spark discharges, called *lightning* flashes, result. These flashes are sometimes several miles in length, and are accompanied by thunder claps and reverberation.

Lightning rods are used to afford protection against damage by atmospheric electricity. These rods are heavy copper conductors, mounted on the exteriors of buildings and structures to be protected, and arranged with their upper ends pointed and directed skyward and their lower ends firmly connected to conductors embedded in the ground. Shielding of power lines and hazardous structures against direct strokes is arranged generally by overhead conductors that are grounded at intervals or by groups of grounded masts.

Lightning rods serve primarily to conduct negative charges from or to the earth. For example, when a positively-charged cloud approaches a region protected by lightning rods, electrons are drawn up from the earth and are dispersed into the atmosphere. These electrons make their way to the cloud where they neutralize at least a part of the original positive charge.

Again, when a negatively-charged cloud approaches the lightning rod, some of its excess charge reaches the earth by way of the rod. In both cases the electric field intensity is reduced and the probability of a direct lightning stroke is lessened.

Generally a lightning rod is not intended to provide a path to ground for a direct stroke, for the very large currents involved would destroy the rod and its circuit to ground. Instead, the rod serves to release or neutralize the charge on a cloud at a relatively slow rate, and to keep the currents in the rod circuit low enough so as to cause no damage.

The protection of electric power and communication lines and their associated apparatus against lightning is effected by means of lightning arresters located at various points in the circuits. These arresters are short air gaps which break down when the surge reaches them and thereby produce temporary low-resistance paths to ground. As soon as the surge has passed, the high resistance of the gap must be restored automatically (often by electromagnetic means), so that the sources of power will not remain short-circuited for more than an instant.

**289. The Edison Effect.**—During the development days of the electric lamp, Edison experimented with a carbon-filament lamp which had a metal plate sealed inside the evacuated bulb and insulated from the filament. He observed that when this plate was connected through a galvanometer with the positive terminal of the filament a current was set up in the instrument, but when the connection was made to the negative terminal of the filament there was no current. This discovery was made in 1883 but its importance was not realized until about twenty years later.

The discovery, subsequently called the Edison Effect, could not be explained at the time, but it is now known that electrons are "evaporated" from hot substances, such as an incandescent filament, and that these electrons are attracted to the plate when it is positive with respect to the filament, setting up an electric current. Further, when the plate is made negative, by connecting it with the negative end of the filament, it repels the electrons which are being evaporated from the filament. Also, since the plate is relatively cool (at least below a dull red heat, no electrons are emitted from it. For these reasons there can be no current when the plate is negative to the filament.

Fig. 386 illustrates a tube with a filament and a plate, connected externally to a galvanometer and two batteries. The filament is heated to incandescence by battery $A$ and the plate is charged positively by battery $B$. Electrons are emitted from the filament because of its high temperature and these are drawn to the plate because of its positive charge. This means that current through the tube is directed from the plate to the filament. If battery $B$ were reversed the current would cease. Because of these facts such a tube may be employed as a rectifier, permitting a current in one direction only, Lesson XXIII. The plate serves as *anode* and the filament as *cathode*. Because the tube contains just these electrodes it is called a *diode*.

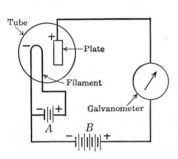

FIG. 386.  Two-element tube or diode

In many tubes a filament is used merely to supply heat to a metal cathode placed over the filament; such tubes are said to be of the *heater type,* and the useful electrons are emitted by the cathode alone. The term *emitter* may also be used for designating the cathode.

**290. Thermionic Emission.**—To explain the emission of electrons, it must be appreciated that the molecules of a solid vibrate in all directions and with varying speeds about their normal positions. The average of these velocities depends upon the temperature of the solid, the higher the temperature the greater the molecular activity. The free electrons in metals behave similarly. An electron located near the surface rarely acquires enough speed at room temperature to pass through the surface and leave the metal. But as the temperature is raised, more and more of the free electrons of a substance reach a speed that is needed to carry them across the surface boundary, and so an appreciable flow of electrons is established from the surface. Since the flow of electrons from the metal depends on its thermal condition, the emission is called *thermionic emission*.

Thermionic emission is not limited to good conductors of electricity which have many free electrons at ordinary temperatures. There are many materials, which are poor conductors of electricity at such temperatures and have but few free electrons, that emit large numbers of electrons when heated to a dull glow. The oxides of calcium, strontium and barium are examples of such materials. These oxides are employed as coatings for filaments and other forms of cathodes for vacuum tubes. Such emitters can be recognized by their cherry-red operating color. It is probable that these oxides generate large numbers of free electrons during the process of heating, perhaps because some of the oxide is reduced to pure metal.

Another material which emits electrons readily is thorium; this is added to tungsten to produce so-called thoriated filaments, which are also commonly used in vacuum tubes. Such filaments are operated at temperatures that give them a yellow heat, while filaments of pure tungsten or platinum are generally operated at white heat.

**291. Vacuum Diodes.**—A vacuum diode, as the name implies, is an exhausted tube containing a plate and an emitter. The emitter may be either a filament or a heater-type cathode. The plate may be of single or double construction; these types of diodes are sketched in Fig. 387. Although the diode may be used for several purposes, its general application is to rectifiers for converting alternating current to direct current.

In common with all electrical devices, a diode is limited in the current it can take and the p.d. it can accommodate. If too great a current is sought the emitter may be found inadequate to supply the electrons necessary. If a vacuum diode is operated with too high a p.d., the electrons may have such high velocities when they arrive at the plate as to heat it to incandescence. The heated plate might then emit sufficiently to set up a flow of electrons to the cathode and, in this way, destroy the rectifying action of the tube. Such a flow of electrons from the plate to the cathode (the regular emitter) is spoken of as an *inverse current,* and the p.d. (maximum value of wave) which tends to establish such a current is known as its *peak inverse potential.* This limiting potential difference as well as the maximum allowable current are important factors in specifying the capacity of any rectifier tube.

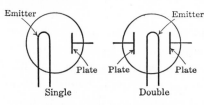

FIG. 387. Types of diodes

If the plate of a tube is made of material which must be raised in temperature above yellow heat before electrons are emitted, then it is safe to have the p.d. at a value which will not bring the plate beyond red heat. Molybdenum is such a material and it is generally employed in most tubes operated at high potentials. The name *kenotron* is often applied to any vacuum diode, but lately this term has been used largely to indicate high-vacuum diodes which operate at high potentials and yield relatively low current values.

**292. Gas Diodes.**—A *gas* diode is similar to a vacuum diode except that it contains a gas or vapor at low pressure. This gas is ionized in the normal operation of the tube and the ionization makes it possible to use a much lower plate potential than would be necessary for the same current in a vacuum diode. For example, a Type 80 high-vacuum double diode requires a p.d. of more than 120 volts between the filament and either plate to pass a momentary current of 0.37 ampere per plate, while a Type 83 mercury-vapor double diode will pass a momentary current of more than 0.67 ampere with only 15 volts applied between its filament and either plate.

The general shapes of the volt-ampere characteristic curves of vacuum and gas diodes are shown in Fig. 388; each shows the variation of plate current when the plate potential is changed. While the gas diode is superior to the vacuum type in many respects, it should be kept in mind that the gas diode cannot withstand the same inverse peak potential as that of the corresponding high-vacuum diode. For this reason gas diodes are seldom employed in rectifier circuits in which the peak inverse potential exceeds 20,000 volts. An undesirable feature of rectifiers employing gas diodes is the tendency to produce radio interference, and this noise is often difficult to eliminate.

The widely used *tungar* battery charger employs a tube containing argon at low pressure; its plate is a carbon button and the emitter is a heavy coiled filament, §268. Other gas diodes are available with various gases for special purposes. Small diodes containing neon gas are used as lamps and are available in capacities ranging down to a small fraction of a watt, §277.

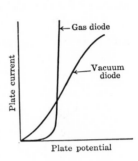

Fig. 388. Volt-ampere characteristics of diodes

**293. Three-Element Vacuum Tubes.**—The vacuum diode was used to some extent in the early days of radio communication styled as a Fleming valve, named after the British investigator Sir (John) Ambrose Fleming (1849-1945). In 1904 he adapted a two-element tube for rectifying the high-frequency alternating currents induced in a receiving aerial, so that their presence could be detected by telephone receivers or relays. Three years later, Lee De Forest, an American inventor, conceived the idea of adding to the diode another element, made in the form of a mesh, for controlling the number of electrons going from filament to plate. The introduction of this mesh or *grid,* as it is called, has rendered the vacuum tube invaluable as a detector of radio waves, as an amplifier of electrical signals, and as a generator of alternating currents ranging in frequency from a fraction of a cycle to billions of cycles per second. Tubes with three elements (emitter, plate and grid) are called triodes.

The effect of the grid in the triode is like that of a shutter which, opening and closing, controls the flow of electrons going through it from filament to plate. This controlling effect of the grid is accomplished by varying its normally negative potential. When the potential is made less negative, the repulsion between the grid and the electrons from the filament is reduced, and the electron flow to the plate increases. When the potential on the grid is made more negative, the repulsion is increased and the plate current diminishes. The normal potential on the grid is produced by a source of e.m.f. called a *grid bias battery.*

Fig. 389 shows the connections of the triode, the three elements being represented by $F$ for filament or emitter, $P$ for plate,

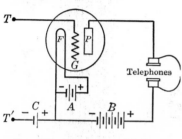

FIG. 389. Three-element tube or triode

and $G$ for grid. The batteries for these elements are lettered $A, B,$ and $C,$ respectively. When the grid is connected to a feeble source of alternating current through terminals $TT'$ there will be alternately a less negative and a more negative potential on the grid, and the electron flow to the plate will be increased and decreased accordingly, thereby varying the direct current through the telephone receivers. In this way the grid serves as a gate-valve in controlling relatively large currents in the plate circuit.

Most low-power high-vacuum tubes are operated with a grid bias potential which makes the grid sufficiently negative so that the applied alternating or signal potential never brings the grid to a positive value. Thus, while the potential on the grid varies, it always remains negative. This prevents electrons from striking the grid and so avoids establishing a current in the circuit that provides the grid potential. Consequently, a vacuum tube with a sufficiently negative bias draws no power from the circuit supplying the signal potential to the grid.

In high-power tubes the filaments are made of tungsten or platinum. In most low-power triodes, the filament consists of a narrow alloy ribbon which is coated with the oxides of calcium or barium, §290. It has been pointed out that such coated emitters operate at considerably lower temperatures and, therefore, require much less power than corresponding tungsten or platinum filaments. The cathodes of all heater-type tubes are coated with these oxides.

**Experiment 110.**—Connect a vacuum triode of the type used in radio receiving sets in the manner shown in Fig. 389, using a galvanometer in the plate circuit instead of the telephone receivers. Bring electrified substances such as hard rubber, glass and sealing wax, near the grid terminal and observe the deflection of the galvanometer with each. Verify the fact that positive and negative grid potentials respectively increase and decrease the plate current.

**294. Amplification Factor of a Triode.**—The behavior of three-element vacuum tubes may be indicated by curves showing the plate current plotted against grid potential. The characteristic curves of Fig. 390 show how the plate current of an ordinary triode radio detector or amplifier is increased for any particular plate potential by making the grid less negative. The curves apply to a number of plate or B-battery potentials $E_b$ applied to a Type 6J5 RCA tube. For example, at a grid potential of $-7.5$ volts, the plate currents are 0.8 milliampere for 150 volts on the plate, 4.5 milliamperes for 200 volts, and 10.3 milliamperes for 250 volts.

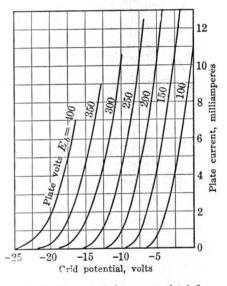

FIG. 390. Characteristic curves of triode, Type 6J5

Filament potential = 6.3 volts.

Another set of characteristic curves, given in Fig. 391, show how the plate current is increased for any particular grid potential by making the plate more positive. The curves correspond to a number of grid or $C$-battery potentials $E_C$ applied to the same type tube. For example, at a plate potential of 200 volts, the plate current is 1.0 milliampere for $-10$ volts on the grid, 3.4 milliamperes for $-8$ volts, and 7.5 milliamperes for $-6$ volts.

The grid potential is much more effective in controlling the plate current than is the plate potential. The *change* in plate potential which will just cancel a potential *change* of 1 volt on the grid, and maintain constant plate current, is called the *amplification factor* of the tube. For example, the left-hand curve of Fig. 391 shows that the tube operating at zero grid potential and with 50 volts on the plate passes a current of 4.3 milliamperes. To maintain the same current with say −8 volts on the grid (middle

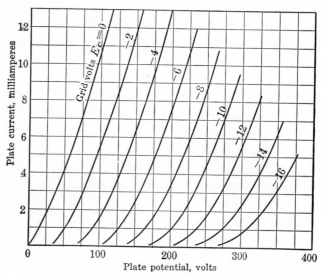

FIG. 391. Plate characteristics of triode, type 6J5

curve), the plate potential must be increased to 210 volts. The potential change on the plate is thus 210 − 50 or 160 volts, while the grid potential change necessary to cancel this plate potential increase is −8 to 0 or 8 volts. Therefore, the amplification factor of the tube is 160 ÷ 8 or 20 for operation in this region of its characteristic.

**Problem 159.**—Calculate the amplification factor of the tube represented by the curves of Fig. 391 in the proximity of a point determined by a grid bias of −6 volts and a plate potential of +200 volts.

Since the plate current at −6 volts on the grid and 200 volts on the plate is 7.5 milliamperes, note the plate potentials at this current value for the grid biases on either side of $E_c = -6$ volts, namely of −4 and −8 volts.

These plate potentials are 160 and 240 volts respectively. If the plate current is to be kept constant at 7.5 milliamperes as the grid bias varies from −4 to −8 volts, the plate potential must increase from 160 to 240 volts. The amplification factor of the tube under these conditions is, therefore, $(240 − 160) \div (8 − 4) = 20$.

**Problem 160.**—Compute the amplification factor of the same tube from the curves of Fig. 390, using as the operating point the conditions of −10 volts on the grid and +250 volts on the plate.

The operating point, −10 volts on the grid and +250 on the plate with a plate current of 4.5 milliamperes, lies between the curves for +300 and +200 volts on the plate. The grid biases corresponding to these plate potentials, at a constant plate current of 4.5 milliamperes, are −12.5 and −7.5 volts. Hence, the amplification factor is $(300 − 200) \div (12.5 − 7.5) = 20$.

**295. Other Characteristics of Triodes.**—In addition to amplification factor, there are two other important operating factors of a triode; these are called plate resistance and transconductance. The *plate resistance* of a triode is the *change* of plate potential divided by the *change* in plate current as the grid bias is kept constant. The plate resistance may be determined by means of the same set of curves, Fig. 391, by drawing a tangent to the operating point, and erecting a right-angled triangle with the tangent as hypotenuse. The ratio of the base of this triangle, measured in volts, to the altitude, measured in amperes, yields the plate resistance in ohms. If this is done for a grid bias of −4 volts and a plate potential of 130 volts, the plate resistance of a Type 6J5 triode is found to be about 10,000 ohms. The conditions for this determination correspond to those for which the amplification factor was calculated, since −4 is the average of 0 and −8 volts, while 130 is the average of 50 and 210 volts.

**Problem 161.**—Calculate the plate resistance of a Type 6J5 tube when the grid bias is −5 volts and the plate potential is 150 volts, making use of the curves of Fig. 390.

A vertical line at a bias of −5 volts intersects the potential curves neighboring that for 150 volts, namely the 200- and 100-volt curves, at 10.3 and 0.7 milliamperes respectively. Thus, at a constant bias of −5 volts, a plate potential change of $200 − 100$ or 100 volts yields a current change of $10.3 − 0.7$ or 9.6 milliamperes. Thus, the plate resistance of this tube under the specified conditions is $100 \div 0.0096 = 10,400$ ohms.

The *transconductance* of a tube is the ratio of the *change* in plate current to the *change* in grid bias when the plate potential is kept constant. It is also the ratio of the amplification factor to the plate resistance, both values being calculated for the same conditions. The transconductance is measured in *mhos* or *micromhos* (1 mho equals 1 million micromhos). For example, a Type 6J5 tube at a grid bias of $-4$ volts and a plate potential of 130 volts has an amplification factor of 20 and a plate resistance of 10,000 ohms; therefore the transconductance of the tube is 20/10,000 or 0.0020 mho or 2000 micromhos. The transconductance is also known as the *mutual conductance* of a tube.

**Problem 162.**—Calculate the transconductance of a type 6J5 tube when the grid bias is $-8$ volts and the plate potential is $+225$ volts.

Referring to Fig. 391 the operating point refers to a plate current of 5.8 milliamperes. If the grid bias is varied between $-10$ and $-6$ volts while the plate potential remains fixed at 225 volts, the plate current varies from 2.4 to 10.8 milliamperes. Therefore, the transconductance under these conditions is $(0.0108 - 0.0024) \div (10.0 - 6.0) = 0.0021$ mho $=$ 2100 micromhos.

The space between the heated emitter and the plate of a tube is obviously occupied by a great many electrons, and therefore this space may be considered quite properly as having a *space charge*. Since this charge is all negative electricity, it will repel electrons which are coming from the emitter and tend to force them back into it, thus limiting the plate current. Making the grid more negative assists the space charge in limiting the electron flow, while making the grid less negative reduces the space charge and allows more electrons to travel to the plate.

As already stated, either increasing the plate potential or making the grid potential less negative, or both, causes an increase in plate current, since more and more of the electrons coming from the emitter are drawn to the plate. Naturally, when all those emitted are drawn to the plate, there is no further use of increasing the plate potential or making the grid less negative. This maximum flow of electrons, or limiting value of plate current, is called the *saturation current;* its value depends entirely upon the nature and temperature of the emitter. It is clear that the emitter temperature must always be high enough to make it possible for the normal plate and grid potentials to control the plate current, otherwise the tube would be useless.

To understand the rectifying action of the three-element tube, assume that 300 volts are used on the plate of a 6J5 triode, Fig. 390, and that the grid is subjected to an alternating potential varying between the maximum values of +5 and −5 volts. Assume further that the grid bias is −15 volts. Then the combination of the fixed bias and the alternating e.m.f. causes the total grid potential to vary from −10 to −20 volts. When the alternating potential passes through its zero value only the steady bias of −15 volts is effective on the grid and then the plate current is 1.5 milliamperes; when at its negative maximum of −20 volts, this current is 0.0 milliamperes; and when at its least negative value, −10 volts, the plate current is 10.0 milliamperes. Consequently, the plate current swings down 1.5 and up 8.5 milliamperes from its normal value of 1.5 milliamperes with −15 volts on the grid; that is, the plate current is an alternating one having positive lobes almost six times as large as its negative lobes. Such a current with the positive lobes overbalancing the negative lobes, gives the same result in a suitable electrical device as produced by a direct current. This principle is made use of in detecting the high frequency oscillations set up in a radio antenna.

The following table gives the operating potentials and currents of some detector and amplifier triodes used in radio receiving sets:

### VACUUM TUBE DATA

| Operation | Type No. of Tube | Filament or Heater, Volts | Filament or Heater, Amperes | Plate Potential, Volts | Plate Current, Milliamperes | Grid Bias, Volts | Amplification Factor | Plate Resistance, Ohms | Mutual Conductance, Micromhos |
|---|---|---|---|---|---|---|---|---|---|
| Detector | 6C5 | 6.3 | 0.3 | 250 | 0.2 | −17 | .... | .... | .... |
| Amplifier | 6C5 | 6.3 | 0.3 | 250 | 8 | −8 | 20 | 10000 | 2000 |
| Amplifier | 6J5 | 6.3 | 0.3 | 250 | 9 | −8 | 20 | 7700 | 2600 |
| Amplifier | 6F5 | 6.3 | 0.3 | 250 | 0.9 | −2 | 100 | 66000 | 1500 |
| Amplifier | 2A3 | 2.5 | 2.5 | 250 | 60 | −45 | 4.2 | 800 | 5250 |

**Experiment 111.**—To measure the characteristics of a triode, set up the circuit shown in Fig. 392, making connections at the tube socket, as viewed from the bottom, to the lugs bearing the numbers indicated. Direct-current instruments $M$ and $V$ are respectively a 5-milliampere ammeter and a 100-volt, 100,000-ohm voltmeter. Potentiometer $P$ should have about 10,000 ohms resistance and have a rating not less than 0.5 watt.

Connect the grid return lead to point $m$ so that the grid potential $E_C$ is —1.5 volts, and set the slider of $P$ so that the tube draws a current $I$ of, say, 3.5 milliamperes. Then observe the reading of the voltmeter and call it $V_1$. Next, change the grid return lead to point $n$ so that $E_C$ is —3.0 volts. Adjust $P$ so that the same value of current is indicated on $M$ as before.

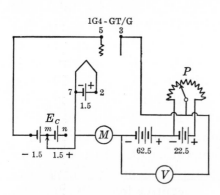

Note the indication of the voltmeter and call it $V_2$. The amplification factor for these conditions is

$$\mu = \frac{V_2 - V_1}{3 - 1.5}$$

Next, with $E_C$ kept constant at —3.0 volts, reset $P$ so that the meter indicates a current in the vicinity of 5 milliamperes. Note this current and the simultaneous reading of the volt-meter; call these values $I_3$ and $V_3$ respectively. Then for these conditions, the plate resistance is

$$r_p = \frac{V_3 - V_2}{I_3 - I}$$

Fig. 392. Test of triode for amplification factor and plate resistance

The tube used is designated 1G4-GT/G and the potentials are expressed in volts.

**296. Gas Discharge Tubes.**—The addition of a grid to a gas-filled diode results in a tube which has found unusually wide appli-cation in electrical communication, control systems, welding, and power circuits. Such a tube is called a *gas discharge tube* and its trade name is a *thyratron*. It affords much larger plate currents than does the vacuum triode.

The outstanding feature of a discharge tube is the character-istic that plate current is not established until the plate potential reaches a certain critical positive value, determined by the amount of grid bias, at which the gas ionizes. Furthermore, this current cannot be varied, as in a vacuum triode, by a change of grid potential, but continues irrespective of grid bias until the plate potential drops practically to zero or the current falls so low that ionization of the gas ceases. The difference of potential between plate and filament need be only about 15 volts, and this *p.d. is practically constant* regardless of the plate current.

Fig. 393 shows a thyratron circuit in which the usual plate battery of a triode is replaced by an alternator. The plate circuit includes the alternator $E$ and a load resistance $R$. The filament $F$ is heated by alternating current supplied through a transformer $T$. The grid circuit extends from the transformer tap $a$ through the bias battery $E_c$ and resistor $R_G$ to the grid $G$. This resistor serves to limit the grid current when the gas ionizes; it is necessary even when the grid bias is negative for then the grid draws positive ions that result from the ionization. With the grid bias positive, as shown, the grid current is that due to electron flow. Current through the thyratron is established only during the half-cycles of e.m.f. from the alternator which make the plate $P$ positive, but the current does not commence in each half-cycle until the plate potential reaches the critical value for the grid bias employed.

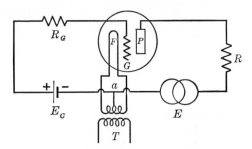

FIG. 393. A thyratron circuit

To make the operation clear, assume that the alternator has an e.m.f. of 150 volts peak value, that the grid bias is +3 volts, that the critical potential of a particular thyratron for this bias is +50 volts on the plate, and that the load resistance is 40 ohms. When the alternator makes the plate positive, no current will be established until the e.m.f. reaches 50 volts, at which value ionization takes place. The p.d. between $a$ and $P$ then falls to about 15 volts, leaving approximately 35 volts across $R$; the current in the load at that instant will be $35 \div 40 = 0.87$ ampere. As the e.m.f. rises, say to 115 volts, the p.d. between $a$ and $P$ remains at 15 volts and, therefore, the p.d. across the load $R$ rises to 100 volts, making the momentary plate current $100 \div 40 = 2.5$ amperes. Thus, the plate current varies with changes in the plate potential supply; it will cease when the e.m.f. of the alternator drops below +15 volts. Obviously, there will be no current when the alternator makes the plate negative.

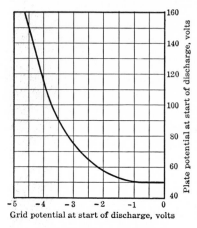

Grid potential at start of discharge, volts

FIG. 394. Typical breakdown curve of a thyratron tube, FG-81

Fig. 394 shows a curve of plate potential plotted against grid potential for a small thyratron tube. Such a curve indicates the plate potentials necessary to initiate plate current for various values of grid bias. For example, if the bias on the tube is set at −3.5 volts, the plate potential necessary to start the current must be at least +90 volts. The following problem illustrates the method of determining the current supplied by the thyratron.

**Problem 163.**—A thyratron, to which the curve of Fig. 394 applies, is used to charge a storage battery requiring 6.6 volts, and the power supply is alternating current of 120 volts r.m.s. value. Assume that the grid potential is −3.5 volts, that the maximum value of the charging current is to be 2.0 amperes, and that the tube drop is 16 volts, i.e., ionization ceases when the p.d. between plate and filament is 16 volts. Construct the shape of the charging current.

The circuit would be the same as in Fig. 393, except that the battery to be charged is also connected in the circuit aPRE. The wave shape of potential is shown as sinusoidal in Fig. 395 and rises to maximum values

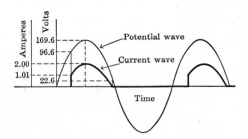

FIG. 395. Graphs of alternating potential and battery charging current

of 120 × 1.414 = 169.6 volts. Current would start in the plate circuit when the instantaneous potential reaches a positive value of 90 + 6.6 = 96.6 volts, since 90 volts are required for a grid bias of −3.5 volts (Fig. 394) and 6.6 volts are needed to balance the e.m.f. of the battery. Immediately after the current is established in the plate circuit of the tube, the p.d.

between the plate and cathode falls to 16 volts. Since the charging current is limited to a peak value of 2 amperes, the series resistance $R$ should have a value of

$$\frac{169.6 - 6.6 - 16}{2} = \frac{147}{2} = 73.5 \text{ ohms}$$

Consequently, the initial current, when the e.m.f. reaches 96.6 volts, is

$$\frac{96.6 - 6.6 - 16}{73.5} = 1.01 \text{ amperes}$$

The current falls to zero when the applied e.m.f. drops to $16 + 6.6$ or 22.6 volts, for potentials below this value provide insufficient potential differences to supply the tube drop and the battery counter e.m.f. The heavy line in Fig. 395 shows the resulting current wave available for charging the battery.

**297. Photo-Tubes.**—Certain materials, such as sodium, potassium and caesium, emit electrons when exposed to light. Such materials are said to be *photosensitive* or *photoemissive,* and they are employed as the cathode surfaces in diodes known as *photo-tubes, photo-cells,* or *photoelectric cells,* also popularly as "electric eyes." These cathodes are generally in the form of thin layers of the photosensitive material deposited either on glass or on a suitable metal. The anode, which collects the electrons emitted from the cathode, is generally a thin rod or loop. A battery or other source of e.m.f. is used to maintain an appropriate p.d. between the electrodes. The electrons emitted are sometimes called *photoelectrons* to indicate their origin.

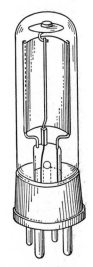

Fig. 396.
Photo-tube
construction

Radio Corporation of America

Photo-tubes are of two types: vacuum and gas-filled. In the vacuum cell, the number of electrons collected by the anode, and therefore the current through the cell, is relatively small. The gas-filled type generally contains a small amount of argon and the pressure is low; this type yields greater currents because the gas molecules are ionized by collision with electrons and other molecules. The gas-filled tube is not as sturdy as the other for it may be damaged if exposed to strong sources of light. Fig. 396 shows the structure of a photo-tube and

Fig. 397 illustrates the characteristics of the vacuum and gas-filled types.

The number of electrons emitted from the photosensitive cathode is practically proportional to the amount of light falling upon it. Because of this fact, photo-tubes, used in connection with vacuum-tube amplifiers, are employed for many purposes. They are used with sound-on-film motion pictures to make audible the speech and tones recorded on the "sound track." Photo-cells are also used in light meters for measuring illumination, in control devices for automatically leveling elevators at each floor of a building, in the printing and perforating of postage stamps, in burglar alarms, in matching colors or making comparisons, in counting operations, and in many other applications.

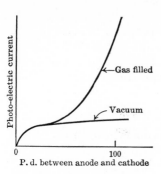

FIG. 397. Characteristics of vacuum and gas-filled photo-tubes

**298. Photovoltaic Cells.**—It has been found that when certain materials are placed in contact and the combination is exposed to light, a displacement of electrons takes place across the contact surface, establishing a difference of potential between the materials of the combination. Such combinations are known as *photovoltaic cells,* and may consist of either a liquid and a solid, or two solids, in contact.

A common example of such a cell employing two solids, consists of a thin coating of cuprous oxide on pure copper. When the cuprous oxide surface of the cell is exposed to light, electrons shift across the contact surface from the oxide to the copper, thus making the copper negative and the oxide positive. In the absence of light, the cell will permit electrons to pass only from the copper to the oxide and, therefore, it can serve as a rectifier. There appears to be a barrier to the flow of electrons from the oxide to the copper, but light which penetrates the oxide seems to overcome it. Such cells, which include the *Weston Photronic cell,* §282, are also known as *barrier layer cells.*

When a photovoltaic cell of cuprous oxide and copper is connected to an external circuit, as shown in Fig. 398, and light falls upon the oxide, the electrons circulate from the oxide to the copper, and through the external circuit back to the oxide. The current, of course, is in the opposite direction, as indicated in the figure. When the external circuit is a low-resistance galvanometer or microammeter, the combination of cell and meter may be used to measure illumination values and is called a *foot-candle meter.* Such devices are also used in photography to determine the proper film exposure, and are styled *exposure meters.* If the microammeter employed is of sufficiently low resistance, its deflection will be almost exactly proportional to the amount of light falling on the cell.

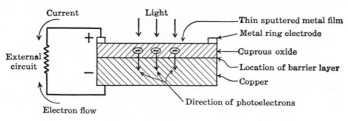

FIG. 398. Electron flow and current in a cuprous oxide-copper photovoltaic cell

Since cuprous oxide is a poor conductor, a large contact surface is necessary between the oxide and the positive terminal of the cell to avoid a high contact resistance. This is obtained by depositing an extremely thin metal film on the cuprous oxide, by an electrical process known as *sputtering.* The sputtered film is so thin that it transmits light readily. A metal ring electrode is used to make connection between the sputtered film and the external circuit.

**299. X-Ray Tubes.**—While experimenting in 1895 with a Crookes vacuum tube excited from an induction coil, William K. Roentgen (1845-1923), a German physicist, discovered that a sensitized photographic plate, protected from daylight but lying near the vacuum tube, showed upon development that it had been exposed. Further investigation indicated that the tube emitted a type of radiation which was not perceptible to the human eye, but was capable of penetrating many substances: wood, sheet metal, and so on. He called this radiation X-rays; the rays are now also spoken of as *Roentgen rays.*

It has been found by experiment that X-rays are produced as the result of the bombardment of metals by electrons going at speeds of from one-tenth to one-half the speed of light, the speed of light being 186,000 miles per second. The electrons are usually obtained by emission from a hot cathode, and acquire high speeds by exhausting the tube to a high degree and by applying a large potential difference between the anode and cathode. The stream of electrons, also called *cathode rays,* strikes the metal of the anode or *target* and puts its molecules into violent vibration. As a result of this bombardment, the anode sets up waves analogous to, but much shorter than, the waves of light, and these waves of invisible radiation are X-rays. The action is somewhat akin to the emission of sound waves from a bell which is continually hit by shot, for in this case also waves are produced by the impact of material particles.

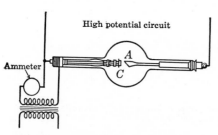

FIG. 399. Hot-cathode X-ray tube

The general shape of an X-ray tube is depicted in Fig. 399. The anode *A* and cathode *C* are connected to a source of high unidirectional potential that is obtained from a high alternating potential either by a mechanical rectifier or more effectively by a kenotron rectifier. The filament *C* is usually formed of a tungsten wire wound into a spiral and is heated by current supplied through a transformer as shown. The target of wrought tungsten is attached to a molybdenum rod and supported by an iron sleeve; the latter helps to radiate the heat evolved.

When different substances are interposed between a protected photographic plate or film and a source of X-rays, the radiation penetrates them to different extents, according to their densities, so that the plate or film, upon development, shows the shadows of the objects interposed. When the hand is so placed near an X-ray tube, the plate is much less affected directly behind the bones than behind the flesh, because the bones are more opaque to the radiation. A print made from such a plate shows deep shadows of the bones and fainter ones of the flesh. Broken bones and foreign objects in the body can be located accurately from such prints. X-ray films and prints are called *radiographs*.

The potential differences ordinarily applied between the cathode and the target of an X-ray tube range from 40,000 to over 200,000 volts, while the currents vary from about 5 to more than 300 milliamperes. These wide ranges are necessary in order to supply X-rays of different penetrating powers and of different intensities. Generally, higher voltages produce X-rays of greater penetrating power while larger currents yield greater amounts of X-rays. Powerful equipments have been developed for inspect-

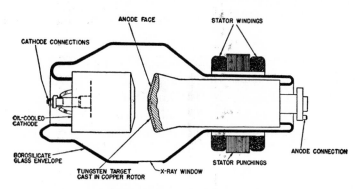

FIG. 400. Modern X-ray tube with revolving anode
General Electric Company

ing welds in thick steel plates and locating defects in heavy castings.

Because of the high potential difference between the electrodes of the tube, the electrons striking the target heat it to rather high temperatures. For this reason the targets of most tubes have external cooling fins. In order to avoid overheating at high outputs, X-ray tubes are now available with rotating targets. In such tubes, a mushroom-shaped anode is attached to the shaft of an induction motor and the entire rotor is enclosed in the tube; the stator of the motor is slipped over the glass envelope. Such motors rotate the target at about 3000 revolutions per minute and the spot where the X-rays are generated is changed so rapidly that the target remains cool enough for safe and efficient operation. Fig. 400 shows a tube of this type in cross section; the bearings are self-lubricating and the electrodes are shaped to confine the electronic bombardment to a distinct path.

Physicians use X-rays not only in making examinations but also for their curative action. Animal tissue undergoes a change in structure when exposed to X-rays and is destroyed by prolonged exposure. In *X-ray therapy* the rays are concentrated upon abnormal or diseased tissue that is to be destroyed.

Because stray X-rays may prove injurious both to the patient and to the person operating an X-ray machine, the tubes are carefully shielded so as to confine the rays to the desired directions. Further, the high potentials that are applied to the tube make it necessary to provide excellent insulation for the whole electrical system.

**300. Fluoroscope.**—It is often desirable to use X-rays for seeing what takes place inside the human body or inside enclosures during short periods of observation. Such observations may be made conveniently by means of a fluoroscope. This device is generally a plate of lead glass coated on one side with a film of barium platino-cyanide, the crystals of which glow or fluoresce when struck by X-rays.

Usually the person making a fluoroscopic examination operates in partial or complete darkness in order that the picture in the fluoroscope may be visible more easily. The coated side of the fluoroscope is placed toward the object under examination so that the observer looks through the lead glass. Such glass is employed because it stops most X-rays and so aids in protecting the observer. To further protect himself, the observer may wear a lead apron, lead gloves, and lead glass goggles. All these precautions are necessary since the practitioner may spend many hours each day at this work; and continued exposure to even minute amounts of X-rays may result in serious burns and injuries. For this reason, beginners in fluoroscopy and radiography should first have adequate instruction in these fields of practice and then begin their work under the direction of experienced technicians.

**301. Piezo-Electric Effect.**—Certain crystals when subjected to pressure are found to become electrically charged at opposite ends or on opposite faces, the charges being greatest when plates are cut from the crystals along definite planes. This phenomenon, called the *piezo-electric effect,* may be utilized when such a crystal is held between two insulated metal plates and pressure is exerted upon them. Rochelle salt, quartz and tourmaline are among the crystals which exhibit this property.

The piezo-electric effect is most pronounced in Rochelle salt, and crystals of this material are used in the manufacture of crystal microphones and phonograph transcribers or "pick-ups." Quartz is used to set up vibrations when its metal coatings are connected to a source of alternating e.m.f. of appropriate high frequency, and to control the frequency of radio-frequency oscillators, §335.

## QUESTIONS

1. What is meant by the expression: "ionization by collision"?
2. Why does an ionized gas glow?
3. Explain the conditions under which corona is produced.
4. What is the purpose of lightning rods?
5. Describe the Edison Effect, and give an explanation for it.
6. Name three materials used as thermionic emitters and describe their operating color.
7. Explain how a diode acts as a rectifier.
8. What is meant by the term "peak inverse potential" as applied to a rectifier tube?
9. How do gas diodes differ in operating characteristics from vacuum diodes?
10. What is meant by a coated cathode?
11. What is the purpose of a grid in a triode?
12. Define the following terms: amplification factor, plate resistance, and transconductance of a triode.
13. Explain how a signal applied to the grid of a triode may be rectified in the plate circuit of that tube.
14. What is a thyratron?
15. Distinguish between vacuum and gas photo-tubes.
16. Name three uses to which photo-cells may be applied.
17. Explain by means of a diagram the construction of a barrier layer cell and indicate the direction of the current when the cell is illuminated.
18. When and by whom were X-rays discovered?
19. What kind of rays are X-rays? and how are they produced?
20. How does the potential difference across the electrodes of an X-ray tube and the current through it affect the character of the rays produced?
21. What is the target in an X-ray tube made of? What methods are used for cooling the targets?

22. For what purpose is a fluoroscope used?
23. What precautions are necessary in X-ray work to protect the patient and operator from injury?
24. What is the piezo-electric effect?

## PROBLEMS

1. From the values of the average velocity of hydrogen molecules and their mean free path mentioned in §286, determine the number of collisions per second. *Ans.* 7.2 billion.
2. The current in a diode changes from 2 to 5 milliamperes when the plate battery potential is increased from +10 to +25 volts. Calculate the plate resistance of the diode. *Ans.* 5000 ohms.
3. A Type 6J5 tube is to be operated at potentials of −7.5 volts on the grid and +200 volts on the plate. Using the curves of Fig. 390, calculate the amplification factor, the plate resistance, and the mutual conductance of this tube under these conditions. *Ans.* 20, 10,600 ohms and 1890 micromhos respectively.
4. Calculate the amplification factor, the plate resistance and the transconductance for a Type 6J5 tube operating with −6 volts on the grid and +150 volts on the plate, using the curves of Fig. 391. *Ans.* 19, 13,000 ohms, and 1460 micromhos respectively.
5. A thyratron having a breakdown characteristic represented by the curve of Fig. 394 is employed in the circuit of Fig. 393 to charge 10 batteries in series, each requiring 6.6 volts. Assume the tube drop to be 16 volts. (a) Calculate the value of the resistance $R$ necessary to limit the instantaneous current to 2 amperes when the r.m.s. value of the alternating potential available is 120 volts. (b) What value of bias for the thyratron would result in the maximum charging of the batteries? (c) At what plate potential on the positive half-cycle would the charging cease, under the conditions stated in (b)? *Ans.* (a) 43.8 ohms; (b) zero; (c) 82.0 volts.
6. Plot the potential and current waves over one cycle of the applied e.m.f. for the thyratron circuit of Problem 5 (b). What is the initial current in the circuit? *Ans.* 0.78 ampere.

# Lesson XXVI

## TELEGRAPHY AND TELEPHONY

Single Morse telegraph—Duplex signaling—The polar duplex—Multiplex telegraphs—The Teletype system—Telephone instruments—The subscriber's set—Manual exchanges—Automatic telephones—Telephone repeaters—Carrier-current transmission—Questions and Problems.

**302. Single Morse Telegraph.**—The first practical method of communicating between two points by electrical means was the telegraph system devised by the American artist and inventor, Samuel F. B. Morse (1791-1872). Such a system permits the transmission of a single message at a time in either direction over an electric circuit, and it is called the *Single Morse* telegraph. The equipment comprises two keys for opening and closing the circuit, a battery for providing the operating current, and two sounders for indicating audibly the duration of the current pulses. Signals are transmitted by manipulating either key in accordance with a code, and are received by listening to the clicks produced by the sounder armature as it is attracted and released by its electromagnet.

The arrangement of the circuit is shown in Fig. 401, wherein the keys are represented by $K$ and $K'$, the batteries by $B$ and $B'$, the sounders by $S$ and $S'$, and the circuit-closing switches by $s$ and $s'$. When no messages are being transmitted, the circuit is kept closed by means of the switches connected in parallel with the keys, maintaining a current throughout the circuit. When the operator at the left station wishes to send a message, he interrupts the current by opening switch $s$ (as shown) and then proceeds to establish current pulses by depressing key $K$ for short

607

or long intervals. Both sounders respond to these current pulses and the signals are interpreted as dots and dashes, various combinations of which represent the letters and numbers of a telegraph code. The distant operator makes a record of the message received and the sending operator listens to his own signals to detect possible errors. When the operator is through sending, he again completes the circuit by means of his switch, thereby enabling the other operator to answer.

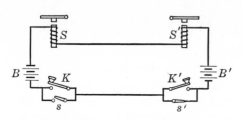

FIG. 401. Single Morse telegraph circuit

To save the expense of one of the line wires between the two stations, the earth is utilized as a conductor. The resistance of this ground-return path is very low because of its enormous cross-sectional area, although the conductivity of the earth's crust is poor. It is necessary, however, that good connections be made to the earth either by driving iron pipes into the ground to reach damp soil or by utilizing municipal water pipes.

On long telegraph lines, relays are used in the line instead of sounders, §110. A relay functions merely to open and close a local circuit rather than to produce an audible response like a sounder; therefore, the relay does not require a heavy armature nor many ampere-turns. The local circuit at each station includes a sounder and a source of e.m.f.

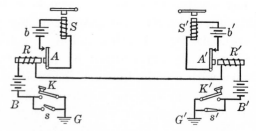

FIG. 402. Telegraph circuit with relays

Fig. 402 shows the circuit of a single Morse telegraph between two stations using relays and a ground return. The line circuit includes batteries $B$ and $B'$, relays $R$ and $R'$, the line, keys $K$ and $K'$ with their switches $s$ and $s'$, and ground from $G$ to $G'$. The two local circuits include the batteries $b$ and $b'$, sounders $S$ and $S'$, and the contacts of armatures $A$ and $A'$. The operation can be traced by considering switch $s'$ at the right-hand station closed and manipulating key $K$ at the other.

Assuming the telegraph line to be perfectly insulated from ground, the current in the circuit can be calculated readily by means of Ohm's Law, §73.

Let

$E$ = total e.m.f. available in the line circuit in volts,
$n$ = number of relays in the line,
$R$ = resistance of each relay in ohms,
$l$ = length of the line in miles,
$r$ = resistance of unit length of line wire in ohms per mile.

Then the current is

$$I = \frac{E}{n \times R + r \times l} \qquad \qquad 132$$

If $I$ be considered as the minimum operating current of the relays, then for a given e.m.f., size of line wire, and resistance of relays, the maximum distance over which signals may be sent is obtained from Formula (132) by solving for $l$, namely

$$l = \frac{E - I \times n \times R}{r \times I} \qquad \qquad 133$$

**Problem 164.**—Over how long a line of No. 13 A.w.g. copper wire could two 20-ohm sounders be operated on 120 volts, if the minimum current to operate the sounders is 0.2 ampere?

From page 115, the resistance of No. 13 wire is 2.04 ohms per 1000 feet, therefore $r = 5.28 \times 2.04$ or 10.8 ohms per mile. The maximum distance for telegraphic transmission over this line is

(133) $\qquad l = \dfrac{120 - 0.2 \times 2 \times 20}{10.8 \times 0.2} = \dfrac{112}{2.16} = 52$ miles

**Problem 165.**—If two 150-ohm relays requiring 0.04 ampere are used instead of the 20-ohm instruments in the preceding problem, what is the maximum distance over which telegraphic signaling is possible on that line?

(133) $\qquad l = \dfrac{120 - 0.04 \times 2 \times 150}{10.8 \times 0.04} = \dfrac{108}{0.432} = 250$ miles

Overhead telegraph lines are supported by glass insulators mounted upon wooden, or sometimes concrete and steel, telegraph poles. These points of support offer leakage current paths to ground and, consequently, not all of the current which starts out on the line reaches the receiving instrument. The insulation of the line in wet weather is much reduced and the received current is then very small. In order to assure sufficient current on a long line under all weather conditions, repeating instruments are introduced at intervals of several hundred miles to retransmit the signals automatically from one section of the line to the next. A repeater for a single Morse telegraph consists of two relays and two transmitters which are electrically and mechanically arranged to allow signaling in either direction.

**Experiment 112.**—Set up a telegraph circuit like that shown in Fig. 401, using either one or both of the batteries illustrated. Operate the circuit in both directions. If it is possible to separate the two stations sufficiently, make use of the earth as a ground return path by utilizing the pipes of the local water supply system.

**303. Duplex Signaling.**—In duplex telegraphy two messages are transmitted simultaneously in opposite directions over a single line circuit, without any interference of the signals either way. Naturally, four operators are required for such a circuit, one sending and one receiving operator at each station. As the message capacity of a duplexed line is twice that of the same line when operated as a single Morse circuit, a corresponding saving is effected in line equipment.

The receiving instrument at each terminal is in circuit at all times ready to respond to signals sent from the other station, but is arranged not to respond to signals sent from its own station. This object is accomplished by using an *artificial line* at each terminal and dividing the winding of each relay so that signal currents from one station will divide between the actual and artificial lines in such a way that the relay at the home station will not operate but the relay at the other station will. The artificial line is an assembly of resistors and capacitors which together simulate the actual line.

The simplest type of duplex telegraph is illustrated in Fig. 403. It is called a *differential duplex* because the neutral relays $R$ and $R'$ each have two windings that are identical as to number of turns and resistance, through which currents may be circulated in the same or opposite directions around the iron core. The corresponding turns of the two windings are wound side by side so as to avoid the formation of consequent magnetic poles, §23, but for clearness the two windings are shown separated in the figure. Each artificial line $A$ and $A'$ has a resistance equal to that of line $L$ plus that of the terminal apparatus from the end-point of the line to ground. Resistors $H$ and $H'$ have resistances that are equal to the internal resistances of batteries $B$ and $B'$ respectively; under this condition the resistance of the circuit is unaltered whether the keys $K$ and $K'$ are on the front or rear contacts.

The transmission of two messages in opposite directions over this duplex telegraph will be described by considering various positions of the keys. If neither key is depressed, the batteries $B$ and $B'$ are disconnected and, therefore, neither relay is actuated.

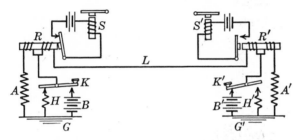

Fig. 403. Differential duplex telegraph

The depression of one key, say $K'$, provides two paths for current from battery $B'$, one through line $L$ to ground $G$ and the other through artificial line $A'$ to ground $G'$. The current divides equally between them and the two parts circulate around the iron core of relay $R'$ in opposite directions. Their magnetomotive forces neutralize each other, the core is left unmagnetized, and the armature of relay $R'$ is not affected. The current in the line $L$ and right-hand coil of relay $R$ completes its path principally through resistor $H$ and ground; as a result, the core of the relay is magnetized and its armature is attracted. Consequently, the depression of key $K'$ causes the actuation of relay $R$ and sounder $S$, but not the instruments of the home station. Similarly, the depression of key $K$ causes the actuation of relay $R'$ and of sounder $S'$.

The depression of both keys connects the two batteries in opposition and, since under this condition there can be no current in the line wire nor in the line coils of the relays, both of these instruments will be actuated by the currents supplied by the home batteries through the coils in the artificial line circuits. The transmission of signals in both directions simultaneously is merely a succession of combinations of the key positions mentioned. Duplex transmission is possible without interference because a relay at one station is energized whenever the key at the other station is depressed regardless of the position of the home key.

The resistances of the artificial lines are experimentally adjusted in practice so that the relays are not affected by movements of the home keys. Their resistance may, however, be calculated on the assumption that the line is perfectly insulated from ground and devoid of capacitance with respect to ground; the result of such a computation is expressed by

$$A = \frac{r \times l}{2} + \frac{1}{2} \sqrt{(r \times l + R)(r \times l + R + 4H)} \qquad 134$$

where $r \times l$ is the total resistance of the line wire, $R$ is the total resistance of each relay, and $H$ is the internal resistance of each battery. When the battery resistance is negligibly small, the resistance of the artificial line reduces to

$$A = r \times l + \frac{R}{2} \qquad 135$$

**Problem 166.**—Two 200-ohm relays are connected to the ends of a 1400-ohm duplex line. What should be the resistance of each artificial line if the internal resistance of each battery is 20 ohms?

$$(134) \quad A = \frac{1400}{2} + \frac{1}{2} \sqrt{(1400 + 200)(1400 + 200 + 80)} = 1520 \text{ ohms}$$

**304. The Polar Duplex.**—The system of duplex telegraphy described in the last section is operated by closing or opening the circuit through keys, thereby increasing or decreasing the current through the relays. Another system operates on *reversal of current direction* rather than by *change of current strength*. It is called a polar duplex because it utilizes polarized relays, §112; Fig. 404 depicts its connections. The polarized relays $P$ and $P'$ are differentially wound, as were the neutral relays in the preceding figure; the keys $K$ and $K'$ control the polarity of the potential applied by the batteries $B$ and $B'$ to the mid-points of the relay windings. The letters $n$ and $s$ on the relay and pole pieces represent their magnetic polarity due to the permanent magnets alone.

When both keys are up, the negative terminals of both batteries are connected to the mid-points of the relay windings. There will be no current in the line nor in the upper coils of the relays because the two batteries of equal e.m.f. oppose each other. There will be current in the lower relay coils and in artificial lines $A$ and $A'$; their directions around the relay cores will be such as to draw the relay armatures away from the sounder contacts and, consequently, both sounders will be idle.

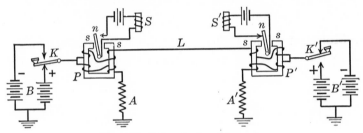

Fig. 404. Polar duplex telegraph

If only key $K$ is depressed, the positive terminal of battery $B$ is connected to the relay and the conditions are exactly as represented in the figure. Each battery supplies current to its own artificial line circuit, and the two batteries assist each other in establishing current in the line $L$. Consequently, there is about twice as much current in the upper coils of the relays as through the lower coils, and so the operation of the relays depends upon the direction of current in their *upper coils*. The current in the upper coil on the left-hand side of relay $P$ aids the south magnetization of the permanent magnet, and the current in its other upper coil opposes the south magnetization there. Thus, the signal current strengthens the left-hand pole and weakens the right-hand pole; these actions cause the armature to stay away from its sounder contact. At the other station, the current in the upper coils of relay $P'$ strengthens the left-hand pole and weakens the right-hand pole and, therefore, the armature closes the local circuit and the sounder $S'$ responds. In like manner the depression of key $K'$ only will operate sounder $S$.

When both keys are closed simultaneously, there will again be no current in the line, because both batteries apply equal positive potential to it. The currents in the lower coils of the relays are now in such a direction as to draw the armatures against the local-circuit contacts, causing both sounders to operate. To summarize, the manipulation of one key controls the operation of the distant sounder, but does not control the home sounder.

By combining the two duplex systems described, Edison in 1874 devised the *quadruplex telegraph* for transmitting four messages simultaneously over a single wire without interference. The *polar side* of the quadruplex circuit provides two channels of communication by means of current reversals, and the other or *neutral side* provides two channels by changes in current intensity.

**305. Multiplex Telegraphs.**—The term multiplex telegraph is applied to those systems of communication which afford several

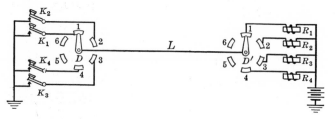

Fig. 405. Scheme of the synchronous multiplex telegraph

telegraph channels over a single wire by utilizing *synchronous distributors* at the terminal stations for assigning the line to corresponding transmitting and receiving devices. The method is illustrated in Fig. 405, with the circuit simplified to provide transmission in one direction only. Four keys are shown connected to contact segments at the transmitting distributor $D$, and four relays are shown joined to segments at the receiving distributor $D'$. The contact arms of the distributors are connected to line $L$, and the ground is utilized as the return path.

When both arms are on contacts 1, key $K_1$ will be in the circuit of relay $R_1$ and control its operation; when the arms are both on contacts 2, key $K_2$ will control relay $R_2$, and so on. By having the arms always in step, each relay will receive only signals transmitted by the key marked with the same subscript.

The speed of these synchronously-revolving arms is made sufficiently great so that they will be coupled with any one channel, say $K_1R_1$, several times during the short interval required to form a dot signal. The current for such a dot signal over any channel is made up of short impulses that are rather widely separated compared with their duration, and the signal is made intelligible by using polarized relays.

Two-way communication may be accomplished by introducing relays at the left-hand and keys at the right-hand stations in Fig. 405; each channel will then be the equivalent of a single Morse circuit as in Fig. 401. Multiplex telegraphy, however, is usually carried out by polar duplex methods. The connection of duplex terminal sets, such as shown in Fig. 404, to the four channel distributors illustrated in Fig. 405, would constitute a quadruple-duplex circuit and afford 4 telegraph channels in each direction over a single line.

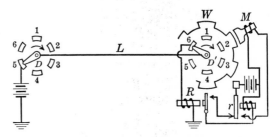

FIG. 406. Method of securing synchronous rotation of distributors

It is essential that the contact arms of both distributors occupy the same relative positions at all times. Such synchronous rotation is secured by the use of motors having tooth-wheel iron armatures and periodically excited field magnets, the contact arms being mounted directly on the motor shaft. Periodic field excitation is obtained by means of a reed that is kept vibrating at its natural frequency. Governing impulses are sent by the distributor at one station during every revolution of its contact arm to control the speed of the motor at the other station.

One circuit arrangement for securing synchronous rotation is shown in Fig. 406; the vibrating reed and distributor motor being shown only at one station. The toothed wheel $W$ of the distributor motor advances one tooth every time the vibrating reed $r$ makes one complete vibration, because a current pulse reaches magnet $M$ every time the reed touches its right-hand contact. The reed is kept in vibration electromagnetically, like the hammer of an electric bell, but its circuit can be controlled by the action of relay $R$ in the governing circuit 5-6.

The vibration rate of the reed at one station is adjusted 1 or 2 per cent faster than that at the other. Suppose that distributor arm $D'$ reaches contact 6 while arm $D$ is still on contact 5, as shown in the figure. Current is established momentarily over line $L$ and through synchronizing relay $R,$ and causes the relay armature to be attracted. This action opens the vibrator circuit for an instant, thereby retarding slightly the vibration of the reed and the rotation of distributor arm $D'$. When both arms are in step in passing over contacts 5, or over contacts 6, the synchronizing circuit is open and no governing impulse is transmitted to the relay.

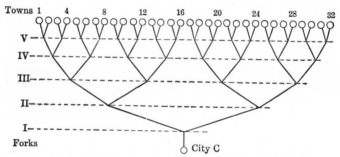

Fig. 407. Illustrating how 32 choices are possible with 5 selections

**306. The Teletype System.**—Hand transmission of telegraph signals at speeds of approximately 150 letters per minute has been largely superseded by mechanical devices operated at higher speeds. The methods involve the manipulation of a keyboard resembling a typewriter for transmitting current impulses, and the receipt of these impulses by a group of relays in proper sequence to select the letters for direct printing on a tape or page. The setting up of the impulses according to a definite code and the translation of them into the letters of the alphabet make use of complicated mechanisms at both stations.

The general plan of selection can be likened to the choice of a road leading from a large city to any one of a number of suburban towns. Fig 407, for example, illustrates a rather systematic road system from city $C$ to towns numbered from 1 to 32. To reach one of these towns requires selecting the correct road at five successive forks I to V; thus, to reach town 20 it is necessary to make the following turns: right, left, left, right right. Similarly, the code used in a printing telegraph system has five impulses for each letter, and their character indicates which of five relays are to be operated for the selection of the letter desired. The 32 possible combinations take care of all letters of the alphabet, some punctuation marks and such functions as space, line space, and return to left of page.

The Teletype system employs the five unit code, but actually has six contacts at the transmitting station and seven at the receiving station to take care of the selecting, controlling, and printing operations. These contacts are closed sequentially by start-and-stop mechanisms that are driven through shafts by small motors at the two stations. The mechanisms start together when a letter or other character is begun and stop when it is completed, thereby synchronism is established between the rotating members at the beginning of each letter; the driving motors need to keep in step only during the short time required for the sending and receiving mechanisms to make one revolution.

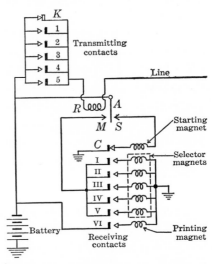

FIG. 408. Simplified circuit of a Teletype station

When a key on the transmitter keyboard is depressed, five selector bars are actuated to determine the character of the current impulses. Each bar moves either to lock its associated sending contact so that it may not be closed, or to leave that contact free to be closed in its proper sequence when the contact arm of the transmitting mechanism passes over it. The bars are then locked in position and the mechanism is released. The subsequent happenings will be explained with the aid of Fig. 408.

In the figure, the transmitting contacts are shown at the top marked $K$ and from 1 to 5, and the receiving contacts are shown below marked $C$ and from I to VI; further, the relay in the line circuit is indicated by $R$ with its armature $A$ and its left and right contact studs $M$ and $S$ respectively. The five selector magnets, the starting and printing magnets, and the battery are designated. In describing the operations, it will be assumed that the station represented is connected to another with identical wiring and that the elements there are designated by the same symbols, but primed.

As the transmitting mechanism is released the line circuit is locked open at contact $K$; this causes relays $R$ and $R'$ to shift their armatures to contact studs $S$ and $S'$. This action energizes the starting magnets at both stations and releases their receiving mechanisms. Immediately thereafter, contacts $C$ and $C'$ are locked open, and the receiving mechanisms at both stations continue to turn for a complete revolution before they are stopped automatically; meanwhile their contact arms touch the various contacts in succession.

First contacts 1, I and I' are touched simultaneously by the respective arms. If transmitting contact 1 is not latched open, it will close momentarily and establish current over the line; relays $R$ and $R'$ will be energized and move their armatures to studs $M$ and $M'$ respectively, thereby actuating the selector magnets associated with contacts I and I'. The three contacts mentioned are then opened but the two selector magnets remain set.

With continued motion of the mechanism, contacts II and II' are closed momentarily as the transmitting arm comes into position to close contact 2. If this contact is latched open, no current is established over the line and the relays shift their armatures to studs $S$ and $S'$. Since contacts $C$ and $C'$ are locked open, neither the starting magnets nor the selector magnets associated with contacts II and II' will operate.

Assuming that contact 3 is not latched open, this contact will close momentarily when contacts III and III' are closed. The line current then causes the relays to make contacts at $M$ and $M'$ and the selector magnets associated with contacts III and III' will be energized. As the respective mechanisms continue to turn, contacts 3, III and III′ will be opened but the selector magnets will remain set. In a similar manner, contacts IV and IV′ are closed at just the right instant to interpret the action at contact 4; so also with contacts V, V′ and 5.

Each selector magnet that is energized moves a notched code bar similar to the selector bar at the transmitter. The resulting arrangement of the five code bars is such that only one set of notches line up across all five bars. As each receiving mechanism approaches the end of its revolution, contacts VI and VI′ are closed and current is established in the printing magnets; these release the printing devices which aιe operated by separate motors. Each of these acts to print all the characters on the machine, but only that letter is printed which corresponds to the alignment of the notches in the five code bars. This letter, of course, corresponds to the key depressed at the transmitter.

Before the transmitting and receiving mechanisms complete their respective revolutions which result in the transmission and printing of a character, the code bars are reset and made ready for a new group of signals. Also, the combination set up at the transmitting contacts is unlatched, and contacts $K$, $C$, and $C'$ are closed. The final pulse resulting from the closing of $K$ brings the armatures of the relays to studs $M$ and $M'$, if these contacts were not already made. The mechanisms come to rest, but the motors operate continuously, the coupling between them being controlled by a clutch.

The Teletype system is designed to transmit up to 460 letters per minute. The motors are rated about 1/16 horsepower and may be either alternating- or direct-current machines; the signals require a direct-current source and the line current is about 60 milliamperes. The system is used for business purposes, such as by brokerage firms and banks, as well as for transmitting fire alarms in cities and broadcasting police alarms over wide areas It may be operated on single Morse or on duplex circuits.

**307. Telephone Instruments.**—The transmission of speech by electrical means was first accomplished in 1876 by Alexander G. Bell (1847-1922), American inventor and physicist. The art of telephony grew rapidly and today there are over 30 million telephones in the United States and about as many again in the rest of the world. Approximately 60 per cent of the total are estimated to be automatic or "dial" telephones. About 125 million calls are completed in this country daily.

The instruments used in telephonic communication consist principally of a *transmitter* for producing a variable current that has the same characteristics as the incident sound waves, and a *receiver* for converting this variable current into sound waves to reproduce the original speech sounds. A complete telephone set includes in addition: an *induction coil* for improving the effectiveness of the transmitter, a *ringer* for attracting attention to an incoming call, and a *hook switch* for shifting the circuit from the idle to the talking connection.

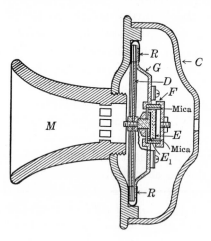

FIG. 409. Telephone transmitter

The transmitter consists essentially of a conducting path of carbon granules; these can be compacted or loosened by the pressure of a diaphragm when activated by the voice, and the resistance of the instrument is lessened or increased.

A cross section of a standard type of transmitter is shown in Fig. 409. The diaphragm *D,* of thin iron or aluminum, is mounted between a hard-rubber mouthpiece *M* and a brass chamber *F* fastened to the metal cup *G.* The chamber contains two polished carbon disks that serve as electrodes; disk *E* is secured to the back of the chamber, and disk $E_1$ is fastened to the center of the diaphragm and carries a mica washer, the outer edge of which is clamped to cup *G* by the chamber *F.* The space between the carbon electrodes is completely closed and is filled with granules of carbon. Sound waves from the person speaking into the mouthpiece cause a vibration of the diaphragm and also of electrode $E_1$ fastened to it; this changes the resistance of the granular carbon and causes a variation in the current through the transmitter. The transmitter parts are mounted in a metal case $C$, and the electrodes are insulated from it by insulating ring $R$.

The receiver contains a small electromagnet to carry the varying current from the transmitter and to set into vibration a thin iron diaphragm mounted nearby. Fig. 410 shows a bipolar receiver of standard design; it consists of a horseshoe permanent magnet $M$ with soft iron pole pieces $P$ and $P_1$, each pole piece being surrounded by a coil of fine copper wire. A circular diaphragm $D$ is clamped at its edge and is kept attracted by the pole pieces, but it does not touch them. The coils on the pole pieces are so connected that a current in one direction through them will tend to strengthen the field of the permanent magnet and a current in the opposite direction will tend to weaken it. The diaphragm will be attracted more when the field is strengthened and less when it is weakened. With an alternating current in the receiver coils, the diaphragm will oscillate to and fro in accordance with the current reversals. When used with a telephone transmitter, the receiver diaphragm will vibrate in the same manner as that of the transmitter, thus reproducing speech.

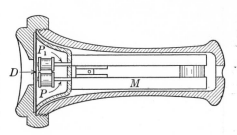

FIG. 410.  Bipolar telephone receiver

**Experiment 113.**—Connect a telephone transmitter and receiver in a series circuit containing a battery of two or three dry cells, the two instruments being placed a dozen yards apart or in two separate rooms. Try it out with another person for one-way transmission of speech. Then verify the fact that when you give the diaphragm of the transmitter a single gentle push with the finger, the receiver will emit a pulse of sound, the loudness of which will increase with the amount of force exerted on the transmitter diaphragm. Explain. Finally, remove the receiver from the circuit and connect it in series with a condenser of 0.5 microfarad capacitance across the usual 110-volt alternating-current service mains; listen for the 60-cycle hum.

Fig. 411 shows a sectional view of a modern telephone handset, with the transmitter at the left and the receiver at the right mounted together in a shell of molded insulation. The transmitter diaphragm is a shallow cone of thin aluminum alloy fastened at its rim, and the receiver diaphragm is a disk of magnetic alloy. The receiver has a bipolar winding on pole pieces of permalloy fastened to two straight bar magnets.

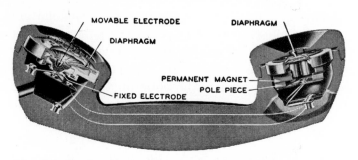

FIG. 411. Handset developed by the Bell Telephone Laboratories

**308. The Subscriber's Set.**—Telephone instruments are arranged in convenient sets for use by subscribers to telephone service, and the sets are connected by line wires to central offices. These offices are equipped with switchboards for interconnecting subscribers' lines, storage batteries for supplying the "talking circuits," and alternating-current generators for signalling purposes. Each subscriber's set is arranged to keep the signaling circuit closed so that the set will be responsive to incoming calls at all times. Lifting the receiver from its support in answering a call automatically closes the talking circuits of a set and the storage battery then supplies the current for two-way telephone conversation.

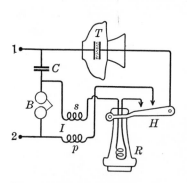

FIG. 412. Connections of a desk set

Fig. 412 shows the connections of a subscriber's desk set that is widely used in this country. It consists of transmitter $T$, receiver $R$, induction coil $I$, ringer or bell $B$, hook switch $H$, and condenser $C$. The ringer is connected in series with the condenser across terminals 1 and 2 of the set, and is generally designed to operate on alternating current having a frequency of 16⅔ cycles per second. When the receiver is off the hook, the switch contacts are closed and both receiver and transmitter are connected in the circuit, which includes the primary winding $p$ and the secondary winding $s$ of the induction coil.

When a person speaks into the transmitter, the resistance of this device varies from instant to instant and the current changes correspondingly in the following circuit: 1, $T$, $H$, $p$, 2 at the home set, the line wires, and 1, $C$, $s$, $R$, $H$, $p$, 2 at some distant telephone set similarly marked. As a result, the person listening at the receiver will hear the sounds made at the transmitter. Further study of the circuit shows that the variation in resistance of the transmitter changes the p.d. across the local circuit consisting of $C, s, R, H$, thereby establishing a current through the secondary winding $s$ of the induction coil. This action induces an e.m.f. in the primary winding $p$ in such a direction as to increase the line current variations initially produced by the changes of transmitter resistance.

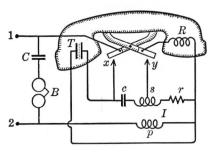

FIG. 413. Connections of a modern handset

The response of the receiver to the actuation of the transmitter is correspondingly greater.

The connections of the modern handset are shown in Fig. 413; it includes transmitter $T$, receiver $R$, ringer $B$, condenser $C$, and induction coil $I$. When the user lifts the handset from its support to engage in conversation, the switch $H$ makes contacts at $x$ and $y$, closing the transmitter and receiver circuits respectively. These circuits are coupled magnetically by the primary and secondary windings $p$ and $s$ of the induction coil. Resistor $r$ and condenser $c$ are added to match the resistance and capacitance of the subscriber's line.

The vibration of the transmitter diaphragm varies the resistance in the circuit 1, $x$, $T$, $p$, 2 and produces corresponding variations of current in a similarly marked circuit of another telephone set where a person is listening. As a result, e.m.f.'s are developed in the secondary winding of the induction coil, and

these produce corresponding current variations in the circuit
*s, y, R, r,* which actuate the receiver accordingly. The connections
of the set are so designed that the receiver will respond very
little to variations of current produced by its own transmitter,
thereby making it unresponsive to extraneous noises picked up
at the home station and hence more effective as a receiver of incoming speech sounds.

**309. Manual Exchanges.**—Telephone calls between subscribers
served by manual telephone exchanges are established and terminated by operators at central offices.

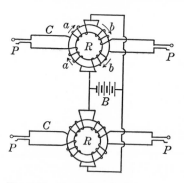

FIG. 414. Cord circuits in a com-
mon-battery exchange

The formation of a communication
channel between two stations connected to a single switchboard proceeds as follows: the calling subscriber
lifts the receiver from the hook, a
lamp associated with the line from
his station and located on the switchboard lights to signal the operator,
the operator connects her telephone
set to the subscriber's line and learns
the number of the station sought, she
establishes line connection with the
wanted subscriber and sends out a signal, that subscriber hears
the ringer and lifts the receiver from the hook, and the two subscribers converse. When the conversation has ended, both subscribers hang their receivers on the hooks, disconnect signals are
displayed at the switchboard, and the operator takes down the
connection.

The functions performed by the operator are carried out with
so-called *cord circuits;* each of these comprises two *plugs* for connection to the *jacks* of the subscriber's lines, a *listening key* for
shunting in the operator's head-set, a *ringing key* for applying
an alternating p.d. to the called subscriber's line, and *supervisory
lamps* to inform the operator when disconnection is desired.

Fig. 414 indicates how the cord circuits are connected to the
common battery of the telephone office; two of them are shown
without the auxiliaries mentioned above except the plugs *P.* It

will be observed that the battery $B$ is not connected in series with each of the cord circuits $C$, but is bridged across them through individual repeating coils $R$, each consisting of four identical windings on a ring-shaped iron core. This is done so that conversation transmitted by one circuit will not be heard on the others supplied by the same battery. For example, suppose an impulse from one station to produce a current directed as shown by the arrows $a$ on the upper repeating coil, and that this will set up a current by transformer action in the other windings of the same coil directed as shown by the arrows $b$; these equal currents pass through the battery in opposite directions and, in consequence, there will be no current fluctuation in it.

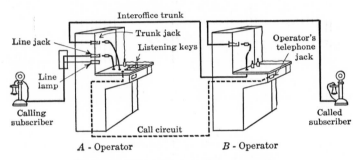

FIG. 415.  Interoffice telephone connection

Communication between stations connected to different central offices is established through two cord circuits, one located at the switchboard of each office. The call is handled at the originating office by the *A-operator*, and she tells the *B-operator* at the terminating office over a *call circuit* to establish connection between an interoffice trunk designated and the wanted subscriber's line. Fig. 415 shows the scheme of connection. On the keyshelf before each A-operator is a call-circuit button for each office to which she may be required to make a connection; the depression of one of these buttons connects her headset with that of a B-operator in the corresponding office.

**310. Automatic Telephones.**—In an automatic or machine-switching telephone system the connections are made by devices set into action directly by the subscribers. The telephone set is of the usual form, but contains in addition a calling switch known as a *dial*. This dial has ten finger holes marked with letters and figures. A letter or figure is dialed by inserting the finger tip in the corresponding hole and turning the dial until the finger strikes a stop; upon releasing the finger the dial returns at a

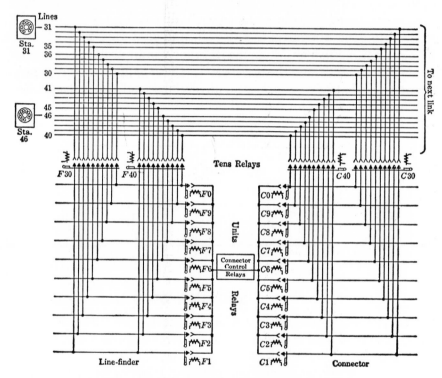

FIG. 416. Automatic telephone exchange for 100 stations
Only 20 lines and one link of the system are shown.

definite rate and sends out an appropriate number of current impulses. This procedure is repeated for each digit of the wanted subscriber's number. Relays or more involved contactors are operated by the current impulses and these devices complete the connections to the station sought. Provision is made for automatic ringing and for the busy signal.

The scheme of connections of a private automatic exchange is illustrated in Fig. 416, which shows an all-relay 100-line system for establishing telephone connection between any two stations.

Only 20 of the lines are indicated and these are drawn horizontally at the top. The lower portion of the figure represents a *link* for connecting any two stations; several of these would be needed to permit simultaneous communication between different pairs of stations, and the additional links would be connected similarly at the right-hand side. The wiring to each station consists of two lines, but only one is shown in the diagram for clearness. Two digits are employed in dialing.

A link consists of the devices necessary to complete the connection between two stations; it includes a *line finder* which locates the calling line, a *connector* which makes contact with the wanted line, and the *connector control relays* which register the number of the wanted station and cause the connector to make contact with it. The finder consists of 10 *tens relays* designated as . . . F30, F40, . . . and 10 *units relays* designated as F1, . . . F9, F0. The connector consists of a similar set of relays designated with a *C* before the number.

When a call is made an idle link is automatically employed for the duration of the call. The finder selects the calling line from the 100 lines in the exchange, and this is done by first selecting the 10-line group containing the calling line and then that particular line from the ten. Thereafter the connector control relays register the number of the desired station, as indicated by the dialing, and set the connector in operation. This device makes the selection of the wanted line in the same manner as the line finder.

Suppose Station 31 to call Station 46 by dialing first 4 and then 6. At an idle finder, the tens relay F30 and the units relay F1 will operate and close their contacts. The former will connect all ten lines 30-39 to the line-finder units relays, and the latter will connect only line 31 through to the connector control relays; the other 9 lines of the group will remain disconnected at the contacts of the units relays F2 to F0. At the connector, the tens relay C40 and the units relay C6 will operate and close their contacts. The former will select the 10-line group 40-49 and the latter will connect with line 46; the other 9 lines in the group will remain disconnected at the contacts of the units relays C1 to C5 and C7 to C0. The circuits of the other 10-line groups will, of course, be open at the contacts of their appropriate tens relays. In this way connection is established between lines 31 and 46.

The completed connection between Stations 31 and 46 may be traced through the link as follows: beginning at Station 31 in the upper left corner, follow the horizontal line to the point where it connects with a vertical line, follow that line down through the contact of relay F30 to the bottom horizontal line, and then follow that line through the contact of relay F1 to the connector control relays; proceed through the contact of relay C6 to a vertical line associated with the C40 relay, follow the vertical line through the contact of this relay to the point where a horizontal line is met, and follow that line toward the left to reach Station 46.

Private automatic exchanges of the type described provide continuous service without an operator and are adapted to plants, hospitals and schools which do not require city trunk connections. When used collaterally with the city system the private exchange relieves the branch operator of all internal or interdepartmental calls.

Automatic telephones for a city system of many central offices involve more complicated mechanisms for completing the connections without the help of operators. A single office may accommodate as many as 10,000 stations. The numbers assigned to the individual stations involve 7 digits, the first 3 designating the name of the central office and the rest the identifying number of the subscriber.

The manner of completing a connection in an automatic city system follows: When a subscriber lifts the receiver from the hook prior to dialing, the line circuit closes and a relay operates at the office. This relay causes an idle line finder to locate the calling subscriber's line terminals, and at the same time a *sender-selector* attached to that finder chooses an idle *sender*. These operations require only a fraction of a second and, when completed, a low humming sound, known as the *dial tone,* will be heard at the calling station. Upon perceiving this signal, the subscriber dials the number desired, and thereafter the procedure is the same whether the called subscriber is served by a manual or by a machine-switching office. The progress of the call in a general way will be traced with the aid of Fig. 417.

The electrical impulses from the dial come through the line finder and sender-selector to the sender, and the latter registers them. These impulses are on a decimal basis, whereas the office trunks and subscribers' lines are in groups of 500. Therefore, the sender translates the impulses to fit the selecting mechanisms used in the system. The sender automatically causes the particular *district-selector,* which is associated with the line finder, to select an idle trunk to the office of the called subscriber.

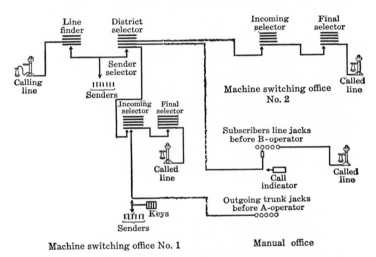

Fig. 417. Schematic plan of connections between machine-switching and manual telephone offices

The trunk leading to the same or to some other machine-switching office terminates on an incoming *selector;* this selector chooses one of a number of other selectors, called *final selectors,* which have access to the subscribers' lines. In a central office of 10,000 subscribers there are 20 groups of final selectors, each having access to 500 subscribers. Consequently, 20 groups of trunks are needed on the incoming selector frames, each group leading to a different frame of final selectors. Thus, the incoming selector, under control of the sender in the originating office, chooses the proper group and selects an idle trunk leading to a final selector; this selector in turn goes through the same process to locate the called subscriber's line. Upon establishing the connection, the sender is released and is ready to be used for another call. If the called line is idle, ringing commences automatically and the signal continues periodically until the subscriber responds; but if the line is busy, an intermittent buzz, recognized as the busy signal, is sent back to the calling subscriber.

When connection is made with a station joined to a manual office, the call is routed from the district selector to the B-operator at that office, where the number desired appears before her in visual form on a *call indicator*. This information, together with the number of the trunk on which the call is being handled, enables the operator to complete the connection by inserting the trunk plug into the jack of the subscriber's line. Calls originating in a manual office and intended for stations joined to a machine-switching office are dialed by the A-operator and may be traced from the figure.

**311. Telephone Repeaters.**—Triodes are used on long telephone lines for amplifying the voice currents. The electrical signal to

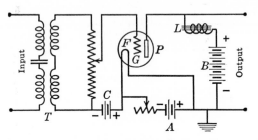

be amplified is applied to the input or grid circuit of the vacuum tube, and the enhanced signal is made available in its output or plate circuit as explained in §294. The tube and its circuits thus constitute a *repeater element* which amplifies telephone signals in one direction.

Fig. 418. Connections of a vacuum-tube repeater element

The connection diagram of such a repeater element is given in Fig. 418, wherein the the incoming signal is received by the primary winding of the input transformer $T$. The e.m.f. induced in the secondary winding is applied to a resistor of high resistance, and a sliding contact is provided so that any desired portion of this e.m.f. may be impressed upon the tube between the filament $F$ and the grid $G$. Battery $B$ supplies the potential to the plate $P$ through choke coil $L$; the latter confines the amplified voice currents to the output circuit indicated by the terminals at the right. Battery $A$ heats the filament to produce the electron flow, and battery $C$ maintains the grid negative to prevent distortion that would result from establishment of current between grid and filament.

A simple method of inserting a repeater element into a telephone line in order to secure two-way transmission is indicated in Fig. 419. The input side of the repeater element $R$ is bridged across the line, and the output side is connected to a winding of the output transformer $O$. Energy entering from line section $L_1$ divides at the repeating station; part is transferred by transformer action to the output circuit of the repeater and is there lost, the other part enters the input circuit of the repeater element and is amplified; little energy is transmitted directly to the line section $L_2$ if the telephone circuit is properly proportioned. The amplified energy from the repeater is then supplied by transformer action to both line sections, but the portion going back to $L_1$ is not usefully employed.

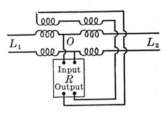

FIG. 419. Telephone repeater set

Another method of introducing a telephone repeater involves a balancing artificial line for each line section, two repeater elements, and two output transformers. This method is used where more than one repeater is required on a line or where two dissimilar lines are to be connected by a repeater.

**312. Carrier-Current Transmission.**—The principle utilized in radio telephony of modulating a high-frequency wave at the transmitter and rectifying this wave at the receiver, as explained in §§322 and 332, has been applied with success to telegraphy and telephony over line wires. This method of increasing the capacity of line circuits is termed *carrier-current* transmission, since alternating currents of different and relatively-high frequencies are employed to "carry" the signal or speech waves. With this method a single circuit, if traffic demanded, might furnish simultaneously 4 two-way telephone channels and 10 telegraph channels in each direction.

While the carrier system is essentially the same for both telegraph and telephone transmission, the following description is limited to telegraphy for the sake of simplicity. The fundamental features are: (a) generation of the several high-frequency e.m.f.'s for furnishing the carrier currents, (b) modulating each carrier current to the variations in strength which characterize the telegraph signals, (c) transmitting the modulated carrier waves and amplifying them if necessary by repeaters, (d) separating the several carrier currents at the receiving terminal according to their frequencies by means of selective circuits, and (e) rectifying the selected carrier currents so as to obtain the original characteristics of the telegraph message.

The carrier currents are generated by vacuum-tube oscillators, §324, and the frequencies of operation are determined by the inductance and capacitance of their associated circuits. Modulation may be effected by merely starting and stopping the carrier current with a key or relay contact in accordance with the telegraph signals. Rectification is accomplished by a vacuum-tube detector or rectifier with a shunt condenser, the resulting direct current being passed through the receiving relay. Thus, each key serves to produce variations of intensity of only one carrier current, and these variations are made intelligible by only one of the receiving relays connected to the line.

The selecting circuits or filters separate the currents of various frequencies and thus make carrier operation possible. They consist of inductance coils and condensers of appropriate size and manner of connection in order to transmit currents of certain frequencies or bands of frequencies and to suppress those of other frequencies. When several filters of different electrical constants are connected in parallel to a common line, then currents of only particular frequencies or bands of frequencies will pass through the filters for which they are individually tuned. Filters comprising a number of sections, each containing inductance coils and condensers, can be designed to transmit currents up to a certain frequency with little attenuation and to suppress those of high frequency, or vice versa; such circuits are called *low-pass filters* and *high-pass filters* respectively.

Fig. 420 gives the schematic diagram of one terminal set of a carrier telegraph system, having two duplex channels, applied to a regular telephone circuit. In addition to using tuned circuits at the receiving end, the diagram also shows them at the sending end in order to keep currents produced at one transmitter out of the circuits of other transmitters. It will be noted that modu-

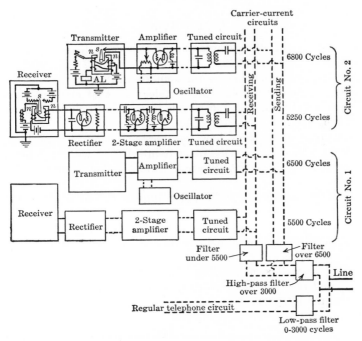

FIG. 420. Carrier-current telegraph circuits

lation is accomplished by making and breaking a short-circuited connection across the input side of a vacuum-tube amplifier. Polarized relays are used as transmitting and receiving instruments to improve the transmission of signals.

Depression of a key actuates the transmitting relay and removes the short-circuit from the input side of the amplifier; such repeated action permits spurts of carrier-frequency current through the selecting circuit to the line. At the other end of the line the modulated carrier current passes through the appropriate tuned circuit into a two-stage amplifier, and then into a third vacuum tube functioning as a rectifier. When the amplified carrier current reaches this tube the direct current in its plate circuit rises to a definite value and operates the receiving relay.

Carrier telegraph operation over a long-distance circuit involves the use of intermediate telephone repeater sets; at each repeating station only one set is needed because it serves to amplify all the carrier currents which the circuit is transmitting.

## QUESTIONS

1. Draw the circuit of a single Morse telegraph line and explain its operation.
2. What is the difference between a sounder and a relay?
3. Make a diagram of a single Morse telegraph that employs relays.
4. What is an artificial line and why is it used on duplex and quadruplex telegraph lines?
5. Make a diagram to show how two messages may be sent in opposite directions over a single wire without interfering with each other.
6. Distinguish between the differential and polar methods of duplex telegraphy.
7. Explain the operation of the polar duplex circuit of Fig. 404 when key $K'$ alone is depressed.
8. How is quadruplex transmission attained?
9. Distinguish between the synchronous multiplex and the carrier-current methods of telegraphy.
10. Describe the method of sending telegraph messages by Teletype transmitters and receiving them as printed letters.
11. Describe the telephone transmitter.
12. Explain the operation of a telephone receiver.
13. Sketch the connections of a subscriber's desk set.
14. What is the purpose of an induction coil in a subscriber's telephone set?
15. What is a cord circuit of a telephone switchboard? and what is it equipped to do?
16. Trace the connections in the 100-line private automatic exchange shown in Fig. 416 from Station 46 to Station 31.
17. How is a call from a subscriber of a manual telephone central office completed to a subscriber of a machine-switching office?
18. Show by a diagram how a repeater element is inserted into a telephone line in order to secure two-way telephonic transmission.
19. Explain the connections of the telephone repeater element shown in Fig. 418.
20. What is an electrical filter? and what can it do?
21. Name the essential elements of a carrier-current telegraph system.

## PROBLEMS

1. If it is desired to transmit over a 5-mile ground-return single Morse telegraph circuit having four 20-ohm sounders and operating on 36 volts, what size copper line wire should be used if the minimum current to actuate the sounders is 0.25 ampere? *Ans.* No. 14 A.w.g.

2. How far would it be possible to telegraph over a line having 5 ohms resistance per mile of length and having a 120-volt battery at each end? Assume that there are ten 150-ohm relays in the circuit, each requiring 0.05 ampere for actuation, and that the line is insulated perfectly. *Ans.* 660 miles.

3. Compute the resistance of each artificial line used on a 1000-ohm duplex line having a 150-ohm relay at each end, (a) neglecting the internal resistance of the current sources, and (b) assuming each of the two sources to have 10 ohms resistance. *Ans.* (a) 1075 ohms; (b) 1085 ohms.

# Lesson XXVII

## ELECTRON TUBE CIRCUITS

Basic functions of electron tubes—Limitations of triodes—Multi-electrode tubes—Vacuum tube amplifiers—Radio-frequency amplifiers—Audio-frequency amplifiers—Push-pull amplifiers—Characteristics of multi-electrode tubes—Calculation of a tube circuit—Detector action—Grid and plate circuit detection—The vacuum tube oscillator—Questions.

**313. Basic Functions of Electron Tubes.**—The two-electrode and three-electrode vacuum and gas filled tubes, described under the headings of diodes and triodes in Lesson XXV, are the prototypes of a number of electron devices called in general *electron tubes*. Such tubes have countless applications, but in reality have only a few basic functions; these functions are *rectification, amplification, oscillation,* and *modulation*. The first two have already been mentioned: rectification is the function involved when a diode is used as a rectifier to change an alternating current into a unidirectional current, §291, and amplification is involved when a triode is used as an amplifier to strengthen a weak signal, §294. The various functions of electron tubes will be considered principally in this lesson, and the application of the tubes in electrical communication and television will be taken up in the lessons to follow.

When an electron tube is used as an amplifier, the amplification must be carried out faithfully, so that a signal may be built up to the required strength without materially altering its form. If the signal delivered by an amplifier is changed in form from that which is applied to its input terminals, the amplifier is said to distort the signal, and the difference between the input and the output forms is called *distortion*. An ideal amplifier simply enlarges a signal but does not change it otherwise.

When a sufficient amount of the output of an amplifier tube is returned in proper fashion to its grid circuit, the tube can operate as a generator of alternating current. In this capacity it is called an oscillator, receiving power from the plate battery, and generating oscillations having a frequency which depends largely upon the constants (resistance, inductance and capacitance) of the oscillatory circuit. A large number of oscillator circuits are available; these differ only in the way power from the plate circuit is fed back to the grid, and in the placement of the oscillatory circuit.

There are many instances in electrical communication where a current of constant amplitude and frequency is used to carry a signal, either audible or otherwise. The process of impressing the signal on such a carrier current is known as modulation, and the circuit arrangement used for this purpose is called a *modu-lator*. A modulator changes the form of the carrier in accordance with the modulating signal. The change may be one of amplitude or of frequency; the former is spoken of as *amplitude modulation* and the latter as *frequency modulation*.

To recover the original signal conveyed by a modulated carrier wave it is necessary to use a *demodulator*. The circuits and functions of modulators and demodulators are practically the same, except that the purpose of one is the reverse of the other.

**314. Limitations of Triodes.**—An important factor in the operation of electron tubes in carrying out their basic functions is the amplication factor, §294. This factor, symbolized by the Greek letter $\mu$, represents the ratio of a change in plate potential to a change in grid potential in the opposite direction such that the plate current will remain unchanged. If, then, an alternating p.d. of value $e_g$ is applied between the grid and cathode of a triode, the effect is the same as introducing an alternating e.m.f. in the plate circuit of value $\mu \times e_g$. Because of structural difficulties, triodes are seldom produced with amplification factors exceeding 100. To achieve higher gains with triodes it is necessary to employ more stages of amplification (that is, additional tubes) and this takes space and adds to the cost.

Fig. 421 shows the electrodes of a triode with the alternating p.d. $e_g$ impressed between grid $G$ and cathode $K$, and its equivalent e.m.f. $\mu \times e_g$ connected between plate $P$ and the cathode. The plate resistance of the tube is indicated by $r_p$, and the resistance of the load by $R_L$. The unidirectional e.m.f.'s of the plate and grid circuits are supplied by batteries marked $E_B$ and $E_C$ respectively, the latter being connected to give the grid a *negative bias*.

While $e_g$ and $\mu \times e_g$ are alternating quantities and change their polarities as the signals change, signs are indicated in the

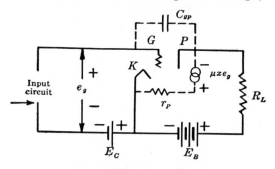

FIG. 421. Equivalent plate e.m.f. and inter-electrode capacitance in a triode

**The dotted portions of the circuit exist within the tube itself.**

figure to represent the condition at a moment when the p.d. $e_g$ of an incoming signal makes the grid less negative. Under such a condition the plate current will increase and, consequently, the polarity of the equivalent e.m.f. $\mu \times e_g$ in the plate circuit is such as to assist the plate battery $E_B$; this polarity is indicated. When $e_g$ reverses, the grid becomes more negative, the polarity of $\mu \times e_g$ changes, and the plate current decreases. In this way the polarity of $e_g$ is related to that of $\mu \times e_g$.

The electrodes of a triode behave exactly like the plates of condensers, and the vacuum or gas within the tube serves as the dielectric. Consequently, there is capacitance between the grid and cathode, between the grid and plate, and between the cathode and plate. Of these small inter-electrode capacitances, the grid-plate capacitance is one of prime importance because it is most disturbing in amplifier circuits employing triodes; this capacitance is indicated by condenser $C_{gp}$ in Fig. 421.

An alternating current can be established through condenser $C_{gp}$, the input circuit, and plate resistance $r_p$; the e.m.f. which is responsible for this current is the equivalent plate e.m.f. $\mu \times e_g$ augmented by the grid potential $e_g$, that is $(\mu + 1) \times e_g$. Thus, because of the grid-plate capacitance $C_{gp}$, energy from the plate circuit of the triode may be fed back to the grid circuit. When this transfer of energy is sufficiently great, the tube and its circuit is virtually transformed into a generator of oscillations, §324. Such transfer of energy in an amplifier renders the tube worthless for amplification. The possibility of oscillation in triode amplifier circuits, especially those intended for operation at radio frequencies, constitutes one of the most serious limitations of triode amplifiers. Such an amplifier may be kept from oscillating by adding a circuit to neutralize the effect of capacitance $C_{gp}$. However, the presence of this capacitance may be advantageous in triodes employed as oscillators, especially at high radio frequencies.

**315. Multi-Electrode Tubes.**—When a triode or three-element electron tube is employed in a radio-frequency circuit as an amplifier, the circuit will tend to oscillate because of the feedback of energy from the plate circuit to the grid circuit by way of the grid-plate capacitance. To avoid this tendency, the amplifier must be neutralized to render this capacitance ineffective. This is done generally by making the tube a part of a balanced bridge circuit. Such neutralization, particularly applicable to radio receivers, was devised by Louis A. Hazeltine in 1919, and receivers so equipped were produced under the trade name of *Neutrodyne* receivers.

A number of circuits are now available for the effective neutralization of the grid-plate capacitance of tubes, but all these arrangements involve a careful balance of the system; such balance may be destroyed by a number of causes, among them merely a change of tubes. While the readjustment of a neutralizing circuit is a relatively simple matter to a trained person, it is generally beyond the ability of the layman. For this reason neutralization of radio receivers was discontinued when a tube with negligible grid-plate capacitance became available.

The reduction of grid-plate capacitance is accomplished by adding another grid to the triode and placing it between the first grid and the plate. The first grid is then known as the *control grid*, and the added one as the *screen grid.*. Tubes so constructed are called *tetrodes*. Their design is depicted in Fig. 422, the grids and plate being arranged concentrically around the cathode. The screen grid of an electron tube virtually shields the control grid electrostatically from the plate and in this way reduces the capacitance between these two elements and eliminates feed back. The signal input to a tetrode is generally applied to the control grid, but there are conditions when it is advantageous to apply the signal to the screen grid.

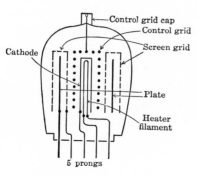

FIG. 422. Construction of a four-element electron tube or tetrode

The elementary circuit of a tetrode is shown in Fig. 423. Herein $E_{C1}$ and $E_{C2}$ represent the batteries or the e.m.f.'s in the circuit of the control grid and screen grid respectively, and the other symbols have the same significance as they have in Fig. 421.

Fig. 424 gives the plate characteristic curves of the Type 24A tube. The region of the characteristic between lines $aa$ and $bb$ implies a negative resistance for the plate circuit of the tube, since the plate current falls with rising plate potential. This region hinders amplification but makes possible the operation

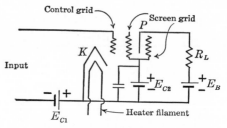

FIG. 423. Connections of an RCA tetrode, type 24A

of a very stable oscillator. Such an oscillator is called a *dynatron oscillator* and the corresponding region of the characteristic is styled the *dynatron region* or *dynatron loop*. The operation of a tetrode as an amplifier is in the region of the curves which lies to the right of line $cc$, for that region yields the least dis-

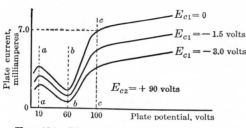

FIG. 424. Plate characteristics of an RCA tetrode, type 24A

tortion since the curves there are practically straight lines.

The negative-resistance characteristic is due to the high velocity of the electrons arriving at the plate. These high-speed particles may actually knock, or splash, out of the plate a very considerable number of electrons; these are known as *secondary electrons* because they result from the action of the fast particles or *primary electrons*. When the conditions are such that the secondary electrons are collected by the screen grid and not by the plate, the operation of the tube is in the dynatron loop.

In order to eliminate the dynatron region of the characteristic which lies to the left of the line *cc* in Fig. 424, the tetrode may be modified by the addition of a third or *suppressor grid*. This grid is located between the screen grid and the plate, and is connected to a point of low potential, usually to the cathode itself. The purpose of the suppressor grid is to prevent secondary electrons from reaching the screen grid. Instead, these electrons are repelled by the suppressor grid and forced back to the plate.

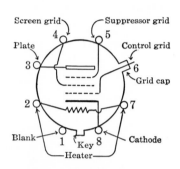

Fig. 425. Bottom view of a 6U7-G pentode and an 8-prong socket

Five-element tubes incorporating an emitter, a control grid, a screen grid, a suppressor grid, and a plate are called *pentodes*. The connections of a 6U7-G RCA pentode with *octal* base are shown in Fig. 425.

Fig. 426 shows the plate characteristic curves of a 6U7-G RCA pentode; the screen grid bias is + 100 volts and the suppressor grid is connected to the cathode with zero bias. The control grid potentials $E_{C1}$ for the four curves range from 0 to −10 volts.

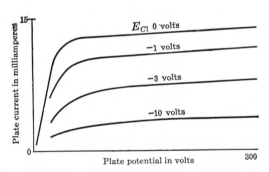

Fig. 426. Plate characteristics of an RCA pentode, type 6U7-G

The addition of the screen and suppressor grids to electron tubes improves their characteristics for certain purposes, but nevertheless new limitations are introduced. Perhaps the most important of these is the power loss resulting from the current in the screen and suppressor grid circuits. This in turn results in prohibitive distortion for any given value of plate battery potential if the potential of the control grid of a pentode is varied over a wide range. The so-called *beam power tube* was developed to overcome this limitation; it is generally employed in the *final stage* of amplifiers. The purpose of all tubes except the last one in such an amplifier is to increase the potential of the impressed signal until it is sufficient to drive the grid of the last or *power stage* tube or tubes.

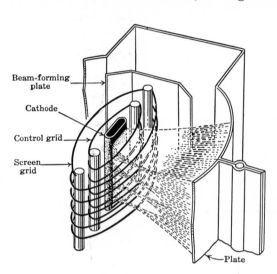

Beam-forming plate

Cathode

Control grid

Screen grid

Plate

FIG. 427. Elements of a beam power tube and their assembly

Dotted lines show formation of beam sheets by grid wires.

The beam power tube is so named because the flow of electrons takes place in beams as a result of two construction features peculiar to this type of tube. The first of these is a pair of beam-forming plates connected to the cathode that allow only those electrons to proceed from it which do not pass around interfering devices such as grid supports, or through those sections of the tube in which the spacing of the electrodes differs from the desired arrangement. The second feature is the arrangement of wires forming the screen grid so as to be just behind the wires of the control grid. As a result, the screen grid lies in the "electron shadow" of the control grid, and the screen grid current is much reduced. In addition, the passage of electrons between the wires of the control and screen grids results in dense concentrations of electrons in a plane between those of the screen and plate, as shown in Fig. 427. These electron concentrations reduce the potential in that plane just as though a suppressor grid were placed there. Thus, suppression is achieved without the use of an actual grid and without the disturbing effects of suppressor grid current. The characteristic curves of a type 6L6 RCA beam power tube are shown in Fig. 428.

Tubes are now available with four and five grids beside emitter and plate; such tubes do not represent basic types but are rather special-purpose tubes. The six-element tube is known as an *hexode* while the seven-element tube is called a *heptode*.

In addition to the multi-electrode tubes mentioned ahead, combinations of tubes are available within the same glass or metal

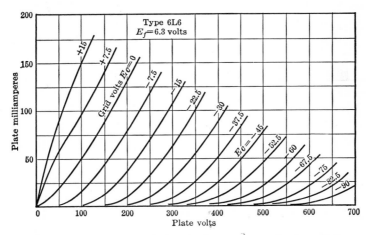

FIG. 428. Plate characteristics of a beam power tube, type 6L6

envelope. An example of this class is the 6B8 *metal tube* which incorporates two diodes and a pentode, all having a common emitter or cathode, and all contained within one metal envelope. Such tubes are available also in glass envelopes. Radio sets, particularly those in the smaller or midget sizes, employ such combination tubes.

**316. Vacuum Tube Amplifiers.**—The general purpose of all amplifiers is to strengthen signals impressed between the control grid and cathode of the successive tubes without introducing excessive distortion. Fig. 429 shows one stage of a resistance-capacitance coupled amplifier which is employed widely in the amplification of either radio- or audio-frequency signals. The tube indicated represents either a triode, or a multi-electrode tube with the intermediate grids omitted for clarity. Such intermediate grids would be connected to the + side of batteries for their biasing potentials, but they are not subject to signal potentials. Gener-

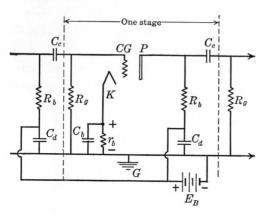

FIG. 429. Resistance-capacitance coupled amplifier

ally, all intermediate grids are connected by relatively large by-pass condensers to the cathode $K$, in order that currents of the same frequency as the signal may be kept out of the "B" battery system. Such currents in the battery system might find their way to other electrodes or tubes operated from the same system, and so produce undesirable interference. Further, since most intermediate grids are connected to the plate supply system through resistors, currents of the signal frequency in these resistors would vary the potentials of such grids and prevent their operation at a constant p.d. with respect to the cathode, as required. The combination of a resistor and its associated condenser connected to a screen grid are shown by $R_d$ and $C'_d$ in Fig. 430.

The cathode bias resistor $r_b$ carries the steady current of the plate circuit provided by battery $E_B$. The unidirectional p.d. produced by this current across that resistor serves to bias the control grid $CG$ negatively, as shown. Condenser $C_b$ of large capacitance is connected across resistor $r_b$ to serve as a short-circuit around that resistor for currents of signal frequncy; the combination of $r_b$ and $C_b$ replaces a grid bias battery generally indicated as $E_c$.

Since the control grid is in the path of electrons moving from cathode $K$ to plate $P$, some electrons strike it accidentally; these would accumulate on $CG$ unless there were a path for them back to $K$. Such a path is provided by resistor $R_g$ of high resistance; the *coupling condenser* $C_c$ cannot serve for this purpose since condensers do not pass direct or steady current.

The plate potential is applied by battery $E_B$ through the coupling resistor $R_b$, and the amplified p.d. delivered by this stage is produced across this resistor. The *decoupling condenser $C_d$* of large capacitance, by-passes the currents of signal frequency and excludes them from the plate battery. Condenser $C_c$ is introduced to make certain that only the grid bias produced across $r_b$ reaches $CG$. If it were omitted from the circuit, the positive potential applied to plate $P$ would be applied to the control grid $CG$ of the following tube.

The operation of the amplifier circuit is as follows: The preceding stages supply an alternating signal p.d. $e_g$ between control grid $CG$ and ground $G$. The condenser $C_b$ by-passes resistor $r_b$, which provides the unidirectional bias for $CG$, so that the input signal is actually applied between $CG$ and $K$. The equivalent plate e.m.f. $\mu \times e_g$ circulates an alternating signal current through the plate circuit of the tube, which includes the coupling resistor $R_b$ and condenser $C_d$. The signal p.d. developed across $R_b$ is applied to the control grid $CG$ of the next tube by way of condenser $C_c$. Generally, a triode is employed in the circuit just described only for operation at audio frequencies, for which the inter-electrode capacitances are negligible. For this reason, these capacitances have been omitted from the diagram.

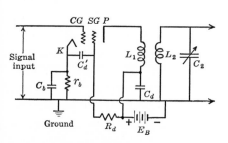

FIG. 430. Radio-frequency amplifier with coupled tuned load

**317. Radio-Frequency Amplifiers.**—Amplifiers used at radio-frequencies generally include a tetrode or other multi-electrode tube and a tuned circuit. Fig. 430 shows such a circuit employing a tetrode having the cathode $K$, plate $P$, and two grids. Coils $L_1$ and $L_2$ are generally of the air-core type and serve to couple the plate circuit to the circuit of $L_2$ and $C_2$ which is tuned by the variable condenser $C_2$. The plate circuit and the $L_2 - C_2$ circuit constitute a pair of *coupled circuits.*

The signal is applied between the control grid $CG$ and ground $G$. The potential supplied to the screen grid $SG$ by battery $E_B$ is reduced by the potential drop on resistor $R_d$. The decoupling condenser $C_d$ by-passes radio-frequency currents from this grid to the cathode $K$. Condensers $C_b$ and $C_d$ by-pass such currents in the plate circuit. The drop on resistor $r_b$ provides the bias for the control grid $CG$, as described in the last section.

The radio-frequency currents in coil $L_1$ induce corresponding e.m.f.'s in coil $L_2$. Condenser $C_2$ tunes the circuit to the desired signal frequency and so establishes a relatively high p.d. across itself and between the control grid and ground of the next tube. All interfering signals finding their way to the input of the amplifier produce only a relatively low p.d. across $C_2$. Thus, the action builds up the desired signal for the next stage of amplification and reduces the effect of interfering signals.

The amplifiers of Figs. 429 and 430 are called *voltage amplifiers* because they build up the p.d. of the signals to a value sufficient for the final stage of amplification, and this latter is called the *power amplifier*.

**318. Audio-Frequency Amplifiers.**—Amplifiers that are intended to operate over the audible range of frequencies may include triodes, although multi-electrode tubes, such as pentodes and beam power tubes, are very often used. Many audio amplifiers, employed as voltage amplifiers, are coupled by the resistance-capacitance method to succeeding tubes, as described in §316. When it is desired to increase the gain per stage using triodes, it is customary to introduce transformer coupling.

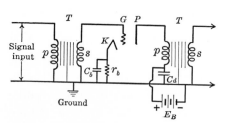

FIG. 431. Transformer-coupled audio amplifier

Fig. 431 shows an audio-frequency amplifier having transformers with grounded iron cores. The transformers $T$ have a ratio of about 1 to 3, so that the e.m.f. supplied by the secondary windings $s$ for establishing a p.d. between grid $G$ and cathode $K$ is about three times that which is applied to the primary windings $p$. The symbols for the other circuit elements have the same significance as in the last section.

When the amplifier of Fig. 431 is used as a power or terminating amplifier, the transformer at the right is omitted and the load, such as a loud speaker, is put in the place of the primary winding) $p$ thus removed.

**Experiment 114.**—To make a test on one stage of an audio-frequency amplifier, connect a triode as shown in Fig. 432 to a 2.5-volt filament transformer $T_1$ and an audio transformer $T_2$ with a turn-ratio of 3 to 1. The numbers on the tube terminals apply to the socket lugs when viewed from the bottom, and the others indicate the battery potentials in volts. Apply 60-cycle alternating current at 120 volts to the primary winding of $T_1$. Impress the p.d. at the input terminals $m$, $n$ to the vertical deflection plates of a simple cathode-ray oscil-

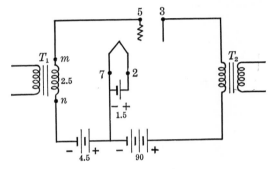

FIG. 432. Test of a 1G4-GT/G triode as an amplifier

loscope, §348, which need not have a sweep circuit, and note the length of the luminous line on the screen. Then connect the output terminals of $T_2$ to the oscilloscope and observe the length of the line again. The ratio of the two lengths gives the amplification of the stage.

If an oscilloscope is not at hand and a vacuum-tube voltmeter is available, then measure the p.d. across $m$, $n$ and across the output terminals of $T_2$ directly. The ratio of these readings gives the amplification of the stage.

**319. Push-Pull Amplifiers.**—All amplifiers introduce a certain amount of distortion, and the amount is generally proportional to the p.d. applied to the grid of the tube. Therefore, in order to keep distortion to a minimum, the input signal must not be too large. This means that generally the power output of the tube must be kept below the power that the tube might develop if considerable distortion were tolerated. However, the *push-pull amplifier* shown in Fig. 433 cancels, to a great extent, the distortion produced in the tubes and permits a large output with faithfulness of reproduction of the input signal. Such devices are often used in the output stage of amplifiers that have high fidelity or high quality. The two tubes represented are triodes, but pentodes and beam power tubes may be used with equal or better results.

The power amplifier is joined to its preceding voltage amplifier by resistance-capacitance coupling and to the load by transformer coupling. The points of similarity of the circuit to those which are described ahead will be noted; the circuit elements shown carry out the same functions and the symbols have the same significance. A by-pass condenser is not needed across the bias resistor $r_b$.

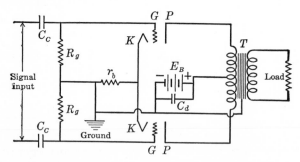

FIG. 433. Push-pull power amplifier using triodes

The power output of the two tubes used in the push-pull arrangement is considerably greater than twice the power which may be drawn from either tube alone. Push-pull amplifiers, also known as *balanced amplifiers,* may be used for audio- or radio-frequency amplification, but in radio-frequency service an air-core transformer is generally substituted for transformer $T$.

Distortion in amplifiers may be ascribed to a series of harmonics that have frequencies which are multiples of the frequency of the signal applied to the input. The output of a balanced amplifier under ideal conditions, that is, with perfectly matched tubes and with input and output circuits perfectly balanced to ground, will not have distortion due to even-numbered harmonics. This accounts for the greater output of push-pull amplifiers.

**320. Characteristics of Multi-Electrode Tubes.**—The three characteristic quantities of a triode considered in §294 and §295, namely, amplification factor, plate resistance, and transconductance, are also used to express the performance of multi-electrode tubes, as explained below.

The amplification factor, when applied to multi-electrode tubes, is defined as the ratio of a change of plate potential in one direction, to the change of control grid potential in the opposite direction, which results in an unchanged plate current. For example, if the plate potential of a Type 24A tetrode (4-element tube), that produces a plate current of 0.005 ampere, is *increased* by 400 volts, the plate current will increase, but it will be brought back to its former value of 0.005 ampere when the control grid potential is *decreased* by one volt. The amplification factor of this type of tube under the conditions stated is 400/1 or 400. The value of this factor will vary slightly under different conditions.

In order to apply the term plate resistance to all types of tubes from diodes to multi-electrode tubes, it is necessary only to define plate resistance as the ratio of the change in potential on the plate to the resulting change of plate current, when the potentials on all the other electrodes are kept constant. For example, a Type 2A5 power pentode (5-element tube) yields a plate current of 0.0500 ampere when the plate potential is 160 volts, the control grid is biased to − 10 volts, and the screen potential is 250 volts. If the plate potential of this tube is increased to 250 volts, while the potentials on all other electrodes are kept constant, the plate current will increase to 0.0525 ampere. Since the changes in plate potential and current are respectively 90 volts and 0.0025 ampere, the plate resistance under these conditions will be 90/0.0025 = 36,000 ohms. This value may change considerably under different tube conditions, such as altering the potentials on the various electrodes.

The significance of transconductance may be extended to multi-electrode tubes by defining it as the ratio of the change of plate current to the change in bias potential on the control grid, when the potentials applied to all other electrodes are kept constant. In the case of 6A4 pentode, with 140 volts on the plate and 180 volts on the screen, a change of control grid bias from − 8 to − 12 volts produces a decrease in plate current from 0.0298 to 0.0210 ampere. Since this change of 0.0088 ampere resulted from a grid bias change of 2 volts, the transconductance of the tube

under these conditions is $0.0088/2 = 0.0044$ mhos, or 4400 micromhos (1 mho = 1,000,000 micromhos). The transconductance of a
tube also varies with changes in the operating potentials on the
tube.

The values for amplification factor, plate resistance, and transconductance of any tube are related to each other. This relation
may be expressed by the formula

$$\text{transconductance} = \frac{\text{amplification factor}}{\text{plate resistance}}$$

Let

$\mu$ = amplification factor,
$r_p$ = plate resistance in ohms,
$m$ = transconductance in mhos.

Then
$$m = \frac{\mu}{r_p}$$
**136**

**Problem 167.**—The plate resistance of a 2A3 triode is 800 ohms and its
transconductance is 5250 micromhos. Calculate the amplification factor for
this tube.

The transconductance of the tube is $5250 \times 10^{-6} = 0.00525$ mhos and
therefore the amplification factor is

(136)        $\mu = m \times r_p = 0.00525 \times 800 = 4.2$

**321. Calculation of a Tube Circuit.**—Following the procedure of
§314, if an alternating signal potential of $e_g$ volts is placed upon the
control grid of a triode or a multi-electrode tube, the plate circuit

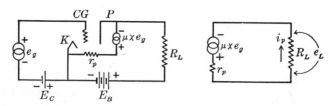

FIG. 434. Amplifier circuit and its equivalent alternating-current plate circuit
The signs associated with $e_g$ and $\mu \times e_g$ are instantaneous polarities.

of that tube reacts as though a signal e.m.f. equal to $\mu \times e_g$ volts
were introduced in the plate circuit. At the left in Fig. 434 is
shown the circuit of a simple amplifier, the tube of which may be
either a triode or a multi-electrode tube with only the control
grid $CG$ indicated. At the right is the equivalent alternating-

current plate circuit consisting of a generator, having an equivalent signal e.m.f. of $\mu \times e_g$ volts, in series with the plate resistance $r_p$ and the load $R_L$; the inter-electrode capacitances are neglected as is permissible in ordinary audio-frequency operation.

Let

$i_p$ = alternating current in plate circuit in amperes,
$e_L$ = alternating p.d. across the load resistance $R_L$,
$P_L$ = power dissipated in the load.

Then, applying Ohm's Law to the equivalent plate circuit, the signal current becomes

$$i_p = \frac{\mu \times e_g}{r_p + R_L} \qquad\qquad 137$$

and the signal p.d. equals $i_p \times R_L$, or

$$e_L = \frac{\mu \times e_g \times R_L}{r_p + R_L} \qquad\qquad 138$$

The signal power dissipated in the load equals $i_p{}^2 \times R_L$ or $i_p \times e_L$; whence the power is

$$P_L = i_p{}^2 R_L = \frac{(\mu \times e_g)^2 \times R_L}{(r_p + R_L)^2} \qquad\qquad 139$$

The voltage amplification of the amplifier is naturally the ratio of the output signal potential $e_L$ to the input signal potential $e_g$. Thus, the voltage amplification of the amplifier is expressed as

$$V.A. = \frac{\mu \times R_L}{r_p + R_L} \qquad\qquad 140$$

The signal potentials and currents mentioned above are alternating potentials and currents, and should not be confused with the unidirectional potentials and currents produced by the grid and plate batteries. If the load has an impedance $Z_L$ rather than merely a resistance $R_L$, then the value of $R_L$ in the foregoing formulas, *except* in the numerator of Formula (140), should be changed to $Z_L = \sqrt{R_L{}^2 + X_L{}^2}$ in accordance with Formula (92), where $X_L$ is the reactance of the load calculated for the frequency of the signal potential $e_g$. It follows that wherever the sum $r_p + R_L$ appears, it should be replaced by $\sqrt{(r_p + R_L)^2 + X_L{}^2}$.

**Problem 168.**—A tube, for which $\mu = 30$ and $r_p = 30{,}000$ ohms, has a signal p.d. of 1 volt, root-mean-square value, applied between the control grid and cathode. Assuming the load to have a resistance of 100,000 ohms, calculate the signal plate current, the corresponding p.d. across the load, the signal power dissipated in that load, and the voltage amplification or gain of the amplifier.

The resistance in the plate circuit is $r_p + R_L = 30,000 + 100,000 = 130,000$ ohms. The plate current is

$$(137) \qquad i_p = \frac{\mu \times e_g}{r_p + R_L} = \frac{30 \times 1}{130,000} = 0.000231 \text{ ampere}$$

The p.d. across the load is

$$(138) \qquad e_L = \frac{\mu \times e_g \times R_L}{r_p + R_L} = \frac{30 \times 1 \times 100,000}{130,000} = 23.1 \text{ volts}$$

The power supplied to the load is

$$(139) \quad P_L = \frac{(\mu \times e_g)^2 \times R_L}{(r_p + R_L)^2} = \frac{(30 \times 1)^2 \times 100,000}{(130,000)^2} = 0.00533 \text{ watt}$$

The voltage gain of the amplifier is

$$(140) \qquad V.A. = \frac{\mu \times R_L}{r_p + R_L} = \frac{30 \times 100,000}{130,000} = 23.1$$

**322. Detector Action.**—A circuit which acts on a received modulated wave for the purpose of recovering the signal or audio component of the wave is called a *detector* or *demodulator*. The basic tube function in the operation of a detector is rectification. Of the various electron tube detector circuits available for radio receiving sets, the simplest utilizes the diode, connected

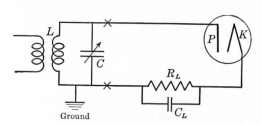

Fig. 435. Circuit of diode detector

as shown in Fig. 435. The electron path from the cathode $K$ to the plate $P$ includes the load $R_L$ with its shunting condenser $C_L$; this path is bridged across the tuned circuit formed of coil $L$ and condenser $C$.

The wave to be detected is composed of a carrier wave that is modulated in amplitude by the signal. It is generally obtained from a radio-frequency voltage amplifier and supplied to a coil coupled with coil $L$. Variable condenser $C$ permits the input circuit of the diode to be tuned to the desired modulated wave, in order to develop a sufficiently high p.d. across this condenser. The coupled circuits associated with the two coils are capable, therefore, of selecting one of a number of available modulated waves and building it up to yield a relatively high p.d. across $C$, while keeping the p.d.'s of the unwanted waves very low.

The capacitance of condenser $C_L$ is so selected that its reactance is low at the frequency of the carrier, and high at the frequency of the modulation. For example, if a carrier of 1,000,000 cycles per second were modulated at 1000 cycles per second, the impedance of circuit $R_L - C_L$ would be low at a million cycles and high at a thousand cycles. The resistance $R_L$ is chosen high as compared with the resistance of the diode in the direction of the current through it.

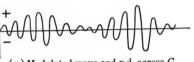

(*a*) Modulated wave and p.d. across *C* if circuit were open at *X X*

If the circuit to the right of ×× were disconnected, the p.d. across condenser $C$ might have the form shown at (*a*) in Fig. 436. This curve is typical of amplitude-modulated waves, the modulation of the carrier would appear as a line connecting the successive peaks of the wave. The frequency of the carrier is the same as the frequency of the modulated wave. Since the load resistance

(*b*) P.d. between *P* and *K* of diode

(*c*) P.d. across $R_L$ and $C_L$

FIG. 436. Action of diode detector
The symbols refer to Fig. 435.

is high it follows that during those half-cycles when plate $P$ is positive, the diode passes current through $R_L$, condenser $C_L$ is charged so that its right plate is positive and the p.d. between the plate and cathode is relatively small. During the negative half-cycles when the tube does not pass current, the total p.d. developed across $C$ is reduced by the potential developed across $R_L$ by the slowly discharging $C_L$, and the difference is available between $P$ and $K$, as shown by curve (*b*).

During the positive half-cycles, when there is current through the tube, condenser $C_L$ is charged at the carrier frequency, and a p.d. is built up across its terminals. Small depressions in this e.m.f. occur during the negative half-cycles of the impressed signal, because $C_L$ discharges slightly through $R_L$, as shown in curve (c) . It may be seen that this curve is practically the envelope of the top one with a superposed ripple; this ripple, exaggerated in the figure, has the same radio frequency as the carrier and is inaudible. The condenser $C_L$ establishes through load $R_L$ a current which is proportional to the ordinates of the lower curve and, therefore, proportional to the modulation of the wave. This signal current may be used directly, which is the case when the load comprises a pair of telephones; more usually, the p.d. across $R_L$ is transferred to an audio-frequency amplifier where its value is increased further.

**323. Grid and Plate Circuit Detection.**—A triode may be employed in detection in one of two ways. When detection or rectification takes place in the grid circuit, the tube and circuit are referred to as a *grid detector;* when this process takes place in the plate circuit, the arrangement is called a *plate circuit detector.*

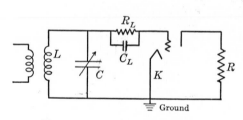

FIG. 437. A triode grid detector

A grid detector is shown in Fig. 437. It will be observed that the grid circuit of the triode corresponds to the diode circuit of Fig. 435, and it will be found that the action between the grid and cathode $K$ is similar to that which takes place between plate $P$ and cathode $K$ of the diode. In addition, the audio-frequency p.d. produced across resistor $R_L$ is transferred, by way of coil $L$, and applied from the grid to $K$. Hence, the audio-frequency signal is amplified by the tube and a much stronger signal is made available in load $R$ of the plate circuit.

If the magnitude of the p.d. across the tuning condenser $C$ of a grid circuit detector is quite large, or if the degree of modulation approaches a maximum, this type of detector is apt to yield excessive distortion. Plate circuit detection avoids this difficulty.

The connections of a plate circuit detector are shown in Fig. 438 and its action is explained with the aid of Fig. 439. The symbols have the same meaning as elsewhere in this lesson. The potential of grid $G$ is biased by battery $E_C$ so that the plate current disappears; under this condition the tube is said to be *biased to cut-off*. The values of

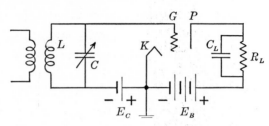

FIG. 438. Arrangement of a plate circuit detector

$E_C$ and $E_B$ are so selected that the variations of potential across condenser $C$ never cause the grid to become positive. Thus, there is never a current between grid $G$ and cathode $K$, and the detector may be styled an *infinite-impedance detector*.

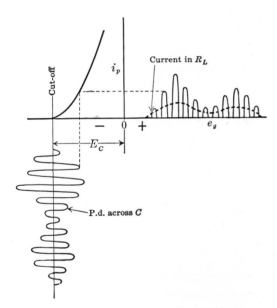

FIG. 439. Action of a plate circuit detector

The symbols refer to Fig. 438.

The variations in a positive direction of the p.d. across condenser $C$ alone cause current in the plate circuit of the triode. Condenser $C_L$, operating as explained in connection with the diode detector, averages this current and the load $R_L$ receives a unidirectional current shown by the dotted line. This current pattern is similar to the modulated wave.

**324. The Vacuum Tube Oscillator.**—Electrical oscillations may be generated by connecting a triode to an oscillatory circuit in such a manner that part of the energy output of the plate circuit is fed back to the grid circuit. The frequency of the oscillations generated is determined largely by the inductance of $L$ and the capacitance of $C$ of the oscillatory circuit. Formula (104) may be employed to calculate the value of this frequency.

**Problem 169.**—An oscillatory circuit has a total inductance of 100 microhenries and a capacitance of 250 micro-microfarads. Find the frequency of the oscillations.

Since 1 henry $= 10^6$ microhenries and 1 farad $= 10^6$ microfarads $= 10^{12}$ micro-microfarads, the values of the circuit constants for use in Formula (104) are: $L = 100 \times 10^{-6}$ henry and $C = 250 \times 10^{-12}$ farads. The frequency of the oscillations generated in cycles per second will be

$$f = \frac{1}{2\pi\sqrt{L \times C}} = \frac{1}{2\pi\sqrt{100 \times 10^{-6} \times 250 \times 10^{-12}}} = \frac{1}{2\pi 10^{-9}\sqrt{100 \times 250}}$$

$$= \frac{10^9}{6.28\sqrt{25,000}} = 1,007,000$$

The frequency of the oscillations actually generated in a circuit differs somewhat from the calculated value, the deviation becoming larger as the frequency increases. This deviation is due to the distributed inductance and capacitance in the circuit and in the tube itself. The grid-to-cathode and the plate-to-cathode resistances in the tube also affect slightly the frequency of the oscillations.

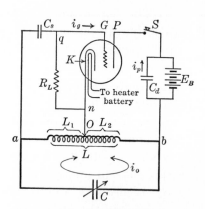

FIG. 440. Hartley oscillator circuit
The oscillatory circuit is shown in heavy lines.

Fig. 440 shows the circuit of the Hartley oscillator, in which the condenser $C$ and the coil $L$ (formed of coils $L_1$ and $L_2$) constitute the oscillatory circuit. To explain the production of oscillations, assume that the heater and the cathode of the tube are at operating temperature when switch $S$ is closed. Electrons in increasing numbers move from the cathode $K$ to the plate $P$, establishing a current in coil $L_2$ directed from $O$ to $b$, and a curent in coil $L_1$ directed from $O$ to $a$; the latter current proceeds through condenser $C$ to $b$. The sum of these currents constitutes the plate current $i_p$ that is established by the plate battery of e.m.f. $E_B$. As $i_p$ approaches a steady value, the charging current of $C$ decreases while the potential across this condenser rises, and the current through $L_2$ approaches a constant value. Presently, the charging of $C$ ceases and the counter e.m.f. in $L$ begins to diminish rapidly because these currents approach constant values. It is well to remember that the condition now being discussed is a *transient condition,* and that the ordinary phase relations of the *steady state* do not apply at this time.

When the counter e.m.f. generated in $L$ falls below the p.d. across $C$, this condenser begins to discharge through $L_1$ and $L_2$ and the resulting current $i_o$ is directed from $a$ to $b$, making $a$ positive with respect to $O$. The p.d. across $L_1$ is transferred through condenser $C_s$ to the grid $G$, making it positive. The current $i_o$ adds to the current in $L_2$, increasing the drop in potential from $O$ to $b$, and causes $O$ to become more positive with respect to $b$ than before. The p.d. between $P$ and $K$, equal to the difference between the e.m.f. $E_B$ and the drop across $L_2$, is now growing smaller. However, in a well adjusted oscillator, the point $O$ is so located that the grid potential at this instant has a greater effect on the plate current than has the decreasing p.d. between $P$ and $K$. As a result, the plate current in $L_2$ rises, thereby increasing the p.d. across this coil and lowering the p.d. between $P$ and $K$ still further.

At the instant when condenser $C$ is completely discharged, the current $i_c$ is a maximum and in the direction from $a$ to $b$. The inductance of $L$ causes $i_o$ to continue beyond the point of complete discharge, so that the condenser actually becomes charged in the opposite direction, with the condenser plate connected to $b$ made positive. As the condenser $C$ approaches full charge in the new direction, the counter e.m.f.'s induced in $L_1$ and $L_2$ again decrease, grid $G$ becomes less positive and plate $P$ more positive with respect to the cathode $K$, and as a result $i_p$ decreases. At the instant the condenser p.d. exceeds that across $L$, condenser $C$ begins to discharge once more through these coils, the current being directed from $b$ to $a$. This current makes $a$ negative with respect to $O$, which in turn is negative to $b$. Thus, the potential of the plate rises with respect to $K$, but the effect of the grid potential exceeds that of the plate, and the plate current $i_p$ is reduced further. As before, the discharge of $C$ continues because of the inductance of $L$ until the condenser is charged once more in the opposite direction. Its subsequent discharge directs current from $a$ to $b$, increases the grid potential in a positive direction, and increases $i_p$, as outlined ahead.

Each successive cycle causes the potentials and currents involved to grow larger until the steady-state condition is established. Then the energy delivered by the plate battery to the oscillating circuit during the time when $i_p$ increases ($G$ is positive), is just equal to the energy dissipated in the circuit during the rest of the cycle, and the oscillations cease growing in amplitude. The plate-circuit oscillations, of course, go through the by-pass condenser $C_d$ rather than through battery $E_B$.

In well-adjusted oscillators, there will be plate current only during the intervals when the grid is positive. This situation is highly desirable because in those intervals point $O$ is positive with respect to point $b$ and the potential difference between $P$ and $K$ is a minimum. As a result the power dissipation at the plate is a minimum and the tube is kept from overheating.

In order that there may be current in the plate circuit of the tube only during those intervals when the oscillations make the grid positive to the cathode, a negative bias battery, with enough e.m.f. to bring the plate current to zero, might be introduced into the grid circuit. Obviously, with such a battery in the circuit, the closing of switch $S$ would not produce plate current, and the circuit would not be self-starting. To avoid this difficulty, a condenser $C_s$ and a grid leak resistor $R_L$ are used instead of a grid bias battery; the combination of $C_s$ and $R_L$ is known as a self-bias system.

Under normal operation, no grid bias battery is used, but the point $O$ is so selected that plate current is established only when the grid is made positive by the alternating potentials generated across $L_1$. If the combination of $R_L$ and $C_s$ were omitted, the grid current $i_g$ would be so large during the positive half-cycle that the grid structure might melt, destroying the tube. However, with this combination in the circuit, electrons collected by the positive grid, leak off to the cathode by way of $R_L$ and also charge condenser $C_s$. The electron stream through $R_L$ while the grid is positive, makes the point $q$ negative with respect to $n$. When this grid current ceases, $C_s$ discharges in a counter-clockwise direction through $R_L$ and maintains this difference of potential. In well-designed

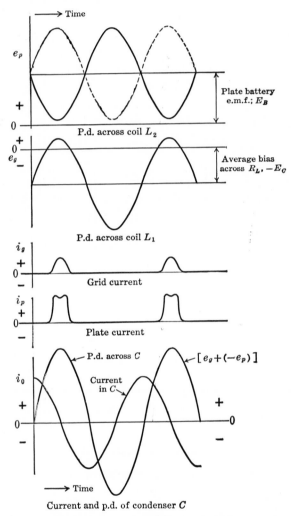

FIG. 441. Steady state conditions in the oscillator of Fig. 440

oscillators, this action establishes point $q$ at such an average negative value with respect to $n$ and the cathode that the grid actually is made positive for only a limited portion of the positive half-cycle and the grid and plate currents are limited accordingly.

The curves in Fig. 441 show the important steady-state operating conditions of the Hartley oscillator, and the center diagrams portray the situation just described. In these diagrams the alternating potentials applied to the plate and grid are represented by $e_p$ and $e_g$ respectively, the plate battery e.m.f. and average grid bias are represented by $E_B$ and $E_C$ respectively, and the currents in the plate, grid and oscillatory circuits are designated by $i_p$, $i_g$ and $i_o$ respectively. The three curves of p.d. are related and the potential difference across $L$ equals that across condenser $C$. The p.d.'s $e_g$ and $e_p$ represent the e.m.f.'s from $a$ to $O$ and from $b$ to $O$, respectively. Therefore, the p.d. from $a$ to $O$, $e_g$, must be added

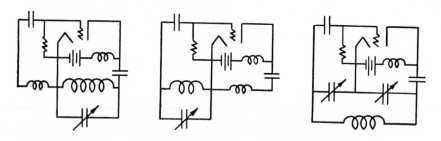

Fig. 442. Various types of oscillators
A—Tuned plate circuit; B—Tuned grid circuit; C—Colpitts circuit.

to the p.d. from $O$ to $b$ or $- e_p$ to yield the p.d. across $C$. The graphs apply also to other types of oscillators in good adjustment.

Fig. 442 shows the connections of some types of vacuum-tube oscillators in common use. The devices indicated have the usual significance, and the tuned oscillatory circuits are shown in heavy lines.

## QUESTIONS

1. Enumerate the basic functions which electron tubes serve to accomplish.
2. What is meant by distortion in an amplifier?
3. Explain the purpose of a modulator.
4. What is meant by inter-electrode capacitance and what are these capacitances in a triode?
5. State two basic limitations of triodes.
6. What is a neutralized amplifier?
7. Name the four elements of a tetrode.
8. Show by means of a diagram the plate-current versus plate-potential curves of a tetrode, and indicate the dynatron region on such curves

9. What is a pentode and in what way is it superior to a tetrode?
10. Distinguish between the purposes of a screen grid and a suppressor grid.
11. Explain what is meant by a beam power tube.
12. Draw the circuit of a resistance-capacitance coupled amplifier, and explain its operation.
13. Explain how a grid bias battery in an amplifier may be supplanted by a combination of a resistor and a condenser.
14. What is the difference between a voltage amplifier and a power amplifier?
15. Draw the circuit and explain the operation of a tuned radio-frequency voltage amplifier.
16. Explain the purpose of a tuned circuit in a radio-frequency amplifier.
17. What is meant by coupled circuits? Mention an example.
18. Why are decoupling condensers used in amplifiers?
19. Draw the circuit of a transformer-coupled amplifier for use at audio frequencies. What is a common turn-ratio of the transformers generally used in such circuits?
20. What is a push-pull amplifier and why is such an amplifier desired?
21. Define amplification factor, plate resistance, and transconductance as applied to multi-electrode tubes.
22. Explain the operation of a diode detector.
23. Give the circuit of a triode grid detector, and of a triode plate circuit detector.
24. Explain the operation of a vacuum tube oscillator.

## PROBLEMS

1. The 242C power triode made by the Western Electric Company has an amplification factor of 12.5 and a transconductance of 3600 micromhos. Calculate its plate resistance. *Ans.* 3470 ohms.
2. A triode, having an amplification factor of 10 and a plate resistance of 10,000 ohms, supplies a load having a resistance of 15,000 ohms. What is the voltage amplification of the stage? *Ans.* 6.
3. A tetrode having an amplification factor of 300 and a plate resistance of 300,000 ohms has a load of 100,000 ohms resistance. If the signal input is 0.05 volt, calculate (a) the p.d. across the load, and (b) the voltage amplification. *Ans.* (a) 3.75 volts; (b) 75.
4. A condenser of 0.0005 microfarad capacitance is to be used with a coil so that the tuned circuit so formed will be tuned to a frequency of 1,500,000 cycles per second. What should be the inductance of the coil? *Ans.* 22.6 microhenries.
5. A vacuum-tube oscillator having an inductance of 0.1 millihenry in its oscillatory circuit is tuned to a frequency of 2 megacycles per second. What should be the capacitance of the tuning condenser? *Ans.* $63.3 \times 10^{-12}$ farads.

# Lesson XXVIII

## RADIO TRANSMISSION

Electromagnetic waves—Frequency and wavelength—Radiation—Natural frequency of circuit—The antenna system—Launching of radio waves from an antenna—Radio telegraph transmitters—Modulation in radio telephony—Radio telephone transmitters—The wavemeter—Frequency control of oscillators—Questions and Problems.

**325. Electromagnetic Waves.**—About 1885, the German physicist Heinrich R. Hertz (1857-1894) showed experimentally that energy can be radiated from an electric circuit and transmitted through space. These radiations, called *electromagnetic waves,* result from changes of current in the circuit. Alternating currents of high frequency yield strong radiations, yet even a fluctuation in a direct current may set up waves that are detectable. In general, a part of the energy supplied to any circuit is radiated into space. Some circuits radiate very little energy, others are expressly designed to radiate large amounts.

An electric current in a circuit produces interlinking of electric and magnetic fields in the space around the circuit, and when the current is changed these fields change accordingly. With an alternating current, the changes repeat themselves cycle after cycle, and the electric and magnetic fields go through similar changes, setting up a succession of electromagnetic waves. Waves so produced are called *radio waves.*

As the frequency of an alternating current in a circuit is increased, the energy radiated from it generally increases, and the resulting radio waves travel farther before their strength is reduced to a negligible value. For this reason, high-frequency

662

currents are employed when the waves are used for communication over long distances. The frequencies in radio communication extend from several thousand cycles per second to over several hundred million. Even higher frequencies were used during the recent war for locating aircraft and submarines by radar, §359, and the methods are now being applied to air and marine transportation in furthering safety.

The field of radio communication really became established in 1901 when the Italian inventor, Guglielmo Marconi (1874-1937), succeeded in receiving a signal sent across the Atlantic. The waves from a radio telegraph station are started and stopped, by the operation of a telegraph key, to form wave trains of short and of longer duration which correspond to the dots and dashes of the International Code. In radio telephony, the continuity of the waves is not changed, but they are moulded in accordance with the variations of the sounds picked up by a telephone transmitter or microphone. In either case, the waves are said to be modulated to correspond with the signals that are being transmitted.

Electromagnetic waves also include light, infra-red and ultra-violet radiations, radio waves, X-rays, and radiations from radio-active substances known as $\gamma$-rays (from the Greek letter gamma). All these waves are of the same character and travel at the same speed, but they differ in wavelength. The following table shows the ranges of wavelength for the several radiations:

ELECTROMAGNETIC SPECTRUM

| Type of Wave | Wavelength |
|---|---|
| Radio | above 30 kilometers to 10 meters |
| Short-wave | 10 meters to 1 meter |
| Ultra short-wave | 1 meter to 0.1 centimeter |
| Infra-red | 0.030 to 0.000076 centimeter |
| Visible light | 0.000076 to 0.000040 centimeter |
| Ultraviolet | 0.000040 to 0.0000013 centimeter |
| X-rays | $10^{-6}$ to $10^{-9}$ centimeter |
| $\gamma$-rays | $10^{-8}$ to $5 \times 10^{-11}$ centimeter |

**326. Frequency and Wavelength.**—Electromagnetic waves travel at a speed of 300,000 kilometers per second or 186,000 miles per second in a vacuum, and the speed is approximately the same in air under normal conditions. If the frequency of the current producing these waves were just 300,000 cycles per second, the waves would travel a distance of 1 kilometer during each current cycle, and this distance would constitute the length of one wave. In general, while the current sweeps through an entire set of instantaneous values in the time taken for completing one cycle, the wave progresses in space a distance of 1 wavelength with a corresponding set of displacements. Fig. 443 shows the relation between the current values and the wave displacements; both are sine curves of arbitrary height and spread. The base line of the current curve is time in seconds or angular motion in electrical degrees, while the base line of the wave curve is distance in meters

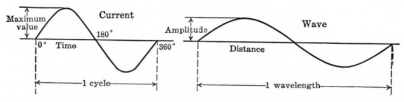

FIG. 443. Correspondence of wavelength with current cycle

or kilometers. The time required to complete one cycle of current is the reciprocal of its frequency. The symbol generally used for wavelength is λ, the Greek letter lambda.

Frequencies in radio communication are often figured in thousands and in millions of cycles per second, and the terms kilocycles (1 kilocycle = 1000 cycles) and megacycles (1 megacycle = 1,000,000 cycles) are used for the sake of convenience.

To FIND THE WAVELENGTH OF AN ELECTROMAGNETIC WAVE IN METERS:

*Divide 300 million by the frequency of the source of oscillations.*

Let
λ = wavelength in meters,
*f* = frequency in cycles per second.

Then

$$\lambda = \frac{300,000,000}{f}$$

**141**

**Problem 170.**—The frequency of alternating current used for generating the radio waves at a particular broadcasting station is 770 kilocycles per second. What is the wavelength of the waves?

(141) $$\lambda = \frac{300,000,000}{770,000} = 390 \text{ meters}$$

**Problem 171.**—A radar set designed for maritime service sends out waves that are 10 centimeters long. What is the frequency of the electrical oscillations in the set?

The wavelength of the waves is 0.1 meter. Hence

(141) $$f = \frac{300,000,000}{\lambda} = \frac{3 \times 10^8}{0.1} = 3 \times 10^9 \text{ cycles per second}$$

Radio waves pass readily through non-conductors of electricity but are absorbed by conductors. When such waves reach a conducting wire, an alternating e.m.f. is generated in it which establishes a current of the same frequency as of the source which produces the waves. This transformation of energy of radio waves to electrical energy is the basis of radio reception.

The circuits of radio receiving sets are adjusted so that they may respond to waves of a chosen length. Then, although there may be many stations transmitting at other wavelengths, practically no *interference* will result. However, a certain amount of it may result when the transmitting or the receiving apparatus does not "tune" sharply.

**327. Radiation.**—A system of wires projecting up from the ground for the purpose of radiating or receiving radio waves is designated as an *antenna*. The usual transmitting antenna consists of a bare wire, carefully insulated at its supporting points to prevent making contact with other structures, and held aloft by means of a suitable tower, mast or pole. One terminal of a generator of high-frequency power is connected to the lower end of the antenna while the other generator terminal is connected to ground. This generator forces electricity up and down the antenna in much the same way that an alternating-current generator would establish a current directed first one way and then the other through a circuit consisting of a coil and a condenser.

All antennas possess inductance and capacitance, the amounts depending upon the design of the wire system. It is because of these circuit constants that a transmitting antenna yields its maximum radiation at a single frequency, known as the *natural frequency* of the antenna. This frequency may be increased somewhat by the addition of a condenser connected between the antenna and the generator, or it may be decreased by the introduction of a coil at that place. It is not good policy to attempt wide changes in the natural frequency of an antenna by the addition of a condenser or a coil, because these additional circuit elements involve losses that reduce the total power supplied to the antenna itself

An analogy of the antenna is found in the steel tuning fork used by musicians. Owing to the elasticity of steel, the fork tends to maintain a fixed shape. When a prong is struck a sharp blow, it is displaced from its normal position and immediately tends to get back to that position, but the inertia of the prong hinders it from doing so. In starting toward its normal position, the prong gains velocity and when it reaches that position, its velocity is a maximum. Then the inertia of the prong keeps it going beyond the normal position, and causes the prong to be displaced in the opposite direction. When its kinetic energy is all converted into potential energy, the prong starts toward its normal position again, and the process continues. The prong swings to and fro until all of the energy has been radiated away in the form of sound waves, or has been converted into heat.

Comparing the behavior of the tuning fork with an electric circuit, it appears that capacitance may be called the "electric springiness" and inductance the "electric inertia" of a circuit. Through the combined effects of inductance and capacitance the electricity in an antenna is made to oscillate to and fro when set into motion by some device like an alternator or an oscillator operating in tune with the circuit. Such oscillation causes electromagnetic waves to be radiated throughout space.

**328. Natural Frequency of Circuit.**—The natural frequency of an oscillating circuit is increased when either the inductance or the capacitance of the circuit is decreased, and vice versa. If either one of these constants is increased and the other is decreased suitably to leave their product unchanged, then the frequency of the circuit will remain the same. These facts are borne out by

Formula (104), which gives the resonant frequency of a circuit of low resistance in terms of the inductance expressed in henries and the capacitance expressed in farads. These units are unduly large in radio practice, and for convenience the millihenry and microfarad are generally used instead. Let

$L_m$ = inductance in millihenries,
$C_M$ = capacitance in microfarads,
$f$ = natural frequency of circuit in cycles per second.

Since 1 henry = 1000 millihenries and 1 farad = $10^6$ microfarads, the natural frequency becomes

$$f = \frac{1}{2\pi\sqrt{L_m \times 10^{-3} \times C_M \times 10^{-6}}} = \frac{10^5}{6.28\sqrt{10L_m \times C_M}} = \frac{5033}{\sqrt{L_m \times C_M}}$$

To find the natural frequency of a circuit:

*Multiply the inductance (in millihenries) by the capacitance (in microfarads), extract the square root of this product, and divide the result into 5033.*

$$f = \frac{5033}{\sqrt{L_m \times C_M}} \qquad\qquad 142$$

This result can be merged with the expression for wavelength, as given by Formula (141), to yield the wavelength of the radiated waves in meters; thus,

$$\lambda = 59,600\sqrt{L_m \times C_M} \qquad\qquad 143$$

**Problem 172.**—A circuit has an inductance of 0.080 millihenry and a capacitance of 0.0016 microfarad. What is the natural frequency of the circuit and what is the wavelength of the radiation it produces?

For this circuit the value of the radical in the preceding equations becomes

$$\sqrt{L_m \times C_M} = \sqrt{0.080 \times 0.0016} = 10^{-2}\sqrt{8 \times 0.16} = \frac{\sqrt{1.28}}{100} = 0.0113$$

consequently the frequency and wavelength will be respectively:

(142) $\qquad f = \dfrac{5033}{0.0113} = 445,000$ cycles per second = 445 kilocycles per second

(143) $\qquad\qquad \lambda = 59,600 \times 0.0113 = 673$ meters

When a circuit is adjusted by altering its inductance or capacitance, or both, so that its resonant frequency is equal to the frequency of the applied e.m.f., the circuit is said to be *tuned* to that frequency.

**329. The Antenna System.**—The design and construction of a transmitting antenna presents many problems of insulation and rigidity. The input to transmitting antennas may be 50 kilowatts of high-frequency power or more, and the potential differences between the radiator and ground are of the order of thousands

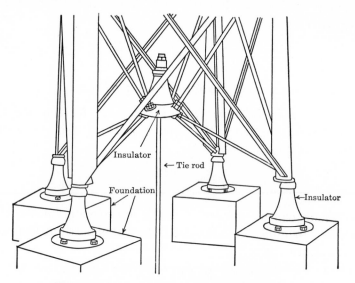

Fig. 444. Lower end of a transmitting antenna

of volts. The wires from which the waves are radiated must be supported by tall masts or towers to keep them securely aloft. Present design of transmitting antennas for the broadcast band seems to favor a single fabricated mast which acts as the radiator as well as the supporting structure. Fig. 444 shows a detailed view of the insulators at the bottom of an antenna to insulate it from the earth.

Transmitting antennas are built in heights varying from $\frac{1}{4}$ to $\frac{5}{8}$ of the wavelength at which the transmitter operates. For a station transmitting on a frequency of 1 million cycles per second, the wavelength is 300 meters; this means that a quarter-wave vertical antenna would have a height of 75 meters or 246 feet.

Fig. 445 shows two common types of antennas mounted between pairs of masts. Such antennas have been used in broadcasting service and on board ship for years, are relatively inexpensive to erect, and are appropriate for the longer waves. The wavelengths of these antennas cannot be calculated by simple formulas. The best approximation for an inverted L-type antenna is to assume the overall length of conductor to equal ¼ of the wavelength. For the T-type radiator, the distance from the lower end of the lead-in wire to one end of the horizontal wire is also about ¼ of the wavelength.

Most antennas operate in conjunction with a ground connection which often utilizes a subsurface metallic structure already pres-

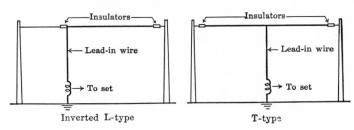

Inverted L-type          T-type

FIG. 445. Usual types of antennas

ent, such as the pipe system of a municipal water supply. In localities where such good ground connections are not available, and where the importance of the radio station warrants the cost, an extensive system of copper conductors is placed in the ground to increase the contact with the earth and so avoid a high resistance in the antenna system. Where the soil is so poorly conducting that even an elaborate direct ground connection yields a prohibitively high resistance in the transmitting antenna circuit, it is necessary to use a *counterpoise*.

A counterpoise is a network of insulated copper conductors spread under the antenna and mounted a few feet above the ground. This network serves as one plate of a condenser, while the conducting stratum of earth considerably below the surface acts as the other plate. In this way the antenna is connected to the conducting layer of earth by means of the series condenser so formed. Sometimes the counterpoise is buried a few feet below the surface of the ground in order to permit the use of the surface for other purposes; in such cases the buried conductors must be well insulated from the earth to avoid large losses.

Quite frequently it is desired to direct the radiation of a transmitter in a given direction, either to avoid interfering wth another transmitter or to serve better a region located in that direction. Such directional antennas consist generally of groups or *arrays of antennas.* A directional antenna may radiate signals in the desired direction from ten to thirty times as strong as those from a non-directional vertical antenna supplied with the same power. Practically all long-distance commercial radio transmission between fixed points is carried on by means of directional antennas. Many broadcasting stations also use arrays of antennas in order to achieve better coverage of neighboring large communities and to avoid interfering with other stations, especially those operating on adjacent channels.

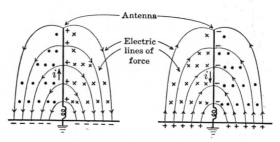

Fig. 446. Magnetic and electric fields around a vertical antenna

**330. Launching of Radio Waves from an Antenna.**—In order to understand how electromagnetic waves are sent out from a transmitting station, consider a vertical antenna, as shown in Fig. 446, with a coil near its base so that the transmitter may be coupled to the antenna. Assume that an alternating current $i$ is set up in the antenna by the transmitter. The diagram at the left shows the situation at a moment when the current is directed upward, and that at the right when the current is downward.

When the direction of $i$ is upward, the antenna is positively charged and the ground is negatively charged, and an electrostatic field is established between them directed as shown by the curved lines in the left-hand diagram. Also, with the current upward, a magnetic field surrounds the antenna directed counterclockwise, as viewed from a point above it. In the sectional view shown, this field is indicated by dots and crosses; the dots represent lines of force directed out of the page and crosses represent lines directed inward. The direction of this field is determined by the Right-hand Rule, §104. While the current is upward, the entire charge passes the point just above the coupling coil, but only a part of it passes any other point higher up on the antenna. As a result, the current $i$ has its largest effective value at the coupling coil, and is zero at the top; accordingly, the magnetic field around the antenna is strongest near its base and weakest at the top. Of course, this field has its greatest strength at each level when the current has its maximum value during the cycle.

The distribution of charge along the antenna makes the p.d. between the antenna and ground greatest at the top and zero at the base. The electric field has its maximum strength when the potential of every point, with respect to ground, has its maximum value during the cycle. At such instants the counter e.m.f. is a maximum and $i$ is zero. Thus, the electric field reaches its maximum value a quarter of a cycle after the magnetic field reaches its maximum.

The right-hand diagram of Fig. 446 shows the situation when the current $i$ is directed downward; it will be observed that the electric and magnetic fields are reversed. In both diagrams only the fields adjacent to the antenna are shown.

Since $i$ is an alternating current, the charge transferred by it flows up and down the antenna. As the lines of force in an electric field terminate on the charges themselves, the ends of these lines of force at the antenna must also move up and down with the charges. At the same time, both the magnetic and electric fields are pushed outward by successively new fields as $i$ continues to change with each cycle. Fig. 447 shows the propagation of the composite field which constitutes the electromagnetic wave. The direction of the electric component is shown by lines with arrows, while the magnetic field is shown by dots and crosses, as before.

The lines of force of the electric field are really surfaces viewed in cross-section in Fig. 447. They enclose the antenna and are concentric with it; at some distance from the antenna these surfaces of the electric field consist of lines of force which are practically vertical. The corresponding surfaces generated by the magnetic lines consist of an infinite number of horizontal circles. Thus, the electric and magnetic components of the electromagnetic field about an antenna are at right angles to each other in space. It has already been pointed out that these components are a quarter-cycle or 90 degrees apart in phase, since one has its maximum strength while the other is zero.

The points $M_m$ and $M_e$ indicate instantaneous positions of maximum magnetic and electric fields respectively, while $m_m$ and $m_e$ indicate points of minimum magnetic and electric fields re-

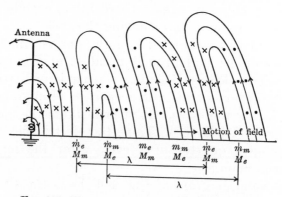

Fig. 447. Waves leaving a transmitting antenna

The dots and crosses indicate magnetic lines of force directed out of and into the page respectively; both the magnetic and electric fields are concentric with the antenna.

spectively. The signs of each are alternately positive and negative outward from the antenna. These points move with the field, the speed of which in air or vacuum is 186,000 miles per second. The length $\lambda$ of the wave extends from point $M_m$ to the second similarly-lettered point beyond, that is, to the next $M_m$ having the same sign; this is also true starting from points $M_e$ as indicated.

**331. Radio Telegraph Transmitters.**—It was shown in §324 that an electron tube can supply continuous and controllable oscillations if it is connected to an oscillatory circuit in which the plate and grid of the tube are properly coupled. These oscillations are transferred to an antenna through a coupling device, such as a coil or condenser, and the energy is radiated from the antenna as explained in the foregoing section. There remains to be shown how the dots and dashes of a code for the transmission of telegraph messages are formed.

Fig 448 illustrates three types of oscillators which are variously coupled to antennas. In each diagram the heavy lines represent the main oscillatory circuit of the transmitter and the lines marked $A$ indicate the antenna. A self-bias system consisting of condenser $C_s$ and grid leak $R_L$ are used instead of a grid bias battery, §324. The tube heater terminals $h$ are connected to suitable transformers. Coils $L$ are radio-frequency choke coils which prevent currents of radio frequency from by-passing condenser $C$.

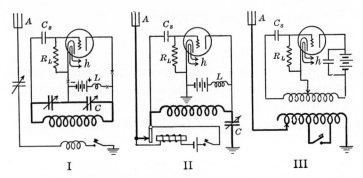

FIG. 448. Types of telegraph transmitters

In the radio telegraph transmitter depicted at I the key is introduced in the antenna circuit, but it may be located instead at the places marked ×. The function of the key is to interrupt the transmission of waves and form short and long wave trains to simulate dots and dashes respectively. However, as will be shown in the next lesson, this method of transmission does not produce audible signals in receivers using crystal or non-oscillating electron-tube detectors. For this reason an e.m.f. of audible frequency, usually of from 500 to 1000 cycles per second, is impressed by means of a buzzer, tuning fork, or other device, upon either the grid or antenna circuit of the oscillator. This arrangement modulates the radiated wave so that the signals will be audible with all systems of reception. A radio telegraph transmitter of this type, known as an interrupted continuous wave transmitter, is shown at II. The interrupting device is at the bottom and operates like any vibrator.

In high-power commercial telegraph transmitters, where it would be impracticable to open either the antenna or oscillator circuits on account of the large currents and high potentials used, the key may be arranged to short-circuit a portion of the antenna inductance, as shown at III. By this action the antenna emits oscillations of one frequency when the key is open, and oscillations of another frequency when closed. Of course, for correct reception, care must be exercised to tune to the proper wave. Such a telegraph transmitter is said to be a compensated continuous wave transmitter.

**332. Modulation in Radio Telephony.**—A radio telegraph transmitter may be converted into a telephone transmitter by substituting a sound modulating system for the telegraph key. Such a system moulds the generated waves to conform to an envelope which has the characteristics of the sound to be transmitted. Since sounds are waves ranging in frequency from about 16 to more than 10,000 cycles per second, modulation may be regarded as a superposition of such audio-frequency waves upon the radio waves generated by the oscillator. This is analogous to the superposition of speech waves on the direct current used in everyday telephone service. The alternating current produced by the oscillator is of constant frequency but the amplitude is varied in accordance with the sound wave so that a curve passing through the successive maxima of the radio-frequency waves represents the sound wave. This type of modulation is known as *amplitude modulation,* often abbreviated a.m.

Fig. 449 shows the individual waves and their resultant. The audio-frequency sound or voice wave is shown at the top; it is often called the *modulation wave.* The carrier wave produced by the high-frequency current in the oscillatory circuit is shown at the right. At the bottom is the modulated wave formed by superposing the voice wave upon the carrier wave.

If an oscillator, operating at a frequency of one million cycles per second, is modulated at a frequency of one thousand cycles per second, the output of the oscillator includes currents of three frequencies, namely: 1,000,000 cycles, 1,001,000 cycles, and 999,000 cycles per second. These frequencies are referred to as the *carrier,* the *upper side frequency,* and the *lower side frequency.* If the million-cycle carrier were modulated by a band of frequencies ranging from 1000 to 5000 cycles per second, the output of the system would include the one million-cycle carrier plus two bands of frequencies, one ranging from 1,001,000 to 1,005,000 cycles and the other from 995,000 to 999,000 cycles per second. These bands are known as the *sidebands* of the system, and are referred to individually as upper and lower sidebands respectively. In most radio broadcasting transmitters, the modulation of the carrier

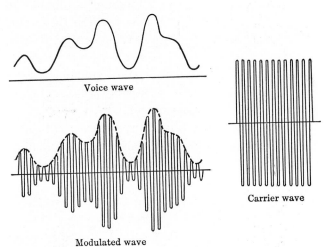

Fig. 449. Modulating high-frequency currents for radio telephony

involves audio frequencies from 30 to about 8000 cycles per second. This results in sidebands approximately 8000 cycles wide.

**333. Radio Telephone Transmitters.**—Modulation in radio telephony may be accomplished by coupling a microphone to the grid circuit of a vacuum-tube oscillator, as shown in Fig. 450. This arrangement, known as *grid modulation,* is very simple and effective in low-power circuits. The sound waves impinging upon the microphone $M$ are converted into corresponding electric currents in the local circuit $H$, and these set up proportional potentials by means of transformer $T$ for impression upon the grid. In this way the grid is subjected to two sets of potential variations, one being the very rapid radio-frequency oscillations for producing the carrier wave, and the other being the relatively slow voice or sound frequency variations.

In the connection diagram, the heavy lines represent the oscillatory circuit. Condenser $C_s$ and grid leak $R_L$ are used for the same purpose as a grid bias battery, as before; $h$ represents the terminals of the cathode heater; $L$ is a radio-frequency choke to prevent short-circuiting the central part of the coil in the oscillatory circuit; and $C_b$ is a by-pass condenser for radio-frequency currents around the secondary winding of the transformer.

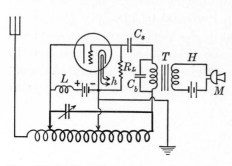

FIG. 450. Radio telephone transmitter using grid modulation

Grid modulation in radio telephony is practical only for transmitters of small output; the most common method of modulation in medium- and high-power systems is the Heising method, illus-

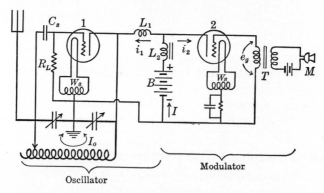

FIG. 451. Radio telephone transmitter using the Heising system of modulation

trated in Fig. 451. It employs at least two tubes: 1 is the oscillator and 2 is the modulator. Battery $B$ supplies potential to the plates of both tubes, and the audio-frequency choke coil $L_2$ keeps the total current to both of them practically constant. The secondary winding of the input transformer $T$ is connected in the grid circuit of the modulator tube. The coils $W_s$ are generally two distinct center-tapped transformer windings which supply power to the filaments of the tubes. Both these coils are secondary windings that may be served by a common primary; this is omitted in the figure for simplicity. Condenser $C_s$ and resistor $R_L$ serve the same purpose as before.

The radio-frequency currents developed by the oscillator circuit are prevented from reaching the battery (as well as the modulator tube) by the radio-frequency choke $L_1$; this is necessary because the usual audio-frequency choke coil may have enough capacitance distributed throughout its winding to pass radio-frequency currents. Radio-frequency power in the battery not only is a waste of energy, but is also a source of danger to the battery and $L_2$.

If the oscillator tube is operating alone, the energy supplied to it by the battery is constant, and the high-frequency current in the antenna will be constant. When a sound is directed into the microphone $M$, the grid of the modulator tube will undergo potential fluctuations, which in turn will cause the plate current of that tube to vary. Since choke $L_2$ will permit the current from $B$ to change but slightly, there will be variations in the plate current of the oscillator in view of the fact that the available energy from the battery, divided between the two tubes, is practically constant. At an instant when the plate current of the modulator increases, the input to the oscillator from $B$ is momentarily reduced; as a result, the energy delivered to the antenna is lessened and the amplitude of the radio wave is reduced. Thus, modulation is effected by causing the modulator tube to absorb energy from a direct-current source of fixed output, the remaining available energy being passed on to the oscillator tube where it is converted to radio-frequency energy. This energy is in turn delivered to the antenna and radiated.

The curves of Fig. 452 show the wave forms of the various currents when the potential $e_g$ for a sustained tone is applied by way of the microphone and transformer to the input of the modulator.

**334. The Wavemeter.**—The oscillator tubes of radio telephone and telegraph transmitters often vary the frequency of their oscillations as a result of variation in the constants of their circuits, of alterations in output, or of changes in the plate battery

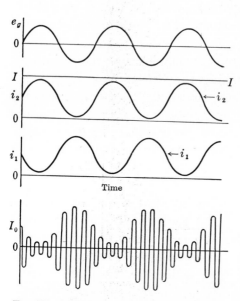

potential. Since such frequency variations cause corresponding changes in wavelength of the radiations emitted and make reception difficult, a close supervision of frequency is necessary to avoid interference with other transmitters. Until recently such supervision could be accomplished only by an instrument known as a *wavemeter*. This device, shown in Fig. 453, usually consists of a coil $L$ of fixed inductance, a condenser $C$ of adjustable capacitance, a suitable shield $S$, and a resonance indicator. The indicator depicted is a heater element $H$ and thermocouple $T$, §143, together with a galvanometer $G$. The deflection of the instrument is approximately proportional to the square of the alternating current through the heater element of the couple.

Fig. 452. Applied p.d. and operating currents in the Heising system of modulation

The symbols used for the ordinates refer to Fig. **451.**

In using a wavemeter to measure the wavelength of a transmitter, the wavemeter is brought near the oscillator and the condenser is varied carefully until a maximum deflection is shown on the galvanometer. For this setting of the condenser the wavelength may be determined by reference to the calibration curve of the instrument. The wavemeter should never be brought closer to the oscillator than is necessary to obtain a reasonable galvanometer deflection.

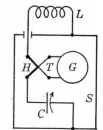

Fig. 453. Wavemeter circuit

The precision of wavemeters varies widely and depends upon the construction of the coil and condenser and upon the sensitivity of the indicator. The manipulation of the wavemeter may also affect its precision. Generally, wavemeters are not instruments of the highest precision.

**335. Frequency Control of Oscillators.**—Although wavemeters may be used to control the frequency of electron-tube oscillators, such control is not accurate enough for commercial radio operation. Furthermore, wavemeters cannot be employed to correct the frequency of an oscillator automatically. The utilization of the piezo-electric effect in quartz does make available an automatic frequency control of extremely high precision for radio-frequency oscillators.

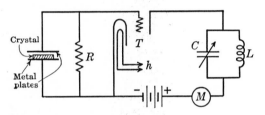

Fig. 454. Crystal-controlled oscillator

If a plate of quartz, properly cut from a crystal of that material, is mounted between two metal plates that are connected to a vacuum tube as shown in Fig. 454, the circuit will oscillate of itself at a frequency depending almost exclusively upon the thickness of the quartz, the manner in which it is cut from the crystal, and the temperature. If the temperature is maintained constant, the frequency may be kept stable to within about 1 part in a million. It is also possible to cut quartz plates from the original crystal so that variations in ordinary room temperature have no effect on oscillators controlled by them.

The tuned circuit in the figure consists of condenser $C$ of variable capacitance and coil $L$ of fixed inductance. The tube $T$ is a triode rated at 10 watts or less as an oscillator, and the instrument $M$ is a milliammeter. The leak resistance $R$ may be as high as several million ohms. Terminals $h$ are connected to a suitable source of direct or alternating current to heat the filament.

When the condenser is varied, a setting is reached at which the pointer of the milliammeter dips decidedly. This dip indicates that the circuit is oscillating; the greater the dip, the stronger will be the oscillations. Generally, the circuit oscillates over only a very small range of condenser settings. The power drawn from the circuit by means of a suitable coupling to coil $L$ is passed on to amplifiers which increase this output to any desired value.

Fig. 455 shows how some quartz plates are cut from the original crystals. The lines $X$, $Y$ and $Z$ are termed the *electrical, mechanical,* and *optic* axes of the crystals respectively. It should be noted that there are three $X$-axes and three $Y$-axes in every quartz crystal. Plates cut perpendicular to the $X$-axis or to the $Y$-axis are called $X$-cut and $Y$-cut plates respectively. The third is called an $AT$ cut plate; its location in the crystal is placed by rotating

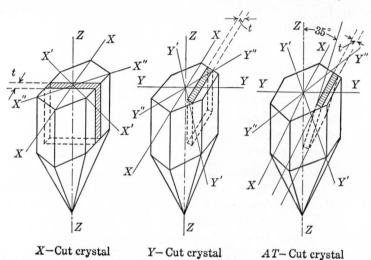

X–Cut crystal        Y–Cut crystal        AT–Cut crystal

Fɪɢ. 455. Three methods of cutting quartz plates for use in controlling oscillators

the plane of a $Y$-cut plate about an edge parallel to an $X$-axis to form an angle of 35 degrees with the plane determined by the $X$ and $Z$ axes.

The frequency of vibration of a quartz plate is inversely proportional to the thickness of the plate. For the three cuts of quartz plates, the frequencies can be expressed with corresponding subscripts as

$$f_x = \frac{107 \times 10^6}{t}$$

$$f_y = \frac{78 \times 10^6}{t}$$

$$f_{at} = \frac{65.4 \times 10^6}{t}$$

where $f$ is expressed in cycles per second, and $t$ is the thickness of the plate in mils or thousanths of an inch. Both $X$-cut and $Y$-cut crystals must be operated at constant temperature. The $AT$-cut quartz plate is not affected by temperature variations in the vicinity of 43° C.

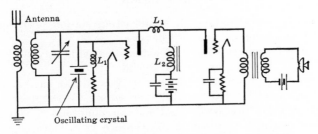

FIG. 456. Crystal-controlled radio telephone transmitter

Fig. 456 illustrates a simple crystal-controlled transmitter used for radio telephony; the devices indicated have the usual significance. Coils $L_1$ and $L_2$ are respectively radio-frequency and audio-frequency chokes.

## QUESTIONS

1. Explain the fundamental principle of radio signaling.
2. What is meant by wavelength of radiation and how is this quantity related to a current cycle?
3. Explain the terms: oscillatory circuit, and natural frequency.
4. How are electromagnetic waves produced?
5. What are the advantages of a good receiving antenna?
6. Describe the construction of a transmitting antenna.
7. How does a counterpoise differ from a direct ground connection?
8. What are directional antennas and why are they used?
9. What are the components of the field about an antenna? What is the relation of these fields in space? in time phase?
10. At what point on an antenna is the p.d. to ground greatest? At what point is the current a maximum?
11. How are radio waves launched at a transmitting antenna?
12. Make a sketch of the appearance of the waves leaving a transmitting antenna.
13. Draw a typical circuit of a radio telegraph transmitter and explain its operation.
14. What is meant by modulation?
15. What does the term side frequency or sideband signify?
16. Describe the grid modulation method in radio telephony.
17. Explain the Heising system of modulation.

18. Draw a circuit of a wavemeter and explain its operation.
19. Make a sketch of a quartz crystal and name all its axes. Point out the original location of an $X$-cut and a $Y$-cut plate of quartz.
20. Draw the circuit of a crystal-controlled telephone transmitter, and explain its operation.

## PROBLEMS

1. Calculate the wavelength of a broadcasting station operating on 710 kilocycles per second. *Ans.* 423 meters.
2. What is the frequency of a station that transmits waves 1.9 meters in length? *Ans.* 158 megacycles per second.
3. Determine the vibration frequency for X-rays that have a wavelength of $10^{-8}$ centimeter. *Ans.* $3 \times 10^{18}$ per second.
4. The yellow light produced by a sodium lamp has a wavelength of 0.0000589 centimeter. What is the frequency of vibration within the source to produce waves of such light? *Ans.* $5.1 \times 10^{14}$ cycles per second.
5. An oscillatory circuit operating at one megacycle has an inductance of 100 microhenries. What should be the capacitance of the tuning condenser? *Ans.* 253 micro-microfarads.
6. A transmitter operating on 1500 kilocycles per second is to have a vertical quarter-wave antenna. How tall should this antenna be? *Ans.* 164 feet.
7. If a broadcasting station operating on 820 kilocycles per second is modulated by a band of frequencies extending from 30 to 8000 cycles per second, what are the sidebands? *Ans.* 820,030 to 828,000 cycles, and 812,000 to 819,970 cycles.
8. Calculate the thickness of an $AT$-cut crystal to operate at a wavelength of 80 meters. *Ans.* 0.0175 inch.

4-13

Palese, G.

(45)

1.) B A          21.) B A
2.) A B          22.) A
3.) B A          23.) A C
4.) C            24.) A B
5.) C B          25.) C
6.) C            26.) C B
7.) B A          27.) C A
8.) C B          28.) C
9.) A C          29.) A C
10.) A           30.) B
11.) B C         31.) C
12.) A B         32.) A
13.) B C         33.) B A
14.) A           34.) C A
15.) B           35.) A
16.) C           36.) C
17.) A           37.) B C
18.) C
19.) C
20.) B C

26. When an ac potential is impressed across a condenser in a purely capacitive circuit, this capacitor is fully charged and the value of circuit current is zero at the instant that the applied voltage –
   (a) reaches either its maximum positive or maximum negative value.
   (b) reaches its zero value.
   (c) remains at a constant value throughout its cycle.

a ___ b ___ c ___

# Lesson XXIX

## RADIO RECEPTION

How radio waves affect the receiving antenna—Receiving antennas—Aims in receiver design—Loud speakers—Tuned radio-frequency receivers—Superheterodyne receivers—Automatic volume control—The idea of frequency modulation—Frequency-modulated radio receivers—The discriminator—Power supply systems—Facsimile transmission—Questions and Problems.

**336. How Radio Waves Affect the Receiving Antenna.**—The electromagnetic waves generated by a transmitting station consist of two components, a magnetic and an electric field, which progress outward from the station. These fields are at right angles to each other in space and are 90 degrees apart in time phase, §330. The magnetic lines of force around a vertical transmitting antenna form circles in a horizontal plane and these circles expand. The motion of such lines, as they approach a vertical receiving antenna, is also horizontal. The field moving past the receiving antenna is another example of the familiar process of magnetic flux cutting a conductor and developing an e.m.f., §144. Thus, the magnetic field of a radio wave induces an e.m.f. in the antenna.

At the same time that the magnetic field sweeps past a receiving antenna and develops an e.m.f. in it, the electric field does likewise. Since any two points on an electric line of force are at different electric potentials, a conductor that coincides with the direction of the electric field is subject to a difference of potential. The magnitude of this p.d. is equal to that between the points in the electric line of force touched by the ends of the conductor. Fig. 457 shows an electric line of force approaching a receiving antenna of height $H$. If the potential on this line at a distance $H$

above the ground is 1 millivolt higher than ground potential, then the p.d. developed in the receiving antenna will be 1 millivolt.

A tall antenna naturally intercepts more magnetic lines of force and also acquires a higher potential from the electric lines of force than a low one, and consequently, a tall antenna is more effective in collecting signals. It should be remembered that all antennas collect not only the desired signals but also unwanted radio-frequency waves, atmospheric static electricity, and all sorts of radiations from nearby electric circuits; obviously, tall antennas also pick up more of such extraneous noises than shorter ones. The heights of receiving antennas should be such as to yield sufficiently strong signals with a minimum of interference.

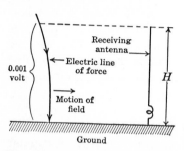

Fig. 457. Development of p.d. in antenna by an electric field

### 337. Receiving Antennas. —Radio

waves of broadcast programs in the United States are generally so strong that only a few feet of wire strung up inside of a building may be adequate as an antenna to achieve fair reception of nearby stations. Because of this condition, one should not minimize the importance of a good receiving antenna, but rather appreciate the conditions which might afford better reception. A vertical wire about 75 feet long generally gives good results over the broadcast band ranging from 500 to 1500 kilocycles.

The e.m.f.'s generated in such antennas are seldom greater than a few millivolts. Therefore, such antennas are not difficult to insulate properly. The supporting structures of commercial receiving antennas must be strong enough to withstand windstorms and designed to avoid destruction by lightning. The arrangement of the wires and their supports should be such as to prevent accidental contact of any part of the conducting system with buildings, electrical transmission lines, or other structures.

Carelessly erected antennas are often responsible for noises heard in radio receivers and may sometimes prove to be fire hazards by causing short circuits in power systems. The layout of a receiving antenna suitable for the broadcast band may depend on the conditions at the point where it is to be erected, and experimentation may be necessary to secure the best results.

In locations where the electromagnetic fields of radio transmitters are sufficiently strong, the usual receiving antenna may be replaced by a loop of wire having relatively small dimensions. Such a *loop antenna* consists of a number of turns of wire mounted in a vertical plane, each side conductor acting as a vertical antenna. The wires on one side attain a higher p.d. than those on the other, and the difference between them is the net e.m.f. available in the loop. It is apparent that this e.m.f. is much less than would be produced in a single vertical antenna having a height equal to the sum of the vertical lengths of the conductors in the loop.

Loop antennas are usually tuned by means of a variable condenser contained in the receiving set. Loop antennas are decidedly directional and should be turned so that the plane of the loop is in the direction from which the radio signals are being received. For this reason the loop is often mounted in such a way as to permit rotation, so that the user may select the position which yields the greatest response. Most broadcast receivers now incorporate loop antennas, making it unnecessary to use other antennas unless the desired signals are too weak for good reception. A terminal is provided so that an external antenna may be coupled to the loop contained within the set.

Portable broadcast receivers always have internal loop antennas. Because of the directional qualities of such loops, it may be necessary to turn the whole receiver in order to improve the reception of weak signals.

**338. Aims in Receiver Design.**—Modern broadcasting stations have been brought to such a high level of excellence that vast improvements in radio receivers were needed to realize fully the benefits of improved transmission. Not only has it been necessary to better the design of receiver circuits, but the electron tubes employed had to be made smaller, more efficient, and thoroughly reliable. Circuit components, such as coils and condensers, are now freer from variations due to aging and to temperature and humidity changes. Tuning controls have been simplified and push-button selection of broadcasting stations has been perfected. The problem of fading also has been virtually solved by the introduc-, tion of automatic volume control, §342.

The power supply system, which provides the current for heating the cathodes and for the plate circuits, is now vastly improved, due largely to the perfection of high-capacitance electrolytic condensers, §166. Such condensers are also used in the receiver itself for by-pass purposes; they are very reliable, cheap, and of unusually small volume and weight.

The term *high fidelity*, as applied to a radio receiver, generally indicates that the set can reproduce in proper proportion all those components of sound which lie in the approximate frequency range from 30 to 8000 cycles per second. Some sets reproduce sounds beyond these limits. In addition to the coverage of this frequency range, a high fidelity set must also be capable of operating at such acoustic output (sound volume) as to convert the available power output of the amplifiers into sound that is free from distortion. Until recently, the limitation of the loud speaker was the major one in determining the quality of reproduction of the set.

The tuning of a high quality radio receiver must be simple and remain constant when once set. Further, the instrument must have high *selectivity* without materially reducing the band of frequencies passed on to the loud speaker. By selectivity is meant the capacity to select one broadcasting station at a time, to the exclusion of all interfering signals from other transmitters.

**339. Loud Speakers.**—The loud speaker of a radio receiver serves the same purpose as a receiver in a telephone circuit, §307; that is, it converts a sound-modulated current into sound waves. In the modern magnetic type of loud speaker, a flexibly mounted voice coil is located in an intense magnetic field produced either by an electromagnet or a permanent magnet. The voice coil carries the modulated current and moves back and forth within the field in accordance with the strength of the current. The coil is attached to a cone or diaphragm which serves as a piston to generate the sound waves in the surrounding air. Fig. 458 shows an electromagnetic loud speaker in cross section. The field coil of this type of speaker is often used as the choke coil in the filter system of the power supply. Speakers making use of permanent magnets instead of electromagnets are lighter, more compact, and often more desirable than the electromagnetic type.

The demand for more and more acoustic volume has led designers to make speakers larger, but these are naturally best adapted to reproduce the lower pitched tones. It has been necessary in high-grade sets to supplement the large loud speaker with another which is better adapted to reproduce the higher tones. These "high-frequency" speakers are quite small and can easily reproduce sounds of frequencies exceeding 8000 cycles per second. When a set incorporates a high- and a low-frequency speaker, they

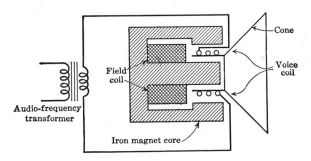

Fig. 458. The electromagnetic loud speaker

are distinguished colloquially as the "tweeter" and the "wooffer," respectively.

### 340. Tuned Radio-Frequency Receivers.

340. Tuned Radio-Frequency Receivers.—Radio receivers now available for the reception of waves with amplitude modulation may be classified in two groups. The earlier group, which dates back to the beginning of broadcasting in 1919, comprises *tuned radio-frequency receivers,* and the later group comprises *superheterodyne receivers.*

Tuned radio-frequency receivers are characterized by a circuit employing only one detector and a radio-frequency amplifier that can be tuned throughout the frequency range of broadcast or other transmitters. Fig. 459 shows the basic circuit of such a receiver. Tubes 1, 2 and 4 function as voltage amplifiers, tube 3 functions as a detector or demodulator, while tubes 5 and 6 constitute the power amplifier. The heaters for the cathodes $K$ of all the tubes are connected in parallel and are supplied with alternating current from a single transformer, and the power for the plate circuits is supplied to terminals $B+$ and $B-$ from a full-wave rectifier and filter of the type described in §346. The power supply system is omitted from the diagram for simplicity.

The radio-frequency transformers RT-1, RT-2 and RT-3 are generally of the air-core type, and their windings have primary coils $L_1$ and secondary coils $L_2$. They are tuned to the frequency of the desired transmitter by means of the condensers $C_1$, $C_2$ and $C_3$, the setting of which is varied simultaneously by a single knob

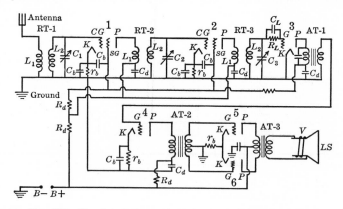

FIG. 459. Circuits of a tuned radio-frequency radio receiver

or dial. The coils of the transformers and their associated tuning condensers constitute three pairs of *tuned radio-frequency coupled circuits*. The first two of these circuits operate in conjunction with the amplifier tetrodes 1 and 2, and the third tuned circuit operates directly into the detector triode 3.

The audio-frequency transformers AT-1, AT-2 and AT-3 are of the iron-core type. The first transfers the output of the detector tube to the first audio-frequency amplifier triode 4, the next delivers power to the final audio-frequency amplifier stage consisting of triodes 5 and 6 connected in push-pull, and the third transformer supplies the output to the voice coil $V$ of the loud speaker $LS$.

Resistors $R_d$ are inserted to provide potential drops in order to yield potentials for the plates $P$ and screen grids $SG$ appropriate to the various tubes. Condensers $C_d$ are decoupling condensers which by-pass the signals to ground and keep them out of the power supply system, where undesirable interaction between the various parts of the circuit might otherwise take place. The potential drop across resistors $r_b$ serves to bias negatively the control grids $CG$ of the radio-frequency amplifiers and the grids $G$ of the audio-frequency amplifiers. Condensers $C_b$ are used with each of these resistors, except that in the push-pull stage, so that no alternating p.d. can exist across them. The functions of condenser $C_L$ and resistor $R_L$ of the grid circuit detector are explained in §323.

**Experiment 115.**—Set up the circuit shown in Fig. 460 to serve as a radio receiver for local stations. $AT$ represents an antenna transformer, $C$ a variable air condenser suitable for the transformer at hand, $P$ a pair of telephone receivers, and $S$ a filament switch. Use a Type 1G4-GT/G triode.

The following data give suitable constants of the devices shown:

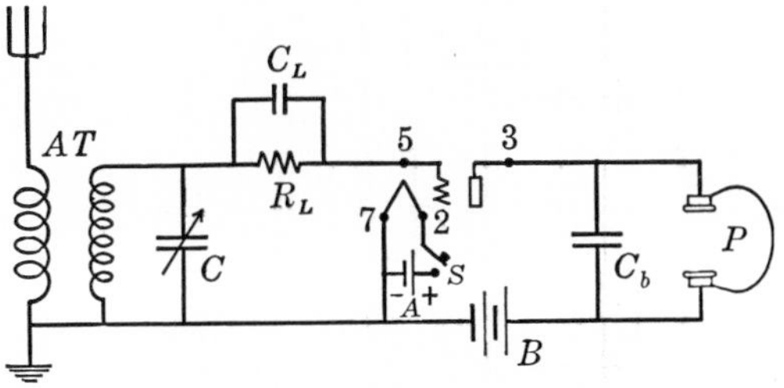

$C_b$ = 500 micro-microfarads,
$C_L$ = 150 micro-microfarads,
$R_L$ = 0.5 megohm,
$P$ = 2000 ohms,
$A$ = 1.5 volts,
$B$ = 45 volts.

A length of 20 feet of wire should be adequate for the antenna.

FIG. 460. A simple radio receiver

## 341. Superheterodyne Receivers.—The second of the two groups of radio receivers mentioned in the previous section includes super-heterodyne receivers, in which the radio-frequency amplification takes place at the carrier frequency of the signal in one part of the set, and at a lower frequency, called the *intermediate frequency*, in another part. These parts are called respectively the radio-frequency (RF) amplifier, and the intermediate-frequency (IF) amplifier. This type of receiver was devised by the American inventor, Edwin H. Armstrong.

The change in frequency from the carrier frequency to the intermediate frequency is produced in the *first detector* tube, which actually functions as a modulator. It operates in conjunction with a radio-frequency oscillator, but in practically all modern sets the first detector and the oscillator are incorporated into a single tube called a *converter*. One or more intermediate-frequency stages of amplification follow the first detector. In a given set, these stages operate at a constant frequency regardless of the frequency of the station being received, and the circuits coupling these stages are tuned by condensers which are set permanently at the factory. The output of the IF amplifier is passed on to the *second detector,* where the signal modulation, originally applied to the carrier at the transmitter, is retrieved. The audio-frequency (AF) amplifier finally builds the signal to a level sufficiently high to operate the loud speaker satisfactorily.

The superheterodyne receiver has two important features to recommend it. The first of these is simplicity and effectiveness

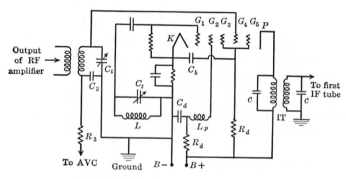

Fig. 461. Circuit of a converter tube

of amplification at the intermediate frequency. The tuned circuits in IF amplifiers are easier to design and, with the associated tubes, generally yield higher and more constant amplification than is the case when operation is carried out at the usual carrier frequencies. The second feature of the superheterodyne is its sharpness of tuning or high selectivity. Such selectivity results from the modulation of the output of the RF amplifier by the oscillator in the set; this action takes place in the first detector or converter tube. The output of this tube is at the intermediate frequency and this is precisely fixed in each set to a value around 455 kilocycles per second. The IF tuned circuits are designed to pass only a band about 5000 cycles wide on either side of this frequency.

Fig. 461 shows the circuits of the converter tube having five grids, $G_1$ to $G_5$. The oscillator is formed by the tube elements

$K$, $G_1$ and $G_2$, serving respectively as cathode, grid and plate. Energy is transferred from the plate ($G_2$) circuit to the grid ($G_1$) circuit by means of the magnetic coupling between coils $L$ and $L_p$. The oscillations generated by this so-called tuned grid circuit oscillator are superposed on the electron stream from the cathode to the actual plate $P$. The signal delivered by the antenna, or received from a previous RF amplifier, if any, is applied to grid $G_4$ which superposes this carrier also on the electron stream from $K$ to $P$. As a result, the modulated carrier from the transmitting station is remodulated by the frequency of the local oscillator, $KG_1G_2$. Grids $G_3$ and $G_5$ are connected to form a shield about grid $G_4$. This shielding is necessary in order to prevent the signal applied to $G_4$ from influencing the frequency of the local oscillator.

The resistors $R_d$ are used to reduce the e.m.f., made available by the power supply at terminals $B+$ and $B-$, to values suitable to the tube elements involved. $C_b$ and $C_d$ are the by-pass and decoupling condensers respectively. The combination of condenser $C_3$ and resistor $R_3$ are used in connection with automatic volume control AVC to be described in the next section. Condenser $C$ serves to tune the intermediate-frequency transformer, IT.

Consider that it is desired to pick up signals of 760 kilocycles per second with a superheterodyne receiver. The condenser in the input circuit of the radio-frequency amplifier tube and condenser $C_t$ in the circuit of the fourth grid of the converter tube are each tuned to the carrier frequency of 760 kilocycles. Condenser $C_t$ in the circuit of the first grid of the converter tube tunes the oscillator to a frequency equal to the difference between the carrier and the intermediate frequency. Assuming the latter frequency in the receiver under consideration to be 455 kilocycles, the oscillator could be tuned to either 305 or 1215 kilocycles. Usually the higher frequency is used because this practice permits more accurate tuning of the circuits associated with the condensers controlled by a common dial or knob. Since the amplitude modulation of currents of one frequency by those of another always results in two new frequencies, namely the sum of the two frequencies and the difference between them, the output of the converter tube includes frequencies of $760 + 1215$ or 1975 kilocycles and $1215 - 760$

or 455 kilocycles. Both the 1975- and 455-kilocycle signals will carry the modulation originally applied to the carrier by the transmitter, but the IF amplifier, being tuned permanently to 455 kilocycles, will only pass the signals of this frequency. The modulated 455-kilocycle wave is amplified effectively and applied to the second detector, where the original audio modulation is separated and applied to the AF amplifier for final amplification before being passed on to the loud speaker.

Now assume that a strong interfering signal on a carrier frequency of 770 kilocycles is present while the 760-kilocycle signal is being received. Since the oscillator of the receiver is tuned, for the reception of the 760-kilocycle signal, at 1215 kilocycles, the result of modulating the 770-kilocycle carrier by the 1215-kilocycle oscillations will be $770 + 1215$ or 1985 kilocycles and $1215 - 770$ or 445 kilocycles. Since the IF amplifier in this receiver passes a band only 10 kilocycles wide, 5 on either side of 455, the only band passed lies between 450 and 460 kilocycles. Accordingly, both components of the 770-kilocycle interfering signal will be rejected by the IF amplifier and the 760-kilocycle station will be received without interference. Since all broadcasting stations in a given area have carriers which differ by at least 10 kilocycles, a well-adjusted superheterodyne receiver will receive signals from any of them, if they are of reasonable strength, without interference. The interference in broadcasting is further minimized by the practice of the Federal Communications Commission of allocating adjacent radio channels only to stations that are widely separated geographically. In localities where a number of broadcasting stations of approximately equal power operate, only a superheterodyne set will receive their signals without interference.

Fig. 462 shows the circuit of a superheterodyne receiver with 5 tubes, excluding the power supply unit with its tube. The three variable condensers, shown as $C_t$ and referred to in connection with the preceding figure, are tuned simultaneously by one control dial, their rotating members being mounted on a common shaft. Condensers $c$ in the intermediate-frequency circuits are tuned to that frequency and have their capacitances fixed once for all. Terminals $B+$ and $B-$ connect to the power supply unit, §346. The significance and function of the various parts of the circuit will be understood from preceding explanations.

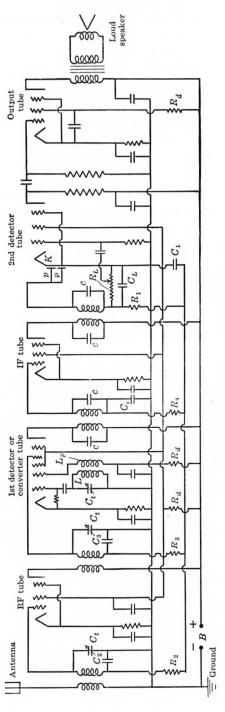

FIG. 462. Circuit of a superheterodyne receiver

The second detector is in reality a combination of a double diode and a pentode. The two plates $p,p$ of the double diode are connected to form a single diode with $K$ as the cathode. The audio signal is available across the combination of $R_L$ and $C_L$. A potentiometer tap on this resistor serves as the manual volume control and transfers the audio signal to the control grid of the pentode, thereby operating the pentode section of this tube as a high-gain AF voltage amplifier. Because of this operation the output of the second detector tube may be applied directly to the output tube, which in this case is a power pentode. The diode rectifier in the second detector tube also supplies automatic volume control to the three preceding tubes by means of the combinations $R_L$ and $C_L$, $R_1$ and $C_1$, $R_4$ and $C_4$. The resistors $R_d$ serve to provide appropriate potentials to the various tube elements as previously explained.

**342. Automatic Volume Control.**—The strength of radio signals received from a distance is likely to vary from time to time in such a manner as to mar the reception of a broadcast program, or to make difficult or impossible the reception of complete messages on commercial radio telegraph and telephone systems. This variation in strength, known as *fading,* results largely from changes in conductivity of the path over which radio waves are received. In order to reduce fading to a minimum, the sensitivity of the receiver must be increased when the received signals grow weak, and reduced when the signals return to normal. Since fading often varies from minute to minute, only an automatic arrangement can be effective against such disturbances. Several arrangements for controlling the volume of sound are now available, and their effectiveness is such that almost every radio receiver now incorporates one; they are known as *automatic volume controls.*

The amplification factor ($\mu$) of certain tubes, called *variable-mu* or *super-control tubes,* varies decidedly when the grid bias potential is varied, the amplification factor being high for a small negative bias, and low for a large negative bias. The signal output of such tubes, therefore, varies from a high value when the grid bias is slightly negative, to a low output when the grid is strongly negative. It is this characteristic of super-control tubes that makes automatic volume control possible.

Generally, a rectifier or detector is incorporated in the receiver, just ahead of the audio-frequency amplifier. This tube rectifies the carrier of the signal received, and produces a unidirectional p.d. across a combination of a resistor shunted by a condenser. By properly selecting the values of $R$ and $C$ in this combination, this p.d. is made to vary proportionally to the strength of the carrier and, consequently, to the received signal. This p.d. is then applied to the variable-mu tubes which may be located in either the RF or the IF amplifier, or in both. Thus, when a strong signal is received, the rectifier or so-called *AVC tube* supplies a large negative bias to the super-control tubes, thereby reducing

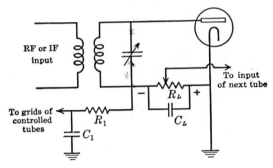

Fig. 463. Diode rectifier used for automatic volume control

the gain of the amplifiers associated with them, and passing along a weaker signal to the audio-frequency amplifier. Conversely, if the received signal fades, the bias fed back by the AVC tube is reduced, the gain of the stages affected is increased, and the signal is brought to normal. In some receiver circuits, the AVC tube is only a part of a multi-purpose tube, the remaining parts acting either as a detector, as an amplifier, or both.

Fig. 463 shows one arrangement for automatic volume control. In this circuit the input from the RF or IF amplifier is supplied to a diode rectifier which includes the loading combination of resistor $R_L$ and condenser $C_L$. Across this combination is available the audio-frequency component of the input signal, together with a rectified signal proportional to the amplitude of the carrier impressed upon the diode. The audio component is taken from the $R_L$-$C_L$ combination and is passed on to the next tube, as shown. The rectified carrier signal is impressed upon the $R_1$-$C_1$ combination which is so designed that it will respond only to slow variations such as result when the impressed signal (and its carrier) fades. The $R_1$-$C_1$ combination supplies these slow variations as additional bias to the tubes served by the AVC and so controls their gains that approximately constant-level signals are passed on by the diode. This bias is applied to the various tubes by way of suitable decoupling networks.

A decoupling network serves to pass most of the alternating current through the condenser and little through the resistor and its associated circuit. To illustrate, the network $R_4$-$C_4$ in Fig. 462 keeps the intermediate-frequency current in the third tube from

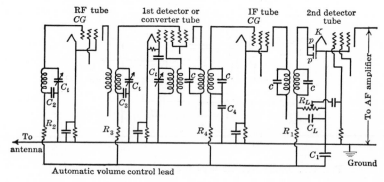

FIG. 464. AVC system of the superheterodyne receiver of Fig. 462

reaching the diode. This is achieved by making the ratio of the resistance of $R_4$ to the reactance of $C_4$ at the operating frequency at least 10 to 1.

Fig. 464 shows the automatic volume control applied to the superheterodyne receiver of Fig. 462. The AVC is applied to the control grid $CG$ of the RF amplifier tube, to the fourth or injection grid of the converter tube, and to the control grid of the IF tube. The audio-frequency output of the diode section of the second detector tube $(K,p,p)$ is taken from the combination of resistor $R_L$ and condenser $C_L$ and applied to the AF amplifier. The groups $R_2$-$C_2$, $R_3$-$C_3$, and $R_4$-$C_4$ are decoupling networks intended to prevent coupling between the diode section of the second detector tube, and those tubes to which the AVC is applied. These networks also prevent undesirable interaction between the various tubes connected to the AVC system.

Resistor $R_L$, connected as a potentiometer, serves also as a manual volume control, since it regulates the audio-frequency potential applied to the first grid of the pentode section of the second detector tube. Condensers $C_t$ are the tuning condensers, and condensers $c$ serve as by-passes for either the carrier or the intermediate radio frequencies.

**343. The Idea of Frequency Modulation.**—One of the most recent developments in radio broadcasting is *frequency modulation* (abbreviated f.m.). This system of modulating the carrier wave was devised by Armstrong, and became commercially available in 1938. Now, many of the larger broadcasting stations have introduced, or are preparing to install, f.m. channels to supplement their regular service, in which the waves are subject to amplitude modulation (a.m.). In the near future the programs of most broadcasting stations will be available on both a.m. and f.m. channels.

The main advantages set forth for f.m. reception are: practical elimination of all noise or static, advancement of high-fidelity reproduction, and reduction of interference between f.m. stations. It has been abundantly demonstrated that reception within the normal service area of an f.m. transmitter is free from noise even in thunderstorms or in the presence of severe man-made static. Currents of audio frequencies as high as 15,000 cycles per second may be transmitted readily with this system of modulation. Further experience may be needed before the claim for freedom from interference is generally accepted.

In order that any radio-frequency carrier may be effectively modulated to transmit a sound, both the pitch (or frequency) and the loudness (or amplitude) of the sound must be imposed in some way upon the carrier. The amplitude of the radio wave emitted by an f.m. transmitter is always constant and is determined only by the power radiated by the station. The basic principles of f.m. transmission are:

*The frequency of the carrier is varied over a range which is proportional to the loudness of the sound.*

*The rate at which this variation takes place is equal to the frequency of the sound.*

To illustrate these principles, let an f.m. transmitter operating on a carrier frequency of 45,000,000 cycles per second vary its

frequency, say a total of 20,000 cycles per second, in order to transmit a certain volume of a tone picked up by a microphone. If this
tone has a pitch of 1000 cycles per second, the frequency of the
transmitter will vary from 44,990,000 to 45,010,000 cycles per second, at the rate of 1000 times a second. This situation is depicted
in Fig. 465. The ordinates of the sine curve show a frequency
deviation of 10,000 cycles (or 0.01 megacycle) per second from
the 45,000,000 cycle (45 megacycle) carrier to represent the chosen
sound volume. The abscissa indicates the time of sweeping through
one complete set of frequency values; since this takes 0.001 sec-

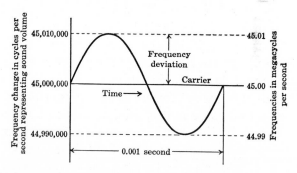

Fig. 465. Instantaneous frequency of an f.m. transmitter for a tone of 1000 cycles
per second at a volume level corresponding to a frequency deviation of 10 kilocycles
per second

ond, 1000 such sets of values can be swept out per second to represent a 1000-cycle tone. If the note were held for two seconds, the
frequency of the transmitter would be varied from 45.01 to 44.99
and back to 45.01 megacycles per second exactly 2000 times in
this interval.

Further, if the volume of the tone picked up were doubled,
the deviation of the carrier frequency would be doubled, ranging
from 44.98 to 45.02 megacycles per second, a difference of 40,000
cycles per second. Should the volume of the tone be tripled, the
frequency would vary over a range of 60,000 cycles per second.
In these examples, the frequency deviation for the three volume
levels of the 1000-cycle note are respectively 10, 20 and 30 kilocycles per second. In each case the frequency would vary from
its maximum to its minimum and back to the maximum frequency
at the rate of 1000 times per second. Furthermore, the amplitude

of the radiated wave from the transmitter would remain constant throughout.

Continuing the illustration, if the tone transmitted were to change from a pitch of 1000 to one of 4000 cycles per second, while maintaining the same loudness as employed in the first case, the radiated wave would vary from 44.99 to 45.01 megacycles per second as before, but now at a rate of 4000 times per second.

The band of frequencies now actively employed in f.m. transmission covers the region from 42 to 50 and from 88 to 106 megacycles per second. In the present allocation of channels, each station is allowed a band extending 100 kilocycles (0.1 megacycle) per second on each side of the carrier. The actual modulation of the carrier may extend only 75 kilocycles per second on each side of the carrier, the remaining 25 serving as a region containing the upper sideband.

The frequency deviation of an f.m. transmitter, that is, the variation of its frequency on either side of the carrier, must not be confused with its sidebands. Such a transmitter does have sidebands and these may include frequencies beginning close to the carrier and extending in both directions well beyond the limits of the frequency deviation. However, f.m. systems used in broadcasting are so designed that the significant components of the side frequencies, which constitute the sidebands, lie within the band assigned to each channel, i.e., within the 200 kilocycles allotted to each channel. In this way interference between adjacent channels is reduced greatly.

**344. Frequency-Modulated Radio Receivers.**—Reception of f.m. signals requires the use of specially constructed receivers. At present, such receivers are of the superheterodyne type, and are designed either for f.m. operation alone, or for both f.m. and a.m. signals, either operation being selected by the shifting of a switch.

The general plan of an f.m. receiver is indicated by the block diagram of Fig. 466. It includes RF, IF and AF amplifiers, an oscillator, a detector or converter, and two other devices to be described later. The RF amplifier does not differ materially from the type used in an a.m. receiver; it serves to amplify the received signals, to increase the selectivity of the receiver, and to prevent oscillations generated by the local oscillator from reaching the antenna or radiating waves to, and interfering with, nearby receivers. The output of the RF amplifier and that of the local oscillator are supplied to the first detector, where currents of the intermediate frequency are generated. The IF amplifier, which follows the first detector, is broadly tuned to this frequency.

To indicate the range over which the IF amplifier must be tuned, assume that the radiation being received is modulated to a deviation of 75 kilocycles per second on either side of the carrier that has a frequency of 42.0 megacycles per second, and assume the intermediate frequency to be fixed at the customary value of

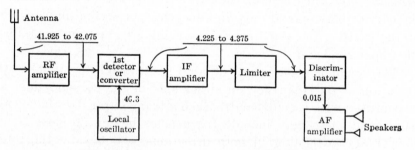

FIG. 466.  Plan of a frequency-modulated receiver
The numbers represent the current frequencies in megacycles per second.

4.3 megacycles per second. The frequency of the oscillator may be either the sum of or the difference between the carrier and intermediate frequencies, §341. As is usual with superheterodyne receivers, whether for a.m. or f.m. operation, the oscillator frequency is taken as the sum frequency; in this case the frequency would be $42.0 + 4.3 = 46.3$ megacycles per second. Obviously, the IF amplifier must be tuned to pass, without appreciable change in amplification, a band of frequencies 75 kilocycles per second on both sides of the intermediate frequency, namely 4.225 to 4.375 megacycles per second. The frequencies of the currents in the various parts of the f.m. receiver are indicated in Fig. 466.

The output of the IF amplifier may be subject to some amplitude modulation that is introduced inadvertently by the circuits employed in the RF and IF amplifiers and the first detector. More important, however, is the undesirable amplitude modulation brought about by static or other electrical noises. The removal of all amplitude modulation, regardless of the cause, is the function of the *limiter*. This device is an IF amplifier stage employing a tube so adjusted as to have the $i_p - e_g$ characteristics shown in Fig. 467.

The outstanding features of the limiter are sharp cut-off and pronounced saturation of plate current $i_p$, both taking place at relatively low values of the signal potential $e_g$ that is applied to the control grid of the tube. This tube and its associated circuit

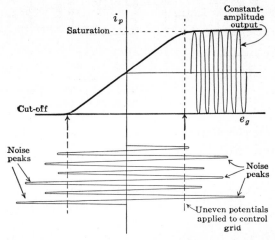

FIG. 467. Action of the limiter in a frequency-modulated receiver

operate at the intermediate frequency and serve as the final stage of the IF amplifier. The figure indicates how an uneven input signal, laden with noise peaks and other forms of amplitude modulation, emerges as a signal of constant amplitude, and is, therefore, free from noise. However, if the input signal to the limiter is not strong enough to drive the tube from cut-off to saturation, as may be the case when a station is sought in a region beyond its normal service area, at least part of the noise present in the signal will pass on and ultimately reach the speakers.

The circuit of a limiter tube is shown in Fig. 468. The pentode (Type 6 SJ 7) has a control grid $CG$, a screen grid $SG$, and a suppressor grid $S$ between the cathode $K$ and plate $P$. The e.m.f. supplied by battery $B$ is about 60 volts.

The signal from the limiter is passed on to the *discriminator*. This stage corresponds somewhat to that of the second detector in an a.m. superheterodyne receiver, but the purpose of the discriminator is to transform the frequency-modulated IF signal to an audio-frequency signal of varying amplitude. A number of circuits are available for this purpose.

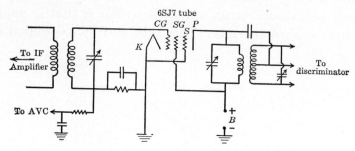

FIG. 468. Circuit of a limiter tube

**345. The Discriminator.**—In order to understand the operation of the discriminator in an f.m. receiver, consideration will first be given to a pair of circuits coupled magneticallly to ascertain the phase relations in them as the frequency of the current is changed. In Fig. 469, the alternating p.d. $E$ in circuit 1 produces a current $i_o$ in it, and establishes a current $i$ of the same frequency in circuit 2. This circuit is composed of coils $L_1$ and $L_2$, assumed to have equal inductance, and a condenser $C$ of fixed capacitance.

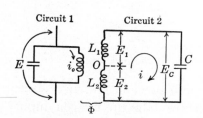

FIG. 469. Circuit supplying power to another coupled to it

When the frequency of $i_o$ in circuit 1 is the same as the resonant frequency of circuit 2, the generated e.m.f. $E_g$ in that circuit will be in phase with the current $i$, and the sum of the counter e.m.f.'s of self-induction in $L_1$ and $L_2$, namely $E_1$ and $E_2$ respectively, will equal the potential drop $E_c$ across the condenser. The magnetic flux $\Phi$ threading all three windings is in phase with $i_o$, which in turn lags the p.d. $E$ in phase by 90 degrees. The generated e.m.f. $E_g$ lags the flux by 90 degrees. Consequently, $E$ is 180 degrees out of phase with $E_g$. These phase relations at resonance are shown in diagram I of Fig. 470.

When the frequency of $i_o$ rises to a value above the resonant frequency of circuit 2, the potential and current relations change to those shown in diagram II. At the higher frequencies circuit 2 becomes inductively reactive, the current $i$ decreases, and the gen-

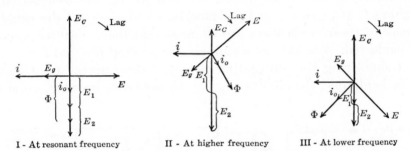

I - At resonant frequency     II - At higher frequency     III - At lower frequency

FIG. 470. Phase relations in a pair of coupled circuits at various frequencies

erated e.m.f. $E_g$ leads this current; $E$ must remain 180 degrees out of phase from $E_g$. On the other hand, when the frequency of $i_o$ drops below that of resonance in circuit 2, this circuit becomes capacitively reactive, the current $i$ decreases, and the generated e.m.f. $E_g$ lags the current; $E$ remains 180 degrees away from $E_g$. Diagram III of the figure represents these relations.

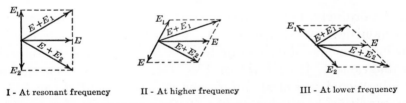

I - At resonant frequency     II - At higher frequency     III - At lower frequency

FIG. 471. Diagrams of potentials active in the operation of the discriminator

In explaining the operation of the discriminator, interest centers about two vector sums, $E$ plus $E_1$ and $E$ plus $E_2$. These potentials from diagrams I, II and III of Fig. 470 are redrawn in Fig. 471, wherein $E$ is shown horizontally in all cases, for convenience. In the diagrams of the latter figure, $E_1$ is reversed in order to show this p.d. with respect to mid-point $O$, Fig. 469. Thus, it may be seen that, at resonance, $E + E_1$ equals in magnitude the sum $E + E_2$. At higher frequencies, $E + E_1$ yields a p.d. greater than $E + E_2$, while at lower frequencies the magnitude of $E + E_2$ is greater than that of $E + E_1$.

The coupled circuits of Fig. 469 are reproduced in Fig. 472 and other elements are added to show the complete circuit of the discriminator. These include the diodes $T_1$ and $T_2$, the load resistors $R_1$ and $R_2$ of equal resistance, the reactor $L_3$, the by-pass condensers $C_1$, $C_2$ and $C_a$, and the blocking condenser $C_b$; the capacitances of these condensers are so large that their reactances may be neglected. The battery terminals are marked $B+$ and $B-$.

Considering the alternating potential drop across $C_a$, $C_2$ and $C_b$ as negligible, the alternating p.d. $E_3$ across $L_3$ becomes equal to

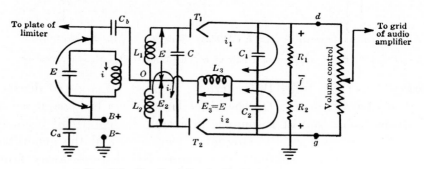

FIG. 472. Circuit of the double-diode discriminator
The diodes $T_1$ and $T_2$ may be within a single envelope.

$E$. Accordingly, the rectified current $i_1$ in the upper diode circuit is established by the p.d. $E + E_1$, while the rectified current $i_2$ in the lower one is establshed by the p.d. $E + E_2$. Thus, by referring to diagrams I, II and III of Fig. 471, it will be seen that the unidirectional potential differences across $R_1$ and $R_2$ are: equal for condition I, greater across $R_1$ than across $R_2$ for condition II, and greater across $R_2$ than across $R_1$ for condition III. This means that, at resonance, the difference of potential between the terminals $d$ and $g$ is zero. For higher frequencies, $i_1$ exceeds $i_2$ and terminal $d$ becomes positive with respect to $g$; at frequencies lower than for resonance, current $i_2$ exceeds $i_1$ and terminal $g$ becomes positive to $d$.

Fig. 473 shows three curves plotted against the frequency of current $i_o$. Curve 1 represents the potential drop $i_1R_1$, produced by the rectified current $i_1$, across points $d$ and $f$ in Fig. 472. Curve 2 shows the drop $i_2 R_2$ from $g$ to $f$ produced by the rectified current $i_2$; it is plotted below the horizontal axis because of the reversal in direction of the potential drop with respect to $f$. The total p.d. between terminals $d$ and $g$ is obtained by adding curves 1

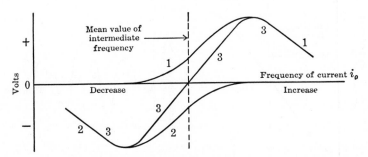

FIG. 473. Variations of potential between terminals $d$ and $g$ of discriminator indicated by curve 3

and 2; the result is curve 3. This curve 3 is the so-called *S-shaped characteristic* of the discriminator, and the practically straight part between the two peaks is the operating zone. It should be remembered that the frequency of $i_o$ is the frequency of the current from the limiter. Applying the output signal of this device to

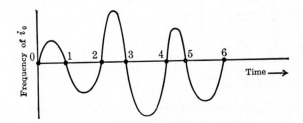

FIG. 474. A frequency-modulated signal

the S-shaped characteristic of the discriminator will reveal the transformation of a frequency-modulated signal to one of audio frequency. The audio output is available between the terminals $d$ and $g$ of the discriminator.

To show the steps involved in the transformation, consider a signal to have the form indicated by the lobes from 0 to 6 in Fig. 474. This is an f.m. signal in the IF range from the limiter plotted as frequency of current $i_o$ against time as abscissas. The manner of converting such a frequency variation into a corresponding amplitude change is indicated in Fig. 475, which shows the frequency-time variation of $i_o$ applied to the characteristic of the

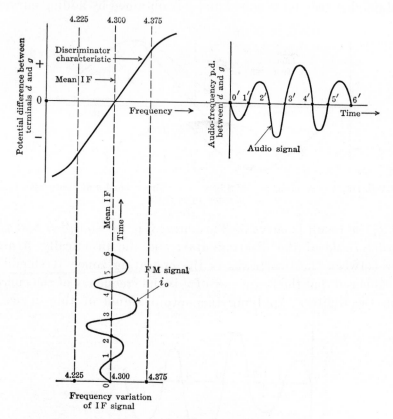

FIG. 475. Transformation of f.m. signal to audio-frequency signal
by the discriminator

Terminals $d$ and $g$ refer to the diagram of Fig. 472, and the frequency values in megacycles per second are those noted in Fig. 466.

discriminator. By projecting points on the curve of $i_o$ upward to the discriminator characteristic and then to the right, there will be obtained the corresponding amplitudes of p.d. available at the terminals of the discriminator. These amplitudes are plotted to a horizontal time scale equal to the vertical time scale of $i_o$, that is, the intervals between points $0'$, $1'$, $2'$, . . . $6'$ on the curve of the resulting audio potentials are equal respectively to the intervals 0, 1, 2, ... 6 on the curve for $i_o$.

Finally, the audio potentials, available between terminals $d$ and $g$ of the discriminator, are applied to a high fidelity audio-frequency amplifier, and this in turn feeds the loud speakers of the f.m. receiver.

The antennas operating with f.m. receivers must function at approximately the same frequencies as those serving television sets; they are described in §356. Frequency modulation is also applicable to carrier current operation over telegraph lines, §312, to reduce the troubles caused by sharp changes of weather.

**346. Power Supply Systems.**—Radio receivers are mostly operated from alternating-current lighting circuits and, consequently, must be equipped to supply the cathode heater currents and the unidirectional potentials needed for the other tube elements of the sets. The equipment, called a *power supply system,* generally comprises a transformer, a diode rectifier, and a filter. The latter is used to smooth the pulsating output of the rectifier so evenly that the unidirectional p.d. at the output will be practically free from ripple.

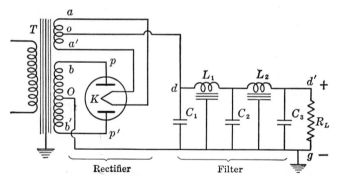

Fig. 476. Full-wave diode rectifier and its filter
The iron cores of transformer $T$ and coils $L_1$ and $L_2$ are grounded.

Fig. 476 shows the connections of a full-wave rectifier operating into a filter and supplying a load represented by $R_L$. The rectifier tube has two plates $p$, $p'$ which are connected to terminals $b$, $b'$ of the high-potential winding of transformer $T$. The filament $K$ of the tube is supplied with power by a low-potential winding

$a$, $a'$ on the same transformer. These windings have center taps at $O$ and $o$ respectively. The filter consists of coils $L_1$ and $L_2$ with condensers $C_1$, $C_2$ and $C_3$.

During the half-cycle when terminal $b$ is positive with respect to the center tap $O$, current will be established in the circuit $b$, $p$, $K$, $o$, $d$, $d'$, $g$, $O$ and back to $b$; this makes $d'$ positive with respect to $g$. During this half-cycle, plate $p'$ is negative with respect to $O$ and is inactive. In the next half-cycle when $p'$ is positive to the filament, there is current in the circuit $b'$, $p'$, $K$, $o$, $d$, $d'$, $g$, $O$ and back to $b'$; this leaves $d'$ still positive with respect to $g$. Thus, the current is unidirectional in the load $R_L$, and only one half of the winding $bb'$ is used during each half-cycle.

The filter depicted is called a *condenser-input filter;* without condenser $C_1$ it would be called a *choke-input filter.* The condenser-input filter is generally recommended only when the rectifier tube is of the vacuum type, such as RCA types 80 and 5Z3. The other is used with gas or vapor-filled tubes, such as RCA types 82 and 83. The choke-input filter is used to prevent possible instantaneous overloads on the rectifier; however, its output affords a lower p.d. than does the condenser-input filter.

The cores and metal casings of transformer $T$ and choke coils $L_1$ and $L_2$ are grounded to the negative side of the system, as are also the metal containers of the condensers, if such are used. This is done to dispose of any induced charges and so prevent the establishment of undesirable potentials on these parts.

The circuit of a half-wave rectifier is the same as in Fig. 476 except that one plate and its associated transformer winding are omitted. In such a circuit there is current through the rectifier only when the plate is positive with respect to the filament. This makes it necessary to construct the filter of larger condensers and inductances, since this network alone must supply the power to the load $R_L$ during the half-cycle when the transformer and tube are inoperative. Usually half-wave rectifiers are not as free from ripples in the output as are full-wave rectifiers.

**347. Facsimile Transmission.**—The commercial transmission of news pictures, maps, cartoons, commercial advertising, and other descriptive material has been in operation for some years over telephone lines, submarine cables and radio networks under the name of facsimile transmission. A number of systems are in use for such service, each one differing somewhat from the others, yet all incorporating certain basic operations. Radio facsimile receivers are now produced at such low cost and of such high degree of reliability that plans have been made to provide radio facsimile broadcasting. A number of radio stations are experimenting with the equipments available and it appears likely that regular facsimile broadcasting may be introduced soon. It is expected that

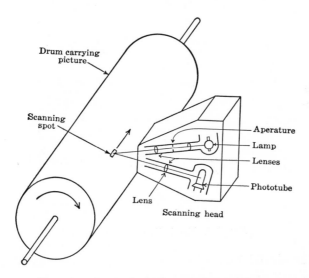

Drum carrying picture
Scanning spot
Aperature
Lamp
Lenses
Phototube
Lens
Scanning head

FIG. 477. Simple facsimile cylindrical scanner

the service will be operated at night, the receiving equipment being turned on and off automatically by means of an electric clock.

The transmission of a picture or page begins with mounting the copy on the cylindrical drum of a *scanner,* and setting this drum in rotation in front of a so-called *scanning head.* This device consists of a lamp, a lens system and a phototube, arranged as in Fig. 477. The light from the lamp is formed into a thin beam by the lens system and this falls upon a tiny spot on the picture; the reflected light from the scanning spot is focused upon the photo-tube. As the cylinder with the picture rotates, the scanning head is moved slowly in a direction parallel to the axis of the cylinder by gears operated from the shaft of the cylinder; by this arrangement every portion of the picture systematically passes the scanning spot. The cylinder revolves about 100 times per minute, and the scanning spot moves about 1 inch per minute. The scanning spot has a size of about 0.010 by 0.006 inch.

When the scanning spot covers a black portion of the picture, the photo-tube receives practically no light; when the spot covers a white portion, it receives a maximum of light. The photo-tube converts the light variations which comprise the picture into correspondingly variable currents; these are amplified and supplied to the receiving instruments. When the transmission is accomplished

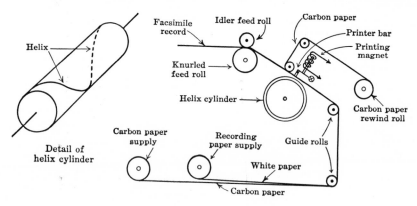

FIG. 478.  Facsimile carbon recorder

by radio, the signal current modulates the carrier wave of the station. Facsimile radio signals are received on superheterodyne receivers employing several stages of IF amplification and incorporating automatic volume control. The output of the second detector is passed on to a powerful audio amplifier before being applied to the *recorder*.

One type of facsimile recorder employed in radio reception makes use of a cylinder having a metal helix protruding slightly from its surface, the helix consisting of a single turn extending over the length of the cylinder, as shown in Fig. 478. The paper used in recording, together with a covering layer of carbon paper, is passed loosely over the helix cylinder. The motion of the paper, about an inch per minute, is controlled by the *knurled feed roll* that is operated through a train of gears from the shaft of a synchronous motor, and the helix cylinder is driven at about 100 revolutions per minute by another gear train from the same motor; as a result the helix cylinder moves in unison with the scanning drum at the transmitter.

A *printing magnet* receives the electrical output of the facsimile receiver; it operates the *printer bar* which extends over the entire length of the helix cylinder. The recording and carbon papers pass between the cylinder and the printer bar. When the set receives a signal corresponding to a black spot on the picture undergoing transmission, the printer bar is forced against the helix cylinder, causing the carbon paper to mark the recording paper at the point where the helix and the printer bar bear on one another. When a signal is received that corresponds to a white spot on the picture, the printer bar is moved away from the cylinder and no marking results. One revolution of the helix cylinder corresponds to one revolution of the scanning drum at the transmitter and records a complete line in the picture. Various synchronizing operations in the receiver make certain that all markings on the recording paper are made in their appropriate places.

The method of facsimile transmission just described requires exact and continuous synchronism between the transmitting and receiving devices. Since electrical power systems are generally not continuously synchronous, but have only constant average frequency, such transmission is practicable only when both the transmitting and receiving equipments receive power from the same source. This requirement limits the range of transmission to the region supplied by the power company. Other, but more complicated, methods are available which overcome this limitation. When facsimile transmission is effected over telephone lines or cables, the same general procedure is employed except that the processing of the signals from the photo-tube at the transmitter is different for each type of circuit.

### QUESTIONS

1. Describe physically how an antenna picks up a radio wave.
2. Explain why a tall antenna collects a stronger signal than does a shorter one.
3. How does a loop antenna operate in receiving a radio signal?
4. State what you understand by the term high fidelity as applied to radio receivers.

5. Show by means of a diagram the construction of an electromagnetic loud speaker.

6. What is a tuned RF receiving set? Explain how this receiver operates.

7. Make a sketch of a pair of coupled circuits, and show how they may be tuned.

8. How does a superheterodyne receiver differ from a tuned RF receiver?

9. What purposes are served by a decoupling network? Where are they used?

10. What is an IF amplifier?

11. How is the IF produced in a superheterodyne set?

12. Explain how radio interference is reduced by using a' superheterodyne receiver.

13. If each tube were allowed to perform one function only, how many tubes would there be in a circuit equivalent to Fig. 459?

14. Give the principle involved in automatic volume control.

15. Show by means of a diagram the difference between a.m. and f.m. reception.

16. In what way does an f.m. wave represent a change of pitch? a change of loudness?

17. Why are the f.m. broadcast channels assigned to such high carrier frequencies?

18. What is the approximate width of the sidebands in f.m. broadcasting? in a.m. broadcasting?

19. What is the function of the first detector in an f.m. receiver?

20. Explain the purpose of a limiter in an f.m. receiver.

21. What is the discriminator in an f.m. set?

22. Explain how a filter removes the ripple or hum in a full-wave rectifier.

23. Describe the recording device of a facsimile transmission system.

## PROBLEMS

1. If the resistor of a decoupling network has a resistance of 0.1 megohm, and the associated condenser is to have a reactance of 0.01 megohm at 455 kilocycles, what should be the capacitance of the condenser? *Ans.* 35 micro-microfarads.

2. Allowing a frequency width of 200 kilocycles per second for every f.m. station, how many channels are provided in the present band of frequencies assigned to f.m. operation between 42 and 50 megacycles per second? *Ans.* 40.

3. An f.m. broadcasting station operates on a frequency of 48 megacycles. If its frequency deviation is limited to 75 kilocycles, what are the values of the limiting frequencies generated by this station? *Ans.* 47.925 to 48.075 megacycles.

4. What should be the frequency of the oscillator in an f.m. receiving set tuned to a 48-megacycle station if the IF amplifier is tuned to 4.3 megacycles? *Ans.* 52.3 megacycles.

# Lesson XXX

## TELEVISION AND NAVIGATIONAL AIDS

Cathode-ray oscilloscope—Electric gun—Saw-tooth wave generators—Vision by electrical means—Iconoscope—Kinescope—Frequency range in television—A typical television receiver—Television receiving antennas—Radio direction finder—Loran—Radar—Other navigational aids—Questions and Problems.

**348. Cathode-Ray Oscilloscope.**—An instrument of great importance in electrical investigations of all sorts is the *cathode-ray oscilloscope*. It makes use of an electron tube of special design for producing a narrow electron beam, for deflecting this beam under controlled conditions, and for observing its motion. The tube comprises a pair of electrodes and two pairs of plates.

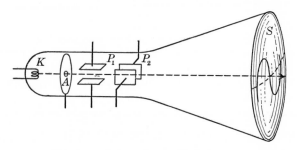

Fig. 479. Cathode-ray oscilloscope tube

The appearance of the cathode-ray tube is shown in Fig. 479. Herein the cathode $K$ is a filament, the anode $A$ is a disk pierced by a hole, and the pairs of plates $P_1$ and $P_2$ are arranged in planes at right angles to each other. Upon heating the filament and maintaining a difference of potential between it and the anode, a stream

of electrons carrying negative charges will pass through the hole
and form what is called a cathode ray. It travels straight ahead
and impinges upon a flourescent screen $S$, producing a tiny luminous spot through excitation of the flourescent material there.

When the plates $P_1$ are charged, the electric field established
between them acts on the electron stream and deflects it; if the
upper plate is positive the electron stream will be deflected upward,
if negative it will be deflected downward. Similarly, when a field
is established between plates $P_2$ the electron stream is deflected
toward or away from the reader depending upon their polarity.

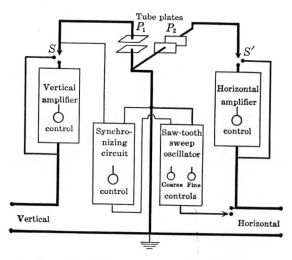

FIG. 480.  Cathode-ray oscilloscope circuits

If the potential differences on the deflecting plates vary from
moment to moment, the electron stream will be deflected accordingly, and the spot on the screen will move about, tracing a luminous pattern that reveals the character of these potential differences.

The cathode-ray oscilloscope includes two high-gain amplifiers, an oscillator of adjustable frequency, and a synchronizing
circuit; these provide a variety of potentials for application to
the tube plates for test purposes. Fig. 480 gives a block diagram
of the circuit arrangement. The outer rectangles represent the
amplifiers, each with a control knob for adjusting the gain. The
amplifier at the left takes the p.d. applied at the lower left terminals
and enlarges it for application to the vertical deflecting plates $P_1$,

and the other amplifier serves the horizontal plates $P_2$ similarly. The amplifiers may be by-passed by turning the switches $S$ and $S'$ to their outer contacts.

When the instrument is used as an oscillograph to show the wave form of an alternating e.m.f., this e.m.f. is included in the circuit of the "vertical amplifier" and its gain is adjusted. If no other provision were made, the trace of the luminous spot would merely be a straight vertical line, its length depending upon the gain employed. However, the trace can be spread out by applying an appropriate p.d. to the input terminals of the "horizontal amplifier." This is usually accomplished by charging the plates $P_2$ at a uniform rate from a condenser and then suddenly discharg-

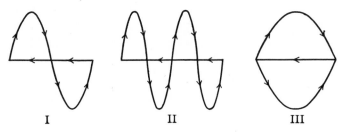

FIG. 481. Oscilloscope traces of a sine wave of e.m.f.

In diagram I the sweep frequency is equal to the frequency of applied p.d.; in II the sweep frequency is half and in III double that of applied p.d. The return sweeps are indicated by horizontal lines.

ing them; each time this is done the luminous spot sweeps across the screen and darts back to the starting point again. The arrangement for obtaining such a to-and-fro motion is called a *saw-tooth sweep oscillator;* it is indicated in the block diagram and has a coarse and a fine adjustment by means of which the frequency of the horizontal motion can be varied. The combination of the two displacements of the spot, therefore, gives a picture on the fluorescent screen of the wave shape of the e.m.f. under investigation.

The frequency of the sweep oscillator can be varied over a wide range. If the frequency is adjusted to coincide with that of the p.d. on the vertical plates $P_1$, the spot will move from left to right while the p.d. goes through exactly one cycle of values, the result will be a steady picture of a complete sine wave as shown at I in Fig. 481. If the frequency of the sweep oscillator is adjusted to be exactly one half that of the p.d. on the vertical plates, the picture on the screen will show two complete waves as at II. When the frequency of the sweep circuit is exactly twice that of the p.d. under investigation the screen will show the loop illustrated at III. The arrows in the figures show the direction in which the luminous spot moves in tracing the wave shapes; of course, these arrows do not appear on the actual screen. The vertical height of the wave trace is controlled by the vertical amplifier, while the horizontal spread of the wave is controlled by the horizontal amplifier.

The synchronizing circuit is employed to facilitate the setting of the frequency of the sweep circuit. A small amount of the p.d. applied to the vertical plates is used to set off, in trigger fashion, the beginning of each sweep of the saw-tooth oscillator. In this way the sweep circuit is, to a degree, locked in step with the wave under study. The degree of locking, or the amount of trigger potential employed, can be controlled and is adjusted to minimum values.

Although not shown in Fig. 480, every oscilloscope includes a power supply system, a focusing control, and a beam intensity control. The focusing control regulates the sharpness of the spot which the electron beam makes on the screen, while the intensity control adjusts the brightness of the spot to the desired amount. The position of the spot on the screen is also adjustable either by means of knobs or by screw-driver controls.

An oscilloscope should always be operated at the minimum of satisfactory brilliance of the pattern on the screen, and the beam should not be allowed to remain stationary too long in one spot for it may burn the fluorescent material on the screen. Attention to these precautions will aid in prolonging the life of a tube.

**349. Electron Gun.**—The arrangement for producing a narrow beam of electrons, for use in a cathode-ray oscilloscope or in other devices, is called an electron gun. It is usually more complicated than that described in the last section where, for simplicity, only two electrodes were considered. The general scheme of an electron gun involves a cathode heated by a filament, a grid, an accelerating electrode, and two anodes. The electron beam originates at the cathode and passes through holes in the thimble-shaped grid and accelerating electrodes, the first being negatively biased and the second positively charged. The grid potential determines the strength of the beam, that is, the number of electrons passing per second through the grid aperture, and the accelerating electrode potential determines the speed of these electrons as they issue from this electrode.

The electron beam next comes under the influence of the first anode, consisting of a metal cylinder with one or more diaphragms, and this serves primarily to focus the beam upon its designated target. The positive potential applied to this anode sets up an electrostatic field which is spoken of as an *electron lens* for the reason that this field focuses the electron beam upon a minute spot in the same manner that an optical lens focuses a beam of light.

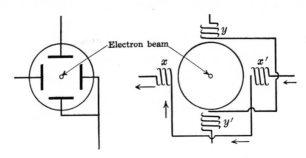

Fig. 482. Electrostatic and electromagnetic methods of deflecting electron beams

The final electrode in the electron gun is the second anode, which carries a high positive potential and serves to accelerate the electrons in the beam to a velocity sufficiently high to produce the desired luminous effect on the target. Often this second or accelerating anode is merely a metallic coating on the inside of the glass envelope of the tube.

Two methods are available for deflecting the electron beam laterally to cover all points of the target. One of these is the electrostatic method already described in the last section, and the other is the electromagnetic method. The end-on view of the tube showing the plates used in electrostatic deflection appears at the left in Fig. 482. These electrodes are *inside* of the glass envelope and generally two adjacent ones are connected and brought out to a common terminal. If the top plate is made positive the beam will move vertically upward, and if negative it will move vertically downward. Similar action takes place sideways if the polarity on the left- and right-hand plates is altered. Thus, by changing the polarity and the amounts of charge on the two sets of electrodes, the beam may be shifted to any desired position within range.

Electromagnetic deflection of an electron beam is accomplished by means of two sets of coils located *outside* the glass envelope of the electron gun, as shown at the right in Fig. 482. Since an electron beam is a current of electricity, such a beam will be shifted if acted upon by a magnetic field, §104. Assume the beam of electrons as moving toward the reader. If the current in coils $xx'$ is directed as indicated by the arrows, the magnetic field will extend from right to left through the tube and the electron beam will be deflected vertically upward. This action can be verified by remembering that a beam of negative electric charges moving in one direction is equivalent to an electric current in the opposite direction. Obviously, a reversal of the field produced by coils $xx'$ would move the beam downward. A downward magnetic field produced by coils $yy'$ results in a motion of the beam to the left, while an upward field from these coils moves the beam to the right. Magnetic fields resulting from the combined action of currents in coils $xx'$ and $yy'$ may be used to shift the beam to any desired position.

The electron gun with its electrodes for electrostatic deflection or its coils for magnetic deflection is used in various electrical measuring devices and indicators as well as in the transmission and recepton of television signals.

**350. Saw-tooth Wave Generator.**—The manner in which the saw-tooth wave generator operates, in connection with the cathode-ray oscilloscope, television apparatus, and other devices, can be explained by considering the effect of introducing a source of unidirectional e.m.f. in a series circuit having resistance and capacitance. Fig. 483 shows the circuit and illustrates its electrical behavior. The instantaneous current produced by the source of e.m.f. $E$ is shown as $i;$ the potential drop across the condenser $C$ is represented by $E_C$ and that across the resistor $R$ is represented by $E_R$. As the condenser charges, building up the potential difference $E_C$ across its terminals, the current falls to zero and the potential drop across the resistor falls proportionately. These facts are indicated by the curves of potential against time. The sum of the ordinates of the two curves is equal to $E$ at all instants, that is, $E = E_R + E_C$.

The combination of a circuit as described and a gas discharge tube results in a saw-tooth wave generator. Fig. 484 shows the circuit and indicates the wave shape produced by it. When the e.m.f. $E$ is first introduced, the p.d. across the condenser $C$ will

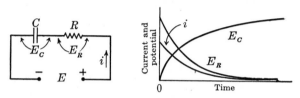

FIG. 483. Current and potential variation in a circuit having resistance and capacitance

rise as shown by the curve $E_C$. Between $O$ and $a$, this potential rise will be almost a straight line if the circuit is properly adjusted. Let $E_1$ be the plate potential which causes a plate current to be established in the gas discharge tube for the value of grid bias employed. Then, when $E_C$ reaches the value $E_1$, the gas tube operates, and the p.d. between the plate and filament drops almost instantly along the line $aa'$. When the value of $E_C$ reaches $E_2$,

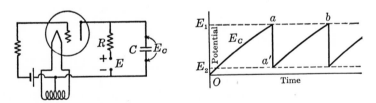

FIG. 484. Circuit of a saw-tooth oscillator or sweep circuit and its operation

not enough current is supplied by source $E$ through resistor $R$ to sustain the ionization in the discharge tube. As a result, the current through the tube ceases, its shunt path around condenser $C$ is eliminated, and the condenser begins to charge through resistor $R$ once more. This builds the potential $E_C$ again to the value $E_1$, this time along the line $a'b$. In this way the operation is repeated over and over again, yielding the saw-tooth wave shape of p.d. illustrated; this is available across the condenser terminals.

If the saw-tooth wave is applied to the horizontal deflection plates of an electrostatically controlled electron gun, its electron beam will be moved horizontally until the potential $E_1$ is reached, at which instant the potential falls quickly to $E_2$ and the beam returns to its starting point. Thus, the beam is swept from right to left, or vice versa, at a definite speed, and is returned at the end of its travel almost instantly to the starting point. For this reason this type of generator is also known as a *sweep circuit*.

When the beam of an electron gun is deflected magnetically, the output p.d. of the saw-tooth generator is applied to the grid of a vacuum tube, and the deflecting coils are connected to its plate circuit.

**351. Vision by Electrical Means.**—The art of reproducing a scene at a distance by means of electrical transmission, called *television,* has made rapid progress in recent years. The technique of television involves the subdivision of the scene into tiny picture areas, the conversion of the illumination of each area into an electrical signal, the orderly transmission of these signals over wire lines or by radio waves, the reversion of the signals at the receiving station into corresponding light pulses, and the reassembly of these pulses in correct sequence to form an image of the original scene. The process is continued repeatedly by scanning the scene 25 times or more per second, and the successive images merge to produce a steady picture because of a peculiarity of the eye called *persistence of vision.* This retentivity of the eye for short periods is also utilized in motion pictures, where the illusion of motion is brought about by projecting a series of still pictures in such rapid succession that the image of one is retained until the next is projected, thereby creating the impression of continuity.

The principal devices needed in television are electron tubes of special design for scanning the scene at one place and reproducing the picture at another. In the RCA television system these tubes are called the *iconoscope* and the *kinescope* respectively; in both, the electron beams are moved to and fro by means of magnetic deflecting coils. Saw-tooth oscillators are used in connection with these tubes for scanning, and the oscillators at the transmitting and receiving stations operate at the same frequency and are kept in step by suitable synchronizing pulses.

**352. Iconoscope.**—In the RCA television system the iconoscope tube is used to convert the variations in light which constitute the scene to be televised into corresponding electrical variations. In its most recent form, the iconoscope is also called the *orthocron*. The major components of this tube, shown in Fig. 485, are the electron gun, its electromagnetic deflecting system, and the screen with its mosaic of photosensitive particles on one side and the signal plate on the other. The second anode is a metallic coating deposited as a ring on the inside of the glass envelope.

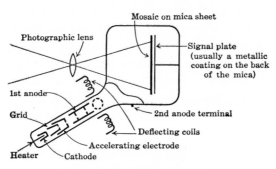

FIG. 485. The RCA iconoscope

The *mosaic* consists of innumerable tiny globules that are photosensitive, which means that they emit electrons under the influence of light. When a scene is focused by the camera lens on the mosaic, each globule emits a number of electrons that is proportional to the amount of light falling upon it. The excess of these electrons, those not attracted to other parts of the mosaic, are collected by the second anode and removed from the tube. Since the globules are insulated from the signal plate by a mica sheet and each globule is virtually insulated from its neighbors, various differences of potential are built up between the elements of the mosaic and the signal plate. These p.d.'s are respectively proportional to the number of electrons emitted by the globules as the result of the light falling upon them.

The electron beam from the gun scans the picture on the mosaic, by moving across it from left to right. This motion of the beam is brought about by a saw-tooth wave of current in the horizontal deflecting coils, as described in §350. When the beam reaches the limit of its travel to the right, it is brought back very quickly to the left in order to begin the scanning of the next line. But while the beam is moving from left to right in the scanning of the first line, the vertical deflecting coil is also operating with a saw-tooth wave generator. The current in this coil moves the beam slowly downward, so that when the beam is returned to the left after scanning the first line it will be in a position to begin the scanning of another line located below the first one. This process continues until the lowest line is scanned, after which the beam is returned quickly to the upper left corner of the mosaic, there to begin a repetition of the whole scanning process.

As the electron beam scans the mosaic, those electrons that were emitted photoelectrically from the globules by the picture focused on the mosaic are replaced by electrons from the beam. The excess electrons are again collected by the second anode and removed. The p.d. between each globule and the signal plate is neutralized, and an electrical pulse is transmitted to the amplifier to which this plate is connected.

Thus, in televising a scene, the camera lens throws a picture of the scene on the iconoscope mosaic and electrons are liberated by the minute sensitized globules which constitute the elements of the mosaic. An element located in a bright part of the picture emits a large number of electrons, while a globule in a darker region emits fewer of them. This emission converts the mosaic into a very large number of charged condensers, each condenser consisting of an individual globule and the signal plate which is back of them all. The mosaic is scanned by the electron beam of the gun, and as each globule is replenished with electrons equal in number to those previously liberated, the tiny condenser is discharged, and the signal plate passes an electrical impulse or signal to the amplifier. The magnitude of each signal is proportional to the amount of light falling on the respective globule in the mosaic. Since the scanning is done in an orderly sequence, the picture may be reconstructed from the signals transmitted by reversing the process at the receiving instrument. The signals resulting from the scanning process in the iconoscope are known as *video signals,* which, freely translated from the Latin, means signals of vision or sight.

**353. Kinescope.**—The device in which the process carried out in the iconoscope is reversed to reconstruct the scene originally televised is called a *kinescope.* It is a tube for converting the video impulses from the transmitting station into minute luminous spots on the fluorescent screen at the receiving station. The transmission between the stations takes place by radio methods; a

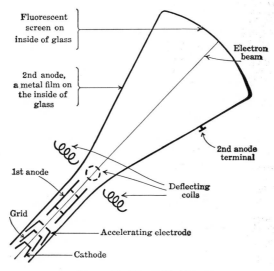

Fig. 486. The RCA kinesope

high-frequency carrier is modulated by the video signals, the short waves are launched and picked up by suitable antennas, and the received currents are amplified and rectified for application to the kinescope.

The design of the kinescope is indicated in Fig. 486; it comprises an electron gun, magnetic deflecting coils, and a screen. The amplified and rectified video signals are applied to the grid and thereby control the intensity of the electron beam; this beam is thus modulated by the signals. The other electrodes of the gun serve to accelerate the electrons and focus the beam upon the fluorescent screen, producing a luminous spot at the point of impact. The currents in the deflecting coils cause this spot to move in the same manner as the beam sweeping over the mosaic of the iconoscope. As the spot on the kinescope moves across the screen, the brilliance of fluorescence changes from point to point under the action of the signals impressed upon the grid. These changes conform to the variations of light and shade in the picture on the iconoscope mosaic, and the picture is reconstructed on the kinescope screen. Since the scanning of a scene in the iconoscope and its reconstruction in the kinescope proceed at a high speed, the eye sees only the composite picture and not the individual luminous points of it. This blending takes place in the eye in the same manner that a number of rapidly changed still pictures give the impression of motion in motion pictures.

As in the iconoscope, the kinescope beam is deflected by pairs of coils placed at right angles to each other and actuated by saw-tooth waves of current. Since the position of the beam in the kinescope must correspond exactly with that of the iconoscpe, *synchronizing pulses* are included in the waves sent out by the transmitter. These synchronizing pulses are separated at the receiver and made to control very accurately the timing of the current in the kinescope deflecting coils.

**354. Frequency Range in Television.**—In order to appreciate certain problems in television, it is necessary to know the width of the sidebands which are needed in this kind of radio transmission. To calculate this width, consideration is given to the most complicated picture to be scanned and to the frequencies that are involved in the scanning process. It is found that such a picture must be divided into 525 lines to meet present-day criteria of satisfactory television. This means that the beams of the electron guns in both iconoscope and kinescope must travel horizontally from left to right 525 times in going from the upper-left corner of the mosaic or screen to the lower-right corner. With this number of lines, the greatest detail in scanning and reproduction would be necessary in transmitting a picture consisting of 525 lines of alternate black and white *squares*.

A section of such a black and white pattern is shown at I in Fig. 487. The variation of light resulting from the scanning of the lowest line of squares in I is indicated at II, and the corresponding electrical pulses delivered by the iconoscope assume

somewhat the same character. Curve III represents the fundamental sinusoidal component of II, and will be considered for
present purposes as the equivalent of curve II. It is evident that
one cycle of this fundamental wave includes one complete black
square and one complete white one.

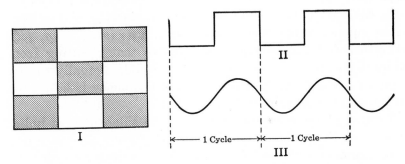

FIG. 487. Translation of black and white pattern into sinusoidal current

To find the frequency range of video signals for transmitting
a rectangular scene, let

$n$ = number of scanning lines in the scene,
$K$ = *aspect ratio* of the scene, that is, the ratio of its width to height,
$F$ = number of complete pictures or *frames* transmitted per second.

Then the frequency range of currents to be transmitted has the
theoretical maximum value of $\frac{1}{2} \times n \times (n \times K) \times F$, or the frequency range is

$$f_m = \frac{n^2 \times K \times F}{2} \qquad\qquad \textbf{144}$$

and this is also the maximum width of the sidebands.

**Problem 173.**—What is the maximum width of television sidebands for
the transmission of 30 frames per second with 525-line scanning, assuming
the width of the picture to be 4/3 of its height.

With 525-line scanning, there will be $4/3 \times 525$ or 700 black or white
elements in each line. Since a black square and its succeeding white one
represents a complete electrical cycle, it follows that 700/2 or 350 cycles
will be transmitted while one line is being scanned. As 525 lines are traced
in 1/30 second, the frequency range will be $350 \times 525 \times 30$ or 5,512,500
cycles per second. This result can be verified by applying Formula (144);
thus

$$f_m = \frac{n^2 \times K \times F}{2} = \frac{(525)^2 \times 4/3 \times 30}{2} = 5{,}512{,}500 \text{ per second}$$

The use of 30 frames per second would result in noticeable flicker. To reduce this effect and to keep the maximum theoretical frequency of modulation to the value calculated above, each frame is scanned in two *fields*. In the first field only the odd-numbered lines are scanned, and in the second only the even-numbered ones. Then, upon completing the scanning of the last odd-numbered line in the first field, the second is begun by starting at the left end of line number two. This process, known as *interlacing*, reduces flicker to a value approximately equal to that resulting from an apparent frequency of 60 frames per second. Actually the frame frequency remains at 30 while the field frequency is 60 interlaced half-frames per second.

Because of the enormous width of the sidebands, as indicated in the foregoing problem, television transmission must be allocated in the region of ultra-high frequencies in the radio band. The sound signals associated with television transmission are carried on an f.m. channel 0.5 megacycle wide and located 0.25 megacycle down from the upper limit of the band allocated to each station. A guard band 0.25 megacycle wide is held vacant between the sound channel and the video channel. The four megacycle band below the guard region is allocated to carry the upper sideband of the video transmission. Since a 5.5125-megacycles band should be available for this purpose, all American stations must filter their upper sidebands in order that they may conform to the 4-megacycle band available. In addition, the lower sideband of these stations is filtered sharply so that only a vestigial sideband 1.25 megacycles wide remains.

The band allocated to television station WNBT, for example, is from 66 to 72 megacycles. The sound is carried on an f.m. channel 0.5 megacycle wide with its carrier at 71.75 megacycles. The guard channel is from 71.25 to 71.50 megacycles. The video carrier is at 67.25 megacycles. The vestigial and upper sidebands are from 66 to 67.25 megacycles and 67.25 to 71.25 megacycles respectively.

**355. A Typical Television Receiver.**—In order to gain a general understanding of the operation of a modern television receiver, a block diagram will be employed. Fig. 488 shows such a diagram for a typical receiver. The antenna receives both picture and sound carrier signals, and passes them on to the radio-frequency selector, by means of which the desired station is tuned in. This selector is an RF amplifier. The output of this selector and that of a local oscillator are fed to the first detector which reduces the frequencies of the picture and sound carriers to, say, 26.1 and 21.6 megacycles per second respectively. These are supplied to the intermediate-frequency amplifiers, which are respectively tuned to these frequencies. The width of the IF bands are approximately 4.0 and 0.3 megacycles for the video and audio channels, respectively. Two stages of IF amplification are used in the typical

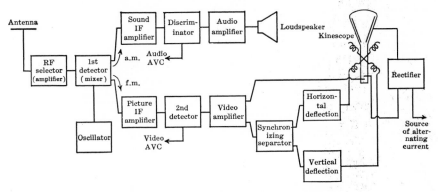

Fig. 488. Block diagram of a typical television set

television receiver for the sound amplifier and five stages for the IF picture amplifier.

The sound channel continues to the discriminator where the audio component is separated from its intermediate-frequency carrier. At this point the automatic volume control (AVC), when employed, is tapped in and arranged to modify the gain of the sound channel. Thereafter, the audio signal is passed through the conventional audio amplifier to the speaker.

The picture channel continues from the intermediate amplifier to its second detector, where the AVC for the picture network is taken, and then to the video amplifier. Here the synchronizing pulses are separated from the video signals, the former passing on and controlling the deflecting circuits, while the latter are applied to the grid of the kinescope to control the illumination of its screen.

The last block includes a high-potential rectifier to supply the anodes and accelerating electrodes of the kinescope with rectified and filtered potentials; these are as high as 7000 volts in some receivers. It also includes a low-potential rectifier, to supply the plate potentials for the various amplifier tubes, and a low-potential alternating-current supply for the cathode heaters for all the tubes of the set.

**356. Television Receiving Antennas.**—Radio waves of short length, such as those now employed in television service, appear

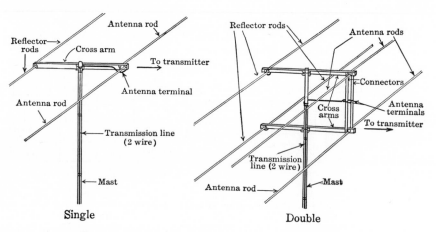

FIG. 489. Television receiving antennas with reflectors

to travel in straight lines and do not follow the earth's surface as do the longer waves used in ordinary broadcasting service. In consequence, television receiving antennas must be designed and installed with much greater care than is exercised with antennas serving the broadcast band of frequencies.

Present practice in television receiving antennas generally specifies a single or a double *dipole antenna,* with or without *reflectors.* A reflector reduces interference and also assists the antenna in picking up the desired signals; its use results generally in a very substantial increase in signal strength. Reflectors are not connected electrically to the antennas. Fig. 489 shows two types of television dipole antennas; the one at the left is single and the other double.

A dipole antenna is generally designed so that its overall length is one-half the wavelength of the waves to be received. If the signals extend over a band of frequencies as in television, the length of the antenna is based on the geometric average wavelength of the band. Taking $f'$ as the frequency in megacycles per second, the overall length of the dipole, expressed in feet, should be

$$L = \frac{492}{f'} \qquad\qquad 145$$

Thus, if an antenna is to serve the band between 60 and 80 megacycles per second, the overall length for the geometric average frequency of $\sqrt{60 \times 80} = 69.3$ megacycles is 7.1 feet, and the length of each rod constituting half of the single dipole antenna is about 42.6 inches. This length is the same for single and double dipoles.

The reflector rods for a television antenna are somewhat longer than the antenna rods. For a frequency of 69.3 megacycles, the overall length of the reflector should be about 7.5 feet, and each reflector rod should measure 45 inches. It should be placed behind the antenna and at a distance yielding the strongest signal, as determined by experiment. In the case of the 69.3 megacycle antenna mentioned, the proper separation of the antenna and its reflector is about 22 inches. The vertical distance between the two sets of antenna rods (and between the two sets of reflectors) is 2 feet. The rods are generally of copper plated steel $\frac{5}{16}$ inch in diameter.

**357. Radio Direction Finder.**—The so-called *radio direction finder* makes it possible to determine, with good accuracy, the direction from which radio waves are being received. It most important application is in the navigation of vessels and airplanes. Bearings may be taken on distant known stations and the location of the direction finder may be determined by triangulation. The finder consists primarily of a vertically-pivoted loop of wire, say 3 feet square and with perhaps ten turns of light wire; this loop is shunted with a variable condenser, and connected to some type of radio receiving apparatus containing an amplifier.

Suppose that the loop, tuned by the condenser, is turned so that its plane is at right angles to the direction of the radio waves to

be received. Then each wave meets both vertical conductors of the
loop at the same instant, and equal but opposing e.m.f.'s are
induced in them. Their resultant is continually zero, and there
will be no current in the loop. When the plane of the loop is turned
parallel to the direction of the wave, the resultant e.m.f. induced
in the loop will be a maximum. Thus, the amount of energy received
by the loop depends upon the angle which
the loop makes with the wave.

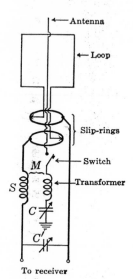

FIG. 490. Radio direc-
tion finder

A pointer, attached to the
frame of the loop and lo-
cated below the slip-rings,
moves over a circular scale
and indicates the bearings.

When the loop is turned to the position of
minimum response, the signals will be coming
from a direction which is at right angles to
the plane of the loop. With the loop in this
position, a very slight change in the angle
between it and the direction of wave propagation makes a great difference in the amount
of energy received and, therefore, in the
strength of the signals. Consequently, the
apparatus is very sensitive when in this position. On the other hand, it is quite insensitive
when the plane of the loop is pointing toward
the transmitting station, because a large
change in the angle produces only a small
change in the strength of the signals.

A loop antenna by itself can be used only
to determine the line along which radio
waves travel from the transmitter to the loop,
for when the loop is turned to such a position
that no signal is received, it is impossible to tell which side of the
loop faces the transmitter. Uncertainty also prevails when the loop
is turned to the position of maximum response, for then it is not
known which edge of the loop points to the transmitter. However,
if a vertical antenna is used in combination with the loop, it is
possible to determine the *sense* of direction from which the radio
waves are being received.

Fig. 490 shows how a small vertical antenna may be combined
with a vertical loop to form a direction finder. The variable condensers C and C' are used in the antenna and loop circuits respectively to tune these circuits to the frequency of the signals to be
received. Generally, the e.m.f. developed in the antenna is much

stronger than the one generated in the loop, and a reduction may be effected by means of the variable radio-frequency transformer $M$.

The response curve of a loop and of a vertical antenna are shown in Fig. 491 at I and II respectively. When the radio waves come from $a$ or $a'$ along the line $aa'$, the *magnitude* of the e.m.f. generated in the loop is proportional to the lengths $op$ or $op'$ in diagram I. Since these lengths are equal, the loop makes no distinction between waves traveling from $a$ to $a'$ and from $a'$ to $a$. The e.m.f. generated in the vertical antenna is proportional to the radius of the circle $q$ in diagram II.

The combination of the loop and vertical antennas yields the response curve shown at I in Fig. 492 by the heavy line; it is called

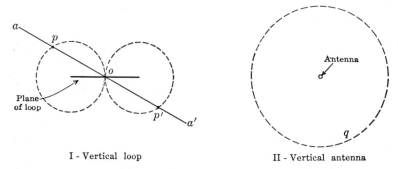

I - Vertical loop                    II - Vertical antenna

FIG. 491. Response curves of loop and straight antennas

a cardioid and is formed by adding the response curves of Fig. 491. Suppose the signal wave is moving from $a$ to $a'$; the cardioid indicates that the response will be proportional to $oq + op$, which is $or$. If the loop is next turned through 180 degrees, the loop e.m.f. remains unchanged in magnitude, but its phase is shifted through 180 degrees to position $op'$. Thus, the resultant e.m.f. is now proportional to $oq - op'$, and since $oq = oq'$, the response is proportional to $oq' - op'$, which is $or'$. In this way the sense of the approaching signal is determined as well as its direction.

Diagram II in Fig. 492 shows the directions of the potentials induced in the loop and antenna when the loop is in the plane of the waves traveling in the direction $a$-$a'$. This diagram shows the output e.m.f. to be equal to the net loop e.m.f. $(e_1 - e_3)$ plus the antenna e.m.f. $e_2$. This condition corresponds to the sum $oq + op = or$ as indicated in diagrams I and II. When the loop is turned through 180 degrees, the e.m.f.'s are as shown in diagrams I and III, where the output is $(e_1 - e_3) - e_2$, corresponding

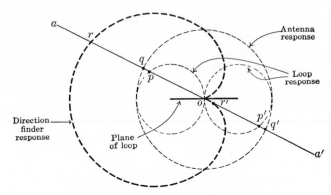

I - Combination of loop and antenna

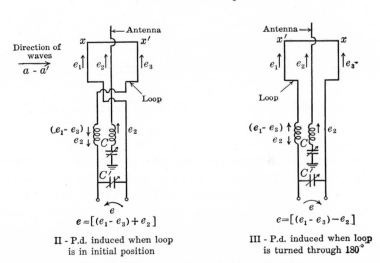

$$e = [(e_1 - e_3) + e_2]$$

II - P.d. induced when loop
is in initial position

$$e = [(e_1 - e_3) - e_2]$$

III - P.d. induced when loop
is turned through 180°

FIG. 492. Response of a radio direction finder

to the condition $oq' - op' = or'$. Since only alternating e.m.f.'s are under consideration, the reversal of $e$ in the two diagrams would not affect the receiver used in detecting the signals. It should be remembered that while $e_1$ and $e_3$ are practically of the same magnitude, they are out of phase and hence their difference is not zero.

**Problem 174.**—A square loop, 1 meter on each side, is used to receive a 50-megacycle signal. If the e.m.f. induced in each vertical side of the loop is 1 millivolt, calculate the net p.d. developed in the loop.

Since the distance between the vertical sides of the loop is 1 meter and the velocity of wave propagation is $3 \times 10^8$ meters per second, the time required for the waves to pass from one vertical side to the other is $1 \div 3 \times 10^8$ second. In this time interval the 50-megacycle wave will pass through

$$\frac{50 \times 10^6}{3 \times 10^8} = 0.167 \text{ cycle} = 0.167 \times 360° = 60°$$

Hence, the two e.m.f.'s are 60 degrees apart in phase. Since they are opposed to each other, the resultant is found by adding two vectors, each representing 1 millivolt, drawn 120 degrees apart. The result is $2 \times 1 \times \cos 60° = 1$ millivolt.

In operation, the loop is turned to the position of maximum signal, or in line $aa'$, with the antenna switch open. Then the switch is closed and the coupling of transformer $M$ is adjusted until the signal received by the combination is zero with the loop in one position, and a maximum with the loop turned through 180 degrees. Under this adjustment the signal delivered to winding $S$ by the antenna is equal in magnitude to the e.m.f. generated in the loop.

All radio direction finders are calibrated by moving a visible transmitter about the finder. This procedure checks the operation of the finder from all angles and determines which edge of the loop faces the advancing wave when the zero-maximum response test is made. After the sense of the advancing wave has been determined, the antenna is switched off and the loop is used alone to determine the position of zero signal. As was pointed out ahead, this position brings the loop into a plane exactly perpendicular to the line of travel of the wave.

**358. Loran.**—One of the scientific developments of World War II that is now proving a valuable aid in navigation is known as "Loran," an abbreviation of *long range navigation*. It is an electronic means for determining the position of a ship or an airplane within a few minutes even in the thickest fog. The system can fix such positions up to 750 miles in daylight and to 1400 miles at night, and the observations do not need correction as do celestial observations. The basic measurement in loran is the *time* of arrival of radio frequency signals from pairs of shore stations and not the *direction* of arrival of such signals as in the direction finder.

The transmitting stations operate in pairs 24 hours a day and radiate in all directions. One station of a pair is called the *master* and the other the *slave* station; there are located from 200 to 400 miles apart. Both send out short pulses at the same recurrence rate, such as 25 per second, while other pairs of stations transmit similar pulses at other definite recurrence rates. The use of pulse signals with individual recurrence rates permits the pulses to be identified at the receiving station, and the difference of the times of their arrival there to be measured. By making such a measurement the navigator at sea or in the air can fix his position by the aid of charts or tables. The charts show families of *loran lines,* one family of lines for each pair of transmitting stations. These lines for a single pair of stations bear symbols that identify the pair and also individual numbers that show the several time differences. The accuracy of a "fix" varies with the distance from the base line between stations; at 1000 miles the error will be less than 5 miles, but nearer the base line the error will be within half a mile.

Loran transmitting stations are identified by the radio frequency of the pulse signal and by the pulse recurrence rate. Four channels of radio frequency are now used, and there are two basic recurrence rates, Low and High, each with eight specific rates, as follows:

RADIO FREQUENCY

| Channel | Kilocycles per Second |
|---------|-----------------------|
| 1 | 1950 |
| 2 | 1850 |
| 3 | 1900 |
| 4 | 1750 |

RECURRENCE RATES

| Specific Rate | Basic Rate (Pulses per second) | |
|---------------|-----|------|
| | Low | High |
| 0 | 25 | $33\frac{3}{9}$ |
| 1 | $25\frac{1}{16}$ | $33\frac{4}{9}$ |
| 2 | $25\frac{2}{16}$ | $33\frac{5}{9}$ |
| 3 | $25\frac{3}{16}$ | $33\frac{6}{9}$ |
| 4 | $25\frac{4}{16}$ | $33\frac{7}{9}$ |
| 5 | $25\frac{5}{16}$ | $33\frac{8}{9}$ |
| 6 | $25\frac{6}{16}$ | 34 |
| 7 | $25\frac{7}{16}$ | $34\frac{1}{9}$ |

The individual signal pulse lasts only 40 millionths of a second, or 40 microseconds. On the 1900-kilocycle channel there would be $1,900,000 \times 0.00004 = 76$ cycles to each pulse.

Fig. 493 represents a portion of a loran map showing the location of the master station at $A$ and the slave station at $B$, together with a few of the loran lines associated with that pair of trans-

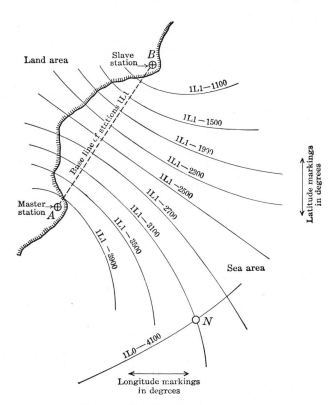

FIG. 493. Portion of a Loran map

mitting stations. The lines bear the symbols 1L1, showing that the stations transmit on Channel 1 (1950 kilocycles) with the L (low) recurrence band using the specific rate 1 ($25\frac{1}{16}$ cycles). Should a navigator receive these signals and measure the time difference of signals from the stations as 3100 microseconds, he would know that he is somewhere along the loran line marked 1L1-3100. He then tunes in a second pair of stations, say the adjacent pair 1L0, which also operates on 1950 kilocycles but with a pulse recurrence rate of 25 cycles. If his time-difference measurement is now 4100 microseconds he will know that he is also located along the loran line 1L0-4100. Hence he must be at the intersection of lines 1L1-3100 and 1L0-4100, or at $N$ in Fig. 493. He can then read the latitude and longitude (omitted from the figure) of point $N$ and the fix is made.

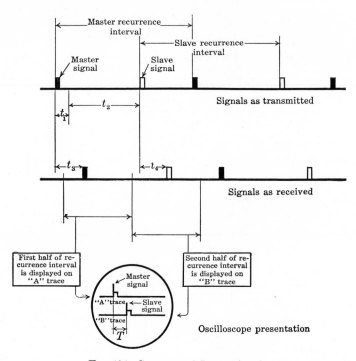

FIG. 494. Sequence of Loran signals

When the master station transmits a signal pulse it travels in all directions and is received by the slave station and all loran receivers within range. The slave station, upon receiving the master pulse and after a predetermined delay, sends out a similar pulse which also reaches all loran receivers within range. These events are repeated over and over again at intervals which, for different pairs of stations, occur from 25 to 34⅓ times per second, as previously listed.

The timing of the signal pulses is shown in Fig. 494. The heavy upper line indicates the time intervals between the transmitted signals, and the lower line shows the intervals between these signals as received. The symbols represent

$t_1$ = time required for master signal to reach slave station,
$t_2$ = time that the slave station waits before sending its signal; it is half the pulse recurrence interval plus an assigned coding delay,
$t_3$ = time required for master signal to travel to receiver,
$t_4$ = time required for slave signal to travel to receiver,
$T$ = loran time difference to be measured.

The signals are received by a navigator on a radio instrument which includes a cathode ray oscilloscope. The appearance of the rectified signals on an oscilloscope screen is shown at the bottom of the figure.

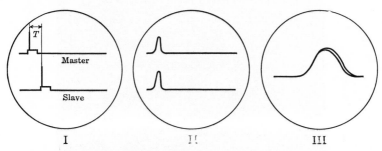

FIG. 495. Signal patterns on oscilloscope screen of Loran receiver
I—Slow sweep; II—Medium-speed sweep; III—Fast sweep.
The time difference to be measured is $T$.

The receiver tunes automatically to any of the loran channels somewhat in the manner of a radio broadcast receiver equipped with pushbuttons. The selection of the recurrence rate involves two controls, one for the basic rate, $L$ or $H$, and the other for the specific rate, 0 to 7. The horizontal sweep on the oscilloscope trace is broken into two equal parts which appear one above the other. The signal from the master station is presented on the upper half and that from the slave station on the lower half, as shown in the figure, and the time difference to be measured is marked $T$. It is this difference of time which determines the navigator's position as along some one loran line associated with the two stations involved.

The time difference may be measured on the oscilloscope scale directly or, more accurately, by aligning or superposing the signal traces by means of coarse and fine delay controls in the receiver. With a slow sweep the rectified signals appear on the screen as vertical lines extending above pedestals, as indicated at I in Fig. 495. With a medium speed sweep the pedestal tops are stretched across the screen as shown at II, and here the signals are aligned vertically. With a fast sweep the signal lobes are expanded further as shown at III, and here the signals are superposed so that their left edges match. When the adjustment

FIG. 496. Control panel of Loran receiver

Sperry Gyroscope Company

has been made the designation for a loran position line, such as 1L1-3100, is read directly from the dials of the control panel. Fig. 496 shows such a panel for a loran receiver; the setting indicates loran line 1H0-0610.

Loran service is already available over almost half of the entire earth's surface. In this country the service is rendered by the U. S. Coast Guard and the maps and tables are obtainable from the U. S. Hydrographic Office at Washington, D. C.

**359. Radar.**—The method of ranging by radio waves, conceived before the recent war and developed tremendously during that conflict, is called "Radar," a contraction of *radio detection and* *r*anging. The technique is now being adopted as a peacetime aid for aerial and marine navigation. Aerial navigators may use radar, when vision is obstructed, to determine altitude, location of mountains, and positions of other aircraft in flight. Marine navigators may use the system at night or in fog to locate coast-lines, icebergs, buoys, and other ships.

The basic principle of radar is the reflection of radio waves from solid objects and the detection of the reflected waves at the same station from which the waves originated. Since the velocity of the waves is known, it is only necessary to measure the time which elapses between the transmission of radio-frequency pulses and the arrival of the reflected waves in order to locate the object which caused the reflection. The effective range of a marine radar extends from a circle of about 100-yard radius around the ship outward to the horizon, which may be from 10 to 15 miles away depending on the height of the antenna. Elevated areas, as well as tall

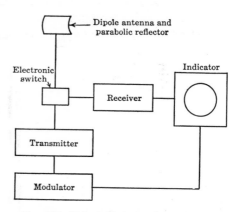

FIG. 497. Principal parts of a radar set

structures beyond the horizon, can also be located as far away as 30 miles if they are in a direct line from the transmitting antenna.

Radar equipment includes an antenna, the transmitter and its modulator, the receiver and its indicator, and the usual power supply systems and auxiliary circuits. The principal elements are indicated in the block diagram of Fig. 497.

The antenna is generally a dipole, §356, with a parabolic reflector; the purpose of the reflector is to focus radio waves into a narrow beam in the same way that the parabolic reflector of a searchlight concentrates light into a pencil-like beam. The antenna assembly is rotated continuously when in use. For this reason its size should be limited, yet the reflector must be large with respect to the length of the radio waves in order that it may reflect them effectively. Both objectives can be met by using very short waves, say from 3 to 10 centimeters long.

The transmitter has an oscillator of special design to generate the very short waves needed in radar; the frequencies corresponding to the wavelength range of from 3 to 10 centimeters are respectively 10,000 to 3000 megacycles per second. The modulator causes the transmitter to radiate its signals in short pulses, usually of 1 microsecond or less, with a recurrence rate of about 1000 pulses per second. The pulses are of high intensity; in fact, the power transmitted in each one may be of the order of several kilowatts.

When the transmitter is active, the radio-frequency power is conveyed to the antenna through an electronic switch which simultaneously short-circuits the input terminals of the receiver to protect that instrument from damage. Immediately after each pulse of power leaves the antenna, the switch removes the short-circuit and connects the receiver to the antenna so that the reflected pulse can be detected.

The electronic switch is essentially a needle spark gap within an enclosure containing gas under pressure. When a pulse is sent out from the transmitter, the high potential causes a spark at the gap and short-circuits the receiver; when the pulse ends, the gas de-ionizes in about four microseconds and the receiver is ready for any returned signal.

The receiver is of the superheterodyne type, §341; it amplifies and rectifies the signal pulse and impresses it upon the cathode-ray oscilloscope of the indicator. Radial scanning is employed, in which the sweep starts from the center of the oscilloscope screen and spirals outward in a direction to match that of the radio beam from the antenna, and then returns quickly to the center. When the echo signal is received, the rectified pulse from the receiver is impressed on the grid which controls the intensity of the electron beam in the oscilloscope. In this way a bright spot appears on the screen for each echo received.

Since the time required for radio waves to reach an obstacle and return to the antenna is determined by the distance of this obstacle from the ship, the distance of a bright spot on the oscilloscope from the center of its screen bears a fixed relation to the distance of the obstacle. The range of the obstacle may be measured by turning a control on the set which moves an expanding circle on the screen to the position of the bright spot which corresponds to that obstacle. The bearing or direction of the obstacle is determined generally by reference to a line from the center to the top of the screen; this line may represent either the lengthwise axis of the ship or the true north-south direction. Bearings from that line are read on a graduated circle around the edge of the screen.

**Problem 175.**—If a radar echo is received at a ship's antenna 25 microseconds after the transmitting pulse is sent out, how far from the ship is the obstacle which caused the echo?

Since the speed of radio waves is 186,000 miles per second, the distance which they travel in 25 microseconds is $186,000 \times 0.000025 = 4.65$ miles. Therefore the obstacle is 2.325 miles from the ship.

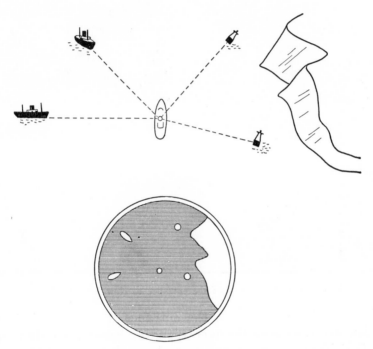

FIG. 498. Relative appearance of a scene and its radar representation

The radar antenna rotates about a vertical axis at a speed up to 20 revolutions per minute, and scans the entire region about the ship with its wave beam. The electron beam of the oscilloscope is synchronized with the antenna and a corresponding trace is made on the screen. The retentivity of the screen material is such that the repeated scannings produce a picture of the region about the ship, obstacles appearing as bright spots on a dark background as illustrated in Fig. 498. Radars employing the higher antenna rotational speeds yield complete pictures, while those operating at lower speeds show only partial pictures which appear behind the scanning beam and fade almost completely before being reproduced again by subsequent scannings.

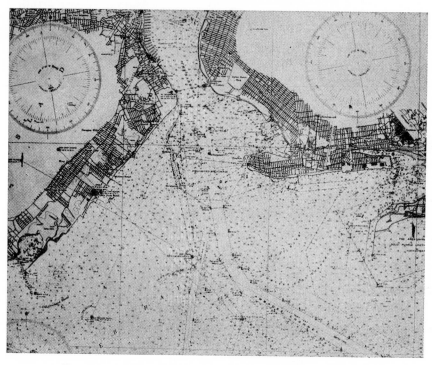

FIG. 499. Nautical map of the entrance to New York Harbor

Fig. 499 shows a map of the entrance to New York Harbor and Fig. 500 illustrates the corresponding radar map. It is to be noted that in radar scenes one obstacle, such as a shore line, may hide another in its shadow.

360. **Other Navigational Aids.**—Experimentation with radar stations along the coast for assisting merchant vessels has been under way for some time. Naturally, more powerful and precise radar signaling would be possible with shore-based stations than would be practicable with ship stations. Small boats and vessels

without radar equipment could be assisted to safe anchorage by utilizing shore-based radar stations.

Beacons that emit very short radio waves are designed to aid aircraft navigation; such a beacon is called "Racon," an abbreviation of *ra*darbea*con*. Racon differs from radar operation in that a radar station depends upon the reflection of one of its

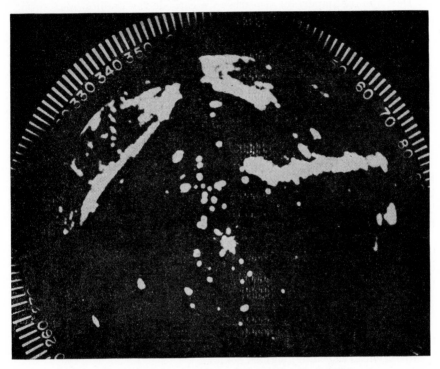

FIG. 500. Radar map of the entrance to New York Harbor

own radio-frequency beams to locate an obstacle, while a racon station is a combination of a receiver and transmitter which sends out a coded signal of its own when triggered by a short-wave signal from an airplane. Thus, racon enables an aerial navigator to locate himself with respect to the station which responds to his interrogating equipment. Since buoys and other navigational markers are small, only a small part of the energy of a radar beam is reflected from them and very little of the reflected energy gets back to the originating station. On the other hand, a racon puts out a large amount of energy which assures dependable indication at relatively large distances. Studies are under way to adapt racon to marine navigation.

## QUESTIONS

1. Describe the important features of a cathode-ray oscilloscope.
2. How is a pattern on an oscilloscope synchronized?
3. What is the procedure in studying the wave shape of an alternating current by means of an oscilloscope?
4. What precautions should be exercised in using a cathode-ray tube?
5. Name the elements of an electron gun and state their purposes.
6. Describe the two methods for deflecting the beam in an electron gun.
7. Draw a saw-tooth wave and indicate the part used in sweeping across the screen of a cathode-ray tube, and the part used to return the beam to the starting point.
8. Explain the operation of a sweep circuit.
9. Describe the construction of the RCA iconoscope.
10. What is the purpose of the mosaic in an iconoscope?
11. How is the beam in an iconoscope deflected?
12. Describe the construction and operation of a kinescope.
13. Explain what is meant by interlacing as applied to television practice. Why is interlacing employed?
14. State the difference between a "field" and a "frame" in television.
15. Explain why television employs such high carrier frequencies.
16. Show by means of a block diagram the important components of a television receiver.
17. Sketch two types of dipole antennas used in television, and include the reflectors.
18. Explain the principle of a radio direction finder. How is the sense of direction of incoming signals found?
19. How is the position of a ship located by means of the loran system?
20. Why are frequencies of several thousand megacycles used in radar?
21. Describe how an obstacle at sea is located by a radar set.

## PROBLEMS

1. Calculate the maximum width of television sidebands for the transmission of 30 frames per second with 441-line scanning, taking the aspect ratio of the picture as 4/3. *Ans.* 3.89 megacycles per second.
2. Determine the over-all length of a half-wave dipole antenna to receive television signals of 50 megacycles per second. *Ans.* 9.84 feet.
3. Specify how a television channel covering the band from 54 to 60 megacycles would be utilized by a standard television transmitter. *Ans.* Sound carrier—59.75 megacycles; Video carrier—55.25 megacycles;

Sideband—55.25 to 59.25 megacycles; Vestigial sideband—54.0 to 55.25 megacycles.

4. A 100-megacycle signal is being received on a square loop that measures 75 centimeters on a side. Assuming the e.m.f. developed in each side of the loop is 500 microvolts, determine the net e.m.f. induced in the loop. *Ans.* 707 microvolts.

5. How many waves are there in a' loran signal pulse lasting 40 microseconds when the station operates on 1750 kilocycles? *Ans.* 70.

6. How many waves are there in a radar signal pulse lasting 1 microsecond when 10 centimeter waves are used in the transmission? *Ans.* 3000.

# APPENDIX

## Mensuration Rules

Area of triangle $= \begin{cases} \frac{1}{2} \text{ (base} \times \text{altitude)}. \\ \sqrt{s(s-a)(s-b)(s-c)}, \text{ where } a, b \text{ and } c \\ \text{are the lengths of the sides and } s = \\ \frac{1}{2} (a + b + c). \end{cases}$

Area of parallelogram = base × altitude.

Area of trapezoid = altitude × ½ sum of parallel sides.

Circumference of circle = diameter × 3.1416.

Diameter of circle $= \begin{cases} \text{circumference} \times 0.3183. \\ 4 \times \text{area} \div \text{circumference}. \end{cases}$

Area of circle $= \begin{cases} \text{diameter squared} \times 0.7854. \\ \text{radius squared} \times 3.1416. \end{cases}$

Area of ellipse = product of diameters × 0.7854.

Area of regular polygon = ½ (sum of sides × apothem).

Lateral surface of cylinder = circumference of base × altitude.

Volume of cylinder = area of base × altitude.

Surface of sphere $= \begin{cases} \text{diameter} \times \text{circumference}. \\ 12.566 \times \text{radius squared}. \end{cases}$

Volume of sphere $= \begin{cases} \text{diameter cubed} \times 0.5236. \\ \text{radius cubed} \times 4.189. \end{cases}$

Surface of pyramid or cone = ½ (circumference of base × slant height).

Volume of cone = ⅓ (area of base × altitude).

## Conversion Table of Lengths

| To reduce | Multiply by | To reduce | Multiply by |
|---|---|---|---|
| Miles to kilometers | 1.6093 | Kilometers to miles | 0.62137 |
| "     " yards | 1760. | "         " meters | 1000. |
| "     " meters | 1609.3 | Meters to miles | 0.0006214 |
| Yards to meters | 0.91440 | "     " yards | 1.0936 |
| "     " feet | 3. | "     " centimeters | 100. |
| Feet to meters | 0.30480 | "     " feet | 3.2808 |
| "     " inches | 12. | Centimeters to milli- | |
| Inches to mils | 1000. | meters | 10. |
| "     " centimeters | 2.5400 | Centimeters to inches | 0.39370 |
| "     " millimeters | 25.400 | Millimeters to inches | 0.039370 |

## Conversion Table of Areas

| To reduce | Multiply by | To reduce | Multiply by |
|---|---|---|---|
| Sq. miles to acres | 640. | Sq. kilometers to sq. miles | 0.3861 |
| Sq. yards to sq. meters | 0.83613 | Sq. meters to sq. yards | 1.1960 |
| Sq. feet to sq. meters | 0.09290 | "    "    " sq. feet | 10.764 |
| Sq. inches to sq. centi- | | Sq. centimeters to sq. inches | 0.15500 |
| meters | 6.4516 | "     "     " circular | |
| Sq. inches to circular mils | 1,273,238. | mils | 197,861. |

### Conversion Table of Volumes

| To reduce | Multiply by | To reduce | Multiply by |
|---|---|---|---|
| Cu. yards to cu. meters | 0.76456 | Cu. meters to cu. yards | 1.3080 |
| Cu. feet to cu. meters | 0.02832 | "    "    " cu. feet | 35.316 |
| "    "    " liters | 28.317 | Liters to cu. feet | 0.035317 |
| Cu. inches to cu. centi- | | Cu. centimeters to cu. | |
| meters | 16.387 | inches | 0.061027 |
| Cu. inches to liters | 0.01639 | Liters to cu. inches | 61.023 |
| Gallons to cu. inches | 231. | "    " cu. centi- | |
| "    " liters | 3.7854 | meters | 1000. |
| Pounds of water to liters | 0.4536 | Liters to gallons | 0.26417 |

### Conversion Table of Weights

| To reduce | Multiply by | To reduce | Multiply by |
|---|---|---|---|
| Tons to kilograms | 907.18 | Kilograms to tons | 0.001102 |
| "    " pounds | 2000. | "    " grams | 1000. |
| Pounds to kilograms | 0.45359 | "    " pounds | 2.2046 |
| "    " ounces | 16. | Grams to milligrams | 1000. |
| Ounces to grams | 28.349 | "    " ounces | 0.03527 |
| "    " grains | 437.5 | "    " grains | 15.432 |
| Grains to grams | 0.06480 | Grains to Troy ounces | 480. |

### Conversion Table of Force, Energy, Power, Speed

| To reduce | Multiply by | To reduce | Multiply by |
|---|---|---|---|
| Pounds to dynes | 444,520. | Dynes to pounds | 0.000002249 |
| Ft.-lbs. to kilogram- | | Kilogram-meters to | |
| meters | 0.13825 | ft.-lbs. | 7.233 |
| Ft.-lbs. to ergs | 13,549,000. | Ergs to ft.-lbs. | 0.0000000738 |
| "    " joules | 1.3549 | Joules to ft.-lbs. | 0.7381 |
| "    per second to | | Horsepower to ft.-lbs. | |
| horsepower | 0.00182 | per second | 550. |
| Horsepower to watts | 746. | Watts to horsepower | 0.001342 |
| B.T.U. to calories | 251.8 | Calories to B.T.U. | 0.003971 |
| Calories to joules | 4.1893 | Joules to calories | 0.2387 |
| Lbs. per sq. foot to kilo- | | Kilograms per sq. meter | |
| grams per sq. meter | 4.8824 | to lbs. per sq. foot | 0.2048 |
| Lbs. per sq. inch to grams | | Grams per sq. centimeter | |
| per sq. centimeter | 70.307 | to lbs. per sq. inch | 0.01422 |
| Miles per hour to feet per | | Feet per sec. to | |
| sec. | 1.4667 | miles per hour | 0.68182 |
| Miles per hour to centi- | | Centimeters per sec. | |
| meters per sec. | 44.704 | to miles per hour | 0.02237 |

## TRIGONOMETRIC FUNCTIONS (*Natural*)

| Angle | Sine | Cosine | Tangent | Angle | Sine | Cosine | Tangent |
|---|---|---|---|---|---|---|---|
| 0° | 0.000 | 1.000 | 0.000 | | | | |
| 1° | .018 | 1.000 | .018 | 46° | .719 | .695 | 1.036 |
| 2° | .035 | 0.999 | .035 | 47° | .731 | .682 | 1.072 |
| 3° | .052 | .999 | .052 | 48° | .743 | .669 | 1.111 |
| 4° | .070 | .998 | .070 | 49° | .755 | .656 | 1.150 |
| 5° | .087 | .996 | .088 | 50° | .766 | .643 | 1.192 |
| 6° | .105 | .995 | .105 | 51° | .777 | .629 | 1.235 |
| 7° | .122 | .993 | .123 | 52° | .788 | .616 | 1.280 |
| 8° | .139 | .990 | .141 | 53° | .799 | .602 | 1.327 |
| 9° | .156 | .988 | .158 | 54° | .809 | .588 | 1.376 |
| 10° | .174 | .985 | .176 | 55° | .819 | .574 | 1.428 |
| 11° | .191 | .982 | .194 | 56° | .829 | .559 | 1.483 |
| 12° | .208 | .978 | .213 | 57° | .839 | .545 | 1.540 |
| 13° | .225 | .974 | .231 | 58° | .848 | .530 | 1.600 |
| 14° | .242 | .970 | .249 | 59° | .857 | .515 | 1.664 |
| 15° | .259 | .966 | .268 | 60° | .866 | .500 | 1.732 |
| 16° | .276 | .961 | .287 | 61° | .875 | .485 | 1.804 |
| 17° | .292 | .956 | .306 | 62° | .883 | .470 | 1.881 |
| 18° | .309 | .951 | .325 | 63° | .891 | .454 | 1.963 |
| 19° | .326 | .946 | .344 | 64° | .899 | .438 | 2.050 |
| 20° | .342 | .940 | .364 | 65° | .906 | .423 | 2.145 |
| 21° | .358 | .934 | .384 | 66° | .914 | .407 | 2.246 |
| 22° | .375 | .927 | .404 | 67° | .921 | .391 | 2.356 |
| 23° | .391 | .921 | .425 | 68° | .927 | .375 | 2.475 |
| 24° | .407 | .914 | .445 | 69° | .934 | .358 | 2.605 |
| 25° | .423 | .906 | .466 | 70° | .940 | .342 | 2.747 |
| 26° | .438 | .899 | .488 | 71° | .946 | .326 | 2.904 |
| 27° | .454 | .891 | .510 | 72° | .951 | .309 | 3.078 |
| 28° | .470 | .883 | .532 | 73° | .956 | .292 | 3.271 |
| 29° | .485 | .875 | .554 | 74° | .961 | .276 | 3.487 |
| 30° | .500 | .866 | .577 | 75° | .966 | .259 | 3.732 |
| 31° | .515 | .857 | .601 | 76° | .970 | .242 | 4.011 |
| 32° | .530 | .848 | .625 | 77° | .974 | .225 | 4.331 |
| 33° | .545 | .839 | .649 | 78° | .978 | .208 | 4.705 |
| 34° | .559 | .829 | .675 | 79° | .982 | .191 | 5.145 |
| 35° | .574 | .819 | .700 | 80° | .985 | .174 | 5.671 |
| 36° | .588 | .809 | .727 | 81° | .988 | .156 | 6.314 |
| 37° | .602 | .799 | .754 | 82° | .990 | .139 | 7.115 |
| 38° | .616 | .788 | .781 | 83° | .993 | .122 | 8.144 |
| 39° | .629 | .777 | .810 | 84° | .995 | .105 | 9.514 |
| 40° | .643 | .766 | .839 | 85° | .996 | .087 | 11.43 |
| 41° | .656 | .755 | .869 | 86° | .998 | .070 | 14.30 |
| 42° | .669 | .743 | .900 | 87° | .999 | .052 | 19.08 |
| 43° | .682 | .731 | .933 | 88° | .999 | .035 | 28.64 |
| 44° | .695 | .719 | .966 | 89° | 1.000 | .018 | 57.29 |
| 45° | .707 | .707 | 1.000 | 90° | 1.000 | .000 | ∞ |

## *Trigonometric Functions for Angles Larger than 90 Degrees*

When the angle lies beyond the first quadrant, the accompanying table of trigonometric functions of any angle $\theta$ can be used by applying the following:

Second Quadrant.............
$$\begin{cases} \sin\ (\ 90 + \theta) = \ \ \ \cos\theta \\ \cos\ (\ 90 + \theta) = -\sin\theta \\ \tan\ (\ 90 + \theta) = -\cot\theta \end{cases}$$

Third Quadrant...............
$$\begin{cases} \sin\ (180 + \theta) = -\sin\theta \\ \cos\ (180 + \theta) = -\cos\theta \\ \tan\ (180 + \theta) = \ \ \ \tan\theta \end{cases}$$

Fourth Quadrant.............
$$\begin{cases} \sin\ (270 + \theta) = -\cos\theta \\ \cos\ (270 + \theta) = \ \ \ \sin\theta \\ \tan\ (270 + \theta) = -\cot\theta \end{cases}$$

# ROSTER OF FORMULAS

| Formula Number | | Page Number |
|---|---|---|
| 37 | $I_p = \dfrac{n \times E}{(n \times R) + r}$ | 160 |
| 38 | $\dfrac{I_s}{I_p} = \dfrac{(m \times n) + 1}{m + n}$ | 161 |
| 39 | $I = \dfrac{E_1 - E_2}{r_1 + r_2}$ | 163 |
| 40 | $T = F \times L$ | 171 |
| 41 | $W = F \times s$ | 172 |
| 42 | $W = 2\pi \times N \times T$ | 173 |
| 43 | $P = \dfrac{W}{t}$ | 175 |
| 44 | $P = \dfrac{p \times L \times A \times N}{33,000}$ | 177 |
| 45 | $W = Q \times E$ | 178 |
| 46 | $W = E \times I \times t$ | 178 |
| 47 | $W = I^2 \times R \times t$ | 179 |
| 48 | $W = \dfrac{E^2 \times t}{R}$ | 179 |
| 49 | $P = E \times I$ | 180 |
| 50 | $\text{kilowatts} = \dfrac{\text{watts}}{1000} = \dfrac{E \times I}{1000}$ | 181 |
| 51 | $\text{horsepower} = \dfrac{\text{watts}}{746} = \dfrac{E \times I}{746}$ | 181 |
| 52 | $P = I^2 \times R$ | 182 |
| 53 | $P = \dfrac{E^2}{R}$ | 183 |
| 54 | $J = \dfrac{W}{H}$ | 187 |
| 55 | $H = 0.239 \times I^2 \times R \times t$ | 188 |
| 56 | $\mathcal{H} = \dfrac{I}{5 \times r}$ | 198 |
| 57 | $\mathcal{H} = \dfrac{\pi \times N \times I}{5 \times r}$ | 200 |

| Formula Number | | Page Number |
|---|---|---|
| 99 | $Y = \dfrac{1}{Z}$ | 387 |
| 100 | $Y = \sqrt{G^2 + S^2}$ | 388 |
| 101 | $G = \dfrac{R}{R^2 + X^2}$ | 388 |
| 102 | $S = \dfrac{X}{R^2 + X^2}$ | 388 |
| 103 | $Y = \sqrt{(G_1 + G_2 + \ldots)^2 + (S_1 + S_2 + \ldots)^2}$ | 389 |
| 104 | $f = \dfrac{1}{2\pi\sqrt{L \times C}}$ | 392 |
| 105 | power factor $= \cos\phi$ | 399 |
| 106 | power factor $= \dfrac{R}{Z}$ | 399 |
| 107 | power factor $= \dfrac{P}{E \times I}$ | 400 |
| 108 | $P = E \times I \times \cos\phi$ | 401 |
| 109 | $E_{AB} = \ldots = 1.73\,E$ | 406 |
| 110 | $I_A = \ldots = 1.73\,I$ | 407 |
| 111 | $\tan\phi = \dfrac{\sin\phi}{\cos\phi} = \dfrac{P_2}{P_1}$ | 408 |
| 112 | $P = \sqrt{3}\,E_l \times I_l \times \cos\phi$ | 410 |
| 113 | percentage regulation $= 100 \times \dfrac{\text{no-load p.d.} - \text{full-load p.d.}}{\text{full-load p.d.}}$ | 444 |
| 114 | efficiency $= \dfrac{\text{output}}{\text{input}}$ | 457 |
| 115 | $e = \dfrac{P}{P + p}$ | 458 |
| 116 | $I = \dfrac{E - \varepsilon}{r}$ | 466 |
| 117 | $P = \dfrac{2\pi \times r \times n \times F}{33{,}000}$ | 469 |

| Formula Number | | Page Number |
|---|---|---|
| 118 | $$P = \frac{2\pi \times n \times T}{33,000}$$ | 470 |
| 119 | $$P = \varepsilon \times I$$ | 470 |
| 120 | $$e = \frac{P - p}{P}$$ | 471 |
| 121 | $$\text{speed regulation} = \frac{\text{no-load speed} - \text{full-load speed}}{\text{no-load speed}}$$ | 477 |
| 122 | $$I = \frac{1000 \times \text{kw.}}{E \times e} = \frac{746 \times \text{hp.}}{E \times e}$$ | 482 |
| 123 | $$CM = \frac{746 \times \text{hp.} \times L \times \rho}{E \times E_d \times e}$$ | 482 |
| 124 | $$\text{slip} = \frac{\text{synchronous speed} - \text{rotor speed}}{\text{synchronous speed}}$$ | 509 |
| 125 | $$\frac{n_2}{n_1} = \frac{E_2}{E_1}$$ | 528 |
| 126 | $$\frac{E_2}{E_1} = \frac{I_1}{I_2}$$ | 529 |
| 127 | $$F = 4\pi \times I_s$$ | 560 |
| 128 | $$\text{efficiency} = \frac{F}{P}$$ | 562 |
| 129 | $$E = \frac{F}{A}$$ | 563 |
| 130 | $$E = \frac{I}{r^2}$$ | 564 |
| 131 | $$F = \frac{E \times A}{C}$$ | 569 |
| 132 | $$I = \frac{E}{n \times R + r \times l}$$ | 609 |
| 133 | $$l = \frac{E - I \times n \times R}{r \times I}$$ | 609 |
| 134 | $$A = \frac{r \times l}{2} + \frac{1}{2}\sqrt{(r \times l + R)(r \times l + R + 4H)}$$ | 612 |
| 135 | $$A = r \times l + \frac{R}{2}$$ | 612 |

# INDEX

ONE Kilowatt = 1000 watts
ONE megawatt = 1,000,000 watts
ONE watt = one millionth of a megawatt
ONE elect. hp. = 746 watts
ONE mech. hp. = 33000 ftlbs per min.
ONE farad = one million microfarads
ONE henry = one million micro henry
ONE micro henry = one million of a henry
ONE milliamper = one thousand of a Amp.
ONE ampere = one thousand milliamper

D.C. Dynamo - Series, Compound, Shunt

## SERIES CKT.

$$I_T = I_1 = I_2 = I_3$$

$$E_T = E_1 \, \text{sum} \, E_2 \, \text{sum} \, E_3$$
$$\text{sum}$$

$$R_T = R_1 + R_2 + R_3$$

## PARALLEL CKT.

$$I_T = I_1 + I_2 + I_3$$

$$E_T = E_1 \neq E_2 = E_3$$

$$R_T = \frac{1}{R_1} + \frac{1}{R_2} + \frac{1}{R_3}$$

choke

LINE